A SURVEY OF MATHEMATICS

Allen R. Angel ■ Christine D. Abbott ■ Dennis C. Runde

Custom Edition for Ocean County College

Taken from:
A Survey of Mathematics with Applications
Expanded Seventh Edition
by Allen R. Angel, Christine D. Abbott and Dennis C. Runde

PEARSON
Custom
Publishing

PEARSON
Addison
Wesley

Cover: *Orange County College monument*

Taken from:

A Survey of Mathematics with Applications
Expanded Seventh Edition
by Allen R. Angel, Christine D. Abbott and Dennis C. Runde
Copyright © 2005 Pearson Education, Inc.
Published by Addison Wesley, Inc.

This special edition published in cooperation with Pearson Custom Publishing.

Printed in the United States of America

10 9 8 7 6 5 4 3 2 1

ISBN 0-536-94644-2

2005360156

MR

Please visit our web site at *www.pearsoncustom.com*

PEARSON CUSTOM PUBLISHING
75 Arlington Street, Suite 300, Boston, MA 02116
A Pearson Education Company

CONTENTS

We present *A Survey of Mathematics with Applications,* seventh edition, with that vision in mind. Our primary goal in writing this book was to give students a text that they can read, understand, and enjoy while learning how mathematics affects the world around them. Numerous applied examples motivate topics. A variety of interesting applied exercises demonstrate the real-life nature of mathematics and its importance in the students' lives.

The text is intended for students who require a broad-based general overview of mathematics, especially those majoring in the liberal arts, elementary education, the social sciences, business, nursing, and allied health fields. It is particularly suitable for those courses that satisfy the minimum competency requirement in mathematics for graduation or transfer.

EXPANDED EDITION

- The expanded version of *A Survey of Mathematics with Applications,* seventh edition, contains all the material covered in the basic text, with additional chapters on *Graph Theory* and *Voting and Apportionment.* While many wished inclusion of these topics, others did not. Therefore, we have written two versions of the book.

NEW TO THIS EDITION

In this edition we made several important improvements in presentation.

- The interior design has been modified, and many new photographs were added to make the book more inviting and motivational. A new, more open design has been used to make the book easier for the student to read.
- **Recreational Mathematics Exercises** have been added in many sections to help make the book more enjoyable to students. These exercises take a variety of forms, from puzzles to exploring new mathematical ideas and concepts. Often, but not always, the material in these exercises is related to the material covered in the section or chapter.
- **Timely Tips** have been added to provide useful and timely information for students. This information often helps students to understand the concepts, or relates the material to other sections of the book.
- A new feature, **Mathematics Everywhere,** has been added. The information provided in these boxes relates mathematics to students' everyday lives. This material will help students to see a need for and gain an appreciation of mathematics.
- Additional interesting Did You Knows . . . and Profiles in Mathematics have been added throughout the book.
- In various exercise sets, the number and variety of exercises has been increased.

- The exercise sets have been reclassified to include: Concept/Writing Exercises; Practice the Skills Exercises; Problem Solving Exercises; Challenge Problem/Group Activity Exercises; Recreational Mathematics; and Internet/Research Activities.
- Sources have been added; up-to-date tables, graphs, and charts make the material more relevant and encourage students to read graphs and analyze data.
- Approximately 40% of the exercises are new.
- The number of writing exercises was increased. The writing exercises are denoted in magenta in the exercise sets.
- The number of examples was increased throughout the text to promote student understanding.

CONTENT REVISION

In addition, we revised and expanded certain topics to introduce new material and to increase understanding.

CHAPTER 1 "Critical Thinking Skills," was updated with exciting and current examples and exercises.

CHAPTER 2 "Sets," includes more information on countable sets and infinite sets.

CHAPTER 3 "Logic," has more exercises and a greater variety of exercises. Certain material has been rewritten for greater clarity.

CHAPTER 4 "Systems of Numeration," covers the ancient Chinese numeration system in more depth. More material on the hexadecimal system is included.

CHAPTER 5 "Number Theory and the Real Number System," was expanded to include additional coverage of Fibonacci numbers. The most current number theory information (largest prime number, most accurate value of pi, etc.) has been included.

CHAPTER 6 "Algebra, Graphs and Functions," has more and a greater variety of examples and exercises dealing with real-life situations.

CHAPTER 7 "Systems of Linear Equations and Inequalities," now has annotations included, and more detailed explanations of certain topics.

CHAPTER 8 "The Metric System," now includes many examples and interesting photographs of real-life (metric) situations taken from around the world. More information is provided on larger and smaller metric units of measurements.

CHAPTER 9 "Geometry," now includes a new section on Transformational Geometry (transformations, symmetry, and tessellations) and additional information on M. C. Escher and his works.

CHAPTER 10 "Mathematical Systems," has additional exercises and examples. We have tied in this material more with real-life situations.

CHAPTER 11 "Consumer Mathematics," includes current interest rates and updated information on items that may be of interest to students including updated material on sources of credit and mutual funds. There is also additional information on stocks, bonds, and mutual funds.

CHAPTER 12 "Probability," has a greater variety of examples and exercises, more examples and exercises have been added that deal with real-life situations. Certain material has been rewritten for greater clarity.

CHAPTER 13 "Statistics," now includes expanded coverage of measures of location. Also, material related to z-scores has been revised.

CHAPTER 14 "Graph Theory," includes more maps from around the world. Important definitions have been highlighted. Certain material has been rewritten for greater clarity.

CHAPTER 15 "Voting and Apportionment," includes current information about voting and elections. There is expanded material on apportionment methods. Certain material has been rewritten for greater clarity.

CONTINUING FEATURES

Several features appear throughout the book, adding interest and provoking thought.

- **Chapter Openers** Interesting and motivational photo essays introduce each chapter and illustrate the real-world nature of the chapter topics.
- **Problem Solving** Beginning in Chapter 1, students are introduced to problem solving and critical thinking. The theme of problem solving is then continued throughout the text, and special problem-solving exercises are presented in the exercise sets.
- **Critical Thinking Skills** In addition to a focus on problem solving, the book also features sections on *Inductive Reasoning* and the important skills of *Estimation* and *Dimensional Analysis.*
- **Profiles in Mathematics** Brief historical sketches and vignettes present the stories of people who have advanced the discipline of mathematics.
- **Did You Know . . .** These colorful, engaging, and lively boxed features highlight the connection of mathematics to history, to the arts and sciences, to technology, and to a broad variety of disciplines.
- **Group Projects** At the end of each chapter are suggested projects that can be used to have students work together. These projects can also be assigned to individual students if desired.
- **Chapter Summaries, Review Exercises, and Chapter Tests** This end-of-chapter material helps students to review material and to prepare for tests.

INSTRUCTOR'S SUPPLEMENTS

Instructor's Edition ISBN 0-321-20566-9

This special edition of the text includes an answer section consisting of answers to all text exercises.

Instructor's Solutions Manual ISBN 0-321-20594-4

This manual contains solutions to all exercises in the text and answers to Group Projects.

Instructor's Testing Manual ISBN 0-321-20595-2

This manual includes three alternate tests per chapter.

PowerPoint Lecture Presentation

Available through http://www.aw-bc.com/suppscentral or at MyMathLab.

This classroom presentation software covers all-important topics from sections in the text.

TestGen with QuizMaster ISBN 0-321-20593-6

TestGen enables instructors to build, edit, print, and administer tests using a computerized bank of questions developed to cover all the objectives of the text. TestGen is algorithmically based so that multiple, yet equivalent, versions of the same question or test can be generated at the click of a button. Instructors can also modify test bank questions or add new questions by using the built-in question editor, which allows users to create graphs, import graphics, insert math notation, and insert variable numbers or text. Tests can be printed or administered on-line via the Internet or another network. Many questions in TestGen can be expressed in a short-answer or multiple-choice form, giving instructors greater flexibility in their test preparation. TestGen comes packaged with QuizMaster, which allows students to take tests on a local area network. The software is available on a dual-platform Windows/Macintosh CD-ROM.

MathXL® www.mathxl.com

MathXL® is a powerful online homework, tutorial, and assessment system that accompanies your Addison-Wesley textbook in mathematics or statistics. With MathXL, instructors can create, edit, and assign online homework and tests using algorithmically generated exercises correlated at the objective level to your textbook. All student work is tracked in MathXL's online gradebook. Students can take chapter tests in MathXL and receive personalized study plans based on their test results. The study plan diagnoses weaknesses and links students directly to tutorial exercises for the objectives they need to study and retest. Students can also access supplemental animations and video clips directly from selected exercises. MathXL is available to qualified adopters. For more information, visit our website at www.mathxl.com.

MyMathLab® www.mymathlab.com

MyMathLab® is a series of text-specific, easily customizable online courses for Addison-Wesley textbooks in mathematics and statistics. MyMathLab is powered by CourseCompass™—Pearson Education's online teaching and learning environment—and by MathXL®—our online homework, tutorial, and assessment system. MyMathLab gives you the tools you need to deliver all or a portion of your course online, whether your students are in a lab setting or working from home. MyMathLab provides a rich and flexible set of course materials, featuring free-response exercises that are algorithmically generated for unlimited practice and mastery. Students can also use online tools, such as video lectures, animations, and a multimedia textbook, to independently improve their understanding and performance. Instructors can use MyMathLab's homework and test managers to select and assign online exercises correlated directly to the textbook, and they can import TestGen tests into MyMathLab for added flexibility. MyMathLab's online gradebook—designed specifically for mathematics and statistics—automatically tracks students' homework and test results and gives the instructor control over how to calculate final grades.

MyMathLab is available to qualified adopters. For more information, visit our website at www.mymathlab.com.

STUDENT'S SUPPLEMENTS

Student's Solutions Manual ISBN 0-321-20597-9

This for-sale manual contains solutions to all odd-numbered exercises and to all review and chapter test exercises.

Guide to CLAST Mathematical Competency ISBN 0-201-61327-1

This special for-sale study guide for use in Florida offers help in preparing for the College Level Academic Skills Test (CLAST). It includes a review of arithmetic, a CLAST pretest, supplementary exercises, and a CLAST posttest.

Videotape Series ISBN 0-321-20596-0

Videotapes presenting the text's topics are available. A qualified college-level mathematics instructor presents worked-out examples and uses visual aids to reinforce the mathematical concepts.

Digital Video Tutor ISBN 0-321-20598-7

The videotape series for this text is provided on CD-ROM, making it easy and convenient for students to watch video segments from a computer at home or on campus. This complete video set, now affordable and portable for students, is ideal for distance learning or extra instruction.

InterActMath® Tutorial Website

Get practice and tutorial help online! This interactive tutorial website provides algorithmically generated practice exercises that correlate directly to the exercises in the text. A detailed worked-out example and guided solution accompany each practice exercise. The website recognizes student errors and provides feedback.

MathXL will help students succeed in their math course!

MathXL is an online homework, tutorial, and assessment system that uses algorithmically generated exercises correlated to the objectives in your textbook. Students can take chapter tests and receive personalized study plans that diagnose weaknesses and link students to areas they need to study and retest. Students can also work unlimited practice exercises that provide tutorial instruction, and they can access animations and video clips directly from selected exercises. An access code is required. For more information go to www.mathxl.com.

MyMathLab

MyMathLab is a complete online course available with this text and is perfect for a lecture-based, self-paced, or online course. This site offers instructors and students a wide variety of resources from dynamic multimedia—video clips, animations, and more—to course management tools. With *MyMathLab,* instructors can customize their online course and help students increase their comprehension and success!

- The entire textbook is available online and is supplemented by multimedia content, such as videos and animations, which is used to explain concepts. With *MyMathLab,* students can work with tutorial exercises tied directly to those in their textbook.

- *MyMathLab* allows students to do practice work and to complete instructor-assigned tests and homework assignments online. Based on their results, *MyMathLab* automatically builds individual study plans that students can use to improve their skills.

MyMathLab requires a student access code. For more information about *MyMathLab,* go to www.mymathlab.com.

Addison-Wesley Math Tutor Center

The Addison-Wesley Math Tutor Center is staffed by qualified math and statistics instructors who provide students with tutoring on examples and odd-numbered exercises from the textbook. Tutoring is available via toll-free telephone, fax, email, or the Internet and White Board technology allows tutors and students to actually see the problems worked while they "talk" in real time over the Internet during tutoring sessions. An access card is required. For more information, go to www.aw-bc.com/tutorcenter.

ACKNOWLEDGMENTS

We would like to thank our spouses Kathy Angel, Jason Abbott, and Kris Runde for their support and encouragement throughout the project. Our spouses helped us in a great many ways, including proofreading, typing, and offering valuable suggestions. We cannot thank them enough for their wonderful support and understanding while we worked on the book.

We would also like to thank our children: Robert and Steven Angel; Matthew and Jake Abbott; and Alex, Nicholas, and Max Runde. They also gave us support and encouragement. They were very understanding when we could not spend as much time with them as we wished because of book deadlines. Without the support and understanding of our families, this book would not be a reality.

We would like to thank Cathy Ferrer of Valencia Community College and Deana Richmond for accuracy checking of the text and answers. They did a very conscientious job. We would also like to thank Sherry Tornwall of the University of Florida for reading through the book and making many valuable suggestions for improving the content of the book.

There are many people at Addison-Wesley who deserve thanks. We would like to thank all those listed on the Library of Congress categorizing page. In particular, we would like to thank Anne Kelly, Senior Acquisitions Editor; Lauren Morse, Project Editor; Cecilia Fleming, Editorial Assistant; Peggy McMahon, Senior Production Supervisor; Becky Anderson, Marketing Manager; Sara Anderson, Associate Media Producer; Barbara Atkinson, Senior Designer; and Karen Guardino, Managing Editor. We would also like to thank Maria McColligan of Nesbitt Graphics, Inc., for her assistance as Production Manager for this project.

Aimee Calhoun and Dick Stewart of Monroe Community College also deserve our thanks for the excellent work they did on the *Student's Solutions Manual* and the *Instructor's Solutions Manual.*

Finally, we would like to thank the reviewers from all editions of the book and all the students who have offered suggestions for improving the book. A list of reviewers for all editions of this book follows. Thanks to all of you for helping make *A Survey of Mathematics with Applications* the most successful Liberal Arts book in the country.

Allen R. Angel

Christine D. Abbott

Dennis C. Runde

REVIEWERS FOR THIS AND PREVIOUS EDITIONS

Frank Asta, *College of DuPage, IL*

*Robin L. Ayers, *Western Kentucky University*

Hughette Bach, *California State University–Sacramento*

Madeline Bates, *Bronx Community College, NY*

Rebecca Baum, *Lincoln Land Community College, IL*

Vivian Baxter, *Fort Hayes State University, KS*

Una Bray, *Skidmore College, NY*

David H. Buckley, *Polk Community College, FL*

Robert C. Bueker, *Western Kentucky University*

Carl Carlson, *Moorhead State University, MN*

Kent Carlson, *St. Cloud State University, MN*

Donald Catheart, *Salisbury State College, MD*

*Yungchen Cheng, *Southwest Missouri State University*

Joseph Cleary, *Massasoit Community College, MA*

Donald Cohen, *SUNY Ag & Tech College at Cobleskill, NY*

David Dean, *Santa Fe Community College, FL*

Charles Downey, *University of Nebraska*

*Annie Droullard, *Polk Community College, FL*

Ruth Ediden, *Morgan State University, MD*

Lee Erker, *Tri-County Community College, NC*

Karen Estes, *St. Petersburg College, FL*

Teklay Fessahaye, *Santa Fe Community College, FL*

Kurtis Fink, *Northwest Missouri State University*

Raymond Flagg, *McPherson College, KS*

Penelope Fowler, *Tennessee Wesleyan College*

Gilberto Garza, *El Paso Community College, TX*

Judith L. Gersting, *Indiana University–Purdue University at Indianapolis*

Lucille Groenke, *Mesa Community College, AZ*

John Hornsby, *University of New Orleans, LA*

Nancy Johnson, *Broward Community College, FL*

Daniel Kimborowicz, *Massasoit Community College, MA*

Mary Lois King, *Tallahassee Community College, FL*

David Lehmann, *Southwest Missouri State University*

Peter Lindstrom, *North Lake College, TX*

James Magliano, *Union College, NJ*

Yash Manchanda, *East Los Angeles College & Fullerton College, CA*

Don Marsian, *Hillsborough Community College, FL*

Marilyn Mays, *North Lake College, TX*

Robert McGuigan, *Westfield State College, MA*

*Wallace H. Memmer, *Brookdale Community College, NJ*

Maurice Monahan, *South Dakota State University*

Julie Monte, *Daytona Beach Community College, FL*

Karen Mosely, *Alabama Southern Community College*

Edwin Owens, *Pennsylvania College of Technology*

Wing Park, *College of Lake County, IL*

Bettye Parnham, *Daytona Beach Community College, FL*

Joanne Peeples, *El Paso Community College, TX*

Nelson Rich, *Nazareth College, NY*

Kenneth Ross, *University of Oregon*

Ronald Ruemmler, *Middlesex County College, NJ*

Rosa Rusinek, *Queensborough Community College, NY*

Len Ruth, *Sinclair Community College, OH*

John Samoylo, *Delaware County Community College, PA*

Sandra Savage, *Orange Coast College, CA*

Gerald Schultz, *Southern Connecticut State University*

Richard Schwartz, *College of Staten Island, NY*

Kara Shavo, *Mercer County Community College, NJ*

Minnie Shuler, *Chipola Junior College, FL*

*Paula R. Stickles, *University of Southern Indiana*

Kristin Stoley, *Blinn College–Bryan, TX*

Steve Sworder, *Saddleback College, CA*

Shirley Thompson, *Moorhead College, GA*

Alvin D. Tinsley, *Central Missouri State University*

*Sherry Tornwall, *University of Florida*

William Trotter, *University of South Carolina*

Sandra Welch, *Stephen F. Austin State University, TX*

Joyce Wellington, *Southeastern Community College, NC*

Sue Welsch, *Sierra Nevada College*

Robert F. Wheeler, *Northern Illinois University*

Susan Wirth, *Indian River Community College, FL*

James Wooland, *Florida State University*

*Judith B. Wood, *Central Florida Community College*

Jean Woody, *Tulsa Community College, OK*

Michael A. Zwick, *Monroe Community College, NY*

*Denotes reviewers for seventh edition.

TO THE STUDENT

Mathematics is an exciting, living study. It has applications that shape the world around you and influence your everyday life. We hope that as you read through this book you will realize just how important mathematics is and gain an appreciation of both its usefulness and its beauty. We also hope to teach you some practical mathematics that you can use in your everyday life and that will prepare you for further courses in mathematics.

Our primary purpose in writing this text was to provide material that you could read, understand, and enjoy. To this end we have used straightforward language and tried to relate mathematical concepts to everyday experiences. We have also provided many detailed examples for you to follow.

The concepts, definitions, and formulas that deserve special attention have been either boxed or set in boldface type. Within each category the exercises are graded so that the more difficult problems appear at the end. The problems with exercise numbers set in color are writing exercises. At the end of most exercise sets are Challenge Problem/Group Activity exercises that contain challenging or exploratory exercises. At the end of each chapter are Group Projects which reinforce the material learned or provide related material.

Each chapter has a summary, review exercises, and a chapter test. When studying for a test, be sure to read the chapter summary, work the review exercises, and take the chapter test. The answers to the odd-numbered exercises, all review exercises, all chapter test exercises, and selected recreational mathematics exercises appear in the answer section in the back of the text. However, you should use the answers only to check your work.

It is difficult to learn mathematics without becoming involved. To be successful, we suggest you read the text carefully *and work each exercise in each assignment in detail.* Check with your instructor to determine which supplements are available for your use.

We welcome your suggestions and your comments. You may contact us at the following address:

Allen Angel
c/o Marketing
Mathematics & Statistics
Addison-Wesley
75 Arlington St., Ste 300
Boston, MA 02116

or by email at:

math@awl.com
Subject: for Allen Angel

Good luck in your adventure in mathematics!

Allen R. Angel

Christine D. Abbott

Dennis C. Runde

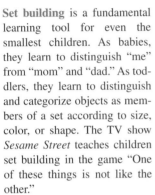

Set building is a fundamental learning tool for even the smallest children. As babies, they learn to distinguish "me" from "mom" and "dad." As toddlers, they learn to distinguish and categorize objects as members of a set according to size, color, or shape. The TV show *Sesame Street* teaches children set building in the game "One of these things is not like the other."

SETS

One of the most basic human impulses is to sort and classify things. Consider yourself, for example. How many different sets are you a member of? You might start with some simple categories, such as whether you are male or female, your age group, and the state you live in. Then you might think about your family's ethnic group, socioeconomic group, and nationality. These are but some of the many ways you could describe yourself to other people.

Of what use is this activity of categorization? As you will see in this chapter, putting elements into sets helps you order and arrange your world. It allows you to deal with large quantities of information. Set building is a learning tool that helps answer the question, "What are the characteristics of this group?"

Sets underlie other mathematical topics, such as logic and abstract algebra. In fact, the book *Eléments de Mathématique,* written by a group of French mathematicians under the pseudonym Nicolas Bourbaki, states, "Nowadays it is possible, logically speaking, to derive the whole of known mathematics from a single source, the theory of sets."

2.1 SET CONCEPTS

We encounter sets in many different ways every day of our lives. A *set* is a collection of objects, which are called *elements* or *members* of the set. For example, the United States is a collection or set of 50 states. The 50 individual states are the members or elements of the set that is called the United States.

A set is *well defined* if its contents can be clearly determined. The set of U.S. presidents is a well-defined set because its contents, the presidents, can be named. The set of the three best movies is not a well-defined set because the word *best* is interpreted differently by different people. In this text, we use only well-defined sets.

Three methods are commonly used to indicate a set: (1) description, (2) roster form, and (3) set-builder notation.

The method of indicating a set by *description* is illustrated in Example 1.

PROFILE IN MATHEMATICS

GEORG CANTOR

Georg Cantor (1845–1918), born in St. Petersburg, Russia, is recognized as the founder of set theory. Cantor's creative work in mathematics was nearly lost when his father insisted that he become an engineer rather than a mathematician. His two major books on set theory, *Foundations of General Theory of Aggregates* and *Contributions to the Founding of the Theory of Transfinite Numbers,* were published in 1883 and 1895, respectively.

┌─ EXAMPLE 1   *Description of Sets*

Write a description of the set containing the elements Monday, Tuesday, Wednesday, Thursday, Friday, Saturday, Sunday.

SOLUTION: The set is the days of the week.   ▲

Listing the elements of a set inside a pair of *braces*, { }, is called *roster form*. The braces are an essential part of the notation because they identify the contents as a set. For example, {1, 2, 3} is notation for the set whose elements are 1, 2, and 3, but (1, 2, 3) and [1, 2, 3] are not sets because parentheses and brackets do not indicate a set. For a set written in roster form, commas separate the elements of the set. The order in which the elements are listed is not important.

Sets are generally named with capital letters. For example, the name commonly selected for the set of *natural numbers* or *counting numbers* is *N*.

Natural Numbers

$$N = \{1, 2, 3, 4, 5, \dots\}$$

The three dots after the 5, called an *ellipsis,* indicate that the elements in the set continue in the same manner. An ellipsis followed by a last element indicates that the elements continue in the same manner up to and including the last element. This notation is illustrated in Example 2(b).

┌─ EXAMPLE 2   *Roster Form of Sets*

Express the following in roster form.

a) Set *A* is the set of natural numbers less than 6.

b) Set *B* is the set of natural numbers less than or equal to 50.

c) Set *P* is the set of planets in Earth's solar system.

SOLUTION:

a) The natural numbers less than 6 are 1, 2, 3, 4, and 5. Thus, set *A* in roster form is
$$A = \{1, 2, 3, 4, 5\}.$$

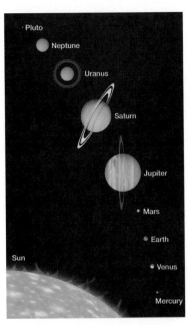

The planets of Earth's solar system.

b) $B = \{1, 2, 3, 4, \ldots, 50\}$. The 50 after the ellipsis indicates that the elements continue in the same manner up to and including the number 50.

c) $P = \{$Mercury, Venus, Earth, Mars, Jupiter, Saturn, Uranus, Neptune, Pluto$\}$

▲

EXAMPLE 3   *The Word* Inclusive

Express the following in roster form.

a) The set of natural numbers between 5 and 8.

b) The set of natural numbers between 5 and 8, inclusive.

SOLUTION:

a) $A = \{6, 7\}$

b) $B = \{5, 6, 7, 8\}$. Note that the word *inclusive* indicates that the values of 5 and 8 are included in the set.

▲

The symbol $\in$, read, is an element of, is used to indicate membership in a set. In Example 3, since 6 is an element of set A, we write $6 \in A$. This may also be written $6 \in \{6, 7\}$. We may also write $8 \notin A$, meaning that 8 is not an element of set A.

Set-builder notation (sometimes called *set-generator notation*) may be used to symbolize a set. Set-builder notation is frequently used in algebra. The following example illustrates its form.

$$D \quad = \quad \{ \quad x \quad | \quad \text{Condition(s)} \}$$

| Set D | is | the set of | all elements x | such that | the condition(s) x must meet in order to be a member of the set. |

Consider $E = \{x \mid x \in N \text{ and } x > 10\}$. The statement is read: "Set E is the set of all the elements x such that x is a natural number and x is greater than 10." The conditions that x must meet to be a member of the set are $x \in N$, which means that x must be a natural number, and $x > 10$, which means that x must be greater than 10. The numbers that meet both conditions are the set of natural numbers greater than 10. Set E in roster form is

$$E = \{11, 12, 13, 14, \ldots\}$$

EXAMPLE 4   *Using Set-Builder Notation*

a) Write set $B = \{1, 2, 3, 4, 5\}$ in set-builder notation.

b) Write, in words, how you would read set B in set-builder notation.

SOLUTION:

a) Since set B consists of the natural numbers less than 6, we write

$$B = \{x \mid x \in N \text{ and } x < 6\}$$

Another acceptable answer is $B = \{x \mid x \in N \text{ and } x \leq 5\}$.

b) Set B is the set of all elements x such that x is a natural number and x is less than 6.

EXAMPLE 5   Roster Form to Set-Builder Notation

a) Write set $C = \{$North America, South America, Europe, Asia, Australia, Africa, Antarctica$\}$ in set-builder notation.

b) Write in words how you would read set C in set-builder notation.

SOLUTION:

a) $C = \{x \mid x \text{ is a continent}\}$.

b) Set C is the set of all elements x such that x is a continent.

EXAMPLE 6   Set-Builder Notation to Roster Form

Write set $A = \{x \mid x \in N \text{ and } 2 \le x < 8\}$ in roster form.

SOLUTION: $A = \{2, 3, 4, 5, 6, 7\}$

EXAMPLE 7   Busiest Ports

The chart shows the 10 busiest U.S. ports in 2000, ranked by tonnage handled. Also given is a map of Texas and its ports. Let set T be the set of ports in Texas that are among the 10 busiest ports in the United States. Write set T in roster form.

Ten Busiest Ports in the U.S., 2000	Total Tonnage
South Louisiana, LA, Port of	217,756,734
Houston, TX	191,419,265
New York, NY and NJ, Port of	138,669,879
New Orleans, LA	90,768,449
Corpus Christi, TX	83,124,950
Beaumont, TX	82,652,554
Huntington-Tristate, WV	78,867,987
Long Beach, CA	70,149,684
Baton Rouge, LA	65,631,084
Texas City, TX	61,585,891

Source: Corps of Engineers, Department of the U.S. Army, U.S. Department of Defense

SOLUTION: By examining the map and the chart we find that four cites appear on both the map and the chart. They are Beaumont, Corpus Christi, Houston, and Texas City. Thus, set $T = \{$Beaumont, Corpus Christi, Houston, Texas City$\}$.

A set is said to be *finite* if it either contains no elements or the number of elements in the set is a natural number. The set $B = \{2, 4, 6, 8, 10\}$ is a finite set because the number of elements in the set is 5, and 5 is a natural number. A set that is not finite is said to be *infinite*. The set of counting numbers is one example of an infinite set. Infinite sets are discussed in more detail in Section 2.6.

Creature Cards

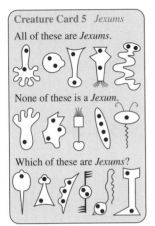

Creature Card 5   *Jexums*

All of these are *Jexums*.

None of these is a *Jexum*.

Which of these are *Jexums*?

We learn to group objects according to what we see as the relevant distinguishing characteristics. One way used by educators to measure this ability is through visual cues. An example can be seen in this test, called "Creature Cards," offered by the Education Development Center. How would you describe membership in the set of Jexums?

Another important concept is equality of sets.

Set A is **equal** to set B, symbolized by $A = B$, if and only if set A and set B contain exactly the same elements.

For example, if set $A = \{1, 2, 3\}$ and set $B = \{3, 1, 2\}$, then $A = B$ because they contain exactly the same elements. The order of the elements in the set is not important. If two sets are equal, both must contain the same number of elements. The number of elements in a set is called its *cardinal number*.

The **cardinal number** of set A, symbolized by $n(A)$, is the number of elements in set A.

Both set $A = \{1, 2, 3\}$ and set $B = \{$England, Brazil, Japan$\}$ have a cardinal number of 3; that is, $n(A) = 3$, and $n(B) = 3$. We can say that set A and set B both have a cardinality of 3.

Two sets are said to be *equivalent* if they contain the same number of elements.

Set A is **equivalent** to set B if and only if $n(A) = n(B)$.

Any sets that are equal must also be equivalent. Not all sets that are equivalent are equal, however. The sets $D = \{$a, b, c$\}$ and $E = \{$apple, orange, pear$\}$ are equivalent, since both have the same cardinal number, 3. Because the elements differ, however, the sets are not equal.

Two sets that are equivalent or have the same cardinality can be placed in *one-to-one correspondence*. Set A and set B can be placed in one-to-one correspondence if every element of set A can be matched with exactly one element of set B and every element of set B can be matched with exactly one element of set A. For example, there is a one-to-one correspondence between the student names on a class list and the student identification numbers because we can match each name with a student identification number.

Consider set S, states, and set C, state capitals.

$$S = \{\text{North Carolina, Georgia, South Carolina, Florida}\}$$

$$C = \{\text{Columbia, Raleigh, Tallahassee, Atlanta}\}$$

Two different one-to-one correspondences for sets S and C follow.

$$S = \{\text{North Carolina, Georgia, South Carolina, Florida}\}$$

$$C = \{\text{Columbia, Raleigh, Tallahassee, Atlanta}\}$$

$$S = \{\text{North Carolina, Georgia, South Carolina, Florida}\}$$

$$C = \{\text{Columbia, Raleigh, Tallahassee, Atlanta}\}$$

Other one-to-one correspondences between sets S and C are possible. Do you know which capital goes with which state?

Null or Empty Set

Some sets do not contain any elements, such as the set of zebras that are in this room.

> The set that contains no elements is called the **empty set** or **null set** and is symbolized by { } or Ø.

Note that {Ø} is not the empty set. This set contains the element Ø and has a cardinality of 1. The set {0} is also not the empty set because it contains the element 0. It also has a cardinality of 1.

EXAMPLE 8   *Natural Number Solutions*

Indicate the set of natural numbers that satisfies the equation $x + 2 = 0$.

SOLUTION: The values that satisfy the equation are those that make the equation a true statement. Only the number -2 satisfies this equation. Because -2 is not a natural number, the solution set of this equation is { } or Ø.   ▲

Universal Set

Another important set is a *universal set*.

> A **universal set,** symbolized by U, is a set that contains all the elements for any specific discussion.

When a universal set is given, only the elements in the universal set may be considered when working the problem. If, for example, the universal set for a particular problem is defined as $U = \{1, 2, 3, 4, \ldots, 10\}$, then only the natural numbers 1 through 10 may be used in that problem.

SECTION 2.1   EXERCISES

Concept/Writing Exercises

In Exercises 1–12, answer each question with a complete sentence.

1. What is a set?

2. What is an ellipsis, and how is it used?

3. What are the three ways that a set can be written? Give an example of each.

4. What is a finite set?

5. What is an infinite set?

6. What are equal sets?

7. What are equivalent sets?

8. What is the cardinal number of a set?

9. What is the empty set?

10. What are the two ways to indicate the empty set?

11. What does a one-to-one correspondence of two sets mean?

12. What is a universal set?

Practice the Skills

In Exercises 13–18, determine whether each set is well defined.

13. The set of people who own large dogs

14. The set of the best Internet web sites

15. The set of states that have a common border with Colorado

16. The set of the four states in the United States having the largest areas

17. The set of astronauts who walked on the moon

18. The set of the nicest entertainers

In Exercises 19–24, determine whether each set is finite or infinite.

19. $\{1, 3, 5, 7, \ldots\}$

20. The set of multiples of 6 between 0 and 90

21. The set of even numbers greater than 19

22. The set of fractions between 1 and 2

23. The set of odd numbers greater than 15

24. The set of cars in the parking lot at the Home Depot store at 770 Jefferson Road, Rochester, New York, on August 1, 2004, at 1:00 P.M.

In Exercises 25–34, express each set in roster form. You may need to use a world almanac or some other reference source.

25. The set of oceans in the world

26. The set of states in the United States whose names begin with the letter I

27. The set of natural numbers between 10 and 178

28. $C = \{x \mid x + 6 = 10\}$

29. $B = \{x \mid x \in N \text{ and } x \text{ is even}\}$

30. The set of states west of the Mississippi River that have a common border with the state of Florida

31. The set of football players over the age of 70 who are still playing in the National Football League

32. The set of states in the United States that have no common border with any other state

33. $E = \{x \mid x \in N \text{ and } 6 \leq x < 72\}$

34. The set of professional baseball players in the major leagues who have hit at least 70 home runs in a season prior to 2002

The list above and to the right shows the estimated price of the seven best-selling digital cameras, ranked by market share, in October 2000. In Exercises 35–38, use the list to represent each of the sets in roster form. Let the seven cameras in the list represent the universal set.

35. The set of best-selling digital cameras with an estimated price greater than $500

36. The set of best-selling digital cameras with an estimated price less than $300

37. The set of best-selling digital cameras with an estimated price between $250 and $650

38. The set of best-selling digital cameras with an estimated price between $500 and $800

Camera	Estimated Price
1. Sony Mavica FD-73	$400
2. Olympus D-360L	$290
3. Sony DSC-S50	$550
4. Sony DSC-S70	$750
5. Kodak DC215	$310
6. H-P Photo Smart C315	$300
7. Sony Mavica FD-90	$700

Source: PC Data (Rochester Democrat and Chronicle)

The following graph shows the federal deficit, in billions of dollars, for 2002 and 2003 and the projected federal deficit for the years 2004–2008. In exercises 39–42, use the graph to represent each of the sets in roster form.

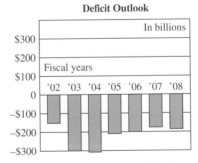

Source: White House Office of Management and Budget

39. The set of years in which the federal deficit or the projected federal deficit is more than $100 billion

40. The set of years in which the federal deficit or the projected federal deficit is between $100 billion and $250 billion

41. The set of years in which the federal deficit or the projected federal deficit is less than $250 billion

42. The set of years in which the federal deficit or the projected federal deficit is more than $250 billion

In Exercises 43–50, express each set in set-builder notation.

43. $B = \{4, 5, 6, 7, 8, 9, 10\}$

44. $A = \{1, 2, 3, 4, 5, 6, 7\}$

45. $C = \{3, 6, 9, 12, \dots\}$

46. $D = \{5, 10, 15, 20, \dots\}$

47. E is the set of odd natural numbers

48. A is the set of national holidays in the United States in September

49. C is the set of months that contain less than 30 days

50. $F = \{15, 16, 17, \dots, 100\}$

In Exercises 51–58, write a description of each set.

51. $A = \{1, 2, 3, 4, 5, 6, 7\}$

52. $D = \{4, 8, 12, 16, 20, \dots\}$

53. $V = \{a, e, i, o, u\}$

54. $S = \{$Bashful, Doc, Dopey, Grumpy, Happy, Sleepy, Sneezy$\}$

55. $C = \{$Casio, Hewlett-Packard, Sharp, Texas Instruments, $\dots\}$

56. $B = \{$Mississippi, Missouri, Yukon, Rio Grande, Arkansas$\}$

57. $B = \{$John Lennon, Ringo Starr, Paul McCartney, George Harrison$\}$

58. $E = \{x \mid x \in N \text{ and } 5 < x \le 12\}$

The following list shows the top 10 media markets, in order, for advertisements for the 2000 elections of the president and members of Congress, through October 10, 2000. In Exercises 59–62, use the list to represent each of the sets in roster form. Let the 10 markets represent the universal set.

59. $\{x \mid x$ is a city in which the number of advertisements was greater than 18,000$\}$

60. $\{x \mid x$ is a city in which the number of advertisements was less than 10,000$\}$

61. $\{x \mid x$ is a city in which the number of advertisements was between 12,500 and 13,000$\}$

62. $\{x \mid x$ is a city in which the number of advertisements was between 13,000 and 14,000$\}$

Market	Number of Ads
1. St. Louis	18,755
2. Kansas City	14,872
3. Seattle	14,234
4. Detroit	13,490
5. Spokane	13,191
6. Grand Rapids	12,436
7. Flint-Saginaw	11,797
8. Philadelphia	11,006
9. Louisville	10,345
10. Scranton	9016

Source: The Hotline and the Brennan Center for Justice

St. Louis, MO

The following graph shows the advertising revenues for Yahoo, in millions of dollars, for the years 1998–2002. In Exercises 63–66, use the graph to represent each of the sets in roster form.

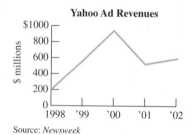

Source: *Newsweek*

63. $\{x \mid x$ is a year in which advertising revenues exceeded $400 million$\}$

64. $\{x \mid x$ is a year in which advertising revenues were less than $300 million$\}$

65. $\{x \mid x$ is a year in which advertising revenues exceeded $500 million but were less than $800 million$\}$

66. $\{x \mid x$ is a year in which advertising revenues exceeded $300 million but were less than $500 million$\}$

In Exercises 67–74, state whether each statement is true or false. If false, give the reason.

67. $\{b\} \in \{a, b, c, d, e, f\}$

68. $b \in \{a, b, c, d, e, f\}$

69. $h \in \{a, b, c, d, e, f\}$

70. Cat in the Hat $\in$ {characters created by Dr. Seuss}

71. $3 \notin \{x \mid x \in N$ and x is odd$\}$

72. Maui $\in$ {capital cities in the United States}

73. *Titanic* $\in$ {top 10 motion pictures with the greatest revenues}

74. $2 \in \{x \mid x$ is an odd natural number$\}$

In Exercises 75–78, for the sets $A = \{2, 4, 6, 8\}$, $B = \{1, 3, 7, 9, 13, 21\}$, $C = \{ \ \}$, and $D = \{\#, \&, \%, \square, *\}$, determine

75. $n(A)$.

76. $n(B)$.

77. $n(C)$.

78. $n(D)$.

In Exercises 79–84, determine whether the pairs of sets are equal, equivalent, both, or neither.

79. $A = \{$circle, triangle, square$\}$,
$B = \{$triangle, circle, square$\}$

80. $A = \{7, 9, 10\}$, $B = \{a, b, c\}$

81. $A = \{$grapes, apples, oranges$\}$,
$B = \{$grapes, peaches, apples, oranges$\}$

82. A is the set of collies.
B is the set of dogs.

83. A is the set of letters in the word *tap*.
B is the set of letters in the word *ant*.

84. A is the set of states.
B is the set of state capitals.

Problem Solving

85. Set-builder notation is often more versatile and efficient than listing a set in roster form. This versatility is illustrated with the two sets.

$$A = \{x \mid x \in N \text{ and } x > 2\}$$
$$B = \{x \mid x > 2\}$$

a) Write a description of set A and set B.

b) Explain the difference between set A and set B.
(*Hint:* Is $4\frac{1}{2} \in A$? Is $4\frac{1}{2} \in B$?)

c) Write set A in roster form.

d) Can set B be written in roster form? Explain your answer.

86. Start with sets

$$A = \{x \mid 2 < x \le 5 \text{ and } x \in N\}$$

and

$$B = \{x \mid 2 < x \le 5\}$$

a) Write a description of set A and set B.

b) Explain the difference between set A and set B.

c) Write set A in roster form.

d) Can set B be written in roster form? Explain your answer.

*A cardinal number answers the question "How many?" An **ordinal number** describes the relative position that an element occupies. For example, Molly's desk is the third desk from the aisle.*

In Exercises 87–90, determine whether the number used is a cardinal number or an ordinal number.

87. John Grisham has written 12 books.

John Grisham

88. Study the chart on page 25 in the book.

89. Lincoln was the sixteenth president of the United States.

90. Emily paid $35 for her new blouse.

91. Describe three sets of which you are a member.

92. Describe three sets that have no members.

93. Write a short paragraph explaining why the universal set and the empty set are necessary in the study of sets.

Challenge Problem/Group Activity

94. a) In a given exercise, a universal set is not specified, but we know that actor Brad Pitt is a member of the universal set. Describe five different possible universal sets of which Brad Pitt is a member.

b) Write a description of one set that includes all the universal sets in part (a).

Recreational Mathematics

95. *Face to Face* Place the eight squares on the left into the diagram on the right so that two squares with a common border will have the same number on both sides of the border. Do not turn the squares or rearrange the numbers within each square.

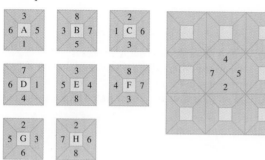

Internet/Research Activity

96. Georg Cantor is recognized as the founder and a leader in the development of set theory. Do research and write a paper on his life and his contributions to set theory and to the field of mathematics. References include history of mathematics books, encyclopedias, and the Internet.

2.2 SUBSETS

In our complex world, we often break larger sets into smaller more manageable sets, called *subsets*. For example, consider the set of people in your class. Suppose we categorize the set of people in your class according to the first letter of their last name (the A's, B's, C's, etc.). When we do this, each of these sets may be considered a subset of the original set. Each of these subsets can be separated further. For example, the set of people whose last name begins with the letter A can be categorized as either male or female or by their age. Each of these collections of people is also a subset. A given set may have many different subsets.

> Set A is a **subset** of set B, symbolized by $A \subseteq B$, if and only if all the elements of set A are also elements of set B.

The symbol $A \subseteq B$ indicates that "set A is a subset of set B." The symbol $\not\subseteq$ is used to indicate "is not a subset." Thus, $A \not\subseteq B$ indicates that set A is not a subset of set B. *To show that set A is not a subset of set B, we must find at least one element of set A that is not an element of set B.*

EXAMPLE 1   *A Subset?*

Determine whether set A is a subset of set B.
a) $A = \{\text{blue jay, robin, cardinal}\}$
    $B = \{\text{blue jay, robin, chickadee, cardinal}\}$

Rainbows

Colors of primary rainbow

Colors of secondary rainbow

Most rainbows we see are primary rainbows, but there are rare moments when a second, fainter rainbow can be seen behind the first. In this secondary rainbow, the light pattern has been reversed. Both rainbows contain the same set of colors, so each set of colors is a subset of the other.

b) $A = \{2, 3, 4, 5\}$ $B = \{2, 3\}$

c) $A = \{x \,|\, x \text{ is a yellow fruit}\}$
    $B = \{x \,|\, x \text{ is a red fruit}\}$

d) $A = \{\text{cassette, compact disc, videotape}\}$
    $B = \{\text{compact disc, videotape, cassette}\}$

SOLUTION:

a) All the elements of set A are contained in set B, so $A \subseteq B$.

b) The elements 4 and 5 are in set A but not in set B, so $A \nsubseteq B$ (A is not a subset of B). In this example, however, all the elements of set B are contained in set A; therefore, $B \subseteq A$.

c) There are fruits, such as bananas, that are in set A that are not in set B, so $A \nsubseteq B$.

d) All the elements of set A are contained in set B, so $A \subseteq B$. Note that set A = set B.

▲

Proper Subsets

Set A is a **proper subset** of set B, symbolized by $A \subset B$, if and only if all the elements of set A are elements of set B and set $A \neq$ set B (that is, set B must contain at least one element not in set A).

Consider the sets $A = \{\text{red, blue, yellow}\}$ and $B = \{\text{red, orange, yellow, green, blue, violet}\}$. Set A is a *subset* of set B, $A \subseteq B$, because every element of set A is also an element of set B. Set A is also a *proper subset* of set B, $A \subset B$, because set A and set B are not equal. Now consider $C = \{\text{car, bus, train}\}$ and $D = \{\text{train, car, bus}\}$. Set C is a subset of set D, $C \subseteq D$, because every element of set C is also an element of set D. Set C, however, is not a proper subset of set D, $C \not\subset D$, because set C and set D are equal sets.

EXAMPLE 2   *A Proper Subset?*

Determine whether set A is a proper subset of set B.

a) $A = \{\text{refrigerator, microwave, dishwasher}\}$
    $B = \{\text{stove, refrigerator, microwave, dishwasher, garbage disposal}\}$

b) $A = \{a, b, c, d\}$ $B = \{a, c, b, d\}$

SOLUTION:

a) All the elements of set A are contained in set B, and sets A and B are not equal; thus, $A \subset B$.

b) Set A = set B, so $A \not\subset B$. (However, $A \subseteq B$.)   ▲

Every set is a subset of itself, but no set is a proper subset of itself. For all sets A, $A \subseteq A$, but $A \not\subset A$. For example, if $A = \{1, 2, 3\}$, then $A \subseteq A$ because every element of set A is contained in set A, but $A \not\subset A$ because set A = set A.

Let $A = \{\ \}$ and $B = \{1, 2, 3, 4\}$. Is $A \subseteq B$? To show $A \not\subseteq B$, you must find at least one element of set A that is not an element of set B. As this cannot be done, $A \subseteq B$ must be true. Using the same reasoning, we can show that *the empty set is a subset of every set, including itself.*

EXAMPLE 3   *Element or Subset?*

Determine whether the following are true or false.

a) $3 \in \{3, 4, 5\}$
b) $\{3\} \in \{3, 4, 5\}$
c) $\{3\} \in \{\{3\}, \{4\}, \{5\}\}$
d) $\{3\} \subseteq \{3, 4, 5\}$
e) $3 \subseteq \{3, 4, 5\}$
f) $\{\ \} \subseteq \{3, 4, 5\}$

SOLUTION:

a) $3 \in \{3, 4, 5\}$ is a true statement because 3 is a member of the set $\{3, 4, 5\}$.

b) $\{3\} \in \{3, 4, 5\}$ is a false statement because $\{3\}$ is a set, and the set $\{3\}$ is not an element of the set $\{3, 4, 5\}$.

c) $\{3\} \in \{\{3\}, \{4\}, \{5\}\}$ is a true statement because $\{3\}$ is an element in the set. The elements of the set $\{\{3\}, \{4\}, \{5\}\}$ are themselves sets.

d) $\{3\} \subseteq \{3, 4, 5\}$ is a true statement because every element of the first set is an element of the second set.

e) $3 \subseteq \{3, 4, 5\}$ is a false statement because the 3 is not in braces, so it is not a set and thus cannot be a subset. The 3 is an element of the set as indicated in part (a).

f) $\{\ \} \subseteq \{3, 4, 5\}$ is a true statement because the empty set is a subset of every set.   ▲

Number of Subsets

How many distinct subsets can be made from a given set? The empty set has no elements and has exactly one subset, the empty set. A set with one element has two subsets. A set with two elements has four subsets. A set with three elements has eight subsets. This information is illustrated in Table 2.1 on page 53. How many subsets will a set with four elements contain?

By continuing this table with larger and larger sets, we can develop a general formula for finding the number of distinct subsets that can be made from any given set.

The **number of distinct subsets** of a finite set A is 2^n, where n is the number of elements in set A.

TABLE 2.1 Number of Subsets

Set	Subsets	Number of Subsets
{ }	{ }	$1 = 2^0$
$\{a\}$	$\{a\}$ { }	$2 = 2^1$
$\{a, b\}$	$\{a, b\}$ $\{a\}, \{b\}$ { }	$4 = 2 \times 2 = 2^2$
$\{a, b, c\}$	$\{a, b, c\}$ $\{a, b\}, \{a, c\}, \{b, c\}$ $\{a\}, \{b\}, \{c\}$ { }	$8 = 2 \times 2 \times 2 = 2^3$

EXAMPLE 4   *Distinct Subsets*

a) Determine the number of distinct subsets for the set $\{S, L, E, D\}$.
b) List all the distinct subsets for the set $\{S, L, E, D\}$.
c) How many of the distinct subsets are proper subsets?

SOLUTION:

a) Since the number of elements in the set is 4, the number of distinct subsets is
   $2^4 = 2 \times 2 \times 2 \times 2 = 16$.

b) $\{S, L, E, D\}$ $\{S, L, E\}$ $\{S, L\}$ $\{S\}$ { }
   $\{S, L, D\}$ $\{S, E\}$ $\{L\}$
   $\{S, E, D\}$ $\{S, D\}$ $\{E\}$
   $\{L, E, D\}$ $\{L, E\}$ $\{D\}$
   $\{L, D\}$
   $\{E, D\}$

c) There are 15 proper subsets. Every subset except $\{S, L, E, D\}$ is a proper subset.

EXAMPLE 5   *Variations of Ice Cream*

Shanna Ruben is going to purchase ice cream at Friendly's Restaurant. To her ice
cream she can add any of the following toppings: hot fudge, whipped cream,
cherries, butterscotch topping, caramel topping, chopped nuts, Reese's Pieces,
M & M's, Gummy Bears. How many different variations of the ice cream and
toppings can be made?

SOLUTION: Shanna can order the ice cream with no extra toppings, any one topping, any two toppings, any three toppings, and so on, up to all nine toppings. One technique used in problem solving is to consider similar problems that you have solved previously. If you think about this problem, you will realize that this problem is the same as, "How many distinct subsets can be made from a set with nine elements?" The number of different variations of the ice cream is the same as the number of possible subsets of a set that has nine elements. There are 2^9 or 512 possible subsets of a set with nine elements, so there are 512 possible variations of the ice cream and toppings.   ▲

DID YOU KNOW

The Ladder of Life

Scientists use sets to classify and categorize knowledge. In biology, the science of classifying all living things is called *taxonomy* and was probably practiced by the earliest cave-dwellers. Over 2000 years ago, Aristotle formalized animal classification with his "ladder of life": higher animals, lower animals, higher plants, lower plants.

Contemporary biologists use a system of classification called the Linnaean system, named after Swedish biologist Carolus Linnaeas (1707–1778). The Linnaean system starts with the smallest unit (member) and assigns it to a specific genus (set) and species (subset).

A zebra, *Equus burchelli*, is a member of the genus *Equus*, as is the horse, *Equus caballus*. Both the zebra and the horse are members of the universal set called the kingdom of animals and the same family, Equidae; they are members of different species (*E. burchelli* and *E. caballus*), however.

Even more general groupings of living things are made according to shared characteristics. The groupings, from most general to most specific are: kingdom, phylum, class, order, family, genus, and species. Each of the groupings is classified into sub groupings. For example, in the sixteenth century, living organisms were classified into two kingdoms, plants and animals. Today, living organisms are classified into six kingdoms called animalia, plantae, archaea, eubacteria, fungi, and protista.

SECTION 2.2   EXERCISES

Concept/Writing Exercises

In Exercises 1–6, answer each question with a complete sentence.

1. What is a subset?

2. What is a proper subset?

3. Explain the difference between a subset and a proper subset.

4. Write the formula for determining the number of distinct subsets for a set with n distinct elements.

5. Write the formula for determining the number of distinct proper subsets for a set with n distinct elements.

6. Can any set be a proper subset of itself? Explain.

Practice the Skills

In Exercises 7–24, answer true or false. If false, give the reason.

7. gold $\subseteq$ {gold, silver, sapphire, emerald}
8. { } $\in$ {knee, ankle, shoulder, hip}
9. { } $\subseteq$ {Tigger, Pooh, Christopher Robin}
10. red $\subset$ {red, green, blue}
11. 5 $\notin$ {2, 4, 6}
12. {Pete, Mike, Amy} $\subseteq$ {Amy, Kaitlyn, Brianna}
13. { } = {Ø}
14. {engineer} $\subseteq$ {architect, physician, attorney, engineer}
15. Ø = { }
16. 0 = { }
17. {0} = Ø
18. {3, 8, 11} $\subseteq$ {3, 8, 11}
19. {swimming} $\in$ {sailing, waterskiing, swimming}
20. {3, 5, 9} $\not\subset$ {3, 9, 5}
21. { } $\subseteq$ { }
22. {1} $\in$ {{1}, {2}, {3}}
23. {US Airways, Delta, American} $\subset$ {American, US Airways, Delta}
24. {b, a, t} $\subseteq$ {t, a, b}

In Exercises 25–32, determine whether $A = B$, $A \subseteq B$, $B \subseteq A$, $A \subset B$, $B \subset A$, or none of these. (There may be more than one answer.)

25. A = {Pepsi, Mountain Dew, Coke, Sprite}
    B = {Pepsi, Coke}
26. $A = \{x \mid x \in N \text{ and } x < 6\}$
    $B = \{x \mid x \in N \text{ and } 1 \leq x \leq 5\}$
27. Set A is the set of states east of the Mississippi River. Set B is the set of states that border the Atlantic Ocean.
28. A = {1, 3, 5, 7, 9}
    B = {3, 9, 5, 7, 6}
29. $A = \{x \mid x \text{ is a brand of ice cream}\}$
    B = {Breyers, Ben & Jerry's, Häagen-Dazs}
30. $A = \{x \mid x \text{ is a sport that uses a ball}\}$
    B = {basketball, soccer, tennis}
31. Set A is the set of natural numbers between 2 and 7. Set B is the set of natural numbers greater than 2 and less than 7.
32. Set A is the set of toys requiring batteries. Set B is the set of toys requiring AA batteries.

In Exercises 33–38, list all the subsets of the sets given.

33. D = Ø
34. A = {○}
35. B = {pen, pencil}
36. C = {apple, peach, banana}

Problem Solving

37. For set A = {a, b, c, d},
    a) list all the subsets of set A.
    b) state which of the subsets in part (a) are not proper subsets of set A.
38. A set contains nine elements.
    a) How many subsets does it have?
    b) How many proper subsets does it have?

In Exercises 39–50, if the statement is true for all sets A and B, write "true." If it is not true for all sets A and B, write "false." Assume that $A \neq \emptyset, U \neq \emptyset$, and $A \subset U$.

39. If $A \subseteq B$, then $A \subset B$.
40. If $A \subset B$, then $A \subseteq B$.
41. $A \subseteq A$
42. $A \subset A$
43. $\emptyset \subset A$
44. $\emptyset \subseteq A$
45. $A \subseteq U$
46. $\emptyset \subset \emptyset$
47. $\emptyset \subset U$
48. $U \subseteq \emptyset$
49. $\emptyset \subseteq \emptyset$
50. $U \subset \emptyset$

51. *Building a House* The Jacobsens are planning to build a house in a new development. They can either build the base model offered by the builder or add any of the following options: deck, hot tub, security system, hardwood flooring. How many different variations of the house are possible?

52. *Computer Upgrade* Jason Jackson is considering having his computer upgraded. He can leave the computer as it is, or he can upgrade any of the following set of items: RAM, modem, video card, hard drive, processor, sound card. How many possible options for upgrading does Jason have?

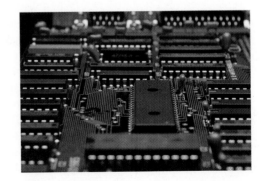

53. *Telephone Features* A customer with Verizon can order telephone service with some, all, or none of the following features: call waiting, call forwarding, caller identification, three-way calling, voice mail, fax line. How many different variations of the set of features are possible?

54. *Hamburger Variations* Customers ordering hamburgers at Vic and Irv's Hamburger stand are always asked, "What do you want on it?" The choices are ketchup, mustard, relish, hot sauce, onions, lettuce, tomato. How many different variations are there for ordering a hamburger?

55. If $E \subseteq F$ and $F \subseteq E$, what other relationship exists between E and F? Explain.

56. How can you determine whether the set of boys is equivalent to the set of girls at a roller-skating rink?

57. For the set $D = \{a, b, c\}$
   a) is a an element of set D? Explain.
   b) is c a subset of set D? Explain.
   c) is $\{a, b\}$ a subset of set D? Explain.

Challenge Problems/Group Activity

58. *Hospital Expansion* A hospital has four members on the board of directors: Arnold, Benitez, Cathy, and Dominique.
   a) When the members vote on whether to add a wing to the hospital, how many different ways can they vote (abstentions are not allowed)? For example, Arnold—yes, Benitez—no, Cathy—no, and Dominique—yes is one of the many possibilities.
   b) Make a listing of all the possible outcomes of the vote. For example, the vote described in part (a) could be represented as (YNNY).

   c) How many of the outcomes given in part (b) would result in a majority supporting the addition of a wing to the hospital? That is, how many of the outcomes have three or more Y's?

Recreational Mathematics

59. How many elements must a set have if the number of proper subsets of the set is $\frac{1}{2}$ of the total number of subsets of the set?

60. If $A \subset B$ and $B \subset C$, must $A \subset C$?

61. If $A \subset B$ and $B \subseteq C$, must $A \subset C$?

62. If $A \subseteq B$ and $B \subseteq C$, must $A \subset C$?

Internet/Research Activity

63. On page 54, we discussed the ladder of life. Do research and indicate all the different classifications in the Linnaean system, from most general to the most specific, in which a koala belongs.

2.3 VENN DIAGRAMS AND SET OPERATIONS

Figure 2.1

A useful technique for picturing set relationships is the Venn diagram, named for the English mathematician John Venn (1834–1923). Venn invented the diagrams and used them to illustrate ideas in his text on symbolic logic, published in 1881.

In a Venn diagram, a rectangle usually represents the universal set, U. The items inside the rectangle may be divided into subsets of the universal set. The subsets are usually represented by circles. In Fig. 2.1, the circle labeled A represents set A, which is a subset of the universal set.

Two sets may be represented in a Venn diagram in any of four different ways (see Fig. 2.2 on page 57). Two sets A and B are *disjoint* when they have no elements in common. Two disjoint sets A and B are illustrated in Fig. 2.2(a). If set A is a proper subset of set B, $A \subset B$, the two sets may be illustrated as in Fig. 2.2(b). If set A contains exactly the same elements as set B, that is, $A = B$, the two sets may be illustrated as in Fig. 2.2(c). Two sets A and B with some elements in common are shown in Fig. 2.2(d), which is regarded as the most general form of a Venn diagram.

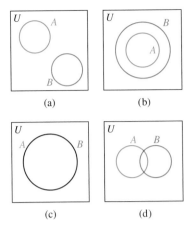

Figure 2.2

Figure 2.3

If we label the regions of the diagram in Fig. 2.2(d) using I, II, III, and IV, we can illustrate the four possible cases with this one diagram, Fig. 2.3.

CASE 1: DISJOINT SETS When sets A and B are disjoint, they have no elements in common. Therefore, region II of Fig. 2.3 is empty.

CASE 2: SUBSETS When $A \subseteq B$, every element of set A is also an element of set B. Thus, there can be no elements in region I of Fig. 2.3. If $B \subseteq A$, however, then region III of Fig. 2.3 is empty.

CASE 3: EQUAL SETS When set A = set B, all the elements of set A are elements of set B and all the elements of set B are elements of set A. Thus, regions I and III of Fig. 2.3 are empty.

CASE 4: OVERLAPPING SETS When sets A and B have elements in common, those elements are in region II of Fig. 2.3. The elements that belong to set A but not to set B are in region I. The elements that belong to set B but not to set A are in region III.

In each of the four cases, any element not belonging to set A or set B is placed in region IV.

Venn diagrams will be helpful in understanding set operations. The basic operations of arithmetic are $+$, $-$, $\times$, and $\div$. When we see these symbols, we know what procedure to follow to determine the answer. Some of the operations in set theory are $'$, $\cup$, and $\cap$. They represent complement, union, and intersection, respectively.

Complement

> The **complement** of set A, symbolized by A', is the set of all the elements in the universal set that are not in set A.

In Fig. 2.4, the shaded region outside of set A within the universal set represents the complement of set A, or A'.

Figure 2.4

┌**EXAMPLE 1**   *A Set and Its Complement*

Given

$$U = \{1, 2, 3, 4, 5, 6, 7, 8\} \text{ and } A = \{1, 3, 4\}$$

find A' and illustrate the relationship among sets U, A, and A' in a Venn diagram.

SOLUTION: The elements in U that are not in set A are 2, 5, 6, 7, 8. Thus, $A' = \{2, 5, 6, 7, 8\}$. The Venn diagram is illustrated in Fig. 2.5.   ▲

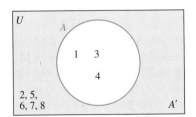

Figure 2.5

Intersection

The word *intersection* brings to mind the area common to two crossing streets. The red car in the figure on the next page is in the intersection of the two streets. The set operation is defined as follows.

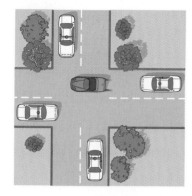

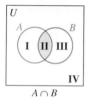

Figure 2.6

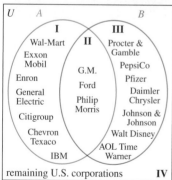

Figure 2.7

The **intersection** of sets A and B, symbolized by $A \cap B$, is the set containing all the elements that are common to both set A and set B.

The shaded region, region II, in Fig. 2.6 represents the intersection of sets A and B.

EXAMPLE 2   *Sets with Overlapping Regions*

Let the universal set, U, represent the set of all U.S. corporations in 2001. Let set A represent the set of the 10 largest U.S. corporations in 2001, based on revenues. Let set B represent the set of the 10 leading U.S. advertisers in 2001 (see the table). Draw a Venn diagram illustrating the relationship between set A and set B.

Ten Largest U.S. Corporations	Ten Leading U.S. Advertisers
Wal-Mart	General Motors
Exxon Mobil	Procter & Gamble
General Motors	Ford Motor Company
Ford Motor Company	PepsiCo
Enron	Pfizer
General Electric	DaimlerChrysler
Citigroup	AOL Time Warner
ChevronTexaco	Phillip Morris
International Business Machines	Walt Disney
Phillip Morris	Johnson & Johnson

Source: *Fortune*, www.adage.com

SOLUTION: First determine the intersection of sets A and B. General Motors, Ford Motor Company, and Phillip Morris are common to both sets. Therefore,

$$A \cap B = \{\text{General Motors, Ford Motor Company, Phillip Morris}\}$$

Place these elements in region II of Fig. 2.7. Now place in region I the elements in set A that have not been placed in region II. Therefore, Wal-Mart, Exxon Mobil, Enron, General Electric, Citigroup, ChevronTexaco, and International Business Machines (IBM) are placed in region I. Complete region III by determining the elements in set B that have not been placed in region II. Thus, Procter & Gamble, PepsiCo, Pfizer, DaimlerChrysler, AOL Time Warner, Walt Disney, and Johnson & Johnson are placed in region III. Finally, place those elements in U that are not in either set outside both circles. This group includes the remaining U.S. corporations, which are placed in region IV.

┌─ EXAMPLE 3   *The Intersection of Sets*

Given

$$U = \{1, 2, 3, 4, 5, 6, 7, 8, 9, 10\}$$
$$A = \{1, 2, 4, 6\}$$
$$B = \{1, 3, 6, 7, 9\}$$
$$C = \{\ \}$$

find

a) $A \cap B.$ b) $A \cap C.$ c) $A' \cap B.$ d) $(A \cap B)'.$

SOLUTION:

a) $A \cap B = \{1, 2, 4, 6\} \cap \{1, 3, 6, 7, 9\} = \{1, 6\}.$ The elements common to both set A and set B are 1 and 6.

b) $A \cap C = \{1, 2, 4, 6\} \cap \{\ \} = \{\ \}.$ There are no elements common to both set A and set C.

c) $\quad A' = \{3, 5, 7, 8, 9, 10\}$
$A' \cap B = \{3, 5, 7, 8, 9, 10\} \cap \{1, 3, 6, 7, 9\}$
$\quad\quad\quad = \{3, 7, 9\}$

d) To find $(A \cap B)'$, first determine $A \cap B$.
$\quad A \cap B = \{1, 6\}$ from part (a)
$\quad (A \cap B)' = \{1, 6\}' = \{2, 3, 4, 5, 7, 8, 9, 10\}$ ▲

Union

The word *union* means to unite or join together, as in marriage, and that is exactly what is done when we perform the operation of union.

> The **union** of set A and set B, symbolized by $A \cup B$, is the set containing all the elements that are members of set A or of set B (or of both sets).

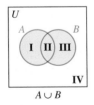

U
A   B
I II III
IV

$A \cup B$

Figure 2.8

The three shaded regions of Fig. 2.8, regions I, II, and III, together represent the union of sets A and B. If an element is common to both sets, it is listed only once in the union of the sets.

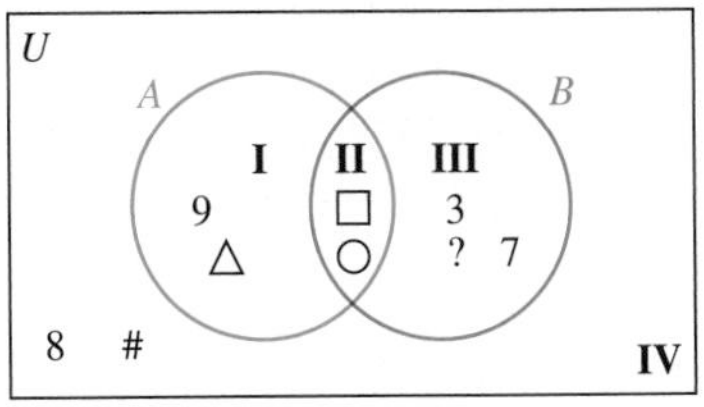

┌─ EXAMPLE 4   *Determining Sets from a Venn Diagram*

Use the Venn diagram in Fig. 2.9 to determine the following sets.

a) U b) A c) B' d) $A \cap B$
e) $A \cup B$ f) $(A \cup B)'$ g) $n(A \cup B)$

SOLUTION:

a) The universal set consists of all the elements within the rectangle, that is, the elements in regions I, II, III, and IV. Thus, $U = \{9, \triangle, \square, \bigcirc, 3, 7, ?, \#, 8\}$.

U
A   B
I II III
9 □ 3
△ ○ ? 7
8 #   IV

Figure 2.9

b) Set A consists of the elements in regions I and II. Thus, $A = \{9, \triangle, \square, \bigcirc\}$.

c) B' consists of the elements outside set B, or the elements in regions I and IV. Thus, $B' = \{9, \triangle, \#, 8\}$.

d) $A \cap B$ consists of the elements that belong to both set A and set B (region II). Thus, $A \cap B = \{\square, \bigcirc\}$.

e) $A \cup B$ consists of the elements that belong to set A or set B (regions I, II, or III). Thus, $A \cup B = \{9, \triangle, \square, \bigcirc, 3, 7, ?\}$.

f) $(A \cup B)'$ consists of the elements in U that are not in $A \cup B$. Thus, $(A \cup B)' = \{\#, 8\}$.

g) $n(A \cup B)$ represents the *number of elements* in the union of sets A and B. Thus, $n(A \cup B) = 7$, as there are seven elements in the union of sets A and B.   ▲

EXAMPLE 5   *The Union of Sets*

Given

$$U = \{1, 2, 3, 4, 5, 6, 7, 8, 9, 10\}$$
$$A = \{1, 2, 4, 6\}$$
$$B = \{1, 3, 6, 7, 9\}$$
$$C = \{\ \}$$

find

a) $A \cup B$.   b) $A \cup C$.   c) $A' \cup B$.   d) $(A \cup B)'$.

SOLUTION:

a) $A \cup B = \{1, 2, 4, 6\} \cup \{1, 3, 6, 7, 9\} = \{1, 2, 3, 4, 6, 7, 9\}$

b) $A \cup C = \{1, 2, 4, 6\} \cup \{\ \} = \{1, 2, 4, 6\}$. Note that $A \cup C = A$.

c) To determine $A' \cup B$, we must determine A'.

$$A' = \{3, 5, 7, 8, 9, 10\}$$
$$A' \cup B = \{3, 5, 7, 8, 9, 10\} \cup \{1, 3, 6, 7, 9\}$$
$$= \{1, 3, 5, 6, 7, 8, 9, 10\}$$

d) Find $(A \cup B)'$ by first determining $A \cup B$, and then find the complement of $A \cup B$.

$$A \cup B = \{1, 2, 3, 4, 6, 7, 9\} \text{ from part (a)}$$
$$(A \cup B)' = \{1, 2, 3, 4, 6, 7, 9\}' = \{5, 8, 10\}$$ ▲

EXAMPLE 6   *Union and Intersection*

Given

$$U = \{a, b, c, d, e, f, g\}$$
$$A = \{a, b, e, g\}$$
$$B = \{a, c, d, e\}$$
$$C = \{b, e, f\}$$

find

a) $(A \cup B) \cap (A \cup C)$.   b) $(A \cup B) \cap C'$.   c) $A' \cap B'$.

SOLUTION:

a) $(A \cup B) \cap (A \cup C) = \{a, b, c, d, e, g\} \cap \{a, b, e, f, g\}$
$= \{a, b, e, g\}$

b) $(A \cup B) \cap C' = \{a, b, c, d, e, g\} \cap \{a, c, d, g\}$
$= \{a, c, d, g\}$

c) $A' \cap B' = \{c, d, f\} \cap \{b, f, g\}$
$= \{f\}$

The Meaning of *and* and *or*

The words *and* and *or* are very important in many areas of mathematics. We use these words in several chapters in this book, including the probability chapter. The word *or* is generally interpreted to mean *union*, whereas *and* is generally interpreted to mean *intersection*. Suppose $A = \{1, 2, 3, 5, 6, 8\}$ and $B = \{1, 3, 4, 7, 9, 10\}$. Then the elements that belong to set A *or* set B are 1, 2, 3, 4, 5, 6, 7, 8, 9, and 10. These are the elements in the union of the sets. The elements that belong to set A *and* set B are 1 and 3. These are the elements in the intersection of the sets.

The Relationship Between $n(A \cup B)$, $n(A)$, $n(B)$, and $n(A \cap B)$

Having looked at unions and intersections, we can now determine a relationship between $n(A \cup B)$, $n(A)$, $n(B)$, and $n(A \cap B)$. Suppose set A has eight elements, set B has five elements, and $A \cap B$ has two elements. How many elements are in $A \cup B$? Let's make up some arbitrary sets that meet the criteria specified and draw a Venn diagram. If we let $A = \{a, b, c, d, e, f, g, h\}$, then set B must contain five elements, two of which are also in set A. Let $B = \{g, h, i, j, k\}$. We construct a Venn diagram by filling in the intersection first, as shown in Fig. 2.10. The number of elements in $A \cup B$ is 11. The elements g and h are in both sets, and if we add $n(A) + n(B)$, we are counting these elements twice.

To find the number of elements in the union of sets A and B, we can add the number of elements in sets A and B and then subtract the number of elements common to both sets.

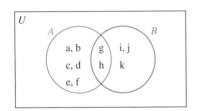

Figure 2.10

For any finite sets A and B,

$$n(A \cup B) = n(A) + n(B) - n(A \cap B)$$

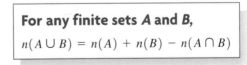

EXAMPLE 7 *How Many Visitors Speak Spanish or French?*

The results of a survey of visitors at the Grand Canyon showed that 25 speak Spanish, 14 speak French, and 4 speak both Spanish and French. How many speak Spanish or French?

SOLUTION: If we let set A be the set of visitors who speak Spanish and let set B be the set of visitors who speak French, then we need to determine $n(A \cup B)$. We can use the above formula to find $n(A \cup B)$.

$$n(A \cup B) = n(A) + n(B) - n(A \cap B)$$
$$n(A \cup B) = 25 + 14 - 4$$
$$= 35$$

Thus, 35 of the visitors surveyed speak either Spanish or French.

EXAMPLE 8   *The Number of Elements in Set A or Set B*

Set A contains 6 letters and 5 numbers. Set B contains 4 letters and 9 numbers. Two letters and 1 number are common to both sets A and B. Find the number of elements in set A or set B.

SOLUTION: You are asked to find the number of elements in set A or set B, which is $n(A \cup B)$. Because $n(A \cup B) = n(A) + n(B) - n(A \cap B)$, if you can determine $n(A)$, $n(B)$, and $n(A \cap B)$, you can solve the problem. Set A contains 6 letters and 5 numbers, so $n(A) = 11$. Set B contains 4 letters and 9 numbers, so $n(B) = 13$. Because 2 letters and 1 number are common to both sets, $n(A \cap B) = 3$.

$$n(A \cup B) = n(A) + n(B) - n(A \cap B)$$
$$= 11 + 13 - 3 = 21$$

Thus, the number of elements in set A or set B is 21.

SECTION 2.3   EXERCISES

Concept/Writing Exercises

In Exercises 1–5, use Fig. 2.2 as a guide to draw a Venn diagram that illustrates the situation described.

1. Set A and set B are disjoint sets.

2. $A \subset B$

3. $B \subset A$

4. $A = B$

5. Set A and set B are overlapping sets.

6. If we are given set A, how do we obtain A complement, A'?

7. How do we obtain the union of two sets A and B, $A \cup B$?

8. In a Venn diagram with two overlapping sets, which region(s) represents $A \cup B$?

9. How do we obtain the intersection of two sets A and B, $A \cap B$?

10. In a Venn diagram with two overlapping sets, which region(s) represents $A \cap B$?

11. a) Which set operation is the word *or* generally interpreted to mean?
b) Which set operation is the word *and* generally interpreted to mean?

12. Give the relationship between $n(A \cup B)$, $n(A)$, $n(B)$, and $n(A \cap B)$.

13. When constructing a Venn diagram with two sets, which region of the diagram do we generally complete first?

14. When constructing a Venn diagram with two sets, which region of the diagram do we generally complete last?

Practice the Skills/Problem Solving

15. *Restaurants* For the sets U, A, and B, construct a Venn diagram and place the elements in the proper regions.

$U = \{$Pizza Hut, Papa John's, McDonald's, Burger King, Wendy's, Roy Rogers, Taco Bell, Subway, Del Taco, Denny's$\}$

$A = \{$Pizza Hut, Papa John's, Wendy's, Roy Rogers, Taco Bell, Denny's$\}$

$B = \{$McDonald's, Burger King, Wendy's, Taco Bell, Subway, Denny's$\}$

16. *Appliances and Electronics* For the sets U, A, and B, construct a Venn diagram and place the elements in the proper regions.

$U = \{$microwave oven, washing machine, dryer, refrigerator, dishwasher, compact disc player, videocassette recorder, computer, camcorder, television$\}$

$A = \{$microwave oven, washing machine, dishwasher, computer, television$\}$

$B = \{$washing machine, dryer, refrigerator, compact disc player, computer, television$\}$

17. *Occupations* The following table shows the fastest-growing occupations based on employment in 2000 and the estimated employment for that profession for 2010. Let the occupations in the table represent the universal set.

Fastest-Growing Occupations, 2000–2010

Occupation	Employment (in thousands of jobs)	
	2000	**2010**
Computer software engineers, applications	380	760
Computer support specialists	506	996
Computer software engineers, system software	317	601
Network and computer systems administrators	229	416
Network systems/data communications analysts	119	211
Desktop publishers	38	63
Database administrators	106	176
Personal/home care aides	414	672
Computer systems analysts	431	689
Medical assistants	329	516

Source: U.S. Department of Labor, Bureau of Labor Statistics

Let $A = $ the set of fastest-growing occupations whose 2000 employment was at least 250,000.

Let $B = $ the set of fastest-growing occupations whose estimated employment in 2010 is at least 650,000.

Construct a Venn diagram illustrating the sets.

18. *Basketball Statistics* The table above and to the right shows the number of times certain basketball players were selected as the National Basketball Association's most valuable player and the number of times the player was the league scoring champion. Let these players represent the universal set.

Player	Most Valuable Player	League Scoring Champion
Michael Jordan	4	10
Dominique Wilkins	0	1
Wilt Chamberlain	2	7
Kareem Abdul-Jabbar	4	2
Shaquille O'Neal	1	2
Earvin Johnson	3	0
Kobe Bryant	0	0
Jerry West	0	1
George Gervin	0	4
Alan Iverson	1	1

Source: National Basketball Association

Michael Jordan

Let $A = $ the set of basketball players that were selected most valuable player at least one time.

Let $B = $ the set of basketball players that were league scoring champion at least one time.

Construct a Venn diagram illustrating the sets.

19. Let U represent the set of U.S. colleges and universities. Let A represent the set of U.S. colleges and universities in the state of North Dakota. Describe A'.

20. Let U represent the set of marbles in a box. Let set B represent the set of marbles that contain some blue coloring. Describe B'.

In Exercises 21–26,

U is the set of insurance companies in the U.S.

A is the set of insurance companies that offer life insurance.

B is the set of insurance companies that offer car insurance.

Describe each of the following sets in words.

21. A'

22. B'

23. $A \cup B$

24. $A \cap B$

25. $A \cap B'$

26. $A \cup B'$

In Exercises 27–32,

U is the set of U.S. corporations.

A is the set of U.S. corporations whose headquarters are in the state of New York.

B is the set of U.S. corporations whose chief executive officer is a woman.

C is the set of U.S. corporations that employ at least 100 people.

Describe the following sets.

27. $A \cap B$

28. $A \cup C$

29. $B' \cap C$

30. $A \cap B \cap C$

31. $A \cup B \cup C$

32. $A' \cup C'$

In Exercises 33–40, use the Venn diagram in Fig. 2.11 to list the set of elements in roster form.

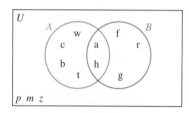

Figure 2.11

33. *A*

34. *B*

35. $A \cap B$

36. *U*

37. $A \cup B$

38. $(A \cup B)'$

39. $A' \cap B'$

40. $(A \cap B)'$

In Exercises 41–48, use the Venn diagram in Fig. 2.12 to list the set of elements in roster form.

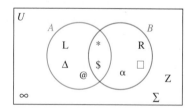

Figure 2.12

41. *A*

42. *B*

43. *U*

44. $A \cup B$

45. $A \cap B$

46. $A \cup B'$

47. $A' \cap B$

48. $(A \cup B)'$

In Exercises 49–58, let

$$U = \{1, 2, 3, 4, 5, 6, 7, 8\}$$
$$A = \{1, 2, 4, 5, 8\}$$
$$B = \{2, 3, 4, 6\}$$

Determine the following.

49. $A \cup B$

50. $A \cap B$

51. B'

52. $A \cup B'$

53. $(A \cup B)'$

54. $A' \cap B'$

55. $(A \cup B)' \cap B$

56. $(A \cup B) \cap (A \cup B)'$

57. $(B \cup A)' \cap (B' \cup A')$

58. $A' \cup (A \cap B)$

In Exercises 59–68, let

$$U = \{a, b, c, d, e, f, g, h, i, j, k\}$$
$$A = \{a, c, d, f, g, i\}$$
$$B = \{b, c, d, f, g\}$$
$$C = \{a, b, f, i, j\}$$

Determine the following.

59. B'

60. $B \cup C$

61. $A \cap C$

62. $A \cup B'$

63. $(A \cap C)'$

64. $(A \cap B) \cup C$

65. $A \cup (C \cap B)'$

66. $A \cup (C' \cup B')$

67. $(A' \cup C) \cup (A \cap B)$

68. $(C \cap B) \cap (A' \cap B)$

Problem Solving

In Exercises 69–82, let

$$U = \{x \mid x \in N \text{ and } x < 10\}$$
$$A = \{x \mid x \in N \text{ and } x \text{ is odd and } x < 10\}$$
$$B = \{x \mid x \in N \text{ and } x \text{ is even and } x < 10\}$$
$$C = \{x \mid x \in N \text{ and } x < 6\}$$

Determine the following.

69. $A \cap B$

70. $A \cup B$

71. $A' \cup B$

72. $(B \cup C)'$

73. $A \cap C'$

74. $A \cap B'$

75. $(B \cap C)'$

76. $(A \cup C) \cap B$

77. $(C \cap B) \cup A$

78. $(C' \cup A) \cap B$

79. $(A' \cup C) \cap B$

80. $(A \cap B)' \cup C$

81. $(A' \cup B') \cap C$

82. $(A' \cap C) \cup (A \cap B)$

83. When will a set and its complement be disjoint? Explain and give an example.

84. When will $n(A \cap B) = 0$? Explain and give an example.

85. *Visiting California* The results of a survey of visitors in Hollywood, California, showed that 27 visited the Hollywood Bowl, 38 visited Disneyland, and 16 visited both the

Hollywood Bowl and Disneyland. How many people visited either the Hollywood Bowl or Disneyland?

Hollywood Bowl

86. *Chorus and Band* At Henniger High School, 46 students sang in the chorus or played in the stage band, 30 students played in the stage band, and 4 students sang in the chorus and played in the stage band. How many students sang in the chorus?

87. Consider the formula

$$n(A \cup B) = n(A) + n(B) - n(A \cap B)$$

a) Show that this relation holds for $A = \{a, b, c, d\}$ and $B = \{b, d, e, f, g, h\}$.
b) Make up your own sets A and B, each consisting of at least six elements. Using these sets, show that the relation holds.
c) Use a Venn diagram and explain why the relation holds for any two sets A and B.

88. The Venn diagram in Fig. 2.13 shows a technique of labeling the regions to indicate membership of elements in a particular region. Define each of the four regions with a set statement. (*Hint: $A \cap B'$ defines region I.*)

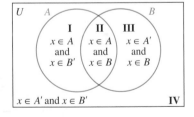

Figure 2.13

In Exercises 89–98, let $U = \{0, 1, 2, 3, 4, 5, \ldots\}$, $A = \{1, 2, 3, 4, \ldots\}$, $B = \{4, 8, 12, 16, \ldots\}$, and $C = \{2, 4, 6, 8, \ldots\}$. Determine the following.

89. $A \cup B$ **90.** $A \cap B$
91. $B \cap C$ **92.** $B \cup C$

93. $A \cap C$ **94.** $A' \cap C$
95. $B' \cap C$ **96.** $(B \cup C)' \cup C$
97. $(A \cap C) \cap B'$ **98.** $U' \cap (A \cup B)$

Challenge Problems/Group Activities

In Exercises 99–106, determine whether the answer is $\varnothing$, A, or U. (Assume $A \neq \varnothing$, $A \neq U$.)

99. $A \cup A'$ **100.** $A \cap A'$
101. $A \cup \varnothing$ **102.** $A \cap \varnothing$
103. $A' \cup U$ **104.** $A \cap U$
105. $A \cup U$ **106.** $A \cup U'$

In Exercises 107–112, determine the relationship between set A and set B if

107. $A \cap B = B$.   **108.** $A \cup B = B$.
109. $A \cap B = \varnothing$.   **110.** $A \cup B = A$.
111. $A \cap B = A$.   **112.** $A \cup B = \varnothing$.

Difference of Two Sets Another set operation is the **difference of two sets**. The difference of two sets A and B, symbolized $A - B$, is defined as

$$A - B = \{x \mid x \in A \text{ and } x \notin B\}$$

Thus, $A - B$ is the set of elements that belong to set A but not to set B. For example, if $U = \{1, 2, 3, 4, 5, 6, 7, 8, 9, 10\}$, $A = \{2, 4, 5, 9, 10\}$, and $B = \{1, 3, 4, 5, 6, 7\}$, then $A - B = \{2, 9, 10\}$ and $B - A = \{1, 3, 6, 7\}$.

In Exercises 113–116, let $U = \{a, b, c, d, e, f, g, h, i, j, k\}$, $A = \{b, c, e, f, g, h\}$, and $B = \{a, b, c, g, i\}$. Determine the following.

113. $A - B$ **114.** $B - A$
115. $A' - B$ **116.** $A - B'$

In Exercises 117–122, let $U = \{1, 2, 3, 4, 5, 6, 7, 8, 9, 10, 11, 12, 13, 14, 15\}$, $A = \{2, 4, 5, 7, 9, 11, 13\}$, and $B = \{1, 2, 4, 5, 6, 7, 8, 9, 11\}$. Determine the following.

117. $A - B$ **118.** $B - A$
119. $(A - B)'$ **120.** $A - B'$
121. $(B - A)'$ **122.** $A \cap (A - B)$

Recreational Mathematics

123. *What Am I?* The poem below gives clues for a 10-letter word discussed in this section. Use the clues to determine the word.

My first is in card and also cat.
My fourth is in top and also in pat.

My third and my seventh are one and the same—
  you'll find them in math and also in game.
My sixth and my eighth, find one you will find two—
  you will find them in open, you will find them in
  shoe.
My second is in work and also in told.
My fifth is in label and also in bold.
My ninth is in number and also in change.
My tenth is in table but never in range.
I have more than one meaning, some say I'm "not."
Although you may want to receive me a lot.

124. *Wordgram* Hidden in the box are the following words
  discussed in this chapter: DIAGRAM, UNION, INTER-

SECTION, SUBSET. You will find them by going letter
to letter either vertically or horizontally. A letter can only
be used once when spelling out a word. Find the words
and make sure you understand the meaning of each word.

N	O	I	E	L	A
T	C	T	S	E	T
S	E	U	B	P	U
R	D	S	R	I	N
E	I	A	G	O	N
T	N	I	R	A	M

2.4 VENN DIAGRAMS WITH THREE SETS AND VERIFICATION OF EQUALITY OF SETS

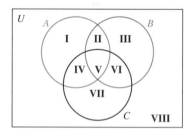

Figure 2.14

Venn diagrams can be used to illustrate three or more sets. For three sets, A, B, and C, the diagram is drawn so the three sets overlap (Fig. 2.14), creating eight regions. The diagrams in Fig. 2.15 emphasize selected regions of three intersecting sets. *When constructing Venn diagrams with three sets, we generally start with region V and work outward*, as explained in the following procedure.

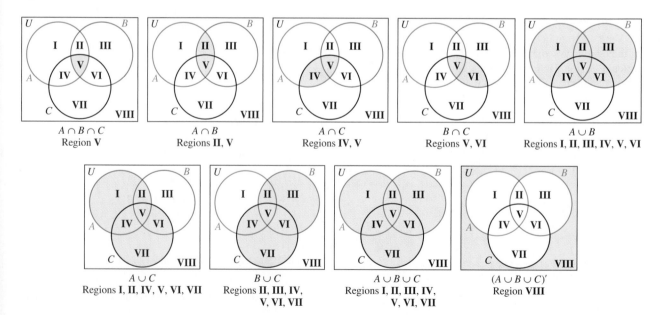

Figure 2.15

General Procedure for Constructing Venn Diagrams with Three Sets, *A*, *B*, and *C*

1. Determine the elements to be placed in region V by finding the elements that are common to all three sets, $A \cap B \cap C$.

2. Determine the elements to be placed in region II. Find the elements in $A \cap B$. The elements in this set belong in regions II and V. Place the elements in the set $A \cap B$ that are not listed in region V in region II. The elements in regions IV and VI are found in a similar manner.

3. Determine the elements to be placed in region I by determining the elements in set *A* that are not in regions II, IV, and V. The elements in regions III and VII are found in a similar manner.

4. Determine the elements to be placed in region VIII by finding the elements in the universal set that are not in regions I through VII.

Example 1 illustrates the general procedure.

EXAMPLE 1   *Constructing a Venn Diagram for Three Sets*

Construct a Venn diagram illustrating the following sets.

$$U = \{1, 2, 3, 4, 5, 6, 7, 8, 9, 10, 11, 12\}$$
$$A = \{1, 5, 8, 9, 10, 12\}$$
$$B = \{2, 4, 5, 9, 10\}$$
$$C = \{1, 3, 5, 8, 9, 11\}$$

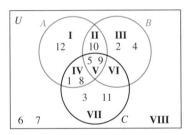

Figure 2.16

SOLUTION: First find the intersection of all three sets. Because the elements 5 and 9 are in all three sets, $A \cap B \cap C = \{5, 9\}$. The elements 5 and 9 are placed in region V in Fig. 2.16. Next complete region II by determining the intersection of sets *A* and *B*.

$$A \cap B = \{5, 9, 10\}$$

$A \cap B$ consists of regions II and V. The elements 5 and 9 have already been placed in region V, so 10 must be placed in region II.

Now determine what numbers go in region IV.

$$A \cap C = \{1, 5, 8, 9\}$$

Since 5 and 9 have already been placed in region V, place the 1 and 8 in region IV. Now determine the numbers to go in region VI.

$$B \cap C = \{5, 9\}$$

Since both the 5 and 9 have been placed in region V, there are no numbers to be placed in region VI. Now complete set *A*. The only element of set *A* that has not previously been placed in regions II, IV, or V is 12. Therefore, place the element 12 in region I. The element 12 that is placed in region I is only in set *A* and not in set *B* or set *C*. Using set *B*, complete region III using the same general procedure used to determine the numbers in region I. Using set *C*, complete region VII by using the same procedure used to complete regions I and III. To determine the elements in region VIII, find the elements in *U* that have not been placed in regions I–VII. The elements 6 and 7 have not been placed in regions I–VII, so place them in region VIII.   ▲

Venn diagrams can be used to illustrate and analyze many everyday problems. One example follows.

EXAMPLE 2   *Blood Types*

Human blood is classified (typed) according to the presence or absence of the specific antigens A, B, and Rh in the red blood cells. Antigens are highly specified proteins and carbohydrates that will trigger the production of antibodies in the blood to fight infection. Blood containing the Rh antigen is labeled positive, +, while blood lacking the Rh antigen is labeled negative, −. Blood lacking both A and B antigens is called type O. Sketch a Venn diagram with three sets A, B, and Rh and place each type of blood listed in the proper region. A person has only one type of blood.

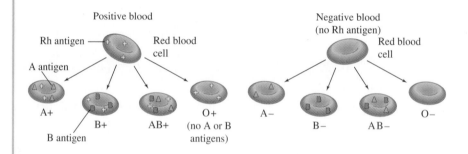

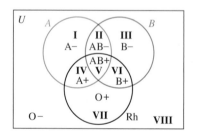

Figure 2.17

SOLUTION: As illustrated in Chapter 1, the first thing to do is to read the question carefully and make sure you understand what is given and what you are asked to find. There are three antigens A, B, and Rh. Therefore, begin by naming the three circles in a Venn diagram with the three antigens; see Fig. 2.17.

Any blood containing the Rh antigen is positive, and any blood not containing the Rh antigen is negative. Therefore, all blood in the Rh circle is positive, and all blood outside the Rh circle is negative. The intersection of all three sets, region V, is AB+. Region II contains only antigens A and B and is therefore AB−. Region I is A− because it contains only antigen A. Region III is B−, region IV is A+, and region VI is B+. Region VII is O+, containing only the Rh antigen. Region VIII, which lacks all three antigens, is O−.   ▲

Verification of Equality of Sets

In this chapter, for clarity we may refer to operations on sets, such as $A \cup B'$ or $A \cap B \cap C$, as *statements involving sets* or simply as *statements*. Now we discuss how to determine if two statements involving sets are equal.

Consider the question: Is $A' \cup B = A' \cap B$ *for all sets A and B*? For the specific sets $U = \{1, 2, 3, 4, 5\}$, $A = \{1, 3\}$, and $B = \{2, 4, 5\}$, is $A' \cup B = A' \cap B$? To answer the question, we do the following.

Find $A' \cup B$	Find $A' \cap B$
$A' = \{2, 4, 5\}$	$A' = \{2, 4, 5\}$
$A' \cup B = \{2, 4, 5\}$	$A' \cap B = \{2, 4, 5\}$

For these sets, $A' \cup B = A' \cap B$, because both set statements are equal to $\{2, 4, 5\}$. At this point you may believe that $A' \cup B = A' \cap B$ for all sets A and B.

If we select the sets $U = \{1, 2, 3, 4, 5\}$, $A = \{1, 3, 5\}$, and $B = \{2, 3\}$, we see that $A' \cup B = \{2, 3, 4\}$ and $A' \cap B = \{2\}$. For this case, $A' \cup B \neq A' \cap B$. Thus, we have proved that $A' \cup B \neq A' \cap B$ for all sets A and B by using a *counterexample*. A counterexample, as explained in Chapter 1, is an example that shows a statement is not true.

In Chapter 1, we explained that proofs involve the use of deductive reasoning. Recall that deductive reasoning begins with a general statement and works to a specific conclusion. To verify, or determine whether set statements are equal for any two sets selected, we use deductive reasoning with Venn diagrams. Venn diagrams are used because they can illustrate general cases. To determine if statements that contain sets, such as $(A \cup B)'$ and $A' \cap B'$, are equal for all sets A and B, we use the regions of Venn diagrams. If both statements represent the same regions of the Venn diagram, then the statements are equal for all sets A and B. See Example 3.

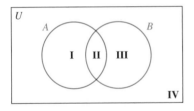

Figure 2.18

┌─**EXAMPLE 3**   *Equality of Sets*

Determine whether $(A \cap B)' = A' \cup B'$ for all sets A and B.

SOLUTION: Draw a Venn diagram with two sets A and B, as in Fig. 2.18. Label the regions as indicated.

Find $(A \cap B)'$

Set	Corresponding Regions
A	I, II
B	II, III
$A \cap B$	II
$(A \cap B)'$	I, III, IV

Find $A' \cup B'$

Set	Corresponding Regions
A'	III, IV
B'	I, IV
$A' \cup B'$	I, III, IV

Both statements are represented by the same regions, I, III, and IV, of the Venn diagram. Thus, $(A \cap B)' = A' \cup B'$ for all sets A and B.   ▲

In Example 3, when we proved that $(A \cap B)' = A' \cup B'$, we started with two general sets and worked to the specific conclusion that both statements represented

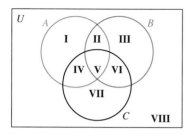

Figure 2.19

MATHEMATICS *Everywhere*

Using Venn Diagrams

A financial planning company uses the following Venn diagram to categorize the financial planning services the company offers. From the diagram, we can see that the company offers financial planning in an "intersection" of the areas investment, retirement, and college planning.

We categorize items on a daily basis, from filing items to planning meals to planning social activities. Children are taught how to categorize items at an early age when they learn how to classify items according to color, shape, and size. Biologists categorize items when they classify organisms according to shared characteristics. A Venn diagram is a very useful tool to help order and arrange items and to picture the relationship between sets.

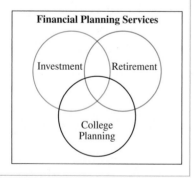

the same regions of the Venn diagram. We showed that $(A \cap B)' = A' \cup B'$ *for all sets A and B*. No matter what sets we choose for A and B, this statement will be true. For example, let $U = \{1, 2, 3, 4, 5, 6, 7, 8, 9, 10\}$, $A = \{3, 4, 6, 10\}$, and $B = \{1, 2, 4, 5, 6, 8\}$.

$$(A \cap B)' = A' \cup B'$$
$$\{4, 6\}' = \{3, 4, 6, 10\}' \cup \{1, 2, 4, 5, 6, 8\}'$$
$$\{1, 2, 3, 5, 7, 8, 9, 10\} = \{1, 2, 5, 7, 8, 9\} \cup \{3, 7, 9, 10\}$$
$$\{1, 2, 3, 5, 7, 8, 9, 10\} = \{1, 2, 3, 5, 7, 8, 9, 10\}$$

We can also use Venn diagrams to prove statements involving three sets.

EXAMPLE 4   *Equality of Sets*

Determine whether $A \cap (B \cup C) = (A \cap B) \cup (A \cap C)$ for all sets, A, B, and C.

SOLUTION: Because the statements include three sets, A, B, and C, three circles must be used. The Venn diagram illustrating the eight regions is shown in Fig. 2.19.

First we will find the regions that correspond to $A \cap (B \cup C)$, and then we will find the regions that correspond to $(A \cap B) \cup (A \cap C)$. If both answers are the same, the statements are equal.

Find $A \cap (B \cup C)$

Set	Corresponding Regions
A	I, II, IV, V
$B \cup C$	II, III, IV, V, VI, VII
$A \cap (B \cup C)$	II, IV, V

Find $(A \cap B) \cup (A \cap C)$

Set	Corresponding Regions
$A \cap B$	II, V
$A \cap C$	IV, V
$(A \cap B) \cup (A \cap C)$	II, IV, V

The regions that correspond to $A \cap (B \cup C)$ are II, IV, and V, and the regions that correspond to $(A \cap B) \cup (A \cap C)$ are also II, IV, and V. The results show that both statements are represented by the same regions, namely, II, IV, and V, and therefore $A \cap (B \cup C) = (A \cap B) \cup (A \cap C)$ for all sets A, B, and C. ▲

In Example 4, we proved that $A \cap (B \cup C) = (A \cap B) \cup (A \cap C)$ for all sets A, B, and C. Show that this statement is true for the specific sets $U = \{1, 2, 3, 4, 5, 6, 7, 8, 9, 10\}$, $A = \{1, 2, 3, 7\}$, $B = \{2, 3, 4, 5, 7, 9\}$, and $C = \{1, 4, 7, 8, 10\}$.

De Morgan's Laws

In set theory, logic, and other branches of mathematics, a pair of related theorems known as De Morgan's laws make it possible to transform statements and formulas into alternative and often more convenient forms. In set theory, *De Morgan's laws* are symbolized as follows.

> **De Morgan's Laws**
>
> 1. $(A \cup B)' = A' \cap B'$
> 2. $(A \cap B)' = A' \cup B'$

Law 2 was verified in Example 3. We suggest that you verify law 1 at this time. The laws were expressed verbally by William of Ockham in the fourteenth century. In the nineteenth century, Augustus De Morgan expressed them mathematically. De Morgan's laws will be discussed more thoroughly in Chapter 3, Logic.

SECTION 2.4   EXERCISES

Concept/Writing Exercises

1. How many regions are created when constructing a Venn diagram with three overlapping sets?

2. When constructing a Venn diagram with three overlapping sets, which region do you generally complete first?

3. When constructing a Venn diagram with three overlapping sets, after completing region V, which regions do you generally complete next?

4. A Venn diagram contains three sets, A, B, and C, as in Fig. 2.14. If region V contains 6 elements and there are 10 elements in $A \cap B$, how many elements belong in region II? Explain.

5. A Venn diagram contains three sets, A, B, and C, as in Fig. 2.14. If region V contains 4 elements and there are 12 elements in $B \cap C$, how many elements belong in region VI? Explain.

6. Give De Morgan's laws.

7. **a)** For $U = \{1, 2, 3, 4, 5\}$, $A = \{1, 4, 5\}$, and $B = \{1, 4, 5\}$, does $A \cup B = A \cap B$?
   b) By observing the answer to part (a), can we conclude that $A \cup B = A \cap B$ for all sets A and B? Explain.
   c) Using a Venn diagram, determine if $A \cup B = A \cap B$ for all sets A and B.

8. What type of reasoning do we use when using Venn diagrams to verify or determine whether set statements are equal?

Practice the Skills

9. Construct a Venn diagram illustrating the following sets.

$$U = \{a, b, c, d, e, f, g, h, i, j\}$$
$$A = \{c, d, e, g, h, i\}$$

$$B = \{a, c, d, g\}$$
$$C = \{c, f, i, j\}$$

10. Construct a Venn diagram illustrating the following sets.

$U = \{$Delaware, Pennsylvania, New Jersey, Georgia, Connecticut, Massachusetts, Maryland, South Carolina, New Hampshire, Virginia, New York, North Carolina, Rhode Island$\}$

$A = \{$New York, New Jersey, Pennsylvania, Massachusetts, New Hampshire$\}$

$B = \{$Delaware, Connecticut, Georgia, Maryland, New York, Rhode Island$\}$

$C = \{$New York, South Carolina, Rhode Island, Massachusetts$\}$

11. Construct a Venn diagram illustrating the following sets.

$U = \{$football, basketball, baseball, gymnastics, lacrosse, soccer, tennis, volleyball, swimming, wrestling, cross-country, track, golf, fencing$\}$

$A = \{$football, basketball, soccer, lacrosse, volleyball$\}$

$B = \{$baseball, lacrosse, tennis, golf, volleyball$\}$

$C = \{$swimming, gymnastics, fencing, basketball, volleyball$\}$

12. Construct a Venn diagram illustrating the following sets.

$U = \{$*The Lion King, Aladdin, Cinderella, Beauty and the Beast, Snow White and the Seven Dwarfs, Toy Story, 101 Dalmatians, The Little Mermaid, Jurassic Park*$\}$

$A = \{$*Aladdin, Toy Story, The Lion King, Snow White and the Seven Dwarfs*$\}$

$B = \{$*Snow White and the Seven Dwarfs, Toy Story, The Lion King, Beauty and the Beast*$\}$

$C = \{$*Snow White and the Seven Dwarfs, Toy Story, Beauty and the Beast, Cinderella, 101 Dalmatians*$\}$

The Lion King

13. Construct a Venn diagram illustrating the following sets.

$U = \{$peach, pear, banana, apple, grape, melon, carrot, corn, orange, spinach$\}$

$A = \{$pear, grape, melon, carrot$\}$

$B = \{$peach, pear, banana, spinach, corn$\}$

$C = \{$pear, banana, apple, grape, melon, spinach$\}$

14. Construct a Venn diagram illustrating the following sets.

$U = \{$Louis Armstrong, Glenn Miller, Stan Kenton, Charlie Parker, Duke Ellington, Benny Goodman, Count Basie, John Coltrane, Dizzy Gillespie, Miles Davis, Thelonius Monk$\}$

$A = \{$Stan Kenton, Count Basie, Dizzy Gillespie, Duke Ellington, Thelonius Monk$\}$

$B = \{$Louis Armstrong, Glenn Miller, Count Basie, Duke Ellington, Miles Davis$\}$

$C = \{$Count Basie, Miles Davis, Stan Kenton, Charlie Parker, Duke Ellington$\}$

15. *Olympic Medals* Consider the chart, which shows countries that won at least 25 medals in the 2000 Summer Olympics. Let the teams shown in the chart represent the universal set.

	Gold	Silver	Bronze	Total
United States	39	25	33	97
Russia	32	28	28	88
China	28	16	15	59
Australia	16	25	17	58
Germany	14	17	26	57
France	13	14	11	38
Italy	13	8	13	34
Cuba	11	11	7	29
Great Britain	11	10	7	28
Korea	8	9	11	28
Romania	11	6	9	26
Netherlands	12	9	4	25

Source: *2001 Time Almanac*

Let A = set of teams that won at least 58 medals.

Let B = set of teams that won at least 20 gold medals.

Let C = set of teams that won at least 10 bronze medals.

Construct a Venn diagram that illustrates the sets A, B, and C.

16. *Popular TV Shows* Let $U = \{$*Friends, CSI, NFL Monday Night Football, Survivor II, E.R., Who Wants to Be a Millionaire—Tues., Who Wants to Be a Millionaire—Wed., Who Wants to Be a Millionaire—Thurs., Who Wants to Be a Millionaire—Sun., Everybody Loves Raymond, 60 Minutes, Law& Order, West Wing*$\}$ Set A represents the five most popular prime time shows on television in 2001–2002, set B represents the five most popular prime-time shows on television in 2000–2001, and set C represents the five most popular prime-time shows on television in 1999–2000 (according to Nielsen Media Research). Then

$A = \{$*Friends, CSI, E.R., Everybody Loves Raymond, Law & Order*$\}$

$B = \{$*Survivor II, E.R., Who Wants to Be a Millionaire—Wed., Who Wants to Be a Millionaire—Tues., Friends*$\}$

$C = \{$*Who Wants to Be a Millionaire—Tues., Who Wants to Be a Millionaire—Thurs., Who Wants to Be a Millionaire—Sun., E.R., Friends*$\}$

Construct a Venn diagram illustrating the sets.

Graduate Schools The accompanying chart on page 73 shows the *U.S News and World Report* top 10 rankings of graduate schools in 2002 in the fields of medicine, education, and business. The universal set is the set of all U.S. graduate schools. In Fig. 2.20, the set indicated as Medical represents the 10 highest-rated medical schools, the set indicated as Education represents the 10 highest-rated graduate education schools, and the set listed as Business represents the 10 highest-rated graduate business schools.

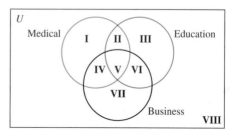

Figure 2.20

Top-Rated Graduate Schools

Medical	Education	Business
1. Harvard	1. Harvard	1. Stanford
2. Johns Hopkins	2. Stanford	2. Harvard
3. Duke	3. Columbia	3. Northwestern
4. University of Pennsylvania	4. UCLA	4. University of Pennsylvania
5. Washington University in St. Louis	5. Vanderbilt	5. M.I.T.
6. Columbia	6. University of California–Berkeley	6. Columbia
7. University of California–San Francisco	7. University of Michigan	7. University of California–Berkeley
8. Yale	8. University of Pennsylvania	8. Duke
9. Stanford	9. University of Wisconsin–Madison	9. University of Chicago
9. University of Michigan (tie)	10. Northwestern	10. University of Michigan

Source: *U.S. News*, www.usnews.com

Indicate in Fig. 2.20 in which region, I–VIII, each of the following belongs.

17. Harvard   **18.** Yale

19. Boston College   **20.** University of California–Berkeley

21. Northwestern   **22.** Duke

Rankings of Metropolitan Areas The table above and to the right, taken from *Places Rated Almanac, Millennium Edition,* shows that almanac's rankings of the overall top 10 metropolitan areas across the United States and Canada. The table also shows the top 10 ranked areas for the categories of transportation and education. The universal set is the set of all metropolitan areas in the United States and Canada. In Fig. 2.21, the set indicated as Overall represents the set of metropolitan areas listed in the table under overall rankings.

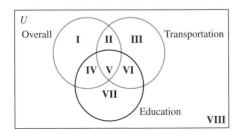

Figure 2.21

The set indicated as Transportation represents the set of metropolitan areas listed in the table under transportation, and the set indicated as Education represents the set of metropolitan areas listed in the table under education.

Rankings of Metropolitan Areas

Overall	Transportation	Education
1. Salt Lake City–Odgen	1. Chicago	1. Raleigh–Durham–Chapel Hill
2. Washington, D.C.	2. Pittsburgh	2. Boston
3. Seattle-Bellevue-Everett	3. New York	3. Albany-Schenectady-Troy
4. Tampa–St. Petersburg–Clearwater	4. Cincinnati	4. St. Louis
5. Denver	5. Detroit	5. Chicago
6. Raleigh–Durham–Chapel Hill	6. Denver	6. Rochester, NY
7. Toronto	7. Atlanta	7. Austin–San Marcos
8. Houston	8. Toronto	8. San Francisco
9. Minneapolis–St. Paul	9. St. Louis	9. Washington, D.C.
10. Phoenix-Mesa	10. Minneapolis–St. Paul	10. Saskatoon

Indicate in Fig. 2.21 in which region, I–VIII, each of the following metropolitan areas belongs.

23. Washington, D.C.   **24.** Pittsburgh

25. Denver   **26.** Houston

27. Rochester, NY   **28.** Chicago

Figures In Exercises 29–40, indicate in Fig. 2.22 the region in which each of the figures would be placed.

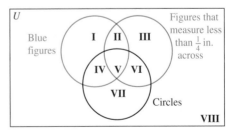

Figure 2.22

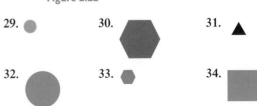

29.   **30.**   **31.**

32.   **33.**   **34.**

35. 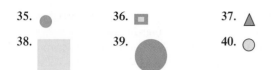 **36.** ▢ **37.** ▲

38. ▢ **39.** ⬤ **40.** ◯

Senate Bills *During a session of the U.S. Senate, three bills were voted on. The votes of six senators are shown below the figure. Determine in which region of Fig.2.23 each senator would be placed. The set labeled Bill 1 represents the set of senators who voted yes on Bill 1, and so on.*

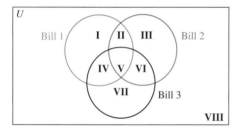

Figure 2.23

Senator	Bill 1	Bill 2	Bill 3
41. Grump	yes	no	no
42. Happi	no	no	yes
43. Turwilliger	no	no	no
44. Dillinger	yes	yes	yes
45. Isaitere	no	yes	yes
46. Smith	no	yes	no

In Exercises 47–60, use the Venn diagram in Fig. 2.24 to list the sets in roster form.

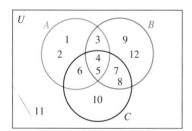

Figure 2.24

47. A **48.** U

49. B **50.** C

51. $A \cap B$ **52.** $A \cap C$

53. $(B \cap C)'$ **54.** $A \cap B \cap C$

55. $A \cup B$ **56.** $B \cup C$

57. $(A \cup C)'$ **58.** $A \cup B \cup C$

59. A' **60.** $(A \cup B \cup C)'$

In Exercises 61–68, use Venn diagrams to determine whether the following statements are equal for all sets A and B.

61. $(A \cup B)'$, $A' \cap B'$

62. $(A \cap B)'$, $A' \cup B$

63. $A' \cup B'$, $A \cap B$

64. $(A \cup B)'$, $(A \cap B)'$

65. $A' \cup B'$, $(A \cup B)'$

66. $A' \cap B'$, $A \cup B'$

67. $(A' \cap B)'$, $A \cup B'$

68. $A' \cap B'$, $(A' \cap B')'$

In Exercises 69–78, use Venn diagrams to determine whether the following statements are equal for all sets A, B, and C.

69. $A \cap (B \cup C)$, $(A \cap B) \cup C$

70. $A \cup (B \cap C)$, $(B \cap C) \cup A$

71. $A \cap (B \cup C)$, $(B \cup C) \cap A$

72. $A \cup (B \cap C)'$, $A' \cap (B \cup C)$

73. $A \cap (B \cup C)$, $(A \cap B) \cup (A \cap C)$

74. $A \cup (B \cap C)$, $(A \cup B) \cap (A \cup C)$

75. $A \cap (B \cup C)'$, $A \cap (B' \cap C')$

76. $(A \cup B) \cap (B \cup C)$, $B \cup (A \cap C)$

77. $(A \cup B)' \cap C$, $(A' \cup C) \cap (B' \cup C)$

78. $(C \cap B)' \cup (A \cap B)'$, $A \cap (B \cap C)$

In Exercises 79–82, use set statements to write a description of the shaded area. Use union, intersection and complement as necessary. More than one answer may be possible.

79. 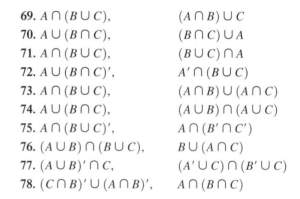 **80.**

81. 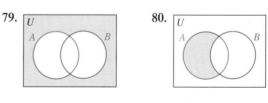 **82.**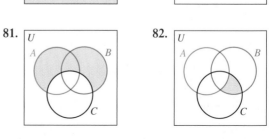

Problem Solving

83. Let

$$U = \{1, 2, 3, 4, 5, 6, 7, 8, 9, 10\}$$
$$A = \{1, 2, 3, 4\}$$
$$B = \{3, 6, 7\}$$
$$C = \{6, 7, 9\}$$

a) Show that $(A \cup B) \cap C = (A \cap C) \cup (B \cap C)$ for these sets.

b) Make up your own sets A, B, and C. Verify that $(A \cup B) \cap C = (A \cap C) \cup (B \cap C)$ for your sets A, B, and C.

c) Use Venn diagrams to verify that $(A \cup B) \cap C = (A \cap C) \cup (B \cap C)$ for all sets A, B, and C.

84. Let

$$U = \{a, b, c, d, e, f, g, h, i\}$$
$$A = \{a, c, d, e, f\}$$
$$B = \{c, d\}$$
$$C = \{a, b, c, d, e\}$$

a) Determine whether $(A \cup C)' \cap B = (A \cap C)' \cap B$ for these sets.

b) Make up your own sets, A, B, and C. Determine whether $(A \cup C)' \cap B = (A \cap C)' \cap B$ for your sets.

c) Determine whether $(A \cup C)' \cap B = (A \cap C)' \cap B$ for all sets A, B, and C.

85. *Blood Types* A hematology text gives the following information on percentages of the different types of blood worldwide.

Type	Positive Blood, %	Negative Blood, %
A	37	6
O	32	6.5
B	11	2
AB	5	0.5

Construct a Venn diagram similar to the one in Example 2 and place the correct percent in each of the eight regions.

86. Define each of the eight regions in Fig. 2.25 using sets A, B, and C and a set operation. (*Hint:* $A \cap B' \cap C'$ defines region I.)

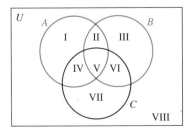

Figure 2.25

87. *Categorizing Contracts* J & C Mechanical Contractors wants to classify its projects. The contractors categorize set A as the set of office building construction projects, set B as the set of plumbing projects, and set C as the set of projects with a budget greater than $300,000.

a) Draw a Venn diagram that can be used to categorize the company projects according to the listed criteria.

b) Determine the region of the diagram that contains office building construction and plumbing projects with a budget greater than $300,000. Describe the region using sets A, B, and C with set operations. Use union, intersection, and complement as necessary.

c) Determine the region of the diagram that contains plumbing projects with a budget greater than $300,000 that are not office building construction projects. Describe the region using sets A, B and C with set operations. Use union, intersection, and complement as necessary.

d) Determine the region of the diagram that contains office building construction and nonplumbing projects whose budget is less than or equal to $300,000. Describe the region using sets A, B, and C with set operations. Use union, intersection, and complement as necessary.

Challenge Problem/Group Activity

88. We were able to determine the number of elements in the union of two sets with the formula

$$n(A \cup B) = n(A) + n(B) - n(A \cap B)$$

Can you determine a formula for finding the number of elements in the union of three sets? In other words, write a formula to determine $n(A \cup B \cup C)$. [*Hint:* The formula will contain each of the following: $n(A)$, $n(B)$, $n(C)$, $n(A \cap B \cap C')$, $n(A \cap B' \cap C)$, $n(A' \cap B \cap C)$, and $2n(A \cap B \cap C)$.]

Recreational Mathematics

89. a) Construct a Venn diagram illustrating four sets, A, B, C, and D. (*Hint:* Four circles cannot be used, and you should end up with 16 *distinct* regions.) Have fun!

b) Label each region with a set statement (see Exercise 86). Check all 16 regions to make sure that *each is distinct*.

90. *Triangle Seek* In the word seek on the next page, you are looking for six-letter words that form triangles. You need to trace out a triangle as you move from the first letter to the last letter and back to the first letter. The first letter of the word can be in any position in the triangle. Triangles may overlap other triangles, and the triangles can point up or down. The word list is below. The word PROPER is shown as an example.

```
S   B   T   R   H   M   D   F   R   T   S
  T   S   J   O   N   B   U   I   E   L   E   M
W   E   E   S   N   E   R   N   I   T   V   O
  P   R   S   A   K   C   P   A   R   N   E   P
O   R   P   O   N   R   R   O   Y   I   M   T
  I   R   J   I   E   E   S   O   C   L   U   S
F   M   U   N   G   R   T   R   N   E   P   P
```

Word List
PROPER
SUBSET
FINITE
NUMBER
ROSTER
PENCIL
REGION

Internet/Research Activity

91. The two Venn diagrams illustrate what happens when colors are added or subtracted. Do research in an art text, an encyclopedia, the Internet, or another source and write a report explaining the creation of the colors in the Venn diagrams, using such terms as union of colors and subtraction (or difference) of colors.

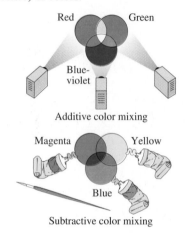

Red   Green

Blue-violet

Additive color mixing

Magenta   Yellow

Blue

Subtractive color mixing

2.5 APPLICATIONS OF SETS

We can solve practical problems involving sets by using the problem-solving process discussed in Chapter 1: Understand the problem, devise a plan, carry out the plan, and then examine and check the results. First determine: What is the problem? or What am I looking for? To devise the plan, list all the facts that are given and how they are related. *Look for key words or phrases* such as "only set *A*," "set *A* and set *B*," "set *A* or set *B*," "set *A* and set *B* and not set *C*." Remember that *and* means intersection, *or* means union, and *not* means complement. The problems we solve in this section contain two or three sets of elements, which can be represented in a Venn diagram. Our plan will generally include drawing a Venn diagram, labeling the diagram, and filling in the regions of the diagram.

Whenever possible, follow the procedure in Section 2.4 for completing the Venn diagram and then answer the questions. Remember, when drawing Venn diagrams, we generally start with the intersection of the sets and work outward.

EXAMPLE 1   *Fitness Equipment*

Fitness for Life health club is considering adding additional cardiovascular equipment. It is considering two types of equipment, treadmills (T) and StairMasters (S). The health club surveyed a sample of members and asked which equipment they had used in the previous month. Of 150 members surveyed, it was determined that

102 used the treadmills.
 71 used the StairMasters.
 40 used both types.

Of those surveyed,

a) how many did not use either the treadmill or the StairMaster?

b) how many used the treadmill but not the StairMaster?

c) how many used the StairMaster but not the treadmill?

d) how many used either the treadmill or StairMaster?

SOLUTION: The problem provides the following information.

The number of members surveyed is 150: $n(U)$ is 150.
The number of members surveyed who used the treadmill is 102: $n(T) = 102$.
The number of members surveyed who used the StairMaster is 71: $n(S) = 71$.
The number of members surveyed who used both the treadmill and the Stair-Master is 40: $n(T \cap S) = 40$.

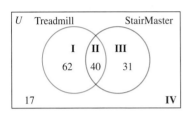

Figure 2.26

We illustrate this information on the Venn diagram shown in Fig. 2.26. We already know that $T \cap S$ corresponds to region II. As $n(T \cap S) = 40$, we write 40 in region II. Set T consists of regions I and II. We know that set T, the members who used the treadmill, contains 102 members. Therefore, region I contains $102 - 40$, or 62 members. We write the number 62 in region I. Set S consists of regions II and III. As $n(S) = 71$, the total in these two regions must be 71. Region II contains 40, leaving $71 - 40$ or 31 for region III. We write 31 in region III.

The total number of members surveyed who used the treadmill or the Stair-Master is found by adding the numbers in regions I, II, and III. Therefore, $n(T \cup S) = 62 + 40 + 31 = 133$. The number in region IV is the difference between $n(U)$ and $n(T \cup S)$. There are $150 - 133$, or 17 members in region IV.

a) The members surveyed who did not use either the treadmill or the StairMaster are those members of the universal set who are not contained in set T or set S. The 17 members in region IV did not use the treadmill or StairMaster.

b) The 62 members in region I are those members surveyed who used the treadmill but not the StairMaster.

c) The 31 members in region III are those members surveyed who used the Stair-Master but not the treadmill.

d) The members in regions I, II, or III are those members surveyed who used either the treadmill or the StairMaster. Thus, $62 + 40 + 31$ or 133 members surveyed used either the treadmill or the StairMaster. Notice that the 40 members in region II who use both types of equipment are included in those members surveyed who used either the treadmill or the StairMaster.

Similar problems involving three sets can be solved, as illustrated in Example 2.

EXAMPLE 2   *Software Purchases*

CompUSA is considering expanding their computer software department. They are considering additional space for three types of computer software: games, educational software, and utility programs. The following information regarding software purchases was obtained from a survey of 893 customers.

545 purchased games.
497 purchased educational software.
290 purchased utility programs.
297 purchased games and educational software.

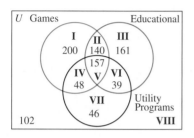

Figure 2.27

196 purchased educational software and utility programs.
205 purchased games and utility programs.
157 purchased all three types of software.

Use a Venn diagram to answer the following questions. How many customers purchased

a) none of these types of software?

b) only games?

c) at least one of these types of software?

d) exactly two of these types of software?

SOLUTION: Begin by constructing a Venn diagram with three overlapping circles. One circle represents games, another educational software, and the third utilities. See Fig 2.27. Label the eight regions.

Whenever possible, work from the center of the diagram outwards. First fill in region V. Since 157 customers purchased all three types of software, we place 157 in region V. Next determine the number to be placed in region II. Regions II and V together represent the customers who purchased both games and educational software. Since 297 customers purchased both of these types of software, the sum of the numbers in these regions must be 297. Since 157 have already been placed in region V, 297 − 157 = 140 must be placed in region II. Now we determine the number to be placed in region IV. Since 205 customers purchased both games and utility programs, the sum of the numbers in regions IV and V must be 205. Since 157 have already been placed in region V, 205 − 157 = 48 must be placed in region IV. Now determine the number to be placed in region VI. A total of 196 customers purchased educational software and utility programs. The numbers in regions V and VI must total 196. Since 157 have already been placed in region V, the number to be placed in region VI is 196 − 157 = 39.

Now that we have determined the numbers for regions V, II, IV, and VI, we can determine the numbers to be placed in regions I, III, and VII. We are given that 545 customers purchased games. The sum of the numbers in regions I, II, IV, and V must be 545. To determine the number to be placed in region I, subtract the amounts in regions II, IV, and V from 545. There must be 545 − 140 − 48 − 157 = 200 in region I. Determine the numbers to be placed in regions III and VII in a similar manner.

$$\text{Region III} = 497 - 140 - 157 - 39 = 161$$
$$\text{Region VII} = 290 - 48 - 157 - 39 = 46$$

Now that we have determined the numbers in regions I through VII, we can determine the number to be placed in region VIII. Adding the numbers in regions I through VII yields a sum of 791. The difference between the total number of customers surveyed, 893, and the sum of the numbers in regions I through VII must be placed in region VIII.

$$\text{Region VIII} = 893 - 791 = 102$$

Now that we have completed the Venn diagram, we can answer the questions.

a) One hundred two customers did not purchase any of these types of software. These customers are indicated in region VIII.

b) Region I represents those customers who purchased only games. Thus, 200 customers purchased only games.

c) The words *at least one* mean "one or more." All those in regions I through VII purchased at least one of the types of software. The sum of the numbers in regions I through VII is 791, so 791 customers purchased at least one of the types of software.

d) The customers in regions II, IV, and VI purchased exactly two of the types of software. Summing the numbers in these regions $140 + 48 + 39$ we find that 227 customers purchased exactly two of these types of software. Notice that we did not include the customers in region V. Those customers purchased all three types of software.   ▲

The procedure to work problems like those given in Example 2 is generally the same. Start by completing region V. Next complete regions II, IV, and VI. Then complete regions I, III, and VII. Finally, complete region VIII. When you are constructing Venn diagrams, be sure to check your work carefully.

TIMELY TIP When constructing a Venn diagram, the most common mistake made by students is forgetting to subtract the number in region V from the respective values in determining the numbers to be placed in regions II, IV, and VI.

EXAMPLE 3   *Birds at the Feeders*

In a bird sanctuary, 41 different species of birds are being studied. Three large bird feeders are constructed, each providing a different type of bird feed. One feeder has sunflower seeds. A second feeder has a mixture of seeds, and the third feeder has small pieces of fruit. The following information was obtained.

> 20 species ate sunflower seeds.
> 22 species ate the mixture.
> 11 species ate the fruit.
> 10 species ate the sunflower seeds and the mixture.
> 4 species ate the sunflower seeds and the fruit.
> 3 species ate the mixture and the fruit.
> 1 species ate all three.

Use a Venn diagram to answer the following questions. How many species ate

a) none of the foods?

b) the sunflower seeds, but neither of the other two foods?

c) the mixture *and* the fruit, but not the sunflower seeds?

d) the mixture *or* the fruit, but not the sunflower seeds?

e) exactly one of the foods?

SOLUTION: The Venn diagram is constructed using the procedure we outlined in Example 2. The diagram is illustrated in Fig. 2.28. We suggest you construct the diagram by yourself now and check your diagram with Fig. 2.28.

a) Four species did not eat any of the food (see region VIII).

b) Seven species (see region I) ate the sunflower seeds but neither of the other two foods.

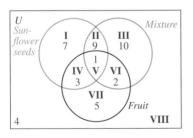

Figure 2.28

c) Those in region VI ate both the mixture and fruit but not the sunflower seeds. Therefore, two species satisfy the criteria.

d) The word *or* in this type of problem means one or the other or both. All the species in regions II, III, IV, V, VI, and VII ate the mixture or the fruit or both. Those in regions II, IV, and V also ate the sunflower seeds. The species that ate the mixture or fruit, but not the sunflower seeds, are found by adding the numbers in regions III, VI, and VII. There are $10 + 2 + 5 = 17$ species that satisfy the criteria.

e) Those species indicated in regions I, III, and VII ate exactly one of the foods. Therefore, $7 + 10 + 5 = 22$ species ate exactly one of the three types of bird food.

SECTION 2.5   EXERCISES

Practice the Skills/Problem Solving

In Exercises 1–15, draw a Venn diagram to obtain the answers.

1. *Landscape Purchases* Agway Lawn and Garden collected the following information regarding purchases from 130 of its customers.

   74 purchased shrubs.
   70 purchased trees.
   41 purchased both shrubs and trees.

   Of those surveyed,
   a) how many purchased only shrubs?
   b) how many purchased only trees?
   c) how many did not purchase either of these items?

2. *Study Locations* At a local college, a survey was taken to determine where students studied on campus. Of 160 students surveyed, it was determined that

   79 studied in the library.
   65 studied in the student lounge.
   43 studied in both the library and the student lounge.

   Of those interviewed,
   a) how many studied in only the library?
   b) how many studied in only the student lounge?
   c) how many did not study in either location?

3. *Real Estate* The Maiello's are moving to Wilmington, Delaware. Their real estate agent located 83 houses listed for sale, in the Wilmington area, in their price range. Of these houses listed for sale,

   47 had a family room.
   42 had a deck.
   30 had a family room and a deck.

   How many had
   a) a family room but not a deck?
   b) a deck but not a family room?
   c) either a family room or a deck?

4. *Toothpaste Taste Test* A drug company is considering manufacturing a new toothpaste. They are considering two flavors, regular and mint. In a sample of 120 people, it was found that

   74 liked the regular.
   62 liked the mint.
   35 liked both types.

   a) How many liked only the regular?
   b) How many liked only the mint?
   c) How many liked either one or the other or both?

5. *Overnight Delivery Services* In San Diego, California, a sample of 444 businesses was surveyed to determine which overnight mailing services they used. The following information was determined.

   189 used Federal Express.
   205 used United Parcel Service.
   122 used Airborne.
    57 used Federal Express and United Parcel Service.
    34 used Federal Express and Airborne.
    30 used United Parcel Service and Airborne.
    22 used all three.

   How many used
   a) none of these services?
   b) only Airborne?
   c) exactly one of the services?
   d) exactly two of the services?
   e) Federal Express or United Parcel Service?

6. *Professional Teams* Thirty-three U.S. cities with large populations were surveyed to determine whether they had a professional baseball team, a professional football team, or a professional basketball team. The following information was determined.

> 16 had baseball.
> 17 had football.
> 15 had basketball.
> 11 had baseball and football.
> 7 had baseball and basketball.
> 9 had football and basketball.
> 5 had all three teams.

How many had
a) only a football team?
b) baseball and football, but not basketball?
c) baseball or football?
d) baseball or football, but not basketball?
e) exactly two teams?

7. *Book Purchases* A survey of 85 customers was taken at Barnes & Noble regarding the types of books purchased. The survey found that

> 44 purchased mysteries.
> 33 purchased science fiction.
> 29 purchased romance novels.
> 13 purchased mysteries and science fiction.
> 5 purchased science fiction and romance novels.
> 11 purchased mysteries and romance novels.
> 2 purchased all three types of books.

How many of the customers surveyed purchased
a) only mysteries?
b) mysteries and science fiction, but not romance novels?
c) mysteries or science fiction?
d) mysteries or science fiction, but not romance novels?
e) exactly two types?

8. *Resorts* In a survey of 65 resorts, it was found that

> 34 provided refrigerators in the guest rooms.
> 30 provided laundry services.
> 37 provided child care services.
> 15 provided refrigerators in the guest rooms and laundry services.

17 provided refrigerators in the guest rooms and child care services.
19 provided laundry services and child care services.
7 provided all three features.

How many of the resorts provided
a) only refrigerators in the guest rooms?
b) exactly one of the features?
c) at least one of the features?
d) exactly two of the features?
e) none of the features?

9. *Transportation* Seventy businesspeople in Sacramento, California, were asked how they traveled to work during the previous month. The following information was determined.

> 28 used public transportation.
> 18 rode in a car pool.
> 37 drove alone.
> 5 used public transportation and rode in a car pool.
> 9 used public transportation and drove alone.
> 4 rode in a car pool and drove alone.
> 3 used all three forms of transportation.

How many of those surveyed
a) only used public transportation?
b) only drove alone?
c) used public transportation and rode in a car pool, but did not drive alone?
d) used public transportation or rode in a car pool, but did not drive alone?
e) used none of these forms of transportation?

10. *Colleges and Universities* In a survey of four-year colleges and universities, it was found that

> 356 offered a liberal arts degree.
> 293 offered a computer engineering degree.
> 285 offered a nursing degree.
> 193 offered a liberal arts degree and a computer engineering degree.
> 200 offered a liberal arts degree and a nursing degree.
> 139 offered a computer engineering degree and a nursing degree.
> 68 offered a liberal arts degree, a computer engineering degree, and a nursing degree.
> 26 offered none of these degrees.

a) How many four-year colleges and universities were surveyed?
Of the four-year colleges and universities surveyed, how many offered
b) a liberal arts degree and a nursing degree, but not a computer engineering degree?
c) a computer engineering degree, but neither a liberal arts degree nor a nursing degree?
d) exactly two of these degrees?
e) at least one of these degrees?

11. *Fastest-Growing Cities* The following census information was collected regarding the 25 largest U.S. cities based on the 2000 population.

5 cities were in Texas.

13 cities had a population greater than 750,000.

11 cities had a population increase greater than 10% from 1990 to 2000.

3 cities had a population greater than 750,000 and were in Texas.

4 cities had a population increase greater than 10% from 1990 to 2000 and were in Texas.

6 cities had a population greater than 750,000 and a population increase greater than 10% from 1990 to 2000.

3 cities had a population greater than 750,000, a population increase greater than 10% from 1990 to 2000, and were in Texas.

How many of the 25 largest cities

a) with a population greater than 750,000 were not in Texas?

b) were in Texas or had a population greater than 750,000?

c) were in Texas and had a population greater than 750,000, but did not have a population increase greater than 10% from 1990 to 2000?

d) were not in Texas, did not have a population greater than 750,000 and did not have a population increase greater than 10% from 1990 to 2000?

12. *Appetizers Survey* Da Tulio's Restaurant hired Dennis Goldstein to determine what kind of appetizers customers liked. He surveyed 100 people, with the following results: 78 liked shrimp cocktail, 56 liked mozzarella sticks, and 35 liked both shrimp cocktail and mozzarella sticks. Every person interviewed liked one or the other or both kinds of appetizers. Does this result seem correct? Explain your answer.

13. *Discovering an Error* An immigration agent sampled cars going from the United States into Canada. In his report, he indicated that of the 85 cars sampled,

35 cars were driven by women.

53 cars were driven by U.S. citizens.

43 cars had two or more passengers.

27 cars were driven by women who are U.S. citizens.

25 cars were driven by women and had two or more passengers.

20 cars were driven by U.S. citizens and had two or more passengers.

15 cars were driven by women who are U.S. citizens and had two or more passengers.

After his supervisor reads the report, she explains to the agent that he made a mistake. Explain how his supervisor knew that the agent's report contained an error.

Challenge Problems/Group Activities

14. *Parks* A survey of 300 parks showed the following.

15 had only camping.

20 had only hiking trails.

35 had only picnicking.

185 had camping.

140 had camping and hiking trails.

125 had camping and picnicking.

210 had hiking trails.

Find the number of parks that

a) had at least one of these features.

b) had all three features.

c) did not have any of these features.

d) had exactly two of these features.

15. *Surveying Farmers* A survey of 500 farmers in a midwestern state showed the following.

125 grew only wheat.

110 grew only corn.

90 grew only oats.

200 grew wheat.

60 grew wheat and corn.

50 grew wheat and oats.

180 grew corn.

Find the number of farmers who

a) grew at least one of the three.

b) grew all three.

c) did not grow any of the three.

d) grew exactly two of the three.

Recreational Mathematics

16. *Number of Elements* A universal set U consists of 12 elements. If sets A, B, and C are proper subsets of U and $n(U) = 12$, $n(A \cap B) = n(A \cap C) = n(B \cap C) = 6$, $n(A \cap B \cap C) = 4$, and $n(A \cup B \cup C) = 10$ determine

a) $n(A \cup B)$ b) $n(A' \cup C)$ c) $n(A \cap B)'$

2.6 INFINITE SETS

On page 44, we state that a finite set is a set in which the number of elements is zero or the number of elements can be expressed as a natural number. On page 45, we define a one-to-one correspondence. To determine the number of elements in a finite set, we can place the set in a one-to-one correspondence with a subset of the set of counting numbers. For example, the set $A = \{\#, ?, \$\}$ can be placed in one-to-one correspondence with set $B = \{1, 2, 3\}$, a subset of the set of counting numbers.

$$A = \{\#, ?, \$\}$$
$$\downarrow \downarrow \downarrow$$
$$B = \{1, 2, 3\}$$

Because the cardinal number of set B is 3, the cardinal number of set A is also 3. Any two sets such as set A and set B that can be placed in a one-to-one correspondence must have the same number of elements (therefore the same cardinality) and must be equivalent sets. Note that $n(A)$ and $n(B)$ both equal 3.

The German mathematician Georg Cantor (1845–1918), known as the father of set theory, thought about sets that were not bounded. He called an unbounded set an *infinite set* and provided the following definition.

An **infinite set** is a set that can be placed in a one-to-one correspondence with a proper subset of itself.

In Example 1, we use Cantor's definition of an infinite set to show that the set of counting numbers is infinite.

EXAMPLE 1   *The Set of Natural Numbers*

Show that $N = \{1, 2, 3, 4, 5, \ldots, n, \ldots\}$ is an infinite set.

SOLUTION: To show that the set N is infinite, we establish a one-to-one correspondence between the counting numbers and a proper subset of itself. By removing the first element from the set of counting numbers, we get the set $\{2, 3, 4, 5, \ldots\}$, which is a proper subset of the set of counting numbers. Now we establish the one-to-one correspondence.

$$\text{Counting numbers} = \{1, 2, 3, 4, 5, \ldots, \quad n \quad, \ldots\}$$
$$\downarrow \downarrow \downarrow \downarrow \downarrow \qquad \downarrow$$
$$\text{Proper subset} \quad = \{2, 3, 4, 5, 6, \ldots, n + 1, \ldots\}$$

Note that for any number, n, in the set of counting numbers, its corresponding number in the proper subset is one greater, or $n + 1$. We have now shown the desired one-to-one correspondence, and thus the set of counting numbers is infinite.   ▲

Note in Example 1 that we showed the pairing of the general terms $n \rightarrow (n + 1)$. Showing a one-to-one correspondence of infinite sets requires showing the pairing of the general terms in the two infinite sets.

In the set of counting numbers, n represents the general term. For any other set of numbers, the general term will be different. The general term in any set should be written in terms of n such that when 1 is substituted for n in the general term, we get the first number in the set; when 2 is substituted for n in the general term, we get the second number in the set; when 6 is substituted for n in the general term, we get the sixth number in the set; and so on.

Consider the set $\{4, 9, 14, 19, \ldots\}$. Suppose we want to write the general term for this set (or sequence) or numbers. What would the general term be? The numbers differ by 5, so the general term will be of the form $5n$ plus or minus some number. Substituting 1 for n yields $5(1)$, or 5. Because the first number in the set is 4, we need to subtract 1 from the 5. Thus, the general term is $5n - 1$. Note that when $n = 1$, the value is $5(1) - 1$ or 4; when $n = 2$, the value is $5(2) - 1$ or 9; when $n = 3$, the value is $5(3) - 1$ or 14; and so on. Therefore, we write the set of numbers with the general term as

$$\{4, 9, 14, 19, \ldots, 5n - 1, \ldots\}$$

Now that you are aware of how to determine the general term of a set of numbers, we can do some more problems involving sets.

EXAMPLE 2   *The Set of Even Numbers*

Show that the set of even counting numbers $\{2, 4, 6, \ldots, 2n, \ldots\}$ is an infinite set.

SOLUTION: First create a proper subset of the set of even counting numbers by removing the first number from the set. Then establish a one-to-one correspondence.

Even counting numbers: $\{2, 4, 6, 8, \ldots, \quad 2n \quad, \ldots\}$
$$\downarrow \downarrow \downarrow \downarrow \qquad \qquad \downarrow$$
Proper subset: $\{4, 6, 8, 10, \ldots, 2n + 2, \ldots\}$

A one-to-one correspondence exists between the two sets, so the set of even counting numbers is infinite.   ▲

EXAMPLE 3   *The Set of Multiples of Three*

Show that the set $\{3, 6, 9, 12, \ldots, 3n, \ldots\}$ is an infinite set.

SOLUTION:

Given set: $\{3, 6, 9, 12, 15, \ldots, \quad 3n \quad, \ldots\}$
$$\downarrow \downarrow \downarrow \downarrow \downarrow \qquad \qquad \downarrow$$
Proper subset: $\{6, 9, 12, 15, 18, \ldots, 3n + 3, \ldots\}$

Therefore, the given set is an infinite set.   ▲

Countable Sets

In his work with infinite sets, Cantor developed ideas on how to determine the cardinal number of an infinite set. He called the cardinal number of infinite sets "transfinite cardinal numbers" or "transfinite powers." He defined a set as *countable* if it is finite or if it can be placed in a one-to-one correspondence with the set of counting numbers. All infinite sets that can be placed in a one-to-one correspondence with the set of counting numbers have cardinal number, *aleph-null*, symbolized $\aleph_0$ (the first Hebrew letter, aleph, with a zero subscript, read "null").

─EXAMPLE 4   *The Cardinal Number of the Set of Even Numbers*

Show that the set of even counting numbers has cardinal number $\aleph_0$.

SOLUTION: In Example 2, we showed that a set of even counting numbers is infinite by setting up a one-to-one correspondence between the set and a proper subset of itself.

   Now we will show that it is countable and has cardinality $\aleph_0$ by setting up a one-to-one correspondence between the set of counting numbers and the set of even counting numbers.

Counting numbers: $N = \{1, 2, 3, 4, \ldots, n, \ldots\}$

$$\downarrow \downarrow \downarrow \downarrow \qquad \downarrow$$

Even counting numbers: $E = \{2, 4, 6, 8, \ldots, 2n, \ldots\}$

For each number n in the set of counting numbers, its corresponding number is $2n$. Since we found a one-to-one correspondence between the set of counting numbers and the set of even counting numbers, the set of even counting numbers is countable. Thus, the cardinal number of the set of even counting numbers is $\aleph_0$; that is, $n(E) = \aleph_0$. As we mentioned earlier, the set of even counting numbers is an infinite set since it can be placed in a one-to-one correspondence with a proper subset of itself. Therefore, the set of even counting numbers is both infinite and countable.   ▲

Any set that can be placed in a one-to-one correspondence with the set of counting numbers has cardinality $\aleph_0$ and is countable.

─EXAMPLE 5   *The Cardinal Number of the Set of Odd Numbers*

Show that the set of odd counting numbers has cardinality $\aleph_0$.

SOLUTION: To show that the set of odd counting numbers has cardinality $\aleph_0$, we need to show a one-to-one correspondence between the counting numbers and the odd counting numbers.

Counting numbers: $N = \{1, 2, 3, 4, 5, \ldots, n, \ldots\}$

$$\downarrow \downarrow \downarrow \downarrow \downarrow \qquad \downarrow$$

Odd counting numbers: $O = \{1, 3, 5, 7, 9, \ldots, 2n - 1, \ldots\}$

Since there is a one-to-one correspondence, the odd counting numbers have cardinality $\aleph_0$; that is, $n(O) = \aleph_0$.   ▲

We have shown that both the odd and even counting numbers have cardinality $\aleph_0$. Merging the odd counting numbers with the even counting numbers gives the set of counting numbers, and we may reason that

$$\aleph_0 + \aleph_0 = \aleph_0$$

This result may seem strange, but it is true. What could such a statement mean? Well, consider a hotel with infinitely many rooms. If all the rooms are occupied, then the hotel is, of course, full. If more guests appear wanting accommodations, will they be turned away? The answer is *no,* for if the room clerk were to reassign each guest to a new room with a room number twice that of the present room, then all the odd-numbered rooms would become unoccupied and there would be space for more guests!

In Cantor's work, he showed that there are different orders of infinity. Sets that are countable and have cardinal number $\aleph_0$ are the lowest order of infinity. Cantor showed that the set of integers and the set of rational numbers (fractions of the form p/q, where $q \neq 0$) are infinite sets with cardinality $\aleph_0$. He also showed that the set of real numbers (discussed in Chapter 5) could not be placed in a one-to-one correspondence with the set of counting numbers and that they have a higher order of infinity, aleph-one, $\aleph_1$.

Welcome to
HOTEL INFINITY

. . . where there's always room for one more. . .

SECTION 2.6   EXERCISES

Concept/Writing Exercises

1. What is an infinite set as defined in this section?
2. **a)** What is a countable set?
   b) How can we determine if a given set has cardinality $\aleph_0$?

Practice the Skills

In Exercises 3–12, show that the set is infinite by placing it in a one-to-one correspondence with a proper subset of it-self. Be sure to show the pairing of the general terms in the sets.

3. $\{7, 8, 9, 10, 11, \dots\}$
4. $\{12, 13, 14, 15, 16, \dots\}$
5. $\{3, 5, 7, 9, 11, \dots\}$
6. $\{20, 22, 24, 26, 28, \dots\}$
7. $\{4, 7, 10, 13, 16, \dots\}$
8. $\{4, 8, 12, 16, 20, \dots\}$
9. $\{6, 11, 16, 21, 26, \dots\}$
10. $\{1, \frac{1}{2}, \frac{1}{3}, \frac{1}{4}, \frac{1}{5}, \dots\}$
11. $\{\frac{1}{2}, \frac{1}{4}, \frac{1}{6}, \frac{1}{8}, \frac{1}{10}, \dots\}$
12. $\{\frac{6}{11}, \frac{7}{11}, \frac{8}{11}, \frac{9}{11}, \frac{10}{11}, \dots\}$

In Exercises 13–22, show that the set has cardinal number $\aleph_0$ by establishing a one-to-one correspondence between the set of counting numbers and the given set. Be sure to show the pairing of the general terms in the sets.

13. $\{6, 12, 18, 24, 30, \dots\}$
14. $\{50, 51, 52, 53, 54, \dots\}$
15. $\{4, 6, 8, 10, 12, \dots\}$
16. $\{0, 2, 4, 6, 8, \dots\}$
17. $\{2, 5, 8, 11, 14, \dots\}$
18. $\{4, 9, 14, 19, 24, \dots\}$
19. $\{5, 8, 11, 14, 17, \dots\}$
20. $\{\frac{1}{2}, \frac{1}{4}, \frac{1}{6}, \frac{1}{8}, \dots\}$
21. $\{\frac{1}{3}, \frac{1}{4}, \frac{1}{5}, \frac{1}{6}, \frac{1}{7}, \dots\}$
22. $\{\frac{1}{2}, \frac{2}{3}, \frac{3}{4}, \frac{4}{5}, \frac{5}{6}, \dots\}$

Challenge Problems/Group Activities

In Exercises 23–26, show that the set has cardinality $\aleph_0$ by establishing a one-to-one correspondence between the set of counting numbers and the given set.

23. $\{1, 4, 9, 16, 25, 36, \dots\}$ 24. $\{2, 4, 8, 16, 32, \dots\}$
25. $\{3, 9, 27, 81, 243, \dots\}$ 26. $\{\frac{1}{3}, \frac{1}{6}, \frac{1}{12}, \frac{1}{24}, \frac{1}{48}, \dots\}$

Recreational Mathematics

In Exercises 27–31, insert the symbol $<$, $>$, or $=$ in the shaded area to make a true statement.

27. $\aleph_0 \quad\rule{1em}{0.6em}\quad \aleph_0 + \aleph_0$

28. $2\aleph_0 \quad\rule{1em}{0.6em}\quad \aleph_0 + \aleph_0$

29. $2\aleph_0 \quad\rule{1em}{0.6em}\quad \aleph_0$

30. $\aleph_0 + 5 \quad\rule{1em}{0.6em}\quad \aleph_0 - 3$

31. $n(N) \quad\rule{1em}{0.6em}\quad \aleph_0$

32. There are a number of paradoxes (a statement that appears to be true and false at the same time) associated with infinite sets and the concept of infinity. One of these, called *Zeno's Paradox*, is named after the mathematician Zeno, born about 496 BC in Italy. According to Zeno's paradox, suppose Achelles starts out 1 meter behind a tortoise. Also, suppose that Achelles walks 10 times as fast as the tortoise crawls. When Achelles reaches the point where the tortoise started, the tortoise is 1/10 of a meter ahead of Achelles. When Achelles reaches the point where the tortoise was 1/10 of a meter ahead, the tortoise is now 1/100 of a meter ahead. And so on. According to Zeno's Paradox, Achelles gets closer and closer to the tortoise but never catches up to the tortoise.

a) Do you believe the reasoning process is sound? If not, explain why not.

b) In actuality, if this were a real situation, would Achelles ever pass the tortoise?

Internet/Research Activities

33. Do research to explain how Cantor proved that the set of rational numbers has cardinal number $\aleph_0$.

34. Do research to explain how it can be shown that the real numbers do not have cardinal number $\aleph_0$.

CHAPTER 2 SUMMARY

IMPORTANT FACTS

Or is generally interpreted to mean *union*.

And is generally interpreted to mean *intersection*.

DE MORGAN'S LAWS

$$(A \cup B)' = A' \cap B'$$
$$(A \cap B)' = A' \cup B'$$

For any sets A and B,

$$n(A \cup B) = n(A) + n(B) - n(A \cap B).$$

Number of distinct subsets of a finite set with n elements is 2^n.

Symbol	Meaning
$\in$	is an element of
$\notin$	is not an element of
$n(A)$	number of elements in set A
$\varnothing$ or $\{\ \}$	the empty set
U	the universal set
$\subseteq$	is a subset of
$\nsubseteq$	is not a subset of
$\subset$	is a proper subset of
$\not\subset$	is not a proper subset of
$'$	complement
$\cup$	union
$\cap$	intersection
$\aleph_0$	aleph-null

CHAPTER 2   REVIEW EXERCISES

2.1, 2.2, 2.3, 2.4, 2.6

In Exercises 1–14, state whether each is true or false. If false, give a reason.

1. The set of counties located in the state of Alabama is a well-defined set.

2. The set of the three best beaches in the United States is a well-defined set.

3. maple $\in$ {oak, elm, maple, sycamore}

4. $\{\ \} \subset \varnothing$

5. $\{3, 6, 9, 12, \ldots\}$ and $\{2, 4, 6, 8, \ldots\}$ are disjoint sets.

6. $\{a, b, c, d, e\}$ is an example of a set in roster form.

7. {computer, calculator, pencil} $=$ {calculator, computer, diskette}

8. {apple, orange, banana, pear} is equivalent to {tomato, corn, spinach, radish}.

9. If $A = \{a, e, i, o, u\}$, then $n(A) = 5$.

10. $A = \{1, 4, 9, 16, \ldots\}$ is a countable set.

11. $A = \{1, 4, 7, 10, \ldots, 31\}$ is a finite set.

12. $\{3, 6, 7\} \subseteq \{7, 6, 3, 5\}$.

13. $\{x \mid x \in N$ and $3 < x \leq 9\}$ is a set in set-builder notation.

14. $\{x \mid x \in N$ and $2 < x \leq 12\} \subseteq \{1, 2, 3, 4, 5, \ldots, 20\}$

In Exercises 15–18, express each set in roster form.

15. Set A is the set of odd natural numbers between 5 and 16.

16. Set B is the set of states that border Nevada.

17. $C = \{x \mid x \in N \text{ and } x < 297\}$

18. $D = \{x \mid x \in N \text{ and } 8 < x \leq 96\}$

In Exercises 19–22, express each set in set-builder notation.

19. Set A is the set of natural numbers between 52 and 100.

20. Set B is the set of natural numbers greater than 63.

21. Set C is the set of natural numbers less than 3.

22. Set D is the set of natural numbers between 23 and 41, inclusive.

In Exercises 23–26, express each set with a written description.

23. $A = \{x \mid x \text{ is a letter of the English alphabet from E through M inclusive}\}$

24. $B = \{\text{penny, nickel, dime, quarter, half-dollar}\}$

25. $C = \{x, y, z\}$

26. $D = \{x \mid 3 \leq x < 9\}$

In Exercises 27–32, let

$$U = \{1, 2, 3, 4, \ldots, 10\}$$
$$A = \{1, 3, 5, 6\}$$
$$B = \{5, 6, 9, 10\}$$
$$C = \{1, 6, 10\}$$

In Exercises 27–32, determine the following.

27. $A \cap B$

28. $A \cup B'$

29. $A' \cap B$

30. $(A \cup B)' \cup C$

31. The number of subsets of set B

32. The number of proper subsets of set A

33. For the following sets, construct a Venn diagram and place the elements in the proper region.

$U = \{\text{lion, tiger, leopard, cheetah, puma, lynx, panther, jaguar}\}$

$A = \{\text{tiger, puma, lynx}\}$

$B = \{\text{lion, tiger, jaguar, panther}\}$

$C = \{\text{tiger, lynx, cheetah, panther}\}$

In Exercises 34–39, use Fig. 2.29 to determine the sets.

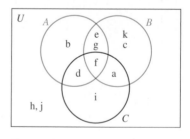

Figure 2.29

34. $A \cup B$

35. $A \cap B'$

36. $A \cup B \cup C$

37. $A \cap B \cap C$

38. $(A \cup B) \cap C$

39. $(A \cap B) \cup C$

Construct a Venn diagram to determine whether the following statements are true for all sets A, B, and C.

40. $(A' \cup B')' = A \cap B$

41. $(A \cup B') \cup (A \cup C') = A \cup (B \cap C)'$

Breakfast Cereals In Exercises 42–47, use the following chart, which shows selected breakfast cereals and some of their nutritional contents for a 1-cup serving. Let the cereals shown represent the universal set.

Cereal	Fat (grams)	Fiber (grams)	Sugar (grams)
Kellogg's Corn Flakes	0	1	2
Kellogg's Product 19	0	1	4
Kellogg's Fruit Loops	1	1	15
Kellogg's All-Bran	2	20	12
Kellogg's Raisin Bran	1.5	8	18
General Mills Wheaties	1	3	4
Kellogg's Special K	0	less than 1	4
General Mills Cinnamon Toast Crunch	3.5	1	10
General Mills Cheerios	2	3	1
General Mills Cookie Crisp	1	0	13

Let A be the set of cereals that contain at least 1 gram of fat.
Let B be the set of cereals that contain at least 3 grams of fiber.
Let C be the set of cereals that contain at least 4 grams of sugar.
Indicate in Fig. 2.30 in which region, I–VIII, each of the following cereals belongs.

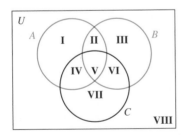

Figure 2.30

42. General Mills Cheerios
43. Kellogg's Raisin Bran
44. Kellogg's Corn Flakes
45. General Mills Cookie Crisp
46. Kellogg's Fruit Loops
47. Kellogg's Special *K*

2.5

48. *Pizza Survey* A pizza chain was willing to pay $1 to each person interviewed about his or her likes and dislikes of types of pizza crust. Of the people interviewed, 200 liked thin crust, 270 liked thick crust, 70 liked both, and 50 did not like pizza at all. What was the total cost of the survey?

49. *Cookie Preferences* The Cookie Shoppe conducted a survey to determine its customers' preferences.
    200 people liked chocolate chip cookies.
    190 people liked peanut butter cookies.
    210 people liked sugar cookies.
    100 people liked chocolate chip cookies and peanut butter cookies.
    150 people liked peanut butter cookies and sugar cookies.
    110 people liked chocolate chip cookies and sugar cookies.
    70 people liked all three.
    5 people liked none of these cookies.

    Draw a Venn diagram, then determine how many people
    a) completed the survey.
    b) liked only peanut butter cookies.
    c) liked peanut butter cookies and chocolate chip cookies, but not sugar cookies.
    d) liked peanut butter cookies or sugar cookies, but not chocolate chip cookies.

50. *TV Choices TV Guide* sent a questionnaire to selected subscribers asking which of the following three reality-based shows they watched on a regular basis. The three shows asked about were *Survivor I*, *Survivor II*, and *Survivor III*. The results of the 510 questionnaires that were returned showed that
    175 watched *Survivor I*.
    227 watched *Survivor II*.
    285 watched *Survivor III*.
    100 watched *Survivor I* and *Survivor II*.
    87 watched *Survivor II* and *Survivor III*.
    96 watched *Survivor I* and *Survivor III*.
    59 watched all three shows.

    Construct a Venn diagram and determine how many people
    a) watched only *Survivor I*.
    b) watched exactly one of these shows.
    c) watched *Survivor II* and *Survivor III*, but not *Survivor I*.
    d) watched *Survivor I* or *Survivor III*, but not *Survivor II*.
    e) watched exactly two of these shows.

2.6

In Exercises 51 and 52, show that the sets are infinite by placing each set in a one-to-one correspondence with a proper subset of itself.

51. $\{2, 4, 6, 8, 10, \dots\}$ 52. $\{3, 5, 7, 9, 11, \dots\}$

In Exercises 53 and 54, show that each set has cardinal number $\aleph_0$ by setting up a one-to-one correspondence between the set of counting numbers and the given set.

53. $\{5, 8, 11, 14, 17, \dots\}$ 54. $\{4, 9, 14, 19, 24, \dots\}$

CHAPTER 2 TEST

In Exercises 1–9, state whether each is true or false. If the statement is false, explain why.

1. $[1, y, 8, \$]$ is equivalent to $\{p, \#, 5, 2\}$.
2. $\{3, 5, 9, h\} = \{9, 5, 3, j\}$
3. $\{star, moon, sun\} \subset \{star, moon, sun, planet\}$
4. $\{7\} \subseteq \{x \mid x \in N \text{ and } x < 7\}$
5. $\{\ \} \not\subset \{0\}$
6. $\{p, q, r\}$ has seven subsets.
7. If $A \cap B = \{\ \}$, then A and B are disjoint sets.
8. For any set A, $A \cup A' = \{\ \}$.
9. For any set A, $A \cap U = A$.

In Exercises 10 and 11, use set

$$A = \{x \mid x \in N \text{ and } x < 9\}.$$

10. Write set A in roster form.
11. Write a description of set A.

In Exercises 12–15, use the following information.

$$U = \{3, 5, 7, 9, 11, 13, 15\}$$
$$A = \{3, 5, 7, 9\}$$
$$B = \{7, 9, 11, 13\}$$
$$C = \{3, 11, 15\}$$

Determine the following.

12. $A \cap B$
13. $A \cup C'$
14. $A \cap (B \cap C)'$
15. $n(A \cap B')$
16. Using the sets provided for Exercises 12–15, draw a Venn diagram illustrating the relationship among the sets.
17. Use a Venn diagram to determine whether

$$A \cap (B \cup C') = (A \cap B) \cup (A \cap C')$$

for all sets A, B, and C. Show your work.

18. *Car Accessories* Auto Accessories Unlimited surveyed 155 customers to determine information regarding car accessories their car had. The results of the surveys showed

    76 had keyless entry.
    90 had a sunroof.
    107 had a compact disc player.
    54 had keyless entry and a compact disc player.
    57 had a sunroof and a compact disc player.
    52 had keyless entry and a sunroof.
    35 had all three accessories.

Construct a Venn diagram and then determine how many customers had
a) exactly one of these accessories.
b) none of these accessories.
c) at least two of these accessories.
d) keyless entry and a sunroof, but not a compact disc player.
e) keyless entry or a sunroof, but not a compact disc player.
f) only a compact disc player.

19. Show that the following set is infinite by setting up a one-to-one correspondence between the set and a proper subset of itself.

$$\{7, 8, 9, 10, \dots\}$$

20. Show that the following set has cardinal number $\aleph_0$ by setting up a one-to-one correspondence between the set of counting numbers and the set.

$$\{1, 3, 5, 7, \dots\}$$

GROUP PROJECTS

Selecting a Family Pet

1. The Wilcox family is considering buying a dog. They have established several criteria for the family dog: It must be one of the breeds listed in the table, must not shed, must be less than 16 in. tall, and must be good with children.

   a) Using the information in the table,* construct a Venn diagram in which the universal set is the dogs listed. Indicate the set of dogs to be placed in each region of the Venn diagram.

   b) From the Venn diagram constructed in part (a), determine which dogs will meet the criteria set by the Wilcox family. Explain.

Breed	Sheds	Less than 16 in.	Good with children
Airedale	no	no	no
Basset hound	yes	yes	yes
Beagle	yes	yes	yes
Border terrier	no	yes	yes
Cairn terrier	no	yes	no
Cocker spaniel	yes	yes	yes
Collie	yes	no	yes
Dachshund	yes	yes	no
Poodle, miniature	no	yes	no
Schnauzer, miniature	no	yes	no
Scottish terrier	no	yes	no
Wirehaired fox terrier	no	yes	no

Classification of the Domestic Cat

2. Read the Did You Know feature on page 54. Do research and indicate the name of the following groupings to which the domestic cat belongs.

   a) Kingdom
   b) Phylum
   c) Class
   d) Order
   e) Family
   f) Genus
   g) Species

Who Lives Where

3. On Diplomat Row, an area of Washington, D.C., there are five houses. Each owner is a different nationality, each has a different pet, each has a different favorite food, each has a different favorite drink, and each house is painted a different color.

   The green house is directly to the right of the ivory house.
   The Senegalese has the red house.
   The dog belongs to the Spaniard.
   The Afghanistani drinks tea.
   The person who eats cheese lives next door to the fox.
   The Japanese eats fish.
   Milk is drunk in the middle house.
   Apples are eaten in the house next to the horse.
   Ale is drunk in the green house.
   The Norwegian lives in the first house.
   The peach eater drinks whiskey.
   Apples are eaten in the yellow house.
   The banana eater owns a snail.
   The Norwegian lives next door to the blue house.

   For each house find
   a) the color.
   b) the nationality of the occupant.
   c) the owner's favorite food.
   d) the owner's favorite drink.
   e) the owner's pet.
   f) Finally, the crucial question is: Does the zebra's owner drink vodka or ale?

*The information is a collection of the opinions of an animal psychologist, Dr. Daniel Tortora, and a group of veterinarians.

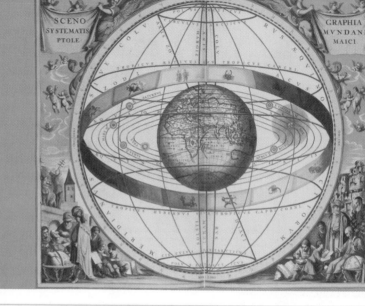

Logical reasoning can tell us whether a conclusion follows from a set of premises, but not whether those premises are true. For example, Greek astronomers, using the assumption that the planets revolved around Earth, correctly predicted the positions of the planets even though their premise was false.

LOGIC

The ancient Greeks were the first people to analyze systematically the way people think and arrive at a conclusion. Aristotle, whose study of logic is presented in a work called *Organon,* is called the father of logic. Since Aristotle's time, the study of logic has been continued by other great mathematicians.

Although most people believe that logic deals with the way people think, it does not. In the study of logic, we use deductive reasoning to analyze complicated situations and come to a reasonable conclusion from a given set of information.

If human thought does not always follow the rules of logic, then why do we study it? Logic enables us to communicate effectively, to make more convincing arguments, and to develop patterns of reasoning for decision making. The study of logic also prepares an individual to better understand other areas of mathematics, computer programming and design, and in general the thought process involved in learning any subject.

3.1   STATEMENTS AND LOGICAL CONNECTIVES

History

The ancient Greeks were the first people to systematically analyze the way humans think and arrive at conclusions. Aristotle (384–322 B.C.) organized the study of logic for the first time in a work called *Organon*. As a result of his work, Aristotle is called the father of logic. The logic from this period, called *Aristotelian logic*, has been taught and studied for more than 2000 years.

Since Aristotle's time, the study of logic has been continued by other great philosophers and mathematicians. Gottfried Wilhelm Leibniz (1646–1716) had a deep conviction that all mathematical and scientific concepts could be derived from logic. As a result, he became the first serious student of *symbolic logic*. One difference between symbolic logic and Aristotelian logic is that in symbolic logic, as its name implies, symbols (usually letters) represent written statements. The forms of the statements in the two types of logic are different. The self-educated English mathematician George Boole (1815–1864) is considered to be the founder of symbolic logic because of his impressive work in this area. Among Boole's publications are *The Mathematical Analysis of Logic* (1847) and *An Investigation of the Law of Thought* (1854). Mathematician Charles Dodgson, better known as Lewis Carroll, incorporated many interesting ideas from logic into his books *Alice's Adventures in Wonderland* and *Through the Looking Glass* and his other children's stories.

Logic has been studied through the ages to exercise the mind's ability to reason. Understanding logic will enable you to think clearly, communicate effectively, make more convincing arguments, and develop patterns of reasoning that will help you in making decisions. It will also help you to detect the fallacies in the reasoning or arguments of others such as advertisers and politicians. Studying logic has other practical applications, such as helping you to understand wills, contracts, and other legal documents.

The study of logic is also good preparation for other areas of mathematics. If you preview Chapter 12, on probability, you will see formulas for the probability of *a* or *b* and the probability of *a* and *b*, symbolized as $P(A \text{ or } B)$ and $P(A \text{ and } B)$, respectively. Special meanings of common words such as *or* and *and* apply to all areas of mathematics. The meaning of these and other special words is discussed in this chapter.

Logic and the English Language

In reading, writing, and speaking, we use many words such as *and, or,* and *if . . . then . . .* to connect thoughts. In logic we call these words *connectives*. How are these words interpreted in daily communication? A judge announces to a convicted offender, "I hereby sentence you to five months of community service *and* a fine of $100." In this case, we normally interpret the word *and* to indicate that *both* events will take place. That is, the person must do community service and must also pay a fine.

Now suppose a judge states, "I sentence you to six months in prison *or* 10 months of community service." In this case, we interpret the connective *or* as meaning the convicted person must either spend the time in jail or do community service, but not both. The word *or* in this case is the *exclusive or*. When the exclusive or is used, one or the other of the events can take place, but *not both*.

In a restaurant a waiter asks, "May I interest you in a cup of soup or a sandwich?" This question offers three possibilities: You may order soup, you may order a sandwich, or you may order both soup and a sandwich. The *or* in this case is the *inclusive or.* When the inclusive or is used, one or the other, *or both* events can take place. *In this chapter, when we use the word* or *in a logic statement, it will mean the* inclusive or *unless stated otherwise.*

If–then statements are often used to relate two ideas, as in the bank policy statement "If the average daily balance is greater than $500, then there will be no service charge." If–then statements are also used to emphasize a point or add humor, as in the statement "If the Cubs win, then I will be a monkey's uncle."

Now let's look at logic from a mathematical point of view.

Statements and Logical Connectives

A sentence that can be judged either true or false is called a *statement*. Labeling a statement true or false is called *assigning a truth value*. Here are some examples of statements.

1. The Brooklyn Bridge goes over San Francisco Bay.
2. Disney World is in Idaho.
3. The Mississippi River is the longest river in the United States.

In each case, we can say that the sentence is either true or false. Statement 1 is false because the Brooklyn Bridge does not go over San Francisco Bay. Statement 2 is false. Disney World is in Florida. By looking at a map or reading an almanac, we can determine that the Mississippi River is the longest river in the United States, and, therefore, statement 3 is true.

The three sentences discussed above are examples of *simple statements* because they convey one idea. Sentences combining two or more ideas that can be assigned a truth value are called *compound statements*. Compound statements are discussed shortly.

Quantifiers

Sometimes it is necessary to change a statement to its opposite meaning. To do so, we use the *negation* of a statement. For example, the negation of the statement "Emily is at home" is "Emily is not at home." The negation of a true statement is always a false statement, and the negation of a false statement is always a true statement. We must use special caution when negating statements containing the words *all, none* (or *no*), and *some.* These words are referred to as *quantifiers.*

Consider the statement "All lakes contain fresh water." We know this statement is false because the Great Salt Lake in Utah contains salt water. Its negation must therefore be true. We may be tempted to write its negation as "No lake contains fresh water," but this statement is also false because Lake Superior contains fresh water. Therefore, "No lakes contain fresh water" is not the negation of "All lakes contain fresh water." The correct negation of "All lakes contain fresh water" is "Not all lakes contain fresh water" or "At least one lake does not contain fresh water" or "Some lakes do not contain fresh water." These statements all imply that at least one lake does not contain fresh water, which is a true statement.

Now consider the statement "No birds can swim." This statement is false, since at least one bird, the penguin, can swim. Therefore, the negation of this statement must be true. We may be tempted to write the negation as "All birds can swim," but because this statement is also false it cannot be the negation. The correct negation of the statement is "Some birds can swim" or "At least one bird can swim," which are true statements.

The Brooklyn Bridge in New York City

Now let's consider statements involving the quantifier *some,* as in "Some students have a driver's license." This is a true statement, meaning that at least one student has a driver's license. The negation of this statement must therefore be false. The negation is "No student has a driver's license," which is a false statement.

Consider the statement "Some students do not ride motorcycles." This statement is true because it means "At least one student does not ride a motorcycle." The negation of this statement must therefore be false. The negation is "All students ride motorcycles," which is a false statement.

The negation of quantified statements is summarized as follows:

Form of statement	Form of negation
All are.	Some are not.
None are.	Some are.
Some are.	None are.
Some are not.	All are.

The following diagram might help you to remember the statements and their negations:

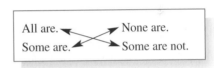

The quantifiers diagonally opposite each other are the negations of each other.

EXAMPLE 1   *Write Negations*

Write the negation of each statement.

a) Some snakes are poisonous.

b) All swimming pools are rectangular.

SOLUTION:

a) Since *some* means "at least one," the statement "Some snakes are poisonous" is the same as "At least one snake is poisonous." Because it is a true statement, its negation must be false. The negation is "No snakes are poisonous," which is a false statement.

b) The statement "All swimming pools are rectangular" is a false statement since some pools are circular, some are oval, and some have other shapes. Its negation must therefore be true. The negation may be written as "Some swimming pools are not rectangular" or "Not all swimming pools are rectangular" or "At least one swimming pool is not rectangular." Each of these statements is true.

Compound Statements

Statements consisting of two or more simple statements are called **compound statements**. The connectives often used to join two simple statements are

and,   or,   if,...then...,   if and only if

In addition, we consider a simple statement that has been negated to be a compound statement. The word *not* is generally used to negate a statement.

To reduce the amount of writing in logic, it is common to represent each simple statement with a lowercase letter. For example, suppose we are discussing the simple statement "Leland is a farmer." Instead of writing "Leland is a farmer" over and over again, we can let p represent the statement "Leland is a farmer." Thereafter we can simply refer to the statement with the letter p. It is customary to use the letters p, q, r, and s to represent simple statements, but other letters may be used instead. Let's now look at the connectives used to make compound statements.

Not Statements

The negation is symbolized by $\sim$ and read "not." For example, the negation of the statement "Steve is a college student" is "Steve is not a college student." If p represents the simple statement "Steve is a college student," then $\sim p$ represents the compound statement "Steve is not a college student." For any statement p, $\sim(\sim p) = p$. For example, the negation of the statement "Steve is not a college student" is "Steve is a college student."

Consider the statement "Inga is not at home." This statement contains the word *not*, which indicates that it is a negation. To write this statement symbolically, we let p represent "Inga *is* at home." Then $\sim p$ would be "Inga is not at home." *We will use this convention of letting letters such as p, q, or r represent statements that are not negated. We will represent negated statements with the negation symbol, $\sim$.*

And Statements

The *conjunction* is symbolized by $\wedge$ and read "and." The $\wedge$ looks like an A (for And) with the bar missing. Let p and q represent the simple statements.

> p: You will perform 5 months of community service.
> q: You will pay a $100 fine.

Then the following is the conjunction written in symbolic form.

$$\underbrace{\text{You will perform 5 months of community service}}_{\uparrow \atop p} \quad \underbrace{\text{and}}_{\uparrow \atop \wedge} \quad \underbrace{\text{you will pay a \$100 fine.}}_{\uparrow \atop q.}$$

The conjunction is generally expressed as *and*. Other words sometimes used to express a conjunction are *but, however,* and *nevertheless.*

EXAMPLE 2 *Write a Conjunction*

Write the following conjunction in symbolic form. The dish is heavy, but the dish is not hot.

SOLUTION: Let *d* and *h* represent the simple statements.

> *d*:   The dish is heavy.
>
> *h*:   The dish is hot.

In symbolic form, the compound statement is $d \wedge \sim h$.   ▲

In Example 2, the compound statement is "The dish is heavy, but the dish is not hot." This statement could also be repesented as "The dish is heavy, but *it* is not hot." In this problem, it should be clear that the word *it* means *the dish*. Therefore, the statement, "The dish is heavy, but it is not hot" would also be symbolized as $d \wedge \sim h$.

Or Statements

The *disjunction* is symbolized by $\vee$ and read "or." The *or* we use in this book (except where indicated in the exercise sets) is the *inclusive or* described on pages 93 and 94.

EXAMPLE 3   *Write a Disjunction*

Let

> *p*:   Maria will go to the circus.
>
> *q*:   Maria will go to the zoo.

Write the following statements in symbolic form.
a) Maria will go to the circus or Maria will go to the zoo.
b) Maria will go to the zoo or Maria will not go to the circus.
c) Maria will not go to the circus or Maria will not go to the zoo.

SOLUTION:
a) $p \vee q$ b) $q \vee \sim p$ c) $\sim p \vee \sim q$ ▲

Because *or* represents the *inclusive or,* the statement "Maria will go to the circus or Maria will go to the zoo" in Example 3(a) may mean that Maria will go to the circus, or that Maria will go to the zoo, or that Maria will go to both the circus *and* the zoo. The statement in Example 3(a) could also be written as "Maria will go to the circus or the zoo."

When a compound statement contains more that one connective, a comma can be used to indicate which simple statements are to be grouped together. When we write the compound statement symbolically, *the simple statements on the same side of the comma are to be grouped together within parentheses.*

For example, "Pink is a singer (*p*) or Geena Davis is an actress (*g*), and Dallas is in Texas (*d*)", is written $(p \vee g) \wedge d$. Note that the *p* and *g* are both on the same side of the comma in the written statement. They are therefore grouped together within parentheses. The statement "Pink is a singer, or Geena Davis is an actress and Dallas is in Texas" is written $p \vee (g \wedge d)$. In this case, *g* and *d* are on the same side of the comma and are therefore grouped together within parentheses.

Geena Davis

EXAMPLE 4 *Understand How Commas Are Used to Group Statements*

Let

p: Dinner includes soup.

q: Dinner includes salad.

r: Dinner includes the vegetable of the day.

Write the following statements in symbolic form.

a) Dinner includes soup, and salad or the vegetable of the day.

b) Dinner includes soup and salad, or the vegetable of the day.

SOLUTION:

a) The comma tells us to group the statement "Dinner includes salad" with the statement "Dinner includes the vegetable of the day." Note that both statements are on the same side of the comma. The statement in symbolic form is $p \land (q \lor r)$.

  In mathematics, we always evaluate the information within the parentheses first. Since the conjunction, $\land$, is outside the parentheses and is evaluated *last,* this statement is considered a *conjunction.*

b) The comma tells us to group the statement "Dinner includes soup" with the statement "Dinner includes salad." Note that both statements are on the same side of the comma. The statement in symbolic form is $(p \land q) \lor r$. Since the disjunction, $\lor$, is outside the parentheses and is evaluated *last,* this statement is considered a *disjunction.*

The information provided in Example 4 is summarized below.

Statement	Symbolic representation	Type of statement
Dinner includes soup, and salad or the vegetable of the day.	$p \land (q \lor r)$	conjunction
Dinner includes soup and salad, or the vegetable of the day.	$(p \land q) \lor r$	disjunction

An important point to remember is that a negation symbol has the effect of negating only the statement that directly follows it. To negate a compound statement, we must use parentheses. When a negation symbol is placed in front of a statement in parentheses, it negates the entire statement in parentheses. The negation symbol in this case is read, "It is not true that . . . " or "It is false that . . . "

EXAMPLE 5 *Change Symbolic Statements to Words*

Let

p: Jozsef is making breakfast

q: Arum is setting the table

Write the following symbolic statements in words.

a) $p \land {\sim}q$ b) ${\sim}p \lor {\sim}q$ c) ${\sim}(p \land q)$

SOLUTION:

a) Jozsef is making breakfast and Arum is not setting the table.

b) Jozsef is not making breakfast or Arum is not setting the table.

c) It is false that Jozsef is making breakfast and Arum is setting the table. ▲

Recall that the word *but* may also be used in a conjunction. Therefore, Example 5(a) could also be written "Jozsef is making breakfast, *but* Arum is not setting the table."

Part (b) of Example 5 is a disjunction, since it can be written $(\sim p) \vee (\sim q)$. Part (c), which is $\sim(p \wedge q)$, is a negation, since the negation symbol negates the entire statement within parentheses. The similarity of these two statements is discussed in Section 3.4.

Occasionally, we come across a *neither–nor* statement, such as "John is neither handsome nor rich." This statement means that John is not handsome *and* John is not rich. If p represents "John is handsome" and q represents "John is rich," this statement is symbolized by $\sim p \wedge \sim q$.

If–Then Statements

The *conditional* is symbolized by $\rightarrow$ and is read "if–then." The statement $p \rightarrow q$ is read "If p, then q."* The conditional statement consists of two parts: the part that precedes the arrow is the *antecedent,* and the part that follows the arrow is the *consequent.*† In the conditional statement $p \rightarrow q$, the p is the antecedent and the q is the consequent.

In the conditional statement $\sim(p \vee q) \rightarrow (p \wedge q)$, the antecedent is $\sim(p \vee q)$ and the consequent is $(p \wedge q)$. An example of a conditional statement is "If you drink your milk, then you will grow up to be healthy." A conditional symbol may be placed between any two statements even if the statements are not related.

Sometimes the word *then* in a conditional statement is not explicitly stated. For example, the statement "If you pass this course, I will buy you a car" is a conditional statement because it actually means "If you pass this course, then I will buy you a car."

EXAMPLE 6 *Write Conditional Statements*

Let

> p: Jennifer goes to the library.
>
> q: Jennifer will study.

Write the following statements symbolically.

a) If Jennifer goes to the library, then she will study.

b) If Jennifer does not go to the library, then she will not study.

c) It is false that if Jennifer goes to the library then she will study.

SOLUTION:

a) $p \rightarrow q$ b) $\sim p \rightarrow \sim q$ c) $\sim(p \rightarrow q)$ ▲

---

*Some books indicate that $p \rightarrow q$ may also be read "p implies q." Many higher-level mathematics books, however, indicate that $p \rightarrow q$ may be read "p implies q" only under certain conditions. Implications are discussed in Section 3.3.

†Some books refer to the antecedent as the hypothesis or premise and the consequent as the conclusion.

┌EXAMPLE 7   *Use Commas When Writing a Symbolic Statement in Words*

Let

p: Jorge is enrolled in calculus.

q: Jorge's major is criminal justice.

r: Jorge's major is engineering.

Write the following symbolic statements in words and indicate whether the statement is a negation, conjunction, disjunction, or conditional.

a) $(q \rightarrow \sim p) \vee r$ b) $q \rightarrow (\sim p \vee r)$

SOLUTION: The parentheses indicate where to place the commas in the sentences.

a) "If Jorge's major is criminal justice then Jorge is not enrolled in calculus, or Jorge's major is engineering." This statement is a disjunction because $\vee$ is outside the parentheses.

b) "If Jorge's major is criminal justice, then Jorge is not enrolled in calculus or Jorge's major is engineering." This is a conditional statement because $\rightarrow$ is outside the parentheses.   ▲

If and Only if Statements

The *biconditional* is symbolized by $\leftrightarrow$ and is read "if and only if." The phrase *if and only if* is sometimes abbreviated as "iff." The statement $p \leftrightarrow q$ is read "p if and only if q."

┌EXAMPLE 8   *Write Statements Using the Biconditional*

Let

p: The printer is working.

q: The ink cartridge is correctly inserted.

Write the following symbolic statements in words.

a) $q \leftrightarrow p$ b) $\sim(p \leftrightarrow \sim q)$

SOLUTION:

a) The ink cartridge is correctly inserted if and only if the printer is working.

b) It is false that the printer is working if and only if the ink cartridge is not correctly inserted.   ▲

You will learn later that $p \leftrightarrow q$ means the same as $(p \rightarrow q) \wedge (q \rightarrow p)$. Therefore, the statement "I will go to college if and only if I can pay the tuition" has the same logical meaning as "If I go to college then I can pay the tuition, and if I can pay the tuition then I will go to college."

The following is a summary of the connectives discussed in this section.

Formal name	Symbol	Read	Symbolic form
Negation	$\sim$	"Not"	$\sim p$
Conjunction	$\wedge$	"And"	$p \wedge q$
Disjunction	$\vee$	"Or"	$p \vee q$
Conditional	$\rightarrow$	"If-then"	$p \rightarrow q$
Biconditional	$\leftrightarrow$	"If and only if"	$p \leftrightarrow q$

Dominance of Connectives

What is the answer to the problem $2 + 3 \times 4$? Some of you might say 20, but others might say 14. If you evaluate $2 + 3 \times 4$ on a calculator by pressing

$$2 \boxed{+} 3 \boxed{\times} 4$$

some may give you the answer 14, whereas others may give you the answer 20. Which is the correct answer? In mathematics, unless otherwise changed by parentheses or some other grouping symbol, multiplication is *always* performed before addition. Thus,

$$2 + 3 \times 4 = 2 + (3 \times 4) = 14$$

The calculators that gave the incorrect answer of 20 are basic calculators that are not programmed according to the order of operations used in mathematics.

Just as an order of operations exists in the evaluation of arithmetic expressions, a dominance of connectives is used in the evaluation of logic statements. How do we evaluate a symbolic logic statement when no parentheses are used? For example, does $p \vee q \rightarrow r$ mean $(p \vee q) \rightarrow r$, or does it mean $p \vee (q \rightarrow r)$? If we are given a symbolic logic statement for which grouping has not been indicated by parentheses or a written logic statement for which grouping has not been indicated by a comma, then we use the dominance of connectives shown in Table 3.1. Note that *the least dominant connective is the negation and the most dominant is the biconditional.*

TABLE 3.1 Dominance of Connectives

Least dominant	1. Negation, $\sim$	Evaluate first
	2. Conjunction, $\wedge$; disjunction, $\vee$	
	3. Conditional, $\rightarrow$	
Most dominant	4. Biconditional, $\leftrightarrow$	Evaluate last

As indicated in Table 3.1, the conjunction and disjunction have the same level of dominance. Thus, to determine whether the symbolic statement $p \wedge q \vee r$ is a conjunction or a disjunction, we have to use grouping symbols (parentheses). When evaluating a symbolic statement that does not contain parentheses, we *evaluate the least dominant connective first and the most dominant connective last*. For example,

Statement	Most dominant connective used	Statement means	Type of statement
$\sim p \vee q$	$\vee$	$(\sim p) \vee q$	Disjunction
$p \rightarrow q \vee r$	$\rightarrow$	$p \rightarrow (q \vee r)$	Conditional
$p \wedge q \rightarrow r$	$\rightarrow$	$(p \wedge q) \rightarrow r$	Conditional
$p \rightarrow q \leftrightarrow r$	$\leftrightarrow$	$(p \rightarrow q) \leftrightarrow r$	Biconditional
$p \vee r \leftrightarrow r \rightarrow \sim p$	$\leftrightarrow$	$(p \vee r) \leftrightarrow (r \rightarrow \sim p)$	Biconditional
$p \rightarrow r \leftrightarrow s \wedge p$	$\leftrightarrow$	$(p \rightarrow r) \leftrightarrow (s \wedge p)$	Biconditional

EXAMPLE 9   *Use the Dominance of Connectives*

Use the dominance of connectives to add parentheses to each statement. Then indicate whether each statement is a negation, conjunction, disjunction, conditional, or biconditional.

a) $p \rightarrow q \vee r$ b) $\sim p \wedge q \leftrightarrow r \vee p$

SOLUTION:

a) The conditional has greater dominance than the disjunction, so we place parentheses around $q \vee r$, as follows:

$$p \rightarrow (q \vee r)$$

It is a conditional statement because the conditional symbol is outside the parentheses.

b) The biconditional has the greatest dominance, so we place parentheses as follows:

$$(\sim p \wedge q) \leftrightarrow (r \vee p)$$

It is a biconditional statement because the biconditional symbol is outside the parentheses.

EXAMPLE 10   *Identify the Type of Statement*

Use the dominance of connectives and parentheses to write each statement symbolically. Then indicate whether each statement is a negation, conjunction, disjunction, conditional, or biconditional.

a) If you are late in paying your rent or you have damaged the apartment then you may be evicted.

b) You are late in paying your rent, or if you have damaged the apartment then you may be evicted.

SOLUTION:

a) Let

p: You are late in paying your rent.
q: You have damaged the apartment.
r: You may be evicted.

No commas appear in the sentence, so we will evaluate it by using the dominance of connectives. Because the conditional has higher dominance than the disjunction, the conditional statement will be evaluated last. Thus, the statements "You are late in paying your rent" and "You have damaged the apartment" are to be grouped together. The statement written symbolically with parentheses is

$$(p \vee q) \to r$$

This is a conditional statement.

b) A comma is used in this statement to indicate grouping, just as parentheses do in arithmetic. The placement of the comma indicates that the statements "You have damaged the apartment" and "You may be evicted" are to be grouped together. Therefore, this statement written symbolically is

$$p \vee (q \to r)$$

This statement is a disjunction. Note that the comma overrides the dominance of connectives and tells us to evaluate the conditional statement before the disjunction.

SECTION 3.1   EXERCISES

Concept/Writing Exercises

1. **a)** What is a simple statement?
   b) What is a compound statement?

2. List the words identified as quantifiers.

3. Write the general form of the negation for statements of the form
   a) none are.
   b) some are not.
   c) all are.
   d) some are.

4. Represent the statement "The ink is not purple" symbolically. Explain your answer.

5. Draw the symbol used to represent the
   a) conditional.
   b) disjunction.
   c) conjunction.
   d) negation.
   e) biconditional.

6. **a)** When the *exclusive or* is used as a connective between two events, can both events take place? Explain.
   b) When the *inclusive or* is used as a connective between two events, can both events take place? Explain.
   c) Which *or*, the *inclusive or* or the *exclusive or*, is used in this chapter?

7. Explain how a comma is used to indicate the grouping of simple statements.

8. List the dominance of connectives from the most dominant to the least dominant.

Practice the Skills/Problem Solving

In Exercises 9–22, indicate whether the statement is a simple statement or a compound statement. If it is a compound statement, indicate whether it is a negation, conjunction, disjunction, conditional, or biconditional by using both the word and its appropriate symbol (for example, "a negation," ~).

9. The sun is shining and the air is crisp.

10. The water in the lake is not drinkable.

11. The figure is a quadrilateral if and only if it has four sides.

12. If the electricity goes out then the standard telephone will still work.

13. Joni Burnette is teaching calculus or she is teaching trigonometry.

14. The book was neither a novel nor an autobiography.

15. The hurricane did $400,000 worth of damage to DeSoto County.

16. Inhibor Melendez will be admitted to law school if and only if he earns his bachelor's degree.

17. It is false that Jeffery Hilt is a high school teacher and a grade school teacher.

18. If Cathy Smith walks 4 miles today then she will be sore tomorrow.

19. Mary Jo Woo ran 4 miles today and she lifted weights for 30 minutes.

20. Nancy Wallin went to the game, but she did not eat a hot dog.

21. It is false that if John Wubben fixes your car then you will need to pay him in cash.

22. If Buddy and Evelyn Cordova are residents of Budville, then they must vote for mayor on Tuesday.

In Exercises 23–34, write the negation of the statement.

23. Some picnic tables are portable.

24. No stock mutual funds have guaranteed yields.

25. All chickens fly.

26. All plants contain chlorophyll.

27. Some turtles do not have claws.

28. No teachers made the roster.

29. No bicycles have three wheels.

30. All horses have manes.

31. Some pine trees do not produce pinecones.

32. No one likes asparagus.

33. Some pedestrians are in the crosswalk.

34. Some dogs with long hair do not get cold.

In Exercises 35–40, write the statement in symbolic form. Let

    p: The tent is pitched.

    q: The bonfire is burning.

35. The tent is not pitched.

36. The tent is pitched and the bonfire is burning.

37. The bonfire is not burning or the tent is not pitched.

38. The bonfire is not burning if and only if the tent is not pitched.

39. If the tent is not pitched, then the bonfire is not burning.

40. The bonfire is not burning, however the tent is pitched.

In Exercises 41–46, write the statement in symbolic form. Let

    p: The charcoal is hot.

    q: The chicken is on the grill.

41. If the chicken is not on the grill then the charcoal is not hot.

42. The chicken is not on the grill if and only if the charcoal is not hot.

43. Neither is the charcoal hot nor is the chicken on the grill.

44. The charcoal is not hot, but the chicken is on the grill.

45. It is false that if the chicken is on the grill then the charcoal is not hot.

46. It is false that the charcoal is hot and the chicken is on the grill.

In Exercises 47–56, write the compound statement in words. Let

    p: Firemen work hard.

    q: Firemen wear red suspenders.

47. $\sim p$ 48. $\sim q$

49. $q \vee p$ 50. $p \wedge q$

51. $\sim p \leftrightarrow \sim q$ 52. $\sim p \rightarrow q$

53. $\sim (q \vee p)$ 54. $\sim p \vee \sim q$

55. $\sim p \wedge \sim q$ 56. $\sim (p \wedge q)$

In Exercises 57–66, write the statements in symbolic form. Let

    p: The temperature is 90°.

    q: The air conditioner is working.

    r: The apartment is hot.

57. If the temperature is 90° or the air conditioner is not working, then the apartment is hot.

58. The apartment is hot if and only if the temperature is not 90°, or the air conditioner is not working.

59. The temperature is 90° and the air conditioner is working, or the apartment is hot.

60. If the apartment is hot and the air conditioner is working, then the temperature is 90°.

61. If the temperature is 90°, then the air conditioner is working or the apartment is not hot.

62. The temperature is not 90° if and only if the air conditioner is not working, or the apartment is not hot.

63. The apartment is hot if and only if the air conditioner is working, and the temperature is 90°.

64. It is false that if the apartment is hot then the air conditioner is not working.

65. If the air conditioner is working, then the temperature is 90° if and only if the apartment is hot.

66. The apartment is hot or the air conditioner is not working, if and only if the temperature is 90°.

In Exercises 67–76, write each symbolic statement in words. Let

p: The water is 70°.

q: The sun is shining.

r: We go swimming.

67. $(p \vee q) \wedge \sim r$

68. $(p \wedge q) \vee r$

69. $\sim p \wedge (q \vee r)$

70. $(q \rightarrow p) \vee r$

71. $\sim r \rightarrow (q \wedge p)$

72. $(q \wedge r) \rightarrow p$

73. $(q \rightarrow r) \wedge p$

74. $\sim p \rightarrow (q \vee r)$

75. $(q \leftrightarrow p) \wedge r$

76. $q \rightarrow (p \leftrightarrow r)$

Dinner Menu In Exercises 77–80, use the following information to arrive at your answers. Many restaurant dinner menus include statements such as the following. All dinners

Welcome to
ANTONIO'S RESTAURANTE

"All dinners are served
with a choice of:
soup or salad, potatoes
or pasta, and carrots or peas"

are served with a choice of: Soup or Salad, and Potatoes or Pasta, and Carrots or Peas. Which of the following selections are permissible? If a selection is not permissible, explain why. See the discussion of the exclusive or *on page 93.*

77. Soup, salad, and peas

78. Salad, pasta, and carrots

79. Soup, potatoes, pasta, and peas

80. Soup, pasta, and potatoes

In Exercises 81–94, (a) add parentheses by using the dominance of connectives and (b) indicate whether the statement is a negation, conjunction, disjunction, conditional, or biconditional (see Example 9).

81. $\sim p \rightarrow q$

82. $\sim p \wedge r \leftrightarrow \sim q$

83. $\sim q \wedge \sim r$

84. $\sim p \vee q$

85. $p \vee q \rightarrow r$

86. $q \rightarrow p \wedge \sim r$

87. $r \rightarrow p \vee q$

88. $q \rightarrow p \leftrightarrow p \rightarrow q$

89. $\sim p \leftrightarrow \sim q \rightarrow r$

90. $\sim q \rightarrow r \wedge p$

91. $r \wedge \sim q \rightarrow q \wedge \sim p$

92. $\sim [p \rightarrow q \vee r]$

93. $\sim [p \wedge q \leftrightarrow p \vee r]$

94. $\sim [r \wedge \sim q \rightarrow q \wedge r]$

In Exercises 95–103, (a) select letters to represent the simple statements and write each statement symbolically by using parentheses and (b) indicate whether the statement is a negation, conjunction, disjunction, conditional, or biconditional (see Example 10).

95. Ruth Bignel retired, but she did not start her concrete business.

96. If the water level is up, then we can go canoeing or we can go rafting.

97. It is false that if your speed is below the speed limit then you will not get pulled over.

98. If dinner is ready then we can eat, or we cannot go to the restaurant.

99. If the food has fiber or the food has vitamins, then you will be healthy.

100. If Corliss is teaching then Faye is in the math lab if and only if it is not a weekend.

101. You may take this course if and only if you did not fail the previous course or you passed the placement test.

102. If the car has gas and the battery is charged then the car will start.

103. The classroom is empty if and only if it is the weekend, or it is 7 A.M.

Challenge Problems/Group Activities

104. *An Ancient Question* If Zeus could do anything, could he build a wall that he could not jump over? Explain your answer.

In Exercises 105 and 106, place parentheses in the statement according to the dominance of connectives. Indicate whether the statement is a negation, conjunction, disjunction, conditional, or biconditional.

105. $\sim q \rightarrow r \vee p \leftrightarrow \sim r \wedge q$

106. $\sim[\sim r \rightarrow p \wedge q \leftrightarrow \sim p \vee r]$

107. a) We cannot place parentheses in the statement $p \vee q \wedge r$. Explain why.
   b) Make up three simple statements and label them p, q, and r. Then write compound statements to represent $(p \vee q) \wedge r$ and $p \vee (q \wedge r)$.
   c) Do you think that the statements for $(p \vee q) \wedge r$ and $p \vee (q \wedge r)$ mean the same thing? Explain.

Internet/Research Activities

108. *Legal Documents* Obtain a legal document such as a will or rental agreement and copy one page of the document. Circle every connective used. Then list the number of times each connective appeared. Be sure to include conditional statements from which the word *then* was omitted from the sentence. Give the page and your listing to your instructor.

109. Write a report on the life and accomplishments of George Boole, who was an important contributor to the development of logic. In your report, indicate how his work eventually led to the development of the computer. References include encyclopedias, history of mathematics books, and the Internet.

3.2 TRUTH TABLES FOR NEGATION, CONJUNCTION, AND DISJUNCTION

A *truth table* is a device used to determine when a compound statement is true or false. Five basic truth tables are used in constructing other truth tables. Three are discussed in this section (Tables 3.2, 3.4, and 3.7), and two are discussed in the next section. Section 3.5 uses truth tables in determining whether a logical argument is valid or invalid.

TABLE 3.2   Negation

	p	$\sim p$
Case 1	T	F
Case 2	F	T

TABLE 3.3

	p	q
Case 1	T	T
Case 2	T	F
Case 3	F	T
Case 4	F	F

Negation

The first truth table is for *negation*. If p is a true statement, then the negation of p, "not p," is a false statement. If p is a false statement, then "not p" is a true statement. For example, if the statement "The shirt is blue" is true, then the statement "The shirt is not blue" is false. These relationships are summarized in Table 3.2. For a simple statement, there are exactly two true–false cases, as shown.

If a compound statement consists of two simple statements p and q, there are four possible cases, as illustrated in Table 3.3. Consider the statement "The test is today and the test covers Chapter 5." The simple statement "The test is today" has two possible truth values, true or false. The simple statement "The test covers Chapter 5" also has two truth values, true or false. Thus, for these two simple statements there are four distinct possible true–false arrangements. Whenever we construct a truth table for a compound statement that consists of two simple statements, we begin by listing the four true–false cases shown in Table 3.3.

Conjunction

To illustrate the conjunction, consider the following situation. You have recently purchased a new house. To decorate it, you ordered a new carpet and new furniture from the same store. You explain to the salesperson that the carpet must be delivered before the furniture. He promises that the carpet will be delivered on Thursday and that the furniture will be delivered on Friday.

To help determine whether the salesperson kept his promise, we assign letters to each simple statement. Let p be "The carpet will be delivered on Thursday" and q be "The furniture will be delivered on Friday." The salesperson's statement written in symbolic form is $p \land q$. There are four possible true–false situations to be considered. (Table 3.4).

TABLE 3.4   Conjunction

	p	q	$p \land q$
Case 1	T	T	T
Case 2	T	F	F
Case 3	F	T	F
Case 4	F	F	F

CASE 1: p is true and q is true. The carpet is delivered on Thursday and the furniture is delivered on Friday. The salesperson has kept his promise and the compound statement is true. Thus, we put a T in the $p \land q$ column.

CASE 2: p is true and q is false. The carpet is delivered on Thursday but the furniture is not delivered on Friday. Since the furniture was not delivered as promised, the compound statement is false. Thus, we put an F in the $p \land q$ column.

CASE 3: p is false and q is true. The carpet is not delivered on Thursday but the furniture is delivered on Friday. Since the carpet was not delivered on Thursday as promised, the compound statement is false. Thus, we put an F in the $p \land q$ column.

CASE 4: p is false and q is false. The carpet is not delivered on Thursday and the furniture is not delivered on Friday. Since the carpet and furniture were not delivered as promised, the compound statement is false. Thus, we put an F in the $p \land q$ column.

Examining the four cases, we see that in only one case did the salesperson keep his promise: in case 1. Therefore, case 1 (T, T) is true. In cases 2, 3, and 4, the salesperson did not keep his promise and the compound statement is false. The results are summarized in Table 3.4, the truth table for the conjunction.

> The **conjunction** $p \land q$ is true only when both p and q are true.

EXAMPLE 1   *Construct a Truth Table*

Construct a truth table for $p \land \sim q$.

SOLUTION: Because there are two statements, p and q, construct a truth table with four cases; see Table 3.5(a). Then write the truth values under the p in the compound statement and label this column 1, as in Table 3.5(b). Copy these truth values directly from the p column on the left. Write the corresponding truth values under the q in the compound statement and call this column 2, as in Table 3.5(c). Copy the truth values for column 2 directly from the q column on the left. Now find the truth values of $\sim q$ by negating the truth values in column 2 and call this column 3,

TABLE 3.5

(a)

	p	q	$p \wedge \sim q$
Case 1	T	T	
Case 2	T	F	
Case 3	F	T	
Case 4	F	F	

(b)

p	q	$p \wedge \sim q$
T	T	T
T	F	T
F	T	F
F	F	F
		1

(c)

p	q	p	$\wedge$	$\sim$	q
T	T	T			T
T	F	T			F
F	T	F			T
F	F	F			F
		1			2

(d)

p	q	p	$\wedge$	$\sim$	q
T	T	T		F	T
T	F	T		T	F
F	T	F		F	T
F	F	F		T	F
		1		3	2

(e)

p	q	p	$\wedge$	$\sim$	q
T	T	T	F	F	T
T	F	T	T	T	F
F	T	F	F	F	T
F	F	F	F	T	F
		1	4	3	2

as in Table 3.5(d). Use the conjunction table, Table 3.4, and the entries in columns 1 and 3 to complete column 4, as in Table 3.5(e). The results in column 4 are obtained as follows:

Row 1:   T $\wedge$ F is F.   Row 2:   T $\wedge$ T is T.

Row 3:   F $\wedge$ F is F.   Row 4:   F $\wedge$ T is F.

The answer is always the last column completed. Columns 1, 2, and 3 are only aids in arriving at the answer in column 4.   ▲

The statement $p \wedge \sim q$ in Example 1 actually means $p \wedge (\sim q)$. In the future, instead of listing a column for q and a separate column for its negation, we will make one column for $\sim q$, which will have the opposite values of those in the q column on the left. Similarly, when we evaluate $\sim p$, we will use the opposite values of those in the p column on the left. This procedure is illustrated in Example 2.

In Example 1, we spoke about *cases* and also *columns*. Consider Table 3.5(e). This table has four cases indicated by the four different rows of the two left hand (unnumbered) columns. The four *cases* are TT, TF, FT, and FF. In every truth table with two letters, we list the four cases (the first two columns) first. Then we complete the remaining columns in the truth table. In Table 3.5(e), after completing the two left-hand columns, we complete the remaining columns in the order indicated by the numbers below the columns. We will continue to place numbers below the columns to show the order in which the columns are completed.

TIMELY TIP When constructing truth tables it is very important to keep your entries in neat columns and rows. If you are using lined paper, put only one row of the table on each line. If you are not using lined paper, using a straightedge may help you correctly enter the information into the truth table's rows and columns.

TABLE 3.6

p	q	~p	∧	~q
T	T	F	F	F
T	F	F	F	T
F	T	T	(F)	F
F	F	T	(T)	T
		1	3	2

┌ EXAMPLE 2   *Construct and Interpret a Truth Table*

a) Construct a truth table for the following statement:

I have not studied and I am not ready for the test.

b) Under which conditions will the compound statement be true?
c) Suppose "I have studied" is a false statement and "I am ready for the test" is a true statement. Is the compound statement given in part (a) true or false?

SOLUTION:

a) First write the simple statements in symbolic form by using simple nonnegated statements.

Let

p: I have studied.

q: I am ready for the test.

Therefore, the compound statement may be written $\sim p \wedge \sim q$. Now construct a truth table with four cases, as shown in Table 3.6

Fill in the column labeled 1 by negating the truth values under p on the far left. Fill in the column labeled 2 by negating the values under q in the second column from the left. Fill in the column labeled 3 by using the columns labeled 1 and 2 and the definition of conjunction.

In the first row, to determine the entry for column 3, we use false for $\sim p$ and false for $\sim q$. Since false $\wedge$ false is false (see case 4 of Table 3.4), we place an F in column 3, row 1. In the second row, we use false for $\sim p$ and true for $\sim q$. Since false $\wedge$ true is false (see case 3 of Table 3.4), we place an F in column 3, row 2. In the third row, we use true for $\sim p$ and false for $\sim q$. Since true $\wedge$ false is false (see case 2 of Table 3.4), we place an F in column 3, row 3. In the fourth row, we use true for $\sim p$ and true for $\sim q$. Since true $\wedge$ true is true (see case 1 of Table 3.4), we place a T in column 3, row 4.

b) The compound statement in part (a) will be true only in case 4 (circled in blue) when both simple statements, p and q, are false, that is, when I have not studied and I am not ready for the test.

c) We are told that p, "I have studied," is a false statement and that q, "I am ready for the test," is a true statement. From the truth table (Table 3.6), we can determine that when p is false and q is true, case 3, the compound statement, is false (circled in red).   ▲

Disjunction

Consider the job description that contains the following requirements.

Civil Technician

Municipal program for redevelopment seeks on-site technician. **The applicant must have a two-year college degree in civil technology or five years of related experience**. Interested candidates please call 555-1234.

Who qualifies for the job? To help analyze the statement, translate it into symbolic form. Let p be "A requirement for the job is a two-year college degree in civil technology" and q be "A requirement for the job is five years of related experience." The statement in symbolic form is $p \vee q$. For the two simple statements, there are four distinct cases (see Table 3.7).

TABLE 3.7   Disjunction

p	q	$p \vee q$
T	T	T
T	F	T
F	T	T
F	F	F

CASE 1: p is true and q is true. A candidate has a two-year college degree in civil technology and five years of related experience. The candidate has both requirements and qualifies for the job. Consider qualifying for the job as a true statement and not qualifying as a false statement. Since the candidate qualifies for the job, we put a T in the $p \vee q$ column.

CASE 2: p is true and q is false. A candidate has a two-year college degree in civil technology but does not have five years of related experience. The candidate still qualifies for the job with the two-year college degree. Thus, we put a T in the $p \vee q$ column.

CASE 3: p is false and q is true. The candidate does not have a two-year college degree in civil technology but does have five years of related experience. The candidate qualifies for the job with the five years of related experience. Thus, we put a T in the $p \vee q$ column.

CASE 4: p is false and q is false. The candidate does not have a two-year college degree in civil technology and does not have five years of related experience. The candidate does not meet either of the two requirements and therefore does not qualify for the job. Thus, we put an F in the $p \vee q$ column.

In examining the four cases, we see that there is only one case in which the candidate does not qualify for the job: case 4. As this example indicates, an *or* statement will be true in every case, except when both simple statements are false. The results are summarized in Table 3.7, the truth table for the disjunction.

The **disjunction**, $p \vee q$, is true when either p is true, q is true, or both p and q are true.

The disjunction $p \vee q$ is false only when p and q are both false.

EXAMPLE 3   *Truth Table with a Negation*

Construct a truth table for $\sim(\sim q \wedge p)$.

SOLUTION: First construct the standard truth table listing the four cases. Then work within parentheses. The order to be followed is indicated by the numbers below the columns (see Table 3.8). Under $\sim q$, column 1, write the negation of the q column. Then, in column 2, copy the values from the p column. Next, complete the *and* column, column 3, using columns 1 and 2 and the truth table for the conjunction. The *and* column is true only when both statements are true, as in case 2. Finally, negate the values in the *and* column, column 3, and place these negated values in column 4. By examining the truth table you can see that the compound statement $\sim(\sim q \wedge p)$ is false only in case 2, that is, when p is true and q is false. ▲

TABLE 3.8

p	q	$\sim$	$(\sim q$	$\wedge$	$p)$
T	T	T	F	F	T
T	F	F	T	T	T
F	T	T	F	F	F
F	F	T	T	F	F
		4	1	3	2

A General Procedure for Constructing Truth Tables

1. Study the compound statement and determine whether it is a negation, conjunction, disjunction, conditional, or biconditional statement, as was done in Section 3.1. The answer to the truth table will appear under $\sim$ if the statement is a negation, under $\wedge$ if the statement is a conjunction, under $\vee$ if the statement is a disjunction, under $\rightarrow$ if the statement is a conditional, and under $\leftrightarrow$ if the statement is a biconditional.

2. Complete the columns under the simple statements, p, q, r, and their negations, $\sim p$, $\sim q$, $\sim r$, within parentheses. If there are nested parentheses (one pair of parentheses within another pair), work with the innermost pair first.

3. Complete the column under the connective within the parentheses. You will use the truth values of the connective in determining the final answer in step 5.

4. Complete the column under any remaining statements and their negations.

5. Complete the column under any remaining connectives. Recall that the answer will appear under the column determined in step 1. If the statement is a conjunction, disjunction, conditional, or biconditional, you will obtain the truth values for the connective by using the last column completed on the left side and on the right side of the connective. If the statement is a negation, you will obtain the truth values by negating the truth values of the last column completed within the grouping symbols on the right side of the negation. Be sure to circle or highlight your answer column or number the columns in the order they were completed.

TABLE 3.9

p	q	(~p	∨	q)	∧	~p
T	T	F	T	T	F	F
T	F	F	F	F	F	F
F	T	T	T	T	T	T
F	F	T	T	F	T	T
		1	3	2	5	4

TABLE 3.10

	p	q	r
Case 1	T	T	T
Case 2	T	T	F
Case 3	T	F	T
Case 4	T	F	F
Case 5	F	T	T
Case 6	F	T	F
Case 7	F	F	T
Case 8	F	F	F

┌ **EXAMPLE 4**   *Use the General Procedure to Construct a Truth Table*

Construct a truth table for the statement $(\sim p \vee q) \wedge \sim p$.

SOLUTION: We will follow the general procedure outlined in the box. This statement is a conjunction, so the answer will be under the conjunction symbol. Complete columns under $\sim p$ and q within the parentheses and call these columns 1 and 2, respectively (see Table 3.9). Complete the column under the disjunction, $\vee$, using the truth values in columns 1 and 2, and call this column 3. Next complete the column under $\sim p$, and call this column 4. The answer, column 5, is determined from the definition of the conjunction and the truth values in column 3, the last column completed on the left side of the conjunction, and column 4.   ▲

So far, all the truth tables we have constructed have contained at most two simple statements. Now we will explain how to construct a truth table that consists of three simple statements, such as $(p \wedge q) \wedge r$. When a compound statement consists of three simple statements, there are eight different true–false possibilities, as illustrated in Table 3.10. To begin such a truth table, write four Ts and four Fs in the column under p. Under the second statement, q, pairs of Ts alternate with pairs of Fs. Under the third statement, r, T alternates with F. This technique is not the only way of listing the cases, but it ensures that each case is unique and that no cases are omitted.

┌ **EXAMPLE 5**   *Construct a Truth Table with Eight Cases*

a) Construct a truth table for the statement "Santana is home and he is not at his desk, or he is sleeping."

b) Suppose that "Santana is home" is a false statement, that "Santana is at his desk" is a true statement, and that "Santana is sleeping" is a true statement. Is the compound statement in part (a) true or false?

SOLUTION:

a) First we will translate the statement into symbolic form.

Let

$$p: \quad \text{Santana is home.}$$
$$q: \quad \text{Santana is at his desk.}$$
$$r: \quad \text{Santana is sleeping.}$$

In symbolic form, the statement is $(p \land \sim q) \lor r$.

Since the statement is composed of three simple statements, there are eight cases. Begin by listing the eight cases in the three left-hand columns; see Table 3.11. By examining the statement, you can see that it is a disjunction. Therefore, the answer will be in the $\lor$ column. Fill out the truth table by working in parentheses first. Place values under p, column 1, and $\sim q$, column 2. Then find the conjunctions of columns 1 and 2 to obtain column 3. Place the values of r in column 4. To obtain the answer, column 5, use columns 3 and 4 and your knowledge of the disjunction.

TABLE 3.11

p	q	r	(p	∧	~q)	∨	r
T	T	T	T	F	F	T	T
T	T	F	T	F	F	F	F
T	F	T	T	T	T	T	T
T	F	F	T	T	T	T	F
F	T	T	F	F	F	(T)	T
F	T	F	F	F	F	F	F
F	F	T	F	F	T	T	T
F	F	F	F	F	T	F	F
			1	3	2	5	4

b) We are given the following:

$$p: \quad \text{Santana is home—false.}$$
$$q: \quad \text{Santana is at his desk—true.}$$
$$r: \quad \text{Santana is sleeping—true.}$$

Therefore, we need to find the truth value of the following case: false, true, true. In case 5 of the truth table, p, q, and r are F, T, and T, respectively. Therefore, under these conditions, the original compound statement is true (as circled in the table).

We have learned that a truth table with one simple statement has two cases, a truth table with two simple statements has four cases, and a truth table with three simple statements has eight cases. In general, *the number of distinct cases in a truth table with n distinct simple statements is* 2^n. The compound statement $(p \lor q) \lor (r \land \sim s)$ has four simple statements, p, q, r, s. Thus, a truth table for this compound statement would have 2^4, or 16, distinct cases.

When we construct a truth table, we determine the truth values of a compound statement for every possible case. If we want to find the truth value of the compound statement for any specific case when we know the truth values of the simple statements, we do not have to develop the entire table. For example, to determine the truth value for the statement

$$2 + 3 = 5 \quad \text{and} \quad 1 + 1 = 3$$

we let p be $2 + 3 = 5$ and q be $1 + 1 = 3$. Now we can write the compound statement as $p \land q$. We know that p is a true statement and q is a false statement. Thus, we can substitute T for p and F for q and evaluate the statement:

$$p \land q$$
$$\text{T} \land \text{F}$$
$$\text{F}$$

Therefore, the compound statement $2 + 3 = 5$ and $1 + 1 = 3$ is a false statement.

EXAMPLE 6   *Determine the Truth Value of a Compound Statement*

Determine the truth value for each simple statement. Then, using these truth values, determine the truth value of the compound statement.

a) 15 is less than or equal to 9.

b) George Washington was the first U.S. president or Abraham Lincoln was the second U.S. president, but there has not been a U.S. president born in Antarctica.

SOLUTION:

a) Let

$$p: \quad 15 \text{ is less than } 9.$$
$$q: \quad 15 \text{ is equal to } 9.$$

The statement "15 is less than or equal to 9" means that 15 is less than 9 or 15 is equal to 9. The compound statement can be expressed as $p \lor q$. We know that both p and q are false statements since 15 is greater than 9. Therefore, substitute F for p and F for q and evaluate the statement:

$$p \lor q$$
$$\text{F} \lor \text{F}$$
$$\text{F}$$

Therefore, the compound statement "15 is less than or equal to 9" is a false statement.

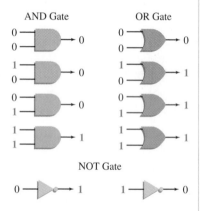
b) Let

> p: George Washington was the first U.S. president.
>
> q: Abraham Lincoln was the second U.S. president.
>
> r: There has been a U.S. president who was born in Antarctica .

The compound statement can be written in symbolic form as $(p \lor q) \land \sim r$. Recall that *but* is used to express a conjunction. We know that p is a true statement and that q is a false statement. We also know that r is a false statement since all U.S. presidents must be born in the United States. Thus, since r is a false statement, the negation, $\sim r$, is a true statement. So we will substitute T for p, F for q, and T for $\sim r$ and then evaluate the statement:

$$(p \lor q) \land \sim r$$
$$(T \lor F) \land T$$
$$T \land T$$
$$T$$

Therefore, the original compound statement is a true statement.

EXAMPLE 7   *OPEC Oil Production*

The Organization of Petroleum Exporting Countries (OPEC) consists of 11 developing nations whose economies are heavily reliant on oil export revenues. Figure 3.1 shows the percentage of total OPEC oil production produced by each of its member nations in 2002. Use this graph to determine the truth value of the following statement:

Saudi Arabia produces the most oil among OPEC nations and Qatar produces more oil than Venezuela, or Indonesia does not produce the least amount of oil among OPEC nations.

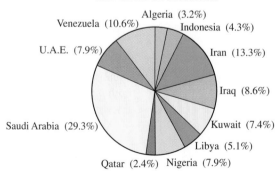

2002 OPEC Oil Production

Source: Energy Information Administration

Figure 3.1

SOLUTION:
Let

p: Saudi Arabia produces the most oil among OPEC nations.

q: Qatar produces more oil that Venezuela.

r: Indonesia produces the least amount of oil among OPEC nations.

The given compound statement can be written in symbolic form as $(p \wedge q) \vee \sim r$. From Fig. 3.1, we see that statement p is true: Saudi Arabia does produce the most oil among OPEC nations. We also see that statement q is false: Venezuela actually produces more oil than Qatar. We also see that statement r is false: two OPEC nations produce less oil than Indonesia. Since r is false, its negation, $\sim r$, is true. Therefore, we substitute T for p, F for q, and T for $\sim r$ and get

$$(p \wedge q) \vee \sim r$$
$$(T \wedge F) \vee T$$
$$F \vee T$$
$$T$$

Thus, the original compound statement is true.

SECTION 3.2   EXERCISES

1. a) How many distinct cases must be listed in a truth table that contains two simple statements?
   b) List all the cases.

2. a) How many distinct cases must be listed in a truth table that contains three simple statements?
   b) List all the cases.

3. a) Construct the truth table for the disjunction, $p \vee q$.
   b) Under what circumstances is the *or* table false?

4. a) Construct the truth table for the conjunction, $p \wedge q$.
   b) Under what circumstances is the *and* table true?

In Exercises 5–20, construct a truth table for the statement.

5. $p \vee \sim p$
6. $p \wedge \sim p$
7. $p \wedge \sim q$
8. $q \vee \sim p$
9. $\sim(p \vee \sim q)$
10. $\sim p \vee \sim q$
11. $\sim(p \wedge \sim q)$
12. $\sim(\sim p \wedge \sim q)$
13. $\sim q \vee (p \wedge r)$
14. $(p \vee \sim q) \wedge r$
15. $r \vee (p \wedge \sim q)$
16. $(r \wedge q) \wedge \sim p$

17. $(r \vee \sim p) \wedge \sim q$
18. $\sim p \wedge (q \vee r)$
19. $(\sim q \wedge r) \vee p$
20. $\sim r \vee (\sim p \wedge q)$

In Exercises 21–30, write the statement in symbolic form and construct a truth table.

21. Meetings are dull and teaching is fun.

22. The stadium is enclosed, but it is not air-conditioned.

23. Bob will get a haircut, but he will not shave his beard.

24. It is false that the class must have at least 15 students or the class will be canceled.

25. It is false that Jasper Adams is a tutor and Mark Russo is a secretary.

26. Mike made pizza and Dennis made a chef salad, but Gil burned the lemon squares.

27. The copier is out of toner, or the lens is dirty or the corona wires are broken.

28. I am hungry, and I want to eat a healthy lunch and I want to eat in a hurry.

29. The Congress must act on the bill, and the president must sign the bill or not sign the bill.

30. Gordon Langeneger likes the PowerMac G4 Cube and he likes the iBook, but he does not like the Pentium IV.

In Exercises 31–42, determine the truth value of the statement if

    a) p is true, q is false, and r is true.
    b) p is false, q is true, and r is true.

31. $\sim p \vee (q \wedge r)$ **32.** $(\sim p \wedge r) \wedge q$

33. $(\sim q \wedge \sim p) \vee \sim r$ **34.** $(\sim p \vee \sim q) \vee \sim r$

35. $(p \wedge \sim q) \vee r$ **36.** $(p \vee \sim q) \wedge \sim(p \wedge \sim r)$

37. $(\sim r \wedge p) \vee q$ **38.** $\sim q \vee (r \wedge p)$

39. $(\sim q \vee \sim p) \wedge r$ **40.** $(\sim r \vee \sim p) \vee \sim q$

41. $(\sim p \vee \sim q) \vee (\sim r \vee q)$ **42.** $(\sim r \wedge \sim q) \wedge (\sim r \vee \sim p)$

In Exercises 43–50, determine the truth value for each simple statement. Then use these truth values to determine the truth value of the compound statement. (You may have to use a reference source such as the Internet or an encyclopedia.)

43. $3 + 5 = 4 + 4$ or $10 - 9 = 9 - 10$

44. $5 < 4$ and $4 < 5$

45. Elvis Presley was a singer or chickens can swim.

Elvis Presley

46. Alaska is the 50th state or Hawaii is a group of islands, and Atlanta is the capital of Alabama.

47. U2 is a rock band and Denzel Washington is an actor, but Jerry Seinfeld is not a comedian.

48. The city of Toronto is in Minnesota or Mexico City is in Texas, and Cairo is in Egypt.

49. Cal Ripken Jr. played football or George Bush was the prime minister of England, and Colin Powell was in the Army.

50. Holstein is a breed of cattle and collie is a breed of dogs, or beagle is not a breed of cats.

Food Consumption In Exercises 51–54, use the chart to determine the truth value of each simple statement. Then determine the truth value of the compound statement.

Annual per capita consumption in pounds:

	1909	2001
Red meat	99	123.5
Poultry	11	66
Fish	11	15
Cheese	4	30
Fats and oils[a]	38	69
Sweeteners[b]	86	154

[a]Added fats and oils
[b]Caloric sweeteners (sugars, honey, corn syrup).
Source: U.S. Department of Agriculture

51. Thirty pounds of cheese were consumed by the average American in 1909, and the average American did not consume 154 pounds of sweeteners in 2001.

52. The per capita consumption of red meat was less for the average American in 2001 than it was in 1909 or the per capita consumption of poultry was greater for the average American in 2001 than it was in 1909.

53. The average American ate approximately the same amount of fish and poultry in 1909, but between 1909 and 2001 the per capita consumption of poultry increased at a rate higher than that of fish.

54. The average American ate approximately nine times as much red meat as fish in 1909, but by 2001 the average American only ate approximately eight times as much red meat as fish.

Sleep Time In Exercises 55–58, use the graph, which shows the number of hours Americans sleep, to determine the truth value of each simple statement. Then determine the truth value of the compound statement.

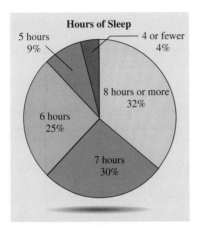

55. It is false that 30% of Americans get 6 hours of sleep each night and 9% get 5 hours of sleep each night.

56. Twenty-five percent of Americans get 6 hours of sleep each night, and 30% get 7 hours of sleep each night or 9% do not get 5 hours of sleep each night.

57. Thirteen percent of Americans get 5 or fewer hours of sleep each night or 32% get 6 or more hours of sleep each night, and 30% get 8 or more hours of sleep each night.

58. Over one-half of all Americans get 7 or fewer hours of sleep each night, and over one-quarter get 6 or fewer hours of sleep each night.

In Exercises 59–62, let

  p: Tanisha owns a convertible.
  q: Joan owns a Volvo.

Translate each statement into symbols. Then construct a truth table for each and indicate under what conditions the compound statement is true.

59. Tanisha owns a convertible and Joan does not own a Volvo.

60. Tanisha does not own a convertible, but Joan owns a Volvo.

61. Tanisha owns a convertible or Joan does not own a Volvo.

62. Tanisha does not own a convertible or Joan does not own a Volvo.

In Exercises 63–66, let

  p: The house is owned by an engineer.
  q: The heat is solar generated.
  r: The car is run by electric power.

Translate each statement into symbols. Then construct a truth table for each and indicate under what conditions the compound statement is true.

63. The car is run by electric power or the heat is solar generated, but the house is owned by an engineer.

64. The house is owned by an engineer and the heat is solar generated, or the car is run by electric power.

65. The heat is solar generated, or the house is owned by an engineer and the car is not run by electric power.

66. The house is not owned by an engineer, and the car is not run by electric power and the heat is solar generated.

Obtaining a Loan In Exercises 67 and 68, read the requirements and each applicant's qualifications for obtaining a loan.

  a) Identify which of the applicants would qualify for the loan.
  b) For the applicants who do not qualify for the loan, explain why.

67. To qualify for a loan of $40,000, an applicant must have a gross income of $28,000 if single, $46,000 combined income if married, and assets of at least $6,000.

  Mrs. Rusinek, married with three children, makes $42,000 on her job. Mr. Rusinek does not have an income. The Rusineks have assets of $42,000.

  Mr. Duncan is not married, works in sales, and earns $31,000. He has assets of $9000.

  Mrs. Tuttle and her husband have total assets of $43,000. One earns $35,000, and the other earns $23,500.

68. To qualify for a loan of $45,000, an applicant must have a gross income of $30,000 if single, $50,000 combined income if married, and assets of at least $10,000.

  Mr. Argento, married with two children, makes $37,000 on his job. Mrs. Argento earns $15,000 at a part-time job. The Argentos have assets of $25,000.

  Ms. McVey, single, has assets of $19,000. She works in a store and earns $25,000.

  Mr. Siewert earns $24,000 and Ms. Fox, his wife, earns $28,000. Their assets total $8000.

69. *Airline Special Fares* An airline advertisement states, "To get the special fare you must purchase your tickets between January 1 and February 15 and fly round trip between March 1 and April 1. You must depart on a Monday, Tuesday, or Wednesday, and return on a Tuesday, Wednesday, or Thursday, and stay over at least one Saturday."

a) Determine which of the following individuals will qualify for the special fare.
b) If the person does not qualify for the special fare, explain why.

Wing Park plans to purchase his ticket on January 15, depart on Monday, March 3, and return on Tuesday, March 18.

Gina Vela plans to purchase her ticket on February 1, depart on Wednesday, March 10, and return on Thursday, April 2.

Kara Shavo plans to purchase her ticket on February 14, depart on Tuesday, March 5, and return on Monday, March 18.

Christos Supernaw plans to purchase his ticket on January 4, depart on Monday, March 8, and return on Thursday, March 11.

Alex Chang plans to purchase his ticket on January 1, depart on Monday, March 3, and return on Monday, March 10.

Problem Solving/Group Activities

In Exercises 70 and 71, construct a truth table for the symbolic statement.

70. $\sim[(\sim(p \vee q)) \vee (q \wedge r)]$

71. $[(q \wedge \sim r) \wedge (\sim p \vee \sim q)] \vee (p \vee \sim r)$

72. On page 113, we indicated that a compound statement consisting of n simple statements had 2^n distinct true–false cases.
  a) How many distinct true–false cases does a truth table containing simple statements p, q, r, and s have?
  b) List all possible true–false cases for a truth table containing the simple statements p, q, r, and s.
  c) Use the list in part (b) to construct a truth table for $(q \wedge p) \vee (\sim r \wedge s)$.
  d) Construct a truth table for $(\sim r \wedge \sim s) \wedge (\sim p \vee q)$.

73. Must $(p \wedge \sim q) \vee r$ and $(q \wedge \sim r) \vee p$ have the same number of trues in their answer columns? Explain.

Internet/Research Activities

74. Digital computers use gates that work like switches to perform calculations. Information is fed into the gates and information leaves the gates, according to the type of gate. The three basic gates used in computers are the NOT gate, the AND gate, and the OR gate. Do research on the three types of gates.
  a) Explain how each gate works.
  b) Explain the relationship between each gate and the corresponding logic connectives *not, and,* and *or.*
  c) Illustrate how two or more gates can be combined to form a more complex gate.

3.3 TRUTH TABLES FOR THE CONDITIONAL AND BICONDITIONAL

Conditional

In Section 3.1, we mentioned that the statement preceding the conditional symbol is called the *antecedent* and that the statement following the conditional symbol is called the *consequent*. For example, consider $(p \vee q) \rightarrow [\sim(q \wedge r)]$. In this statement, $(p \vee q)$ is the antecedent and $[\sim(q \wedge r)]$ is the consequent.

Now we will look at the truth table for the conditional. Suppose I make the following promise to you: "If you get an A in this class, then I will buy you a car." Consider the statement within the quotation marks. Assume this statement is true except when I have actually broken my promise to you.

Let

p: You get an A.

q: I buy you a car.

Translated into symbolic form, the statement becomes $p \rightarrow q$. Let's examine the four cases shown in Table 3.12.

CASE 1: (T, T) You get an A, and I buy a car for you. I have met my commitment, and the statement is true.

CASE 2: (T, F) You get an A, and I do not buy a car for you. I have broken my promise, and the statement is false.

What happens if you don't get an A? If you don't get an A, I no longer have a commitment to you, and therefore I cannot break my promise.

CASE 3: (F, T) You do not get an A, and I buy you a car. I have not broken my promise, and therefore the statement is true.

CASE 4: (F, F) You do not get an A, and I don't buy you a car. I have not broken my promise, and therefore the statement is true.

The conditional statement is false when the antecedent is true and the consequent is false. In every other case the conditional statement is true.

> The **conditional statement** $p \rightarrow q$ is true in every case except when p is a true statement and q is a false statement.

TABLE 3.12 Conditional

p	q	p → q
T	T	T
T	F	F
F	T	T
F	F	T

TABLE 3.13

p	q	~p	→	q
T	T	F	T	T
T	F	F	T	F
F	T	T	T	T
F	F	T	F	F
		1	3	2

TABLE 3.14

p	q	r	p	→	(~q	∧	r)
T	T	T	T	F	F	F	T
T	T	F	T	F	F	F	F
T	F	T	T	T	T	T	T
T	F	F	T	F	T	F	F
F	T	T	F	T	F	F	T
F	T	F	F	T	F	F	F
F	F	T	F	T	T	T	T
F	F	F	F	T	T	F	F
			4	5	1	3	2

EXAMPLE 1 *A Truth Table with a Conditional*

Construct a truth table for the statement $\sim p \rightarrow q$.

SOLUTION: Since this is a conditional statement, the answer will lie under the $\rightarrow$. Fill out the truth table by placing the appropriate values under $\sim p$, column 1, and under q, column 2 (see Table 3.13). Then, using the information given in the truth table for the conditional and the truth values in columns 1 and 2, determine the solution, column 3. In row 1, the antecedent, $\sim p$, is false and the consequent, q, is true. Row 1 is F $\rightarrow$ T, which according to row 3 of Table 3.12, is T. Likewise, row 2 of Table 3.13 is F $\rightarrow$ F, which is T. Row 3 is T $\rightarrow$ T, which is T. Row 4 is T $\rightarrow$ F, which is F. ▲

EXAMPLE 2 *A Conditional Truth Table with Three Simple Statements*

Construct a truth table for the statement $p \rightarrow (\sim q \wedge r)$.

SOLUTION: Since this is a conditional statement, the answer will lie under the $\rightarrow$. Work within the parentheses first. Place the truth values under $\sim q$, column 1, and r, column 2 (Table 3.14). Then take the conjunction of columns 1 and 2 to obtain column 3. Next, place the truth values under p in column 4. To determine the answer, column 5, use columns 3 and 4 and your knowledge of the conditional statement. Column 4 represents the truth values of the antecedent, and column 3 represents the truth values of the consequent. Remember that the conditional is false only when the antecedent is true and the consequent is false, as in cases (rows) 1, 2, and 4 of column 5. ▲

┌─EXAMPLE 3   *Examining an Advertisement*

An advertisement for Perky Morning coffee makes the following claim: "If you drink Perky Morning coffee, then you will not be sluggish and you will have a great day." Translate the statement into symbolic form and construct a truth table.

SOLUTION: Let

p:	You drink Perky Morning coffee.
q:	You will be sluggish.
r:	You will have a great day.

In symbolic form, the claim is

$$p \rightarrow (\sim q \wedge r)$$

This symbolic statement is identical to the statement in Table 3.14, and the truth tables are the same. Column 3 represents the truth values of $(\sim q \wedge r)$, which corresponds to the statement "You will not be sluggish and you will have a great day." Note that column 3 is true in cases (rows) 3 and 7. In case 3, since *p* is true, you drank Perky Morning coffee. In case 7, however, since *p* is false, you did not drink Perky Morning coffee. From this information we can conclude that it is possible for you to not be sluggish and for you to have a great day without drinking Perky Morning coffee.   ▲

A truth table alone cannot tell us whether a statement is true or false. It can, however, be used to examine the various possibilities.

Biconditional

The *biconditional statement*, $p \leftrightarrow q$, means that $p \rightarrow q$ and $q \rightarrow p$, or, symbolically, $(p \rightarrow q) \wedge (q \rightarrow p)$. To determine the truth table for $p \leftrightarrow q$, we will construct the truth table for $(p \rightarrow q) \wedge (q \rightarrow p)$ (Table 3.15). Table 3.16 shows the truth values for the biconditional statement.

TABLE 3.15

p	**q**	**(p**	$\rightarrow$	**q)**	$\wedge$	**(q**	$\rightarrow$	**p)**
T	T	T	T	T	T	T	T	T
T	F	T	F	F	F	F	T	T
F	T	F	T	T	F	T	F	F
F	F	F	T	F	T	F	T	F
		1	3	2	7	4	6	5

TABLE 3.16   Biconditional

p	**q**	$p \leftrightarrow q$
T	T	T
T	F	F
F	T	F
F	F	T

The **biconditional statement,** $p \leftrightarrow q$, is true only when *p* and *q* have the same truth value, that is, when both are true or both are false.

EXAMPLE 4   *A Truth Table Using a Biconditional*

Construct a truth table for the statement $p \leftrightarrow (q \rightarrow \sim r)$.

SOLUTION: Since there are three letters, there must be eight cases. The parentheses indicate that the answer must be under the biconditional (Table 3.17). Use columns 3 and 4 to obtain the answer in column 5. When columns 3 and 4 have the same truth values, place a T in column 5. When columns 3 and 4 have different truth values, place an F in column 5.

TABLE 3.17

p	q	r	p	$\leftrightarrow$	(q	$\rightarrow$	~r)
T	T	T	T	F	T	F	F
T	T	F	T	T	T	T	T
T	F	T	T	T	F	T	F
T	F	F	T	T	F	T	T
F	T	T	F	T	T	F	F
F	T	F	F	F	T	T	T
F	F	T	F	F	F	T	F
F	F	F	F	F	F	T	T
			4	5	1	3	2

In the preceding section, we showed that finding the truth value of a compound statement for a specific case does not require constructing an entire truth table. Example 5 illustrates this technique for the conditional and the biconditional.

EXAMPLE 5   *Determine the Truth Value of a Compound Statement*

Determine the truth value of the statement $(q \leftrightarrow r) \rightarrow (\sim p \wedge r)$ when p is true, q is false, and r is true.

SOLUTION: Substitute the truth value for each simple statement:

$$(q \leftrightarrow r) \rightarrow (\sim p \wedge r)$$
$$(F \leftrightarrow T) \rightarrow (F \wedge T)$$
$$F \quad \rightarrow \quad F$$
$$T$$

For this specific case, the statement is true.

EXAMPLE 6   *Determine the Truth Value of a Compound Statement*

Determine the truth value for each simple statement. Then use the truth values to determine the truth value of the compound statement.

a) If 15 is an even number, then 29 is an even number.

b) Northwestern University is in Illinois and Marquette University is in Alaska, if and only if Purdue University is in Alabama.

SOLUTION:

a) Let

$$p: \quad \text{15 is an even number.}$$
$$q: \quad \text{29 is an even number.}$$

Then the statement "If 15 is an even number, then 29 is an even number" can be written $p \rightarrow q$. Since 15 is not an even number, p is a false statement. Also, since 29 is not an even number, q is a false statement. We substitute F for p and F for q and evaluate the statement:

$$p \rightarrow q$$
$$F \rightarrow F$$
$$T$$

Therefore, "If 15 is an even number, then 29 is an even number" is a true statement.

b) Let

$$p: \quad \text{Northwestern University is in Illinois.}$$
$$q: \quad \text{Marquette University is in Alaska.}$$
$$r: \quad \text{Purdue University is in Alabama.}$$

The original compound statement can be written $(p \wedge q) \leftrightarrow r$. By checking the Internet or other references we can find that Northwestern University is in Illinois, Marquette University is in Wisconsin, and Purdue University is in Indiana. Therefore, p is a true statement, but q and r are false statements. We will substitute T for p, F for q, and F for r and evaluate the compound statement:

$$(p \wedge q) \leftrightarrow r$$
$$(T \wedge F) \leftrightarrow F$$
$$F \quad \leftrightarrow F$$
$$T$$

Therefore, the original compound statement is true.   ▲

EXAMPLE 7   *Using Real Data in Compound Statements*

The graph in Fig. 3.2 on page 123 represents the U.S. government budget expenditures for fiscal year 2002. Use this graph to determine the truth value of the following compound statements.

a) If social programs account for 17% of the budget then interest on the national debt accounts for 12% of the budget.

b) If physical and community development account for 9% of the budget and social programs account for 37% of the budget, then law enforcement and general government account for 10% of the budget.

SOLUTION:

a) Let

$$p: \quad \text{Social programs account for 17\% of the budget.}$$
$$q: \quad \text{Interest on the national debt accounts for 12\% of the budget.}$$

Then the original compound statement can be written $p \rightarrow q$. We can see from Fig. 3.2 that both p and q are true statements. Substitute T for p and T for q and evaluate the statement:

$$p \rightarrow q$$
$$T \rightarrow T$$
$$T$$

Therefore, "If social programs account for 17% of the budget then interest on the national debt accounts for 12% of the budget" is a true statement.

2002 United States Federal Government Budget Expenditures

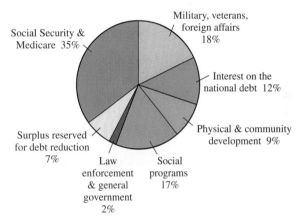

Source: *United States Office of Management and Budget*

Figure 3.2

b) Let

p: Physical and community development account for 9% of the budget.

q: Social programs account for 37% of the budget.

r: Law enforcement and general government account for 10% of the budget.

Then the original compound statement can be written $(p \wedge q) \rightarrow r$. We can see from Fig. 3.2 that p is true, q is false, and r is false. Substitute T for p and F for q and r and evaluate the statement:

$$(p \wedge q) \rightarrow r$$
$$(T \wedge F) \rightarrow F$$
$$F \quad \rightarrow F$$
$$T$$

Therefore, the original compound statement, "If physical and community development account for 9% of the budget and social programs account for 37% of the budget, then law enforcement and general government account for 10% of the budget," is true. ▲

Self-Contradictions, Tautologies, and Implications

Two special situations can occur in the truth table of a compound statement: The statement may always be false, or the statement may always be true. We give such statements special names.

A **self-contradiction** is a compound statement that is always false.

When every truth value in the answer column of the truth table is false, then the statement is a self-contradiction.

TABLE 3.18

p	q	(p ↔ q)	∧	(p	↔	~q)
T	T	T	F	T	F	F
T	F	F	F	T	T	T
F	T	F	F	F	T	F
F	F	T	F	F	F	T
		1	5	2	4	3

┌ EXAMPLE 8   *All Falses, a Self-Contradiction*

Construct a truth table for the statement $(p \leftrightarrow q) \wedge (p \leftrightarrow \sim q)$.

SOLUTION: See Table 3.18. In this example, the truth values are false in each case of column 5. This statement is an example of a self-contradiction or a *logically false statement*.   ▲

A **tautology** is a compound statement that is always true.

When every truth value in the answer column of the truth table is true, the statement is a tautology.

┌ EXAMPLE 9   *All Trues, a Tautology*

Construct a truth table for the statement $(p \wedge q) \rightarrow (p \vee r)$.

SOLUTION: The answer is given in column 3 of Table 3.19. The truth values are true in every case. Thus, the statement is an example of a tautology or a *logicallly true statement*.

TABLE 3.19

p	q	r	(p ∧ q)	→	(p ∨ r)
T	T	T	T	T	T
T	T	F	T	T	T
T	F	T	F	T	T
T	F	F	F	T	T
F	T	T	F	T	T
F	T	F	F	T	F
F	F	T	F	T	T
F	F	F	F	T	F
			1	3	2

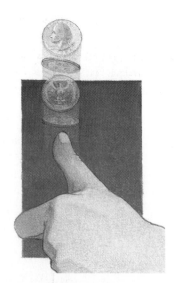

"Heads I win, tails you lose." Do you think that this statement is a tautology, self-contradiction, or neither? See Problem-Solving Exercise 81.

The conditional statement $(p \wedge q) \rightarrow (p \vee r)$ is a tautology. Conditional statements that are tautologies are called *implications*. In Example 9, we can say that $p \wedge q$ implies $p \vee r$.

An **implication** is a conditional statement that is a tautology.

In any implication the antecedent of the conditional statement implies the consequent. In other words, if the antecedent is true, then the consequent must also be true. That is, the consequent will be true whenever the antecedent is true.

TABLE 3.20

p	q	[(p ∧ q)	∧	p]	→	q
T	T	T	T	T	T	T
T	F	F	F	T	T	F
F	T	F	F	F	T	T
F	F	F	F	F	T	F
		1	3	2	5	4

EXAMPLE 10   *An Implication?*

Determine whether the conditional statement $[(p \wedge q) \wedge p] \rightarrow q$ is an implication.

SOLUTION: If the conditional statement is a tautology, the conditional statement is an implication. Because the conditional statement is a tautology (see Table 3.20), the conditional statement is an implication. The antecedent $[(p \wedge q) \wedge p]$ implies the consequent q. Note that the antecedent is true only in case 1 and that the consequent is also true in case 1. ▲

SECTION 3.3   EXERCISES

1. **a)** Construct the truth table for the conditional statement $p \rightarrow q$.
   b) Explain when the conditional statement is true and when it is false.

2. **a)** Construct the truth table for the biconditional statement $p \leftrightarrow q$.
   b) Explain when the biconditional statement is true and when it is false.

3. **a)** Explain the procedure to determine the truth value of a compound statement when specific truth values are provided for the simple statements.
   b) Follow the procedure in part (a) and determine the truth value of the symbolic statement
   $$[(p \leftrightarrow q) \vee (\sim r \rightarrow q)] \rightarrow \sim r$$
   when p = true, q = true, and r = false.

4. What is a tautology?

5. What is a self-contradiction?

6. What is an implication?

In Exercises 7–16, construct a truth table for the statement.

7. $\sim q \rightarrow \sim p$

8. $p \rightarrow \sim q$

9. $\sim(q \rightarrow p)$

10. $\sim(p \leftrightarrow q)$

11. $\sim q \leftrightarrow p$

12. $(p \leftrightarrow q) \rightarrow p$

13. $p \leftrightarrow (q \vee p)$

14. $(\sim q \wedge p) \rightarrow \sim q$

15. $q \rightarrow (p \rightarrow \sim q)$

16. $(p \vee q) \leftrightarrow (p \wedge q)$

In Exercises 17–26, construct a truth table for the statement.

17. $r \wedge (\sim q \rightarrow p)$

18. $p \rightarrow (q \vee r)$

19. $(q \leftrightarrow p) \wedge \sim r$

20. $q \leftrightarrow (r \wedge p)$

21. $(q \vee \sim r) \leftrightarrow \sim p$

22. $(p \wedge r) \rightarrow (q \vee r)$

23. $(\sim r \vee \sim q) \rightarrow p$

24. $[r \wedge (q \vee \sim p)] \leftrightarrow \sim p$

25. $(p \rightarrow q) \leftrightarrow (\sim q \rightarrow \sim r)$

26. $(\sim p \leftrightarrow \sim q) \rightarrow (\sim q \leftrightarrow r)$

In Exercises 27–32, write the statement in symbolic form. Then construct a truth table for the symbolic statement.

27. If I drink a glass of water, then I will have a better complexion and I will sleep better.

28. The goalie will make the save if and only if the stopper is in position, or the forward cannot handle the ball.

29. The class has been canceled if and only if the teacher is not here, or we will study together in the library.

30. If the lake rises then we can go canoeing, and if the canoe has a hole in it then we cannot go canoeing.

31. If Mary Andrews does not send me an e-mail then we can call her, or we can write to Mom.

32. It is false that if Eileen Jones went to lunch, then she cannot take a message and we will have to go home.

In Exercises 33–38, determine whether the statement is a tautology, self-contradiction, or neither.

33. $p \rightarrow \sim q$
34. $(p \vee q) \leftrightarrow \sim p$
35. $p \wedge (q \wedge \sim p)$
36. $(p \wedge \sim q) \rightarrow q$
37. $(\sim q \rightarrow p) \vee \sim q$
38. $[(p \rightarrow q) \vee r] \leftrightarrow [(p \wedge q) \rightarrow r]$

In Exercises 39–44, determine whether the statement is an implication.

39. $p \rightarrow (p \wedge q)$
40. $(p \wedge q) \rightarrow (p \vee q)$
41. $(q \wedge p) \rightarrow (p \wedge q)$
42. $(p \vee q) \rightarrow (p \vee \sim r)$
43. $[(p \rightarrow q) \wedge (q \rightarrow p)] \rightarrow (p \leftrightarrow q)$
44. $[(p \vee q) \wedge r] \rightarrow (p \vee q)$

In Exercises 45–56, if p is true, q is false, and r is true, find the truth value of the statement.

45. $p \rightarrow (\sim q \wedge r)$
46. $\sim p \rightarrow (q \vee r)$
47. $(q \wedge \sim p) \leftrightarrow \sim r$
48. $p \leftrightarrow (\sim q \wedge r)$
49. $(\sim p \wedge \sim q) \vee \sim r$
50. $\sim [p \rightarrow (q \wedge r)]$
51. $(p \wedge r) \leftrightarrow (p \vee \sim q)$
52. $(\sim p \vee q) \rightarrow \sim r$
53. $(\sim p \leftrightarrow r) \vee (\sim q \leftrightarrow r)$
54. $(r \rightarrow \sim p) \wedge (q \rightarrow \sim r)$
55. $\sim [(p \vee q) \leftrightarrow (p \rightarrow \sim r)]$
56. $[(\sim r \rightarrow \sim q) \vee (p \wedge \sim r)] \rightarrow q$

In Exercises 57–64, determine the truth value for each simple statement. Then, using the truth values, determine the truth value of the compound statement.

57. If $10 + 5 = 15$, then $56 \div 7 = 8$.

58. If 2 is an even number and 6 is an odd number, then 15 is an odd number.

59. A triangle has four sides or a square has three sides, and a rectangle has four sides.

60. Seattle is in Washington and Portland is in Oregon, or Boise is in California.

61. Dell makes computers, if and only if Gateway makes computers or Canon makes printers.

62. Spike Lee is a movie director, or if Halle Berry is a schoolteacher then George Clooney is a circus clown.

Halle Berry

63. Valentine's Day is in February or President's Day is in March, and Thanksgiving is in November.

64. Honda makes automobiles or Honda makes motorcycles, if and only if Toyota makes cereal.

In Exercises 65–68, use the information provided about the moons for the planets Jupiter and Saturn on page 127 to determine the truth values of the simple statements. Then determine the truth value of the compound statement.

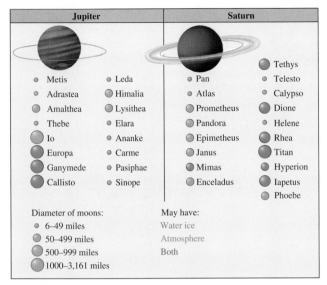

Source: *Time* Magazine

65. *Jupiter's Moons* Io has a diameter of 1000–3161 miles or Thebe may have water, and Io may have atmosphere.

66. *Moons of Saturn* Titan may have water and Titan may have atmosphere, if and only if Janus may have water.

67. *Moon Comparisons* Phoebe has a larger diameter than Rhea if and only if Callisto may have water ice, and Calypso has a diameter of 6–49 miles.

68. *Moon Comparisons* If Jupiter has 16 moons or Saturn does not have 18 moons, then Saturn has 7 moons that may have water ice.

In Exercises 69 and 70, use the graphs to determine the truth values of each simple statement. Then determine the truth value of the compound statement.

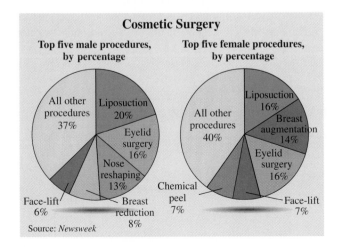

Cosmetic Surgery

Source: *Newsweek*

69. *Most Common Cosmetic Surgery* The most common cosmetic surgery procedure for females is liposuction or the most common procedure for males is eyelid surgery, and 20% of male cosmetic surgery is for nose reshaping.

70. *Face-lifts and Eyelid Surgeries* 7% of female cosmetic surgeries are for face-lifts and 10% of male cosmetic surgeries are for face-lifts, if and only if males have a higher percent of eyelid surgeries than females.

In Exercises 71–76, suppose both of the following statements are true.

   p: Muhundan spoke at the teachers' conference.

   q: Muhundan received the outstanding teacher award.

Find the truth values of each compound statement.

71. If Muhundan spoke at the teachers' conference, then Muhundan received the outstanding teacher award.

72. If Muhundan did not speak at the teachers' conference, then Muhundan did not receive the outstanding teacher award.

73. If Muhundan did not speak at the teachers' conference, then Muhundan received the outstanding teacher award.

74. Muhundan did not receive the outstanding teacher award if and only if Muhundan spoke at the teachers' conference.

75. Muhundan received the outstanding teacher award if and only if Muhundan spoke at the teachers' conference.

76. If Muhundan did not receive the outstanding teacher award, then Muhundan did not speak at the teachers' conference.

77. *A New Computer* Your parents make the following statement to your sister, "If you get straight A's this semester, then we will buy you a new computer." At the end of the semester your parents buy your sister a new computer. Can you conclude that your sister got straight A's? Explain.

78. *Job Interview* Consider the statement "If your interview goes well, then you will be offered the job." If you are interviewed and then offered the job, can you conclude that your interview went well? Explain.

Problem Solving/Group Activities

In Exercises 79 and 80, construct truth tables for the symbolic statement. Use the dominance of connectives (see Section 3.1) as needed.

79. $p \lor q \to \sim r \leftrightarrow p \land \sim q$

80. $[(r \to \sim q) \to \sim p] \lor (q \leftrightarrow \sim r)$

81. Is the statement "Heads I win, tails you lose" a tautology, a self-contradiction, or neither? Explain your answer.

82. Construct a truth table for
   a) $(p \lor q) \rightarrow (r \land s)$.
   b) $(q \rightarrow \sim p) \lor (r \leftrightarrow s)$.

Recreational Mathematics

83. *Cat Puzzle* Solve the following puzzle. The Joneses have four cats. The parents are Tiger and Boots, and the kittens are Sam and Sue. Each cat insists on eating out of its own bowl. To complicate matters, each cat will eat only its own brand of cat food. The colors of the bowls are red, yellow, green, and blue. The different types of cat food are Whiskas, Friskies, Nine Lives, and Meow Mix. Tiger will eat Meow Mix if and only if it is in a yellow bowl. If Boots is to eat her food, then it must be in a yellow bowl. Mrs. Jones knows that the label on the can containing Sam's food is the same color as his bowl. Boots eats Whiskas. Meow Mix and Nine Lives are packaged in a brown paper bag. The color of Sue's bowl is green if and only if she eats Meow Mix. The label on the Friskies can is red. Match each cat with its food and the bowl of the correct color.

84. *The Youngest Triplet* The Barr triplets have an annoying habit: Whenever a question is asked of the three of them, two tell the truth and the third lies. When I asked them which of them was born last, they replied as follows.

   Mary: Katie was born last.
   Katie: I am the youngest.
   Annie: Mary is the youngest.

   Which of the Barr triplets was born last?

Internet/Research Activity

85. Select an advertisement from the Internet, a newspaper, or a magazine that makes or implies a conditional statement. Analyze the advertisement to determine whether the consequent necessarily follows from the antecedent. Explain your answer. (See Example 3.)

3.4 EQUIVALENT STATEMENTS

Equivalent statements are an important concept in the study of logic.

> Two statements are **equivalent,** symbolized ⇔ ,* if both statements have exactly the same truth values in the answer columns of the truth tables.

Sometimes the words *logically equivalent* are used in place of the word *equivalent.*

   To determine whether two statements are equivalent, construct a truth table for each statement and compare the answer columns of the truth tables. If the answer columns are identical, the statements are equivalent. If the answer columns are not identical, the statements are not equivalent.

⌐EXAMPLE 1   *Equivalent Statements*

Show that the following two statements are equivalent.

$$[p \lor (q \lor r)]   [(p \lor q) \lor r]$$

---
*The symbol ≡ is also used to indicate equivalent statements.

SOLUTION: Construct a truth table for each statement (see Table 3.21).

TABLE 3.21

p	q	r	[p	∨	(q ∨ r)]	[(p ∨ q)	∨	r]
T	T	T	T	T	T	T	T	T
T	T	F	T	T	T	T	T	F
T	F	T	T	T	T	T	T	T
T	F	F	T	T	F	T	T	F
F	T	T	F	T	T	T	T	T
F	T	F	F	T	T	T	T	F
F	F	T	F	T	T	F	T	T
F	F	F	F	F	F	F	F	F
			1	3	2	1	3	2

Because the truth tables have the same answer (column 3 for both tables), the statements are equivalent. Thus, we can write

$$[p \lor (q \lor r)] \Leftrightarrow [(p \lor q) \lor r].$$

▲

EXAMPLE 2   *Are the Following Equivalent Statements?*

Determine whether the following statements are equivalent.

a) If you work hard and obey all of the rules, then you will succeed in life.

b) If you do not work hard or do not obey all of the rules, then you will not succeed in life.

SOLUTION: First write each statement in symbolic form, then construct a truth table for each statement. If the answer columns of both truth tables are identical, then the statements are equivalent. If the answer columns are not identical, then the statements are not equivalent.

Let

p: You work hard.
q: You obey all of the rules.
r: You will succeed in life.

In symbolic form, the statements are

a) $(p \land q) \rightarrow r$.   b) $(\sim p \lor \sim q) \rightarrow \sim r$.

The truth tables for these statements are given in Tables 3.22 and 3.23, respectively, on page 130. The answers in the columns labeled 5 are not identical, so the statements are not equivalent.

TABLE 3.22

p	q	r	(p	∧	q)	→	r
T	T	T	T	T	T	T	T
T	T	F	T	T	T	F	F
T	F	T	T	F	F	T	T
T	F	F	T	F	F	T	F
F	T	T	F	F	T	T	T
F	T	F	F	F	T	T	F
F	F	T	F	F	F	T	T
F	F	F	F	F	F	T	F
			1	3	2	5	4

TABLE 3.23

p	q	r	(~p	∨	~q)	→	~r
T	T	T	F	F	F	T	F
T	T	F	F	F	F	T	T
T	F	T	F	T	T	F	F
T	F	F	F	T	T	T	T
F	T	T	T	T	F	F	F
F	T	F	T	T	F	T	T
F	F	T	T	T	T	F	F
F	F	F	T	T	T	T	T
			1	3	2	5	4

EXAMPLE 3   *Which Statements Are Logically Equivalent?*

Determine which statement is logically equivalent to "It is not true that the tire is both out of balance and flat."

a) If the tire is not flat, then the tire is not out of balance.

b) The tire is not out of balance or the tire is not flat.

c) The tire is not flat and the tire is not out of balance.

d) If the tire is not out of balance, then the tire is not flat.

SOLUTION: To determine whether any of the choices are equivalent to the given statement, first write the given statements and the choices in symbolic form. Then construct truth tables and compare the answer columns of the truth tables.

Let

$$p: \quad \text{The tire is out of balance.}$$
$$q: \quad \text{The tire is flat.}$$

The given statement may be written "It is not true that the tire is out of balance and the tire is flat." The statement is expressed in symbolic form as $\sim(p \wedge q)$. Using p and q as indicated, choices (a) through (d) may be expressed symbolically as

a) $\sim q \rightarrow \sim p$.   b) $\sim p \vee \sim q$.   c) $\sim q \wedge \sim p$.   d) $\sim p \rightarrow \sim q$.

Now construct a truth table for the given statement (Table 3.24 on page 131) and each possible choice, given in Table 3.25(a) through (d). By examining the truth tables, we see that the given statement, $\sim(p \wedge q)$, is logically equivalent to choice (b), $\sim p \vee \sim q$. Therefore, the correct answer is "The tire is not out of balance or the tire is not flat." This statement is logically equivalent to the statement "It is not true that the tire is both out of balance and flat."

TABLE 3.24

p	q	$\sim$	$(p$	$\wedge$	$q)$
T	T	F	T	T	T
T	F	T	T	F	F
F	T	T	F	F	T
F	F	T	F	F	F
		4	1	3	2

TABLE 3.25

		(a)			(b)			(c)			(d)		
p	q	$\sim q$	$\rightarrow$	$\sim p$	$\sim p$	$\vee$	$\sim q$	$\sim q$	$\wedge$	$\sim p$	$\sim p$	$\rightarrow$	$\sim q$
T	T	F	T	F	F	F	F	F	F	F	F	T	F
T	F	T	F	F	F	T	T	T	F	F	F	T	T
F	T	F	T	T	T	T	F	F	F	T	T	F	F
F	F	T	T	T	T	T	T	T	T	T	T	T	T

In the preceding section, we showed that $p \leftrightarrow q$ has the same truth table as $(p \rightarrow q) \wedge (q \rightarrow p)$. Therefore, these statements are equivalent, a useful fact for Example 4.

┌ **EXAMPLE 4** *Write an Equivalent Biconditional Statement*

Write the following statement as an equivalent biconditional statement: "If the tree produces acorns then the tree is an oak and if the tree is an oak then the tree produces acorns."

SOLUTION: An equivalent statement is "The tree produces acorns if and only if the tree is an oak." ▲

De Morgan's Laws

Example 3 showed that a statement of the form $\sim(p \wedge q)$ is equivalent to a statement of the form $\sim p \vee \sim q$. Thus, we may write $\sim(p \wedge q) \Leftrightarrow \sim p \vee \sim q$. This equivalent statement is one of two special laws called De Morgan's laws. The laws, named after Augustus De Morgan, an English mathematician, were first introduced in Section 2.4, where they applied to sets.

> **De Morgan's Laws**
> 1. $\sim(p \wedge q) \Leftrightarrow \sim p \vee \sim q$
> 2. $\sim(p \vee q) \Leftrightarrow \sim p \wedge \sim q$

You can demonstrate that De Morgan's second law is true by constructing and comparing truth tables for $\sim(p \vee q)$ and $\sim p \wedge \sim q$. Do so now.

When using De Morgan's laws, if it becomes necessary to negate an already negated statement, use the fact that $\sim(\sim p)$ is equivalent to p. For example, the negation of the statement "Today is not Monday" is "Today is Monday."

┌ **EXAMPLE 5** *Use De Morgan's Laws*

Select the statement that is logically equivalent to "The sun is not shining but it is not raining."

a) It is not true that the sun is shining and it is raining.

b) It is not raining or the sun is not shining.

c) The sun is shining or it is raining.

d) It is not true that the sun is shining or it is raining.

SOLUTION: To determine which statement is equivalent, write each statement in symbolic form.

Let

p: The sun is shining.

q: It is raining.

The statement "The sun is not shining but it is not raining" written symbolically is $\sim p \wedge \sim q$. Recall that the word *but* means the same as the word *and*. Now, write parts (a) through (d) symbolically.

a) $\sim(p \wedge q)$ b) $\sim q \vee \sim p$ c) $p \vee q$ d) $\sim(p \vee q)$

De Morgan's law shows that $\sim p \wedge \sim q$ is equivalent to $\sim(p \vee q)$. Therefore, the answer is (d): "It is not true that the sun is shining or it is raining." ▲

EXAMPLE 6   *Using De Morgan's Laws to Write an Equivalent Statement*

Write a statement that is logically equivalent to "It is not true that tomatoes are poisonous or eating peppers cures the common cold."

SOLUTION: Let

p: Tomatoes are poisonous.

q: Eating peppers cures the common cold.

The given statement is of the form $\sim(p \vee q)$. Using the second of De Morgan's laws, we see that an equivalent statement in symbols is $\sim p \wedge \sim q$. Therefore, an equivalent statement in words is "Tomatoes are not poisonous and eating peppers does not cure the common cold." ▲

Consider $\sim(p \wedge q) \Leftrightarrow \sim p \vee \sim q$, one of De Morgan's laws. To go from $\sim(p \wedge q)$ to $\sim p \vee \sim q$, we negate both the p and the q within parentheses; change the conjunction, $\wedge$, to a disjunction, $\vee$; and remove the negation symbol preceding the left parentheses and the parentheses themselves. We can use a similar procedure to obtain equivalent statements. For example,

$$\sim(\sim p \wedge q) \Leftrightarrow p \vee \sim q$$
$$\sim(p \wedge \sim q) \Leftrightarrow \sim p \vee q$$

We can use a similar procedure to obtain equivalent statements when a disjunction is within parentheses. Note that

$$\sim(\sim p \vee q) \Leftrightarrow p \wedge \sim q$$
$$\sim(p \vee \sim q) \Leftrightarrow \sim p \wedge q$$

EXAMPLE 7   *Using De Morgan's Laws to Write an Equivalent Statement*

Use De Morgan's laws to write a statement logically equivalent to "Benjamin Franklin was not a U.S. president, but he signed the Declaration of Independence."

SOLUTION: Let

p: Benjamin Franklin was a U.S. president.

q: Benjamin Franklin signed the Declaration of Independence.

The statement written symbolically is $\sim p \wedge q$. Earlier we showed that

$$\sim p \wedge q \Leftrightarrow \sim(p \vee \sim q)$$

Therefore, the statement "It is false that Benjamin Franklin was a U.S. president or Benjamin Franklin did not sign the Declaration of Independence" is logically equivalent to the given statement.

There are strong similarities between the topics of sets and logic. We can see them by examining De Morgan's laws for sets and logic.

De Morgan's laws: set theory	De Morgan's laws: logic
$(A \cap B)' = A' \cup B'$	$\sim(p \wedge q) \Leftrightarrow \sim p \vee \sim q$
$(A \cup B)' = A' \cap B'$	$\sim(p \vee q) \Leftrightarrow \sim p \wedge \sim q$

The complement in set theory, $'$, is similar to the negation, $\sim$, in logic. The intersection, $\cap$, is similar to the conjunction, $\wedge$; and the union, $\cup$, is similar to the disjunction, $\vee$. If we were to interchange the set symbols with the logic symbols, De Morgan's laws would remain, but in a different form.

Both $'$ and $\sim$ can be interpreted as *not*.

Both $\cap$ and $\wedge$ can be interpreted as *and*.

Both $\cup$ and $\vee$ can be interpreted as *or*.

For example, the set statement $A' \cup B$ can be written as a statement in logic as $\sim a \vee b$.

Statements containing connectives other than *and* and *or* may have equivalent statements. To illustrate this point, construct truth tables for $p \rightarrow q$ and for $\sim p \vee q$. The truth tables will have the same answer columns and therefore the statements are equivalent. That is,

$$p \rightarrow q \Leftrightarrow \sim p \vee q$$

With these equivalent statements, we can write a conditional statement as a disjunction or a disjunction as a conditional statement. For example, the statement "If the game is polo, then you ride a horse" can be equivalently stated as "The game is not polo or you ride a horse."

To change a conditional statement to a disjunction, negate the antecedent, change the conditional symbol to a disjunction symbol, and keep the consequent the same. To change a disjunction statement to a conditional statement, negate the first statement, change the disjunction symbol to a conditional symbol, and keep the second statement the same.

┌ EXAMPLE 8   *Rewriting a Disjunction as a Conditional Statement*

Write a conditional statement that is logically equivalent to "The Oregon Ducks will win or the Oregon State Beavers will lose." Assume that the negation of winning is losing.

SOLUTION: Let

$$p: \quad \text{The Oregon Ducks will win.}$$
$$q: \quad \text{The Oregon State Beavers will win.}$$

The original statement may be written symbolically as $p \vee \sim q$. To write an equivalent statement, negate the first statement, p, change the disjunction symbol to a conditional symbol, and keep the second statement the same. Symbolically, the equivalent statement is $\sim p \rightarrow \sim q$. The equivalent statement in words is "If the Oregon Ducks lose, then the Oregon State Beavers will lose."   ▲

Negation of the Conditional Statement

Now we will discuss how to negate a conditional statement. To negate a statement we use the fact that $p \rightarrow q \Leftrightarrow \sim p \vee q$ and De Morgan's laws. Examples 9 and 10 show the process.

┌ EXAMPLE 9   *The Negation of a Conditional Statement*

Determine a statement equivalent to $\sim(p \rightarrow q)$.

SOLUTION: Begin with $p \rightarrow q \Leftrightarrow \sim p \vee q$, negate both statements, and use De Morgan's laws.

$$p \rightarrow q \Leftrightarrow \sim p \vee q$$
$$\sim(p \rightarrow q) \Leftrightarrow \sim(\sim p \vee q) \quad \text{Negate both statements}$$
$$\Leftrightarrow p \wedge \sim q \quad \text{De Morgan's laws}$$

Therefore, $\sim(p \rightarrow q)$ is equivalent to $p \wedge \sim q$.   ▲

┌ EXAMPLE 10   *Write an Equivalent Statement*

Write a statement equivalent to

"It is false that if the dog is snoring then the dog cannot sleep in our bedroom."

SOLUTION: Let

$$p = \text{the dog is snoring}$$
$$q = \text{the dog can sleep in our room}$$

Then the given statement can be represented symbolically as $\sim(p \rightarrow \sim q)$. Using the procedure illustrated in Example 9 we can determine that $\sim(p \rightarrow \sim q)$ is equivalent to $p \wedge q$. Verify this yourself now. Therefore, an equivalent statement is "The dog is snoring and the dog can sleep in our bedroom."   ▲

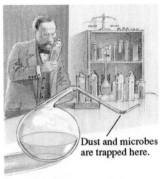

Dust and microbes are trapped here.

L ogical reasoning is often used by scientists as they develop theories. Logical reasoning often also plays a part in developing procedures to test theories. Sometimes, their theories are supported by experimental evidence and are accepted. Other times, their theories are contradicted by the evidence and are rejected. For example, Aristotle observed that bugs appeared in spoiling meat and reasoned that life arose spontaneously from nonliving matter. With advances in technology, scientists have had more means at their disposal to test their theories. To refute Aristotle's claim of spontaneous generation of life, Louis Pasteur in 1862 conducted an experiment by isolating some meat broth in a sterile flask to demonstrate that the bugs Aristotle observed grew from microscopic life forms too small to be seen.

Variations of the Conditional Statement

We know that $p \rightarrow q$ is equivalent to $\sim p \lor q$. Are any other statements equivalent to $p \rightarrow q$? Yes, there are many. Now let's look at the variations of the conditional statement to determine whether any are equivalent to the conditional statement. *The variations of the conditional statement are made by switching and/or negating the antecedent and the consequent of a conditional statement.* The variations of the conditional statement are the *converse* of the conditional, the *inverse* of the conditional, and the *contrapositive* of the conditional.

Listed here are the variations of the conditional with their symbolic form and the words we say to read each one.

Variations of the Conditional Statement

Name	Symbolic form	Read
Conditional	$p \rightarrow q$	"If p, then q"
Converse of the conditional	$q \rightarrow p$	"If q, then p"
Inverse of the conditional	$\sim p \rightarrow \sim q$	"If not p, then not q"
Contrapositive of the conditional	$\sim q \rightarrow \sim p$	"If not q, then not p"

To write the converse of the conditional statement, switch the order of the antecedent and the consequent. To write the inverse, negate both the antecedent and the consequent. To write the contrapositive, switch the order of the antecedent and the consequent and then negate both of them.

Are any of the variations of the conditional statement equivalent? To determine the answer, we can construct a truth table for each variation, as shown in Table 3.26. It reveals that the conditional statement is equivalent to the contrapositive statement and that the converse statement is equivalent to the inverse statement.

TABLE 3.26

p	q	Conditional $p \rightarrow q$	Contrapositive $\sim q \rightarrow \sim p$	Converse $q \rightarrow p$	Inverse $\sim p \rightarrow \sim q$
T	T	T	T	T	T
T	F	F	F	T	T
F	T	T	T	F	F
F	F	T	T	T	T

EXAMPLE 11   *The Converse, Inverse and Contrapositive*

For the conditional statement "If the song contains sitar music, then the song was written by George Harrison," write the

a) converse.   b) inverse.   c) contrapositive.

A sitar

SOLUTION:

a) Let

p: The song contains sitar music.

q: The song was written by George Harrison.

The conditional statement is of the form $p \rightarrow q$, so the converse must be of the form $q \rightarrow p$. Therefore, the converse is "If the song was written by George Harrison, then the song contains sitar music."

b) The inverse is of the form $\sim p \rightarrow \sim q$. Therefore, the inverse is "If the song does not contain sitar music, then the song was not written by George Harrison."

c) The contrapositive is of the form $\sim q \rightarrow \sim p$. Therefore, the contrapositive is "If the song was not written by George Harrison, then the song does not contain sitar music."   ▲

EXAMPLE 12   *Determine the Truth Values*

Let

p: The number is divisible by 9.

q: The number is divisible by 3.

Write the following statements and determine which are true.

a) The conditional statement, $p \rightarrow q$

b) The converse of $p \rightarrow q$

c) The inverse of $p \rightarrow q$

d) The contrapositive of $p \rightarrow q$

SOLUTION:

a) *Conditional statement:* $(p \rightarrow q)$
   If the number is divisible by 9, then the number is divisible by 3. This statement is true. A number divisible by 9 must also be divisible by 3, since 3 is a divisor of 9.

b) *Converse of the conditional:* $(q \rightarrow p)$
   If the number is divisible by 3, then the number is divisible by 9. This statement is false. For instance, 6 is divisible by 3, but 6 is not divisible by 9.

c) *Inverse of the conditional:* $(\sim p \rightarrow \sim q)$
   If the number is not divisible by 9, then the number is not divisible by 3. This statement is false. For instance, 6 is not divisible by 9, but 6 is divisible by 3.

d) *Contrapositive of the conditional:* $(\sim q \rightarrow \sim p)$
   If the number is not divisible by 3, then the number is not divisible by 9. The statement is true, since any number that is divisible by 9 must be divisible by 3.   ▲

EXAMPLE 13   *Use the Contrapositive*

Use the contrapositive to write a statement logically equivalent to "If the boat is 24 ft long, then it will not fit into the boathouse."

SOLUTION: Let

p: The boat is 24 ft long.

q: The boat will fit into the boathouse.

The given statement written symbolically is

$$p \to \sim q$$

The contrapositive of the statement is

$$q \to \sim p$$

Therefore, an equivalent statement is "If the boat will fit into the boathouse, then the boat is not 24 ft long." ▲

The contrapositive of the conditional is very important in mathematics. Consider the statement "If a^2 is not a whole number, then a is not a whole number." Is this statement true? You may find this question difficult to answer. Writing the statement's contrapositive may enable you to answer the question. The contrapositive is "If a is a whole number, then a^2 is a whole number." Since the contrapositive is a true statement, the original statement must also be true.

EXAMPLE 14   *Which Are Equivalent?*

Determine which, if any, of the following statements are equivalent. You may use De Morgan's laws, the fact that $p \to q \Leftrightarrow \sim p \vee q$, information from the variations of the conditional, or truth tables.

a) If you leave by 9 A.M., then you will get to your destination on time.

b) You do not leave by 9 A.M. or you will get to your destination on time.

c) It is false that you get to your destination on time or you did not leave by 9 A.M.

d) If you do not get to your destination on time, then you did not leave by 9 A.M.

SOLUTION: Let

p: You leave by 9 A.M.

q: You will get to your destination on time.

In symbolic form, the four statements are

a) $p \to q$.   b) $\sim p \vee q$.   c) $\sim(q \vee \sim p)$.   d) $\sim q \to \sim p$.

Which of these statements are equivalent? Earlier in this section, you learned that $p \to q$ is equivalent to $\sim p \vee q$. Therefore, statements (a) and (b) are equivalent. Statement (d) is the contrapositive of statement (a). Therefore, statement (d) is also equivalent to statement (a) and statement (b). All these statements have the same truth table (Table 3.27 on page 138).

Now let's look at statement (c). If we use De Morgan's laws on statement (c), we get

$$\sim(q \vee \sim p) \Leftrightarrow \sim q \wedge p$$

TABLE 3.27

p	q	(a) $p \rightarrow q$	(b) $\sim p \vee q$	(d) $\sim q \rightarrow \sim p$
T	T	T	T	T
T	F	F	F	F
F	T	T	T	T
F	F	T	T	T

If $\sim q \wedge p$ was one of the other statements, then $\sim(q \vee \sim p)$ would be equivalent to that statement. Because $\sim q \wedge p$ does not match any of the other choices, it does not necessarily mean that $\sim(q \vee \sim p)$ is not equivalent to the other statements. To determine whether $\sim(q \vee \sim p)$ is equivalent to the other statements, we will construct its truth table (Table 3.28) and compare the answer column with the answer columns in Table 3.27.

TABLE 3.28   (c)

p	q	$\sim$	(q	$\vee$	$\sim p$)
T	T	F	T	T	F
T	F	T	F	F	F
F	T	F	T	T	T
F	F	F	F	T	T
		4	1	3	2

None of the three answer columns of the truth table in Table 3.27 are the same as the answer column of the truth table in Table 3.28. Therefore $\sim(q \vee \sim p)$ is not equivalent to any of the other statements. Therefore, statements (a), (b), and (d) are equivalent to each other.   ▲

DID YOU KNOW

Fuzzy Logic

Modern computers, like truth tables, work with only two values, 1 or 0 (equivalent to true or false in truth tables). This constraint prevents a computer from being able to reason as the human brain can and prevents a computer from being able to evaluate items involving vagueness or value judgments that so often occur in real-world situations. For example, a binary computer will have difficulty evaluating the subjective statement "the air is warm."

Fuzzy logic uses the concept: Everything is a matter of degree. Fuzzy logic manipulates vague concepts such as *bright* and *fast* by assigning values between 0 and 1 to each item. For example, suppose *bright* is assigned a value of 0.80; then *not bright* is assigned a value of $1 - 0.8 = 0.20$. As the value assigned to *bright* changes, so does the value assigned to *not bright*. Not p is always $1 - p$, where $0 < p < 1$. Fuzzy logic is used to operate cameras, air conditioners, subways, and many other devices where the change in one condition changes another condition. For example, when it is bright outside, the camera's lens aperture opens less, and when it is overcast, the camera's lens aperture opens more. How many other devices can you name that may use fuzzy logic? See Problem-Solving Exercises 87 and 88.

SECTION 3.4 EXERCISES

Concept/Writing Exercises

1. What are equivalent statements?

2. Explain how you can determine whether two statements are equivalent.

3. Suppose two statements are connected with the biconditional and the truth table is constructed. If the answer column of the truth table has all trues, what must be true about these two statements? Explain.

4. Write De Morgan's laws for logic.

5. For a statement of the form $p \rightarrow q$, symbolically indicate the form of the
   a) converse.
   b) inverse.
   c) contrapositive.

6. Which of the following are equivalent statements?
   a) The converse
   b) The contrapositive
   c) The inverse
   d) The conditional

7. Write a disjunctive statement that is logically equivalent to $p \rightarrow q$.

8. Write a conjunction involving two conditional statements that is logically equivalent to $p \leftrightarrow q$.

Practice the Skills

In Exercises 9–18, use De Morgan's laws to determine whether the two statements are equivalent.

9. $\sim p \vee \sim q, \sim(p \wedge q)$

10. $\sim(p \vee q), \sim p \wedge \sim q$

11. $\sim(p \wedge q), \sim p \wedge \sim q$

12. $\sim(p \wedge q), \sim p \wedge q$

13. $\sim(p \vee \sim q), \sim p \wedge q$

14. $\sim(p \wedge q), \sim(q \vee \sim p)$

15. $(\sim p \vee \sim q) \rightarrow r, \sim(p \wedge q) \rightarrow r$

16. $q \rightarrow \sim(p \wedge \sim r), q \rightarrow \sim p \vee r$

17. $\sim(p \rightarrow \sim q), p \wedge q$

18. $\sim(\sim p \rightarrow q), \sim p \wedge \sim q$

In Exercises 19–30, use a truth table to determine whether the two statements are equivalent.

19. $p \rightarrow q, \sim p \vee q$

20. $\sim p \rightarrow q, p \wedge q$

21. $(p \wedge q) \wedge r, p \wedge (q \wedge r)$

22. $p \rightarrow q, \sim q \rightarrow \sim p$

23. $(p \vee q) \vee r, p \vee (q \vee r)$

24. $p \vee (q \wedge r), \sim p \rightarrow (q \wedge r)$

25. $p \wedge (q \vee r), (p \wedge q) \vee r$

26. $\sim(q \rightarrow p) \vee r, (p \vee q) \wedge \sim r$

27. $(p \rightarrow q) \wedge (q \rightarrow r), (p \rightarrow q) \rightarrow r$

28. $\sim q \rightarrow (p \wedge r), \sim(p \vee r) \rightarrow q$

29. $(p \rightarrow q) \wedge (q \rightarrow p), (p \leftrightarrow q)$

30. $[\sim(p \rightarrow q)] \wedge [\sim(q \rightarrow p)], \sim(p \leftrightarrow q)$

Problem Solving

In Exercises 31–38, use De Morgan's laws to write an equivalent statement for the sentence.

31. It is false that the Mississippi River runs through Ohio or the Ohio River runs through Mississippi.

32. It is false that the printer is out of toner and the fax machine is out of paper.

33. The snowmobile was neither an Arctic Cat nor was it a Ski-Do.

34. The pot roast is hot, but it is not well done.

35. The hotel does not have a weight room or the conference center does not have an auditorium.

36. Robert Farinelli is an authorized WedgCor dealer or he is not going to work for Prism Construction Company.

37. If we go to Cozumel, then we will go snorkeling or we will not go to Senior Frogs.

38. If Phil Murphy buys us dinner, then we will not go to the top of the CN Tower but we will be able to walk to the Red Bistro Restaurant.

In Exercises 39–44, use the fact that $p \rightarrow q$ is equivalent to $\sim p \vee q$ to write an equivalent form of the given statement.

39. If you drink a glass of orange juice, then you will get a full day supply of folic acid.

40. Nick-at-Nite is showing *Family Ties* or they are showing *The Facts of Life*.

41. Bob the Tomato visited the nursing home or he did not visit the Cub Scout meeting.

42. If John Peden will buy a Harley-Davidson, then he will not buy a Honda.

43. It is false that if the plumbers meet in Kansas City then the Rainmakers will provide the entertainment.

44. Mary Beth Headlee organized the conference or John Waters does not work at Sinclair Community College.

In Exercises 45–48, use the fact that $(p \rightarrow q) \wedge (q \rightarrow p)$ is equivalent to $p \leftrightarrow q$ to write the statement in an equivalent form.

45. If it is cloudy then the front is coming through, and if the front is coming through then it is cloudy.

46. If Model Road is closed then we use Kirkwood Road, and if we use Kirkwood Road then Model Road is closed.

47. The chemistry teacher teaches mathematics if and only if there is a shortage of mathematics teachers.

48. John Deere will hire new workers if and only if the city of Dubuque will pay to retrain the workers.

In Exercises 49–56, write the converse, inverse, and contrapositive of the statement. (For Exercises 55 and 56, use De Morgan's laws.)

49. If the book is interesting, then I will finish the book in 1 week.

50. If the dryer is making a loud noise, then you need to replace the blower fan.

51. If you finish your homework, then you can watch television.

52. If Bob Dylan records a new CD, then he will go on tour.

53. If that annoying paper clip shows up on my computer screen, then I will scream.

54. If the remote control is not within my reach, then I will watch the same channel all night.

55. If the sun is shining, then we will go down to the marina and we will take out the sailboat.

56. If the apple pie is baked, then we will eat a piece of pie and we will save some pie for later.

In Exercises 57–64, write the contrapositive of the statement. Use the contrapositive to determine whether the conditional statement is true or false.

57. If a natural number is not divisible by 5, then the natural number is not divisible by 10.

58. If the opposite sides of the quadrilateral are not parallel, then the quadrilateral is not a parallelogram.

59. If a natural number is divisible by 3, then the natural number is divisible by 6.

60. If $1/n$ is not a natural number, then n is not a natural number.

61. If two lines do not intersect in at least one point, then the two lines are parallel.

62. If $\dfrac{m \cdot a}{m \cdot b} \neq \dfrac{a}{b}$, then m is not a counting number.

63. If the sum of the interior angles of a polygon do not measure $360°$, then the polygon is not a quadrilateral.

64. If a and b are not both even counting numbers, then the product of a and b is not an even counting number.

In Exercises 65–80, determine which, if any, of the three statements are equivalent (see Example 14).

65. a) Maria has not retired or Maria is still working.
   b) If Maria is still working, then Maria has not retired.
   c) If Maria has retired, then Maria is not still working.

66. a) If today is Monday, then tomorrow is not Wednesday.
   b) It is false that today is Monday and tomorrow is not Wednesday.
   c) Today is not Monday or tomorrow is Wednesday.

67. a) The car is not reliable and the car is noisy.
   b) If the car is not reliable, then the car is not noisy.
   c) It is false that the car is reliable or the car is not noisy.

68. a) The house is not made of wood or the shed is not made of wood.
   b) If the house is made of wood, then the shed is not made of wood.
   c) It is false that the shed is made of wood and the house is not made of wood.

69. a) Today is not Sunday or the library is open.
   b) If today is Sunday, then the library is not open.
   c) If the library is open, then today is not Sunday.

70. a) If you are fishing at 1 P.M., then you are driving a car at 1 P.M.
   b) You are not fishing at 1 P.M. or you are driving a car at 1 P.M.
   c) It is false that you are fishing at 1 P.M. and you are not driving a car at 1 P.M.

71. a) The grass grows and the trees are blooming.
   b) If the trees are blooming, then the grass does not grow.
   c) The trees are not blooming or the grass does not grow.

72. a) Johnny Patrick is chosen as department chair if and only if he is the only candidate.
   b) If Johnny Patrick is chosen as department chair then he is the only candidate, and if Johnny Patrick is the only candidate then he is chosen as department chair.
   c) Johnny Patrick is not chosen as department chair and he is not the only candidate.

73. a) It is false that if you do not drink milk then your cholesterol count will be lower.
   b) Your cholesterol count will be lower if and only if you drink milk.
   c) It is false that if you drink milk then your cholesterol count will not be lower.

74. a) Bruce Springsteen will not go on tour if and only if Clarence Clemmons does not play the saxophone in his band.
   b) It is false that Bruce Springsteen will go on tour if and only if Clarence Clemmons does not play the saxophone in his band.
   c) If Bruce Springsteen goes on tour, then Clarence Clemmons plays saxophone in his band.

Clarence Clemmons (left) and Bruce Springsteen

75. a) If the pay is good and today is Monday, then I will take the job.
   b) If I do not take the job, then it is false that the pay is good or today is Monday.
   c) The pay is good and today is Monday, or I will take the job.

76. a) If you are 18 years old and a citizen of the United States, then you can vote in the presidential election.
   b) You can vote in the presidential election, if and only if you are a citizen of the United States and you are 18 years old.
   c) You cannot vote in the presidential election, or you are 18 years old and you are not a citizen of the United States.

77. a) The package was sent by Federal Express, or the package was not sent by United Parcel Service but the package arrived on time.
   b) The package arrived on time, if and only if it was sent by Federal Express or it was not sent by United Parcel Service.
   c) If the package was not sent by Federal Express, then the package was not sent by United Parcel Service but the package arrived on time.

78. a) If we put the dog outside or we feed the dog, then the dog will not bark.
   b) If the dog barks, then we did not put the dog outside and we did not feed the dog.
   c) If the dog barks, then it is false that we put the dog outside or we feed the dog.

79. a) The car needs oil, and the car needs gas or the car is new.
   b) The car needs oil, and it is false that the car does not need gas and the car is not new.
   c) If the car needs oil, then the car needs gas or the car is not new.

80. a) The mortgage rate went down, if and only if Tim purchased the house and the down payment was 10%.
   b) The down payment was 10%, and if Tim purchased the house then the mortgage rate went down.
   c) If Tim purchased the house, then the mortgage rate went down and the down payment was not 10%.

81. If p and q represent two simple statements, and if $p \rightarrow q$ is a false statement, what must be the truth value of the converse, $q \rightarrow p$? Explain.

82. If p and q represent two simple statements, and if $p \rightarrow q$ is a false statement, what must be the truth value of the inverse, $\sim p \rightarrow \sim q$? Explain.

83. If p and q represent two simple statements, and if $p \rightarrow q$ is a false statement, what must be the truth value of the contrapositive, $\sim q \rightarrow \sim p$? Explain.

84. If p and q represent two simple statements, and if $p \rightarrow q$ is a true statement, what must be the truth value of the contrapositive, $\sim q \rightarrow \sim p$? Explain.

Challenge Problems/Group Activities

85. We learned that $p \rightarrow q \Leftrightarrow \sim p \vee q$. Determine a conjunctive statement that is equivalent to $p \rightarrow q$. (*Hint:* There are many answers.)

86. Determine whether $\sim[\sim(p \vee \sim q)] \Leftrightarrow p \vee \sim q$. Explain the method(s) you used to determine your answer.

87. In an appliance or device that uses fuzzy logic, a change in one condition causes a change in a second condition. For example, in a camera, if the brightness increases, the lens aperture automatically decreases to get the proper exposure on the film. Name at least 10 appliances or devices that make use of fuzzy logic and explain how fuzzy logic is used in each appliance or device. See the Did You Know on page 138.

88. In symbolic logic, a statement is either true or false (consider true to have a value of 1 and false a value of 0). In fuzzy logic, nothing is true or false, but everything is a matter of degree. For example, consider the statement "The sun is shining." In fuzzy logic, this statement may have a value between 0 and 1 and may be constantly changing. For example, if the sun is partially blocked by clouds, the value of this statement may be 0.25. In fuzzy logic, the values of connective statements are found as follows for statements p and q.

Not p has a truth value of $1 - p$.

$p \wedge q$ has a truth value equal to the lesser of p and q.

$p \vee q$ has a truth value equal to the greater of p and q.

$p \rightarrow q$ has a truth value equal to the lesser of 1 and $1 - p + q$.

$p \leftrightarrow q$ has a truth value equal to $1 - |p - q|$, that is, 1 minus the absolute value* of p minus q.

Suppose the statement "p: The sun is shining" has a truth value of 0.25 and the statement "q: Mary is getting a tan" has a truth value of 0.20. Find the truth value of

a) $\sim p$.   b) $\sim q$.

c) $p \wedge q$.   d) $p \vee q$.

e) $p \rightarrow q$.   f) $p \leftrightarrow q$.

Recreational Mathematics

89. Unscramble the following letters to form the names of five important terms in the study of logic.

a) ACINNLIDOOT

b) DATOONCLIBINI

c) RIENSEV

d) ROCESVEN

e) ARTSOCINVOTEPI

Internet/Research Activities

90. Do research and write a report on fuzzy logic.

91. Read one of Lewis Carroll's books and write a report on how he used logic in the book. Give at least five specific examples.

92. Do research and write a report on the life and achievements of Augustus De Morgan. Indicate in your report his contributions to sets and logic.

3.5 SYMBOLIC ARGUMENTS

In the preceding sections of this chapter, we used symbolic logic to determine the truth value of a compound statement. We now extend those basic ideas to determine whether symbolic arguments are valid or invalid.

*Absolute values are discussed in Section 13.8.

Consider the statements:

> If Jason is a singer, then he is well known.
>
> Jason is a singer.

If you accept these two statements as true, then a conclusion that necessarily follows is that

> Jason is well known.

These three statements in the following form constitute a symbolic argument.

Premise 1:   If Jason is a singer, then he is well known.
Premise 2:   Jason is a singer.
Conclusion: Therefore, Jason is well known.

A *symbolic argument* consists of a set of *premises* and a *conclusion*. It is called a symbolic argument because we generally write it in symbolic form to determine its validity.

> An **argument is valid** when its conclusion necessarily follows from a given set of premises.
>   An **argument is invalid** or a **fallacy** when the conclusion does not necessarily follow from the given set of premises.

An argument that is not valid is invalid. The argument just presented is an example of a valid argument, as the conclusion necessarily follows from the premises. Now we will discuss a procedure to determine whether an argument is valid or invalid. We begin by writing the argument in symbolic form. To write the argument in symbolic form, we let p and q be

p: Jason is a singer.
q: Jason is well known.

Symbolically, the argument is written

Premise 1: $p \rightarrow q$
Premise 2: p
Conclusion: $\therefore q$ (The three-dot triangle is read "therefore.")

Write the argument in the following form.

If   [*premise 1* **and** *premise 2*] **then** *conclusion*
       [$(p \rightarrow q)$ $\wedge$ p] $\rightarrow$ q

Then construct a truth table for the statement $[(p \rightarrow q) \wedge p] \rightarrow q$ (Table 3.29 on page 144). *If the truth table answer column is true in every case, then the statement is a tautology, and the argument is valid. If the truth table is not a tautology, then the argument is invalid.* Since the statement is a tautology (see column 5), the conclusion necessarily follows from the premises and the argument is valid.

TABLE 3.29

p	q	[(p → q)	∧	p]	→	q
T	T	T	T	T	T	T
T	F	F	F	T	T	F
F	T	T	F	F	T	T
F	F	T	F	F	T	F
		1	3	2	5	4

Once we have demonstrated that an argument in a particular form is valid, all arguments with exactly the same form will also be valid. In fact, many of these forms have been assigned names. The argument form just discussed,

$$p \rightarrow q$$
$$p$$
$$\therefore q$$

is called the *law of detachment*, or *modus ponens*.

EXAMPLE 1   *Determining Validity without a Truth Table*

Determine whether the following argument is valid or invalid.

If the water is warm, then the moon is made of cheese.
The water is warm.
∴ The moon is made of cheese.

SOLUTION: Translate the argument into symbolic form.

Let

w: The water is warm.
m: The moon is made of cheese.

In symbolic form the argument is

$$w \rightarrow m$$
$$w$$
$$\therefore m$$

This argument is also the law of detachment, and therefore it is a valid argument. ▲

Note that the argument in Example 1 is valid even though the conclusion, "The moon is made of cheese," is a false statement. It is also possible to have an invalid argument in which the conclusion is a true statement. When an argument is valid, the conclusion necessarily follows from the premises. It is not necessary for the premises or the conclusion to be true statements in an argument.

Procedure to Determine Whether an Argument Is Valid

1. Write the argument in symbolic form.
2. Compare the form of the argument with forms that are known to be valid or invalid. If there are no known forms to compare it with, or you do not remember the forms, go to step 3.
3. If the argument contains two premises, write a conditional statement of the form

$$[(\text{premise } 1) \wedge (\text{premise } 2)] \rightarrow \text{conclusion}$$

4. Construct a truth table for the statement in step 3.
5. If the answer column of the truth table has all trues, the statement is a tautology, and the argument is valid. If the answer column does not have all trues, the argument is invalid.

Examples 1 through 4 contain two premises. When an argument contains more that two premises, step 3 of the procedure will change slightly, as will be explained shortly.

─EXAMPLE 2   *Determining Validity with a Truth Table*

Determine whether the following argument is valid or invalid.

> If you score 90% on the final exam, then you will get an A in the course.
> You will not get an A in the course.
> ───
> ∴ You do not score 90% on the final exam.

SOLUTION: We first write the argument in symbolic form.

Let

$$p: \quad \text{You score 90\% on the final exam.}$$
$$q: \quad \text{You will get an A in the course.}$$

In symbolic form, the argument is

$$p \rightarrow q$$
$$\underline{\sim q}$$
$$\therefore \sim p$$

As we have not tested an argument in this form, we will construct a truth table to determine whether the argument is valid or invalid. We write the argument in the form $[(p \rightarrow q) \wedge \sim q] \rightarrow \sim p$, and construct a truth table (Table 3.30 on page 146). Since the answer, column 5, has all T's, the argument is valid.

TABLE 3.30

p	q	[(p → q)	∧	~q]	→	~p
T	T	T	F	F	T	F
T	F	F	F	T	T	F
F	T	T	F	F	T	T
F	F	T	T	T	T	T
		1	3	2	5	4

The argument form in Example 2 is an example of the *law of contraposition*, or *modus tollens*.

EXAMPLE 3   *Another Symbolic Argument*

Determine whether the following argument is valid or invalid.

> The grass is green or the grass is full of weeds.
> The grass is not green.
> ∴ The grass is full of weeds.

SOLUTION: Let

> p: The grass is green.
> q: The grass is full of weeds.

In symbolic form, the argument is

$$p \lor q$$
$$\frac{\sim p}{\therefore q}$$

As this form is not one of those we are familiar with, we will construct a truth table. We write the argument in the form $[(p \lor q) \land \sim p] \to q$. Next we construct a truth table, as shown in Table 3.31. The answer to the truth table, column 5, is true in *every case*. Therefore, the statement is a tautology, and the argument is valid.

TABLE 3.31

p	q	[(p ∨ q)	∧	~p]	→	q
T	T	T	F	F	T	T
T	F	T	F	F	T	F
F	T	T	T	T	T	T
F	F	F	F	T	T	F
		1	3	2	5	4

The argument form in Example 3 is an example of *disjunctive syllogism*. Other standard forms of arguments are given in the following chart.

Standard Forms of Arguments

Valid Arguments	Law of Detachment	Law of Contraposition	Law of Syllogism	Disjunctive Syllogism
	$p \rightarrow q$	$p \rightarrow q$	$p \rightarrow q$	$p \vee q$
	$\underline{p \quad\quad}$	$\underline{\sim q \quad\quad}$	$\underline{q \rightarrow r}$	$\underline{\sim p \quad}$
	$\therefore q$	$\therefore \sim p$	$\therefore p \rightarrow r$	$\therefore q$

Invalid Arguments	Fallacy of the Converse	Fallacy of the Inverse		
	$p \rightarrow q$	$p \rightarrow q$		
	$\underline{q \quad\quad}$	$\underline{\sim p \quad}$		
	$\therefore p$	$\therefore \sim q$		

As we saw in Example 1, it is not always necessary to construct a truth table to determine whether or not an argument is valid. The next two examples will show how we can identify an argument as one of the standard arguments given in the chart above.

EXAMPLE 4   *Identifying the Law of Syllogism in an Argument*

Determine whether the following argument is valid or invalid.

> If my laptop battery is dead, then I use my home computer.
> If I use my home computer, then my kids will play outside.
> ∴ If my laptop battery is dead, then my kids will play outside.

SOLUTION: Let

p: My laptop battery is dead.
q: I use my home computer.
r: My kids will play outside.

In symbolic form, the argument is

$$p \rightarrow q$$
$$\underline{q \rightarrow r}$$
$$\therefore p \rightarrow r$$

The argument is in the form of the law of syllogism. Therefore, the argument is valid, and there is no need to construct a truth table. ▲

EXAMPLE 5   *Identifying Common Fallacies in Arguments*

Determine whether the following arguments are valid or invalid.

a)

> If it is snowing, then we put salt on the driveway.
> We put salt on the driveway.
> ∴ It is snowing.

b)

> If it is snowing, then we put salt on the driveway.
> It is not snowing.
> ∴ We do not put salt on the driveway.

SOLUTION:

a) Let

$$p: \quad \text{It is snowing.}$$
$$q: \quad \text{We put salt on the driveway.}$$

In symbolic form, the argument is

$$p \rightarrow q$$
$$\underline{q}$$
$$\therefore p$$

This argument is in the form of the fallacy of the converse. Therefore, the argument is a fallacy, or invalid.

b) Using the same symbols defined in the solution to part (a), in symbolic form, the argument is

$$p \rightarrow q$$
$$\underline{\sim p}$$
$$\therefore \sim q$$

This argument is in the form of the fallacy of the inverse. Therefore, the argument is a fallacy, or invalid.   ▲

TIMELY TIP If you are not sure whether an argument with two premises is one of the standard forms or if you do not remember the standard forms, you can determine whether a given argument is valid or invalid by using a truth table. To do so, follow the boxed procedure on page 145.

In Example 5b) if you did not recognize that this argument was of the same form as the Fallacy of the Inverse you could construct the truth table for the conditional statement

$$[(p \rightarrow q) \wedge \sim p] \rightarrow \sim q$$

The true-false values under the conditional column, →, would be T, T, F, T. Since the statement is not a tautology, the argument is invalid.

Now we consider an argument that has more than two premises. When an argument contains more than two premises, the statement we test, using a truth table, is formed by taking the conjunction of all the premises as the antecedent and the conclusion as the consequent. For example, if an argument is of the form

$$p_1$$
$$p_2$$
$$\underline{p_3}$$
$$\therefore c$$

We evaluate the truth table for $[p_1 \wedge p_2 \wedge p_3] \rightarrow c$. When we evaluate $[p_1 \wedge p_2 \wedge p_3]$, it makes no difference whether we evaluate $[(p_1 \wedge p_2) \wedge p_3]$, or $[p_1 \wedge (p_2 \wedge p_3)]$ because both give the same answer. In Example 6, we evaluate $[p_1 \wedge p_2 \wedge p_3]$ from left to right, that is, $[(p_1 \wedge p_2) \wedge p_3]$.

EXAMPLE 6   *An Argument with Three Premises*

Use a truth table to determine whether the following argument is valid or invalid.

If Donna has a pet, then Donna owns a snail.
Donna owns a snail or Donna drives a truck.
Donna drives a truck or Donna has a pet.
∴ Donna has a pet.

SOLUTION: This argument contains three simple statements.

Let

p: Donna has a pet.
q: Donna owns a snail.
r: Donna drives a truck.

In symbolic form, the argument is

$$p \rightarrow q$$
$$q \vee r$$
$$\underline{r \vee p}$$
$$\therefore p$$

Write the argument in the form

$$[(p \rightarrow q) \wedge (q \vee r) \wedge (r \vee p)] \rightarrow p.$$

Now construct the truth table (Table 3.32 on page 150). The answer, column 7, is not true in every case. Thus, the argument is a fallacy, or invalid.

TABLE 3.32

p	q	r	[(p → q)	∧	(q ∨ r)	∧	(r ∨ p)]	→	p
T	T	T	T	T	T	T	T	T	T
T	T	F	T	T	T	T	T	T	T
T	F	T	F	F	T	F	T	T	T
T	F	F	F	F	F	F	T	T	T
F	T	T	T	T	T	T	T	F	F
F	T	F	T	T	T	F	F	T	F
F	F	T	T	T	T	T	T	F	F
F	F	F	T	F	F	F	F	T	F
			1	3	2	5	4	7	6

Let's now investigate how we can arrive at a valid conclusion from a given set of premises.

EXAMPLE 7   *Determine a Logical Conclusion*

Determine a logical conclusion that follows from the given statements. "If you own a house, then you will pay property tax. You own a house. Therefore, . . ."

SOLUTION: If you recognize a specific form of an argument, you can use your knowledge of that form to draw a logical conclusion.

Let

$$p: \quad \text{You own a house.}$$
$$q: \quad \text{You will pay property tax.}$$

The argument is of the following form.

$$p \rightarrow q$$
$$\underline{p \quad\quad\quad}$$
$$\therefore \; ?$$

If the question mark is replaced with a q, this argument is of the form of the law of detachment. A logical conclusion is "Therefore, you will pay property tax."

SECTION 3.5   EXERCISES

Concept/Writing Exercises

1. What does it mean when an argument is valid?

2. What does it mean when an argument is a fallacy?

3. Is it possible for an argument to be valid if its conclusion is false? Explain your answer.

4. Is it possible for an argument to be invalid if the premises are all true? Explain your answer.

5. Is it possible for an argument to be valid if the premises are all false? Explain your answer.

6. Explain how to determine whether an argument with premises p_1 and p_2 and conclusion c is a valid or invalid argument.

In Exercises 7–10, (a) indicate the form of the valid argument and (b) write an original argument in words for each form.

7. Disjunctive syllogism   8. Law of contraposition

9. Law of syllogism   10. Law of detachment

In Exercises 11 and 12, (a) indicate the form of the fallacy, and (b) write an original argument in words for each form.

11. Fallacy of the inverse   12. Fallacy of the converse

Practice the Skills

In Exercises 13–32, determine whether the argument is valid or invalid. You may compare the argument to a standard form or use a truth table.

13. $p \to q$
$\dfrac{p}{\therefore q}$

14. $p \to q$
$\dfrac{\sim p}{\therefore q}$

15. $p \land \sim q$
$\dfrac{q}{\therefore \sim p}$

16. $\sim p \lor q$
$\dfrac{q}{\therefore p}$

17. $\sim p$
$\dfrac{p \lor q}{\therefore \sim q}$

18. $p \to q$
$\dfrac{\sim q}{\therefore \sim p}$

19. $q \to p$
$\dfrac{\sim q}{\therefore \sim p}$

20. $p \lor q$
$\dfrac{\sim q}{\therefore p}$

21. $\sim p \to q$
$\dfrac{\sim q}{\therefore \sim p}$

22. $q \land \sim p$
$\dfrac{\sim p}{\therefore q}$

23. $p \to q$
$\dfrac{q \to r}{\therefore p \to r}$

24. $q \land p$
$\dfrac{q}{\therefore \sim p}$

25. $p \leftrightarrow q$
$\dfrac{q \land r}{\therefore p \lor r}$

26. $p \leftrightarrow q$
$\dfrac{q \to r}{\therefore \sim r \to \sim p}$

27. $r \leftrightarrow p$
$\dfrac{\sim p \land q}{\therefore p \land r}$

28. $p \lor q$
$\dfrac{r \land p}{\therefore q}$

29. $p \to q$
$q \lor r$
$\dfrac{r \lor p}{\therefore p}$

30. $p \to q$
$q \to r$
$\dfrac{r \to p}{\therefore q \to p}$

31. $p \to q$
$r \to \sim p$
$\dfrac{p \lor r}{\therefore q \lor \sim p}$

32. $p \leftrightarrow q$
$p \lor r$
$\dfrac{q \to r}{\therefore q \lor r}$

Problem Solving

In Exercises 33–50, (a) translate the argument into symbolic form and (b) determine if the argument is valid or invalid. You may compare the argument to a standard form or use a truth table.

33. If Will Smith wins an Academy Award, then he will retire from acting.
Will Smith did not win an Academy Award.

∴ Will Smith will not retire from acting.

Will Smith (see Exercise 33)

34. If the president of the art club resigned, then the vice president becomes president.
The vice president becomes president of the art club.

∴ The president of the art club resigned.

35. If the baby is a boy, then we will name him Alexander Martin.
The baby is a boy.

∴ We will name him Alexander Martin.

36. If I can get my child to preschool by 8:45 A.M., then I can take the 9:00 A.M. class.
If I can take the 9:00 A.M. class, then I can be done by 2:00 P.M.

∴ If I can get my child to preschool by 8:45 A.M., then I can be done by 2:00 P.M.

37. If monkeys can fly, then scarecrows can dance.
Scarecrows cannot dance.

∴ Monkeys cannot fly.

38. Rob Calcatera will go on sabbatical or Frank Cheek will teach logic.
Frank Cheek will not teach logic.

∴ Rob Calcatera will go on sabbatical.

39. If the orange was left on the tree for 1 year, then the orange is ripe.
The orange is ripe.

∴ The orange was left on the tree for 1 year.

40. If you pass general chemistry then you can take organic chemistry.
You pass general chemistry.

∴ You can take organic chemistry.

41. The X-games will be held in San Diego or they will be held in Corpus Christi.
The X-games will not be held in San Diego.

∴ The X-games will be held in Corpus Christi.

42. If Nicholas Thompson teaches this course, then I will get a passing grade.
I did not get a passing grade.

∴ Nicholas Thompson did not teach the course.

43. If it is cold, then graduation will be held indoors.
If graduation is held indoors, then the fireworks will be postponed.

∴ If it is cold, then the fireworks will be postponed.

44. If Miles Davis played with Louis Armstrong, then Charlie Parker played with Dizzy Gillespie.
Miles Davis did not play with Louis Armstrong.

∴ Charlie Parker did not play with Dizzy Gillespie.

45. If the canteen is full, then we can go for a walk.
We can go for a walk and we will not get thirsty.

∴ If we go for a walk, then the canteen is not full.

46. Bryce Canyon National Park is in Utah or Bryce Canyon National Park is in Arizona.
If Bryce Canyon National Park is in Arizona, then it is not in Utah.

∴ Bryce Canyon National Park is not in Arizona.

47. It is snowing and I am going skiing.
If I am going skiing, then I will wear a coat.

∴ If it is snowing, then I will wear a coat.

48. The garden has vegetables or the garden has flowers.
If the garden does not have flowers, then the garden has vegetables.

∴ The garden has flowers or the garden has vegetables.

49. If the house has electric heat, then the Flynns will buy the house.
If the price is not less than $100,000, then the Flynns will not buy the house.

∴ If the house has electric heat, then the price is less than $100,000.

50. If there is an atmosphere, then there is gravity.
If an object has weight, then there is gravity.

∴ If there is an atmosphere, then an object has weight.

In Exercises 51–60, translate the argument into symbolic form. Then determine whether the argument is valid or invalid.

51. If the prescription was called in to Walgreen's, then you can pick it up by 4:00 P.M. You cannot pick it up by 4:00 P.M. Therefore, the prescription was not called in to Walgreen's.

52. The printer has a clogged nozzle or the printer does not have toner. The printer has toner. Therefore, the printer has a clogged nozzle.

53. The television is on or the plug is not plugged in. The plug is plugged in. Therefore, the television is on.

54. If the cat is in the room, then the mice are hiding. The mice are not hiding. Therefore, the cat is not in the room.

55. The test was easy and I received a good grade. The test was not easy or I did not receive a good grade. Therefore, the test was not easy.

56. If Bonnie passes the bar exam, then she will practice law. Bonnie will not practice law. Therefore, Bonnie did not pass the bar exam.

57. The baby is crying but the baby is not hungry. If the baby is hungry then the baby is crying. Therefore, the baby is hungry.

58. If the car is new, then the car has air conditioning. The car is not new and the car has air conditioning. Therefore, the car is not new.

59. If the football team wins the game, then Dave played quarterback. If Dave played quarterback, then the team is not in second place. Therefore, if the football team wins the game, then the team is in second place.

60. The engineering courses are difficult and the chemistry labs are long. If the chemistry labs are long, then the art tests are easy. Therefore, the engineering courses are difficult and the art tests are not easy.

In Exercises 61–67, using the standard forms of arguments and other information you have learned, supply what you believe is a logical conclusion to the argument. Verify that the argument is valid for the conclusion you supplied.

61. If you eat an entire bag of M & M's, your face will break out.
You eat an entire bag of M & M's.
Therefore, . . .

62. If the temperature hits 100°, then we will go swimming.
We did not go swimming.
Therefore, . . .

63. A tick is an insect or a tick is an arachnid.
A tick is not an insect.
Therefore, . . .

64. If Margaret Chang arranges the conference, then many people will attend the conference.
If many people attend the conference, then our picture will be in the paper.
Therefore, . . .

65. If you close the deal, then you will get a commission.
You did not get a commission.
Therefore, . . .

66. If you do not read a lot, then you will not gain knowledge.
You do not read a lot.
Therefore, . . .

67. If you do not pay off your credit card bill, then you will have to pay interest.
If you have to pay interest, then the bank makes money.
Therefore, . . .

Challenge Problems/Group Activities

68. Determine whether the argument is valid or invalid.

If Lynn wins the contest or strikes oil, then she will be rich.
If Lynn is rich, then she will stop working.

∴ If Lynn does not stop working, she did not win the contest.

69. Is it possible for an argument to be invalid if the conjunction of the premises is false in every case of the truth table? Explain your answer.

Recreational Mathematics

70. René Descartes was a seventeenth-century French mathematician and philosopher. One of his most memorable statements is, "I think, therefore, I am." This statement is the basis for the following joke.

Descartes walks into an inn. The innkeeper asks Descartes if he would like something to drink. Descartes replies, "I think not," and promptly vanishes into thin air!

This joke can be summarized in the following argument: If I think, then I am. I think not. Therefore, I am not.
a) Represent this argument symbolically.
b) Is this a valid argument?
c) Explain your answer using either a standard form of argument or using a truth table.

Internet/Research Activities

71. Show how logic is used in advertising. Discuss several advertisements and show how logic is used to persuade the reader.

72. Find examples of valid (or invalid) arguments in printed matter such as newspaper or magazine articles. Explain why the arguments are valid (or invalid).

3.6 EULER DIAGRAMS AND SYLLOGISTIC ARGUMENTS

In the preceding section, we showed how to determine the validity of *symbolic arguments* using truth tables and comparing the arguments to standard forms. This section presents another form of argument called a *syllogistic argument*, better known by the shorter name *syllogism*. The validity of a syllogistic argument is determined by using Euler (pronounced "oiler") diagrams, as is explained shortly.

Syllogistic logic, a deductive process of arriving at a conclusion, was developed by Aristotle in about 350 B.C. Aristotle considered the relationships among the four types of statements that follow.

All _____ are _____.

No _____ are _____.

Some _____ are _____.

Some _____ are not _____.

Examples of these statements are: *All doctors are tall. No doctors are tall. Some doctors are tall. Some doctors are not tall.* Since Aristotle's time, other types of statements have been added to the study of syllogistic logic, two of which are

_____ is a _____.

_____ is not a _____.

Examples of these statements are: *Maria is a doctor. Maria is not a doctor.*

The difference between a symbolic argument and a syllogistic argument can be seen in the following chart. Symbolic arguments use the connectives *and, or, not, if–then*, and *if and only if.* Syllogistic arguments use the quantifiers *all, some,* and *none*, which were discussed in Section 3.1.

Symbolic Arguments Versus Syllogistic Arguments

	Words or phrases used	Method of determining validity
Symbolic argument	and, or, not, if-then, if and only if	Truth tables or by comparison with standard forms of arguments
Syllogistic argument	all are, some are, none are, some are not	Euler diagrams.

As with symbolic logic, the premises and the conclusion together form an argument. An example of a syllogistic argument is

All German shepherds are dogs.

All dogs bark.

∴ All German shepherds bark.

This is an example of a valid argument. Recall from the previous section that an argument is *valid* when its conclusion necessarily follows from a given set of premises. Recall that an argument in which the conclusion does not necessarily follow from the given premises is said to be an *invalid argument* or a *fallacy*.

Before we give another example of a syllogism, let's review the Venn diagrams discussed in Section 2.3 in relationship with Aristotle's four statements.

All *A*s are *B*s	No *A*s are *B*s	Some *A*s are *B*s	Some *A*s are not *B*s
If an element is in set *A*, then it is in set *B*.	If an element is in set *A*, then it is not in set *B*.	There is at least one element that is in both set *A* and set *B*.	There is at least one element that is in set *A* that is not in set *B*.

One method used to determine whether an argument is valid or is a fallacy is by means of an *Euler diagram*, named after Leonhard Euler (1707–1783), who used circles to represent sets in syllogistic arguments. The technique of using Euler diagrams is illustrated in Example 1.

EXAMPLE 1   *Using a Euler Diagram*

Determine whether the following syllogism is valid or invalid.

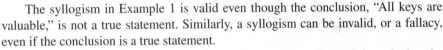

All keys are made of brass.

All things made of brass are valuable.

∴ All keys are valuable.

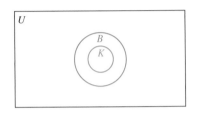

Figure 3.3

SOLUTION: To determine whether this syllogism is valid or not valid, we will construct an Euler diagram. We begin with the first premise, "All keys are made of brass." As shown in Fig. 3.3, the inner blue circle labeled *K* represents the set of all keys and the outer red circle labeled *B* represents the set of all brass objects. The first premise requires that the inner blue circle must be entirely contained within the outer red circle. Next, we will represent the second premise, "All things made of brass are valuable." As shown in Fig. 3.4, the outermost black circle labeled *V* represents the set of all valuable objects. The second premise dictates that the blue circle, representing the set of brass objects, must be entirely contained within the black circle, representing the set of valuable objects. Now, examine the completed Euler diagram in Fig. 3.4. Note that the premises force the set of keys to be within the set of valuable objects. Therefore, the argument is valid, since the conclusion, "All keys are valuable," necessarily follows from the set of premises. ▲

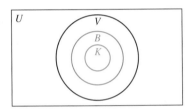

Figure 3.4

The syllogism in Example 1 is valid even though the conclusion, "All keys are valuable," is not a true statement. Similarly, a syllogism can be invalid, or a fallacy, even if the conclusion is a true statement.

When we determine the validity of an argument, we are determining whether the conclusion necessarily follows from the premises. When we say that an argument is valid, we are saying that if all the premises are true statements, then the conclusion must also be a true statement.

The form of the argument determines its validity, not the particular statements. For example, consider the syllogism

All Earth people have two heads.

All people with two heads can fly.

∴ All Earth people can fly.

The form of this argument is the same as that of the previous valid argument in Example 1. Therefore, this argument is also valid.

EXAMPLE 2   *Is the Syllogism Valid?*

Determine whether the following syllogism is valid or is invalid.

All pilots have good vision.

Kaitlyn is a pilot.

∴ Kaitlyn has good vision.

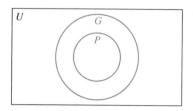

Figure 3.5

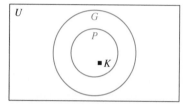

Figure 3.6

SOLUTION: The statement "All pilots have good vision" is illustrated in Fig. 3.5. The second premise, "Kaitlyn is a pilot," tells us that Kaitlyn must be placed in the inner circle (see Fig. 3.6). The Euler diagram illustrates that we must accept the conclusion "Kaitlyn has good vision" as true (when we accept the premises as true). Therefore, the argument is valid. ▲

In both Example 1 and Example 2, we had no choice as to where the second premise was to be placed in the Euler diagram. In Example 1, the set of brass objects had to be placed inside the set of valuable objects. In Example 2, Kaitlyn had to be placed inside the set of people with good vision. Often when determining the truth value of a syllogism, a premise can be placed in more than one area in the diagram. *We always try to draw the Euler diagram so that the conclusion does not necessarily follow from the premises. If that can be done, then the conclusion does not necessarily follow from the premises and the argument is invalid.* If we cannot show that the argument is invalid, only then do we accept the argument as valid. We illustrate this process in Example 3.

EXAMPLE 3   *Ballerinas and Athletes*

Determine whether the following syllogism is valid or is invalid.

> All ballerinas are athletic.
> Keyshawn is athletic.
> ∴ Keyshawn is a ballerina.

SOLUTION: The statement "All ballerinas are athletic" is illustrated in Fig. 3.7(a). The next premise "Keyshawn is athletic" tells us that Keyshawn must be placed in the set of athletic people. Two diagrams in which both premises are satisfied are shown in Fig. 3.7(b) and (c). By examining Fig. 3.7(b), however, we see that Keyshawn is not a ballerina. Therefore, the conclusion "Keyshawn is a ballerina" does not necessarily follow from the set of premises. Thus, the argument is invalid, or a fallacy.

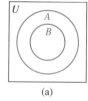

    (a)   (b)   (c)

Figure 3.7 ▲

EXAMPLE 4   *Parrots and Chickens*

Determine whether the following syllogism is valid or invalid.

> No parrots eat chicken.
> Fletch does not eat chicken.
> ∴ Fletch is a parrot.

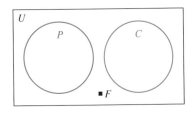

Figure 3.8

SOLUTION: The diagram in Fig. 3.8 satisfies the two given premises and also shows that Fletch is not a parrot. Therefore, the argument is invalid, or is a fallacy.   ▲

Note that in Example 4 if we placed Fletch in circle *P*, the argument would appear to be valid. Remember that *whenever testing the validity of an argument, always try to show that the argument is invalid.* If there is any way of showing that the conclusion does not necessarily follow from the premises, then the argument is invalid.

EXAMPLE 5   *A Syllogism Involving the Word Some*

Determine whether the following syllogism is valid or invalid.

All *A*s are *B*s.

Some *B*s are *C*s.

∴ Some *A*s are *C*s.

SOLUTION: The statement "All *A*s are *B*s" is illustrated in Fig. 3.9. The statement "Some *B*s are *C*s" means that there is at least one *B* that is a *C*. We can illustrate this set of premises in four ways, as illustrated in Fig. 3.10.

Figure 3.9

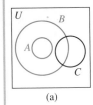   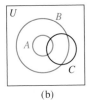   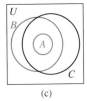   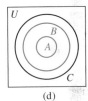

(a)   (b)   (c)   (d)

Figure 3.10

In all four illustrations, we see that (1) all *A*s are *B*s and (2) some *B*s are *C*s. The conclusion is "Some *A*s are *C*s." Since at least one of the illustrations, Fig. 3.10(a), shows that the conclusion does not necessarily follow from the given premises, the argument is invalid.   ▲

EXAMPLE 6   *Cowboys and Debutantes*

Determine whether the following syllogism is valid or invalid.

No cowboys drink lemonade.

All debutantes drink lemonade.

∴ No cowboys are debutantes.

SOLUTION: The first premise tells us that cowboys and the people who drink lemonade are disjoint sets—that is, sets that do not intersect—as shown in Fig. 3.11. The second premise tells us that the set of debutantes is a subset of the people who drink lemonade. Therefore, the circle representing the set of debutantes must go within the circle representing the set of people who drink lemonade.

The set of debutantes and the set of cowboys cannot be made to intersect without violating a premise. Thus, no cowboys can be debutantes, and the syllogism is valid. Note that we did not say that this conclusion is true, only that the argument is valid.   ▲

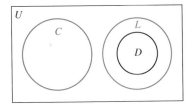

Figure 3.11

SECTION 3.6   EXERCISES

Concept/Writing Exercises

1. If an Euler diagram can be drawn in which the conclusion does not necessarily follow from the premises, what can be said about the syllogistic argument under consideration?

2. If an Euler diagram can only be drawn in a way in which the conclusion necessarily follows from the premises, what can be said about the syllogistic argument under consideration?

3. What does it mean when we determine that an argument is valid?

4. Explain the differences between a symbolic argument and a syllogistic argument.

5. Can an argument be valid if the conclusion is a false statement? Explain your answer.

6. Can an argument be invalid if the conclusion is a true statement? Explain.

Practice the Skills/Problem Solving

In Exercises 7–30, use an Euler diagram to determine whether the syllogism is valid or invalid.

7. All cows give milk.
   Mags is a cow.
   ∴ Mags gives milk.

8. All cordless telephones have antennas.
   All things with antennas are insects.
   ∴ All cordless telephones are insects.

9. No apples are citrus fruits.
   All Granny Smiths are apples.
   ∴ No Granny Smiths are citrus fruits.

10. All dolphins are mammals.
    All mammals are vertebrates.
    ∴ All dolphins are vertebrates.

11. All theme parks have walkways.
    Metropolitan Community College has walkways.
    ∴ Metropolitan Community College is a theme park.

12. All golfers have rain gear.
    John Pearse has rain gear.
    ∴ John Pearse is a golfer.

13. No horses buck.
    Palominos are horses.
    ∴ Palominos do not buck.

14. No jockeys weigh more than 200 pounds.
    Deb Otto is not a jockey.
    ∴ Deb Otto weighs more than 200 pounds.

15. Some mushrooms are poisonous.
    A morel is a mushroom.
    ∴ A morel is poisonous.

16. Some policemen are polite.
    Jarod Harshbarger is a policeman.
    ∴ Jarod Harshbarger is not polite.

17. Some farmers are politicians.
    Some politicians are senators.
    ∴ Some farmers are senators.

18. Some professional golfers give golf lessons.
    All people who belong to the PGA are professional golfers.
    ∴ All people who belong to the PGA give golf lessons.

Tiger Woods

19. No tennis players are wrestlers.
Allison is not a wrestler.

∴ Allison is a tennis player.

20. Some soaps float.
All things that float are lighter than water.

∴ Some soaps are lighter than water.

21. Some people love mathematics.
All people who love mathematics love physics.

∴ Some people love physics.

22. Some desks are made of wood.
All paper is made of wood.

∴ Some desks are made of paper.

23. No *x*s are *y*s.
No *y*s are *z*s.

∴ No *x*s are *z*s.

24. All pilots can fly.
All astronauts can fly.

∴ Some pilots are astronauts.

25. Some dogs wear glasses.
Fido wears glasses.

∴ Fido is a dog.

26. All rainy days are cloudy.
Today it is cloudy.

∴ Today is a rainy day.

27. All sweet things taste good.
All things that taste good are fattening.
All things that are fattening put on pounds.

∴ All sweet things put on pounds.

28. All books have red covers.
All books that have red covers contain 200 pages.
Some books that contain 200 pages are novels.

∴ All books that contain 200 pages are novels.

29. All country singers play the guitar.
All country singers play the drums.
Some people who play the guitar are rock singers.

∴ Some country singers are rock singers.

Bonnie Raitt

30. Some hot dogs are made of turkey.
All things made of turkey are edible.
Some things that are made of beef are edible.

∴ Some hot dogs are made of beef.

Challenge Problem/Group Activity

31. Statements in logic can be translated into set statements: for example, $p \wedge q$ is similar to $P \cap Q$; $p \vee q$ is similar to $P \cup Q$; and $p \rightarrow q$ is equivalent to $\sim p \vee q$, which is similar to $P' \cup Q$. Euler diagrams can also be used to show that arguments similar to those discussed in Section 3.5 are valid or invalid. Use Euler diagrams to show that the symbolic argument is invalid.

$$p \rightarrow q$$
$$\underline{p \vee q}$$
$$\therefore \sim p$$

Internet/Research Activity

32. Leonhard Euler is considered one of the greatest mathematicians of all time. Do research and write a report on Euler's life. Include information on his contributions to sets and to logic. Also indicate other areas of mathematics in which he made important contributions. References include encyclopedias, history of mathematics books, and the Internet.

CHAPTER 3 SUMMARY

IMPORTANT FACTS

Quantifiers

Form of Statement	Form of Negation
All are.	Some are not.
None are.	Some are.
Some are.	None are.
Some are not.	All are.

Summary of connectives

Formal Name	Symbol	Read	Symbolic Form
Negation	$\sim$	not	$\sim p$
Conjunction	$\wedge$	and	$p \wedge q$
Disjunction	$\vee$	or	$p \vee q$
Conditional	$\rightarrow$	if–then	$p \rightarrow q$
Biconditional	$\leftrightarrow$	if and only if	$p \leftrightarrow q$

Basic truth tables

Negation

p	~p
T	F
F	T

p	q	$p \wedge q$	$p \vee q$	$p \rightarrow q$	$p \leftrightarrow q$
		Conjunction	Disjunction	Conditional	Biconditional
T	T	T	T	T	T
T	F	F	T	F	F
F	T	F	T	T	F
F	F	F	F	T	T

De Morgan's laws

$$\sim(p \wedge q) \Leftrightarrow \sim p \vee \sim q$$
$$\sim(p \vee q) \Leftrightarrow \sim p \wedge \sim q$$

Other equivalent forms

$$p \rightarrow q \Leftrightarrow \sim p \vee q$$
$$\sim(p \rightarrow q) \Leftrightarrow p \wedge \sim q$$
$$p \leftrightarrow q \Leftrightarrow [(p \rightarrow q) \wedge (q \rightarrow p)]$$

Variations of the conditional statement

Name	Symbolic Form	Read
Conditional	$p \rightarrow q$	If p, then q.
Converse of the conditional	$q \rightarrow p$	If q, then p.
Inverse of the conditional	$\sim p \rightarrow \sim q$	If not p, then not q.
Contrapositive of the conditional	$\sim q \rightarrow \sim p$	If not q, then not p.

Standard forms of arguments
Valid arguments

Law of Detachment	Law of Contraposition	Law of Syllogism	Disjunctive Syllogism
$p \rightarrow q$	$p \rightarrow q$	$p \rightarrow q$	$p \vee q$
p	$\sim q$	$q \rightarrow r$	$\sim p$
$\therefore q$	$\therefore \sim p$	$\therefore p \rightarrow r$	$\therefore q$

Invalid arguments

Fallacy of the Converse	Fallacy of the Inverse
$p \rightarrow q$	$p \rightarrow q$
q	$\sim p$
$\therefore p$	$\therefore \sim q$

Symbolic argument vs. syllogistic argument

	Words or Phrases Used	Method of Determining Validity
Symbolic argument	and, or, not, if–then, if and only if	Truth tables or by comparison with standard forms of arguments
Syllogistic argument	all are, some are, none are, some are not	Euler diagrams

CHAPTER 3   REVIEW EXERCISES

3.1

In Exercises 1–6, write the negation of the statement.

1. Some rock bands play ballads.
2. Some bananas are not ripe.
3. No chickens have lips.
4. All panthers are endangered.

5. All pens use ink.
6. No rabbits wear glasses.

In Exercises 7–12, write each compound statement in words.

    p: The coffee is Maxwell House.
    q: The coffee is hot.
    r: The coffee is strong.

7. $p \vee q$
8. $\sim q \wedge r$
9. $q \rightarrow (r \wedge \sim p)$
10. $p \leftrightarrow \sim r$
11. $\sim p \leftrightarrow (r \wedge \sim q)$
12. $(p \vee \sim q) \wedge \sim r$

3.2

In Exercises 13–18, use the statements for p, q, and r as in Exercises 7–12 to write the statement in symbolic form.

13. The coffee is strong and the coffee is hot.
14. If the coffee is Maxwell House, then it is strong.
15. If the coffee is strong then the coffee is hot, or the coffee is not Maxwell House.
16. The coffee is hot if and only if the coffee is Maxwell House, and the coffee is not strong.
17. The coffee is strong and the coffee is hot, or the coffee is not Maxwell House.
18. It is false that the coffee is strong and the coffee is hot.

In Exercises 19–24, construct a truth table for the statement.

19. $(p \vee q) \wedge \sim p$
20. $q \leftrightarrow (p \vee \sim q)$
21. $(p \vee q) \leftrightarrow (p \vee r)$
22. $p \wedge (\sim q \vee r)$
23. $p \rightarrow (q \wedge \sim r)$
24. $(p \wedge q) \rightarrow \sim r$

3.2, 3.3

In Exercises 25–28, determine the truth value of the statement.

25. If 7 is an odd number, then 11 is an even number.
26. The St. Louis Arch is in St. Louis or Abraham Lincoln is buried in Grant's Tomb.

27. If Oregon borders the Pacific Ocean or California borders the Atlantic Ocean, then Minnesota is south of Texas.
28. $15 - 7 = 22$ or $4 + 9 = 13$, and $9 - 8 = 1$.

In Exercises 29 and 30, the circle graph shows the sources and percentages of Oregon's electricity sources in 2002. Use the graph to determine the truth value of each simple statement. Then determine the truth value of the compound statement.

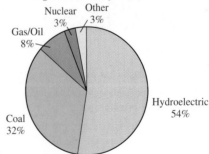

Oregon's Electricity Sources

Source: Renewable Northwest Project

29. Thirty-two percent of Oregon's electricity sources are coal if and only if 54% of Oregon's electricity sources are hydroelectric sources, or 38% of Oregon's electricity sources are nuclear.
30. If 3% of Oregon's electricity sources are gas/oil, then 45% of Oregon's electricity sources are coal and 3% of Oregon's electricity comes from other sources.

3.3

In Exercises 31–34, determine the truth value of the statement when p is T, q is F, and r is F.

31. $(p \rightarrow \sim r) \vee (p \wedge q)$ **32.** $(p \vee q) \leftrightarrow (\sim r \wedge p)$

33. $\sim r \leftrightarrow [(p \vee q) \leftrightarrow \sim p]$ **34.** $\sim[(q \wedge r) \rightarrow (\sim p \vee r)]$

3.4

In Exercises 35–38, determine whether the pairs of statements are equivalent. You may use De Morgan's laws, the fact that $(p \rightarrow q) \Leftrightarrow (\sim p \vee q)$, truth tables, or equivalent forms of the conditional statement.

35. $\sim p \vee \sim q$ $\sim p \leftrightarrow q$

36. $\sim p \rightarrow \sim q$ $p \vee \sim q$

37. $\sim p \vee (q \wedge r)$ $(\sim p \vee q) \wedge (\sim p \vee r)$

38. $(\sim q \rightarrow p) \wedge p$ $\sim(\sim p \leftrightarrow q) \vee p$

In Exercises 39–43, use De Morgan's laws or the fact that $(p \rightarrow q) \Leftrightarrow (\sim p \vee q)$ to write an equivalent statement for the given statement.

39. Johnny Cash is in the Rock and Roll Hall of Fame and India Arie recorded *Acoustic Soul*.

India Arie

40. Her foot fell asleep or she has injured her ankle.

41. It is not true that Altec Lansing only produces speakers or Harman Kardon only produces stereo receivers.

42. Travis Tritt did not win an Academy Award and Randy Jackson does not do commercials for Milk Bone Dog Biscuits.

43. If the temperature is not above 32°, then we will go ice fishing at O'Leary's Lake.

In Exercises 44–48, write the (a) converse, (b) inverse, and (c) contrapositive for the given statement.

44. If you hear a beautiful songbird today, then you enjoy life.

45. If you followed the correct pattern, then the quilt has a uniform design.

46. If Maureen Gerald is not in attendance, then she is helping at the school.

47. If the desk is made by Winner's Only and the desk is in the Rose catalog, then we will not buy a desk at Miller's Furniture.

48. If you get straight A's on your report card, then I will let you attend the prom.

In Exercises 49–52, determine which, if any, of the three statements are equivalent.

49. a) If the temperature is over 80°, then the air conditioner will come on.
  b) The temperature is not over 80° or the air conditioner will come on.
  c) It is false that the temperature is over 80° and the air conditioner will not come on.

50. a) The screwdriver is on the workbench if and only if the screwdriver is not on the counter.
  b) If the screwdriver is not on the counter, then the screwdriver is not on the workbench.
  c) It is false that the screwdriver is on the counter and the screwdriver is not on the workbench.

51. a) If $2 + 3 = 6$, then $3 + 1 = 5$.
  b) $2 + 3 = 6$ if and only if $3 + 1 \neq 5$.
  c) If $3 + 1 \neq 5$, then $2 + 3 \neq 6$.

52. a) If the sale is on Tuesday and I have money, then I will go to the sale.
  b) If I go to the sale, then the sale is on Tuesday and I have money.
  c) I go to the sale, or the sale is on Tuesday and I have money.

3.5, 3.6

In Exercises 53–58, determine whether the argument is valid or invalid.

53. $p \rightarrow q$ **54.** $p \wedge q$
  $\dfrac{\sim p}{\therefore q}$ $\dfrac{q \rightarrow r}{\therefore p \rightarrow r}$

55. Nicole is in the hot tub or she is in the shower.
  Nicole is in the hot tub.
  ─────────────────────
  ∴ Nicole is not in the shower.

56. If the car has a sound system, then Rick will buy the car. If the price is not less than $18,000, then Rick will not buy the car. Therefore, if the car has a sound system, then the price is less than $18,000.

57. All plumbers wear overalls.
  Some electricians wear overalls.
  ─────────────────────
  ∴ Some electricians are plumbers.

58. Some submarines are yellow.
  All dandelions are yellow.
  ─────────────────────
  ∴ Some dandelions are submarines.

CHAPTER 3 TEST

In Exercises 1–3, write the statement in symbolic form.

> *p*:   Ann is the secretary.
>
> *q*:   Dick is the vice president.
>
> *r*:   Elaine is the president.

1. Ann is the secretary but Elaine is the president, or Dick is not the vice president.

2. If Elaine is the president then Dick is the vice president, or Ann is not the secretary.

3. It is false that Elaine is the president if and only if Dick is not the vice president.

In Exercises 4 and 5, use p, q, and r as above to write each symbolic statement in words.

4. $p \leftrightarrow (q \wedge r)$ 5. $\sim(p \rightarrow \sim r)$

In Exercises 6 and 7, construct a truth table for the given statement.

6. $[\sim(p \rightarrow r)] \wedge q$ 7. $(q \leftrightarrow \sim r) \vee p$

In Exercises 8 and 9, find the truth value of the statement.

8. $2 + 6 = 8$ or $7 - 12 = 5$.

9. Scissors can cut paper or a dime has the same value as two nickels, if and only if Louisville is a city in Kentucky.

In Exercises 10 and 11, given that p is true, q is false, and r is true, determine the truth value of the statement.

10. $(r \vee q) \leftrightarrow (p \wedge \sim q)$

11. $[\sim(r \rightarrow \sim p)] \wedge (q \rightarrow p)$

12. Determine whether the pair of statements are equivalent.

$\sim p \vee q, \qquad \sim(p \wedge \sim q)$

In Exercises 13 and 14, determine which, if any, of the three statements are equivalent.

13. a) If the bird is red, then it is a cardinal.
    b) The bird is not red or it is a cardinal.
    c) If the bird is not red, then it is not a cardinal.

14. a) It is not true that the test is today or the concert is tonight.
    b) The test is not today and the concert is not tonight.
    c) If the test is not today, then the concert is not tonight.

15. *Translate the following argument into symbolic form. Determine whether the argument is valid or invalid by comparing the argument to a recognized form or by using a truth table.*

    If the soccer team wins the game, then Sue played fullback. If Sue played fullback, then the team is in second place. Therefore, if the soccer team wins the game, then the team is in second place.

16. *Use an Euler diagram to determine whether the syllogism is valid or is a fallacy.*

    All cars have engines.
    Some things with engines use gasoline.
    ∴ Some cars use gasoline.

In Exercises 17 and 18, write the negation of the statement.

17. All leopards are spotted.

18. Some jacks-in-the-box are electronic.

19. Write the converse, inverse, and contrapositive of the conditional statement, "If the garbage truck comes, then today is Saturday."

20. Is it possible for an argument to be valid when the conclusion is a false statement? Explain your answer.

GROUP PROJECTS

Switching Circuits

1. An application of logic is *switching circuits*. There are two basic types of electric circuits: *series circuits* and *parallel circuits*. In a series circuit, the current can flow in only one path; see Fig. 3.12. In a parallel circuit the current can flow in more than one path; see Fig. 3.13.

Series circuit

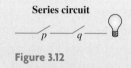

Figure 3.12

Parallel circuit

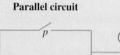

Figure 3.13

In Figs. 3.12 and 3.13, the p and q represent switches that may be opened or closed. In the series circuit in Fig. 3.12, if both switches are closed, the current will reach the bulb and the bulb will light. In the parallel circuit in Fig. 3.13, if either switch p or switch q is closed, or if both switches are closed, the current will reach the bulb and the bulb will light.

a) How many different open/closed arrangements of the two switches in Fig. 3.12 are possible? List all the possibilities.

b) Series circuits are represented using conjunctions. The circuit in Fig. 3.12 may be represented as $p \land q$. Construct a four-row truth table to represent the series circuit. Construct the table with columns for p, q, and $p \land q$. The statement $p \land q$ represents the outcome of the circuit (either the bulb lighting or the bulb not lighting). Represent a closed switch with the number 1, an open switch with the number 0, the bulb lighting with the number 1, and the bulb not lighting with the number 0. For example, if both switches are closed, the bulb will light, and so we write the first row of the truth table as

p	q	$p \land q$
1	1	1

c) How is the truth table determined in part (b) similar to the truth table for $p \land q$ discussed in earlier sections of this chapter?

d) Parallel circuits are represented using disjunctions. The circuit in Fig. 3.13 may be represented as $p \lor q$. Construct a truth table to represent the parallel circuit. Construct the table with columns for p, q, and $p \lor q$. The statement $p \lor q$ represents the outcome of the circuit (either the bulb lighting or the bulb not lighting). Use 1's and 0's as indicated in part (b).

e) How is the truth table determined in part (d) similar to the truth table for $p \lor q$ discussed in earlier sections of this chapter?

f) Represent the following circuit as a symbolic logic statement using parentheses. Explain how you determined your answer.

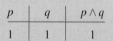

g) Draw a circuit to represent the logic statement $p \land (q \lor r)$. Explain how you determined your answer.

Computer Gates

2. Gates in computers work on the same principles as switching circuits. The three basic types of gate are the NOT gate, the AND gate, and the OR gate. Each is illustrated along with a table that indicates current flow entering and exiting the gate. If current flows into a NOT gate, then no current exits, and vice versa. Current exits an AND gate only when both inputs have a current flow. Current exits an OR gate if current flows through either, or both, inputs. In the table, a 1 represents a current flow and a 0 indicates no current flow. For example, in the AND gate, if there is a current flow in input A (I_a has a value of 1) and no current flow in input B (I_b has a value of 0), there is no current flow in the output (O has a value of 0); see row 2 of the AND Gate table.

NOT gate

Input ▷○ Output

AND gate   **OR gate**

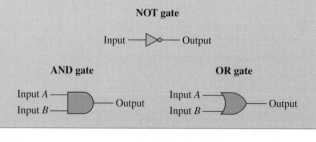

NOT gate

I	O
1	0
0	1

AND gate

I_a	I_b	O
1	1	1
1	0	0
0	1	0
0	0	0

OR gate

I_a	I_b	O
1	1	1
1	0	1
0	1	1
0	0	0

a) If 1 is considered true and 0 is considered false, explain how these tables are similar to the *not, and,* and *or* truth tables.

For the inputs indicated in the following figures determine whether the output is 1 or 0.

b)

c)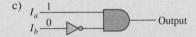

d)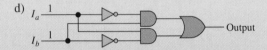

e) What values for I_a and I_b will give an output of 1 in the figure in part (d)? Explain how you determined your answer.

f) Construct a truth table using 1's and 0's for the following gate. Your truth table should have columns I_a, I_b, and O and should indicate the four possible cases for the inputs and each corresponding output.

Logic Game

3. a) Shown is a photograph of a logic game at the Ontario Science Centre. There are 12 balls on top of the game board, numbered from left to right, with ball 1 on the extreme left and ball 12 on the extreme right. On the platform in front of the players are 12 buttons, one corresponding to each of the balls. When 6 buttons are pushed, the 6 respective balls are released. When 1 or 2 balls reach an *and* gate or an *or* gate, a single ball may or may not pass through the gate. The object of the game is to select a proper combination of 6 buttons that will allow 1 ball to reach the bottom. Using your knowledge of *and* and *or*, select a combination of 6 buttons that will result in a win. (There is more than one answer.) Explain how you determined your answer.

b) Construct a game similar to this one where 15 balls are at the top and 8 must be selected to allow 1 ball to reach the bottom.

c) Indicate all solutions to the game you constructed in part (c).

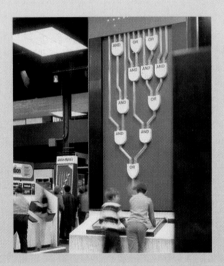

One of the earliest reasons that human beings needed numbers was for reckoning time, marking off days in the lunar month, so the seasonal changes that dictated human activity could be anticipated. The Mayans, the Egyptians, and the ancient Britons constructed monumental stone observatories that enabled them to mark the passage of the seasons, especially the summer solstice, using the alignment of the sun as a guide. The photo is Stonehenge in England.

SYSTEMS OF NUMERATION

The number system we use—called the Hindu–Arabic system—seems to be a permanent, unchanging means of communicating quantities. However, just as languages evolve over time, so do numerical symbols that represent numbers.

Mathematics began with the practical problem of counting and record keeping. People had to count their herds, the passage of days, and objects of barter. They used physical objects—stones, shells, fingers—to represent the objects counted.

As primitive cultures grew from villages to cities, the complexity of human activities increased. Now people needed better ways of recording and communicating. It was a revolutionary step when people started using physical objects to represent not only specific objects like sheep and grain, but also the concept of pure quantity.

Through the course of human history, the evolution of numeration systems has expanded our knowledge and abilities for record keeping, communication, and computation. As a society's numeration system changes, so do the capabilities of that society. Without an understanding of the binary number system, the computer as we know it today could not exist. Without the computer, our lifestyle would not be as it is today.

4.1 ADDITIVE, MULTIPLICATIVE, AND CIPHERED SYSTEMS OF NUMERATION

Just as the first attempts to write were made long after the development of speech, the first representation of numbers by symbols came long after people had learned to count. A tally system using physical objects, such as scratch marks in the soil or on a stone, notches on a stick, pebbles, or knots on a vine, was probably the earliest method of recording numbers.

In primitive societies, such a tally system adequately served the limited need for recording livestock, agriculture, or whatever was counted. As civilization developed, however, more efficient and accurate methods of calculating and keeping records were needed. Because tally systems are impractical and inefficient, societies developed symbols to replace them. For example, the Egyptians used the symbol ∩ and the Babylonians used the symbol ❮ to represent the number we symbolize by 10.

A *number* is a quantity, and it answers the question "How many?" A *numeral* is a symbol such as ∩, ❮, or 10 used to represent the number. We think a number but write a numeral. The distinction between number and numeral will be made here only if it is helpful to the discussion.

In language, relatively few letters of the alphabet are used to construct a large number of words. Similarly, in arithmetic, a small variety of numerals can be used to represent all numbers. In general, when writing a number, we use as few numerals as possible. One of the greatest accomplishments of humankind has been the development of systems of numeration, whereby all numbers are "created" from a few symbols. Without such systems, mathematics would not have developed to its present level.

> A **system of numeration** consists of a set of numerals and a scheme or rule for combining the numerals to represent numbers.

Four types of numeration systems used by different cultures are the topic of this chapter. They are additive (or repetitive), multiplicative, ciphered, and place-value systems. You do not need to memorize all the symbols, but you should understand the principles behind each system. By the end of this chapter, we hope that you better understand the system we use, the *Hindu–Arabic system*, and its relationship to other types of systems.

Additive Systems

An additive system is one in which the number represented by a particular set of numerals is simply the sum of the values of the numerals. The additive system of numeration is one of the oldest and most primitive types of numeration systems. One of the first additive systems, the Egyptian hieroglyphic system, dates back to about 3000 B.C. The Egyptians used symbols for the powers of 10: 10^0 or 1, 10^1 or 10, 10^2 or $10 \cdot 10$, 10^3 or $10 \cdot 10 \cdot 10$, and so on. Table 4.1 on page 168 lists the Egyptian hieroglyphic numerals with the equivalent Hindu–Arabic numerals.

To write the number 600 in Egyptian hieroglyphics, we write the numeral for 100 six times: ୨୨୨୨୨୨ .

TABLE 4.1 Egyptian Hieroglyphics

Hindu–Arabic Numerals	Egyptian Numerals	Description
1	I	Staff (vertical stroke)
10	∩	Heel bone (arch)
100	९	Scroll (coiled rope)
1,000	ℓ	Lotus flower
10,000	∫	Pointing finger
100,000	⬿	Tadpole (or whale)
1,000,000	⚡	Astonished person

EXAMPLE 1   *From Egyptian to Hindu–Arabic Numerals*

Write the following numeral as a Hindu–Arabic numeral.

$$\text{llꝯ९९९९ll}$$

SOLUTION:

$$10{,}000 + 10{,}000 + 100 + 100 + 100 + 100 + 1 + 1 = 20{,}402 \qquad \blacktriangle$$

EXAMPLE 2   *From Hindu–Arabic to Egyptian Numerals*

Write 43,628 as an Egyptian numeral.

SOLUTION:

$$43{,}628 = 40{,}000 + 3000 + 600 + 20 + 8$$

$$\text{))))ℓℓℓ९९९९९९∩∩llllllll} \qquad \blacktriangle$$

In this system, the order of the symbols is not important. For example, $\overset{\displaystyle\mathsf{⬿\ ll}}{\mathsf{९९\ ∩}}$ and ll९९⬿∩ both represent 100,212.

Users of additive systems easily accomplished addition and subtraction by combining or removing symbols. Multiplication and division were more difficult; they were performed by a process called *duplation and mediation* (see Section 4.5). The Egyptians had no symbol for zero, but they did have an understanding of fractions. The symbol ⌣ was used to take the reciprocal of a number; thus, ꝶ meant $\frac{1}{3}$ and ꝶ was $\frac{1}{11}$. Writing large numbers in the Egyptian Hieroglyphics system takes longer than in other systems because so many symbols have to be listed. For example, 45 symbols are needed to represent the number 99,999.

The Roman numeration system, a second example of an additive system, was developed later than the Egyptian system. Roman numerals (Table 4.2) were used in most European countries until the eighteenth century. They are still commonly seen on buildings, on clocks, and in books. Roman numerals are selected letters of the Roman alphabet.

TABLE 4.2 Roman Numerals

Roman numerals	I	V	X	L	C	D	M
Hindu–Arabic numerals	1	5	10	50	100	500	1000

Roman Numerals

R oman numerals remained popular on large clock faces long after their disappearance from daily transactions because they are easier to read from a distance than Hindu–Arabic numerals. The clock shown in this photo is in Vancouver, Canada.

The Roman system has two advantages over the Egyptian system. The first is that it uses the subtraction principle as well as the addition principle. Starting from the left, we add each numeral unless its value is smaller than the value of the numeral to its right. In that case, we subtract its value from the value of the numeral to its right. Only the numbers 1, 10, 100, 1000, ... can be subtracted, and they can only be subtracted from the next two higher numbers. For example, C (100) can be subtracted only from D (500) or M (1000). The symbol DC represents $500 + 100$, or 600, and CD represents $500 - 100$, or 400. Similarly, MC represents $1000 + 100$, or 1100, and CM represents $1000 - 100$, or 900.

EXAMPLE 3   *A Roman Numeral*

Write MMCCCLXII as a Hindu–Arabic numeral.

SOLUTION: Since each numeral is larger than the one on its right, no subtraction is necessary.

$$\text{MMCCCLXII} = 1000 + 1000 + 100 + 100 + 100 + 50 + 10 + 1 + 1$$
$$= 2362$$

EXAMPLE 4   *A Roman Numeral Involving a Subtraction*

Write DCXLVI as a Hindu–Arabic numeral.

SOLUTION: Checking from left to right, we see that X (10) has a smaller value than L (50). Therefore, XL represents $50 - 10$, or 40.

$$\text{DCXLVI} = 500 + 100 + (50 - 10) + 5 + 1 = 646$$

EXAMPLE 5   *Writing a Roman Numeral*

Write 289 as a Roman numeral.

SOLUTION:

$$289 = 200 + 80 + 9 = 100 + 100 + 50 + 10 + 10 + 10 + 9$$

(Nine is treated as $10 - 1$.)

$$289 = \text{CCLXXXIX}$$

In the Roman numeration system, a symbol does not have to be repeated more than three consecutive times. For example, the number 646 would be written DCXLVI instead of DCXXXXVI.

The second advantage of the Roman numeration system over the Egyptian numeration system is that it makes use of the multiplication principle for numbers over 1000. A bar above a symbol or group of symbols indicates that the symbol or symbols are to be multiplied by 1000. Thus, $\overline{V} = 5 \times 1000 = 5000$, $\overline{X} = 10 \times 1000 = 10{,}000$, and $\overline{CD} = 400 \times 1000 = 400{,}000$. Other examples are, $\overline{VI} = 6 \times 1000 = 6000$, $\overline{XIX} = 19 \times 1000 = 19{,}000$, and $\overline{XCIV} = 94 \times 1000 = 94{,}000$. This greatly reduces the number of symbols needed to write large numbers. Still, it requires 19 symbols, including the bar, to write the number 33,888 in Roman numerals. Write the number 33,888 in Roman numerals now.

Multiplicative Systems

Multiplicative numeration systems are more similar to our Hindu–Arabic system than are additive systems. The number 642 in a multiplicative system might be written (6) (100) (4) (10) (2) or

$$
\begin{array}{c}
6 \\
100 \\
4 \\
10 \\
2
\end{array}
$$

Note that no addition signs are needed to represent the number. From this illustration, try to formulate a rule explaining how multiplicative systems work.

The principle example of a multiplicative system is the traditional Chinese system. The numerals used in this system are given in Table 4.3.

TABLE 4.3 Traditional Chinese Numerals

Traditional Chinese numerals	零	一	二	三	四	五	六	七	八	九	十	百	千
Hindu–Arabic numerals	0	1	2	3	4	5	6	7	8	9	10	100	1000

Chinese numerals are always written vertically. The number on top will be a number from 1 to 9 inclusive. This number is to be multiplied by the power of 10 below it. The number 20 is written

$$
\left.\begin{array}{c} 二 \\ 十 \end{array}\right\} 2 \times 10 = 20
$$

The number 400 is written

$$
\left.\begin{array}{c} 四 \\ 百 \end{array}\right\} 4 \times 100 = 400
$$

EXAMPLE 6 *A Traditional Chinese Numeral*

Write 538 as a Chinese numeral.

SOLUTION:

$$
538 = \begin{cases} 500 = & \begin{cases} 5 & 五 \\ 100 & 百 \end{cases} \\ 30 = & \begin{cases} 3 & 三 \\ 10 & 十 \end{cases} \\ 8 = & \quad 8 \quad 八 \end{cases}
$$

Note that in Example 6 the units digit, the 8, is not multiplied by a power of the base.

When writing Chinese numerals, there are some special cases that need to be considered. When writing a number between 11 and 19 it is not necessary to include the 1 before the 10. Thus, the number 18 would be written 十八 rather than 一十八. Another special case involves the use of zero.

When more than one consecutive zero occurs (except at the end of a number) you need to write a zero, but only once for two or more consecutive zeros. Zeros are not included at the end of numbers. The top two illustrations that follow show how zeros are used within a number and the bottom two show that zeros are not used at the end of a number.

$$406 = \begin{array}{l} 四 \\ 百 \end{array}\Big\}\; 4 \times 100 = 400$$
$$零\} \;0 \times 10 = 0$$
$$六\} \;6 \qquad\quad = 6$$

$$4006 = \begin{array}{l} 四 \\ 千 \end{array}\Big\}\; 4 \times 1000 = 4000$$
$$零\}\begin{array}{l}0 \times 100, \\ 0 \times 10\end{array} = 0$$
$$六\} \;6 \qquad\quad = 6$$

$$460 = \begin{array}{l} 四 \\ 百 \end{array}\Big\}\; 4 \times 100 = 400$$
$$\begin{array}{l} 六 \\ 十 \end{array}\Big\}\; 6 \times 10 = 60$$

$$4600 = \begin{array}{l} 四 \\ 千 \end{array}\Big\}\; 4 \times 1000 = 4000$$
$$\begin{array}{l} 六 \\ 百 \end{array}\Big\}\; 6 \times 100 = 600$$

EXAMPLE 7   *Traditional Chinese Numerals*

Write the following as traditional Chinese numerals.
a) 7080   **b)** 7008

SOLUTION: In part (a) there is one zero between the 7 and the 8. In part (b) there are two zeros between the 7 and the 8. As just mentioned, the symbol for zero is used only once in each of those numbers.

a)
$$7080 = \begin{array}{l} 七 \\ 千 \end{array}\Big\}\; 7 \times 1000$$
$$零\}\; 0 \times 100$$
$$\begin{array}{l} 八 \\ 十 \end{array}\Big\}\; 8 \times 10$$

b)
$$7008 = \begin{array}{l} 七 \\ 千 \end{array}\Big\}\; 7 \times 1000$$
$$零\}\begin{array}{l}0 \times 100, \\ 0 \times 10\end{array}$$
$$八\}\; 8$$

▲

TIMELY TIP   Notice the difference between our Hindu–Arabic numeration system, which is a positional numeration system, and the Chinese system, which is a multiplicative numeration system. Consider the number 5678. Below we show how that number would be written in Chinese numerals if the Chinese system was a positional value system similar to ours.

Multiplicative		**Positional Value**	
五	5	五	5
千	1000	六	6
六	6	七	7
百	100	八	8
七	7		
十	10		
八	8		

Note that the multiples of base 10 are removed when writing the number as a positional value number. We will discuss positional value systems in more detail shortly.

Ciphered Systems

A ciphered numeration system is one in which there are numerals for numbers up to and including the base and for multiples of the base. The numbers represented by a particular set of numerals is the sum of the values of the numerals.

Ciphered numeration systems require the memorization of many different symbols but have the advantage that numbers can be written in a compact form. The ciphered numeration system that we discuss is the Ionic Greek system (see Table 4.4). The Ionic Greek system was developed in about 3000 B.C., and it used letters of their alphabet for numerals. Other ciphered systems include the Hebrew, Coptic, Hindu, Brahmin, Syrian, Egyptian Hieratic, and early Arabic systems.

TABLE 4.4   Ionic Greek Numerals

1	α	alpha	60	ξ	xi
2	β	beta	70	o	omicron
3	γ	gamma	80	π	pi
4	δ	delta	90	Q	koph[*]
5	ϵ	epsilon	100	ρ	rho
6	ζ	vau[*]	200	σ	sigma
7	ζ	zeta	300	τ	tau
8	η	eta	400	υ	upsilon
9	θ	theta	500	ϕ	phi
10	ι	iota	600	χ	chi
20	κ	kappa	700	ψ	psi
30	λ	lambda	800	ω	omega
40	μ	mu	900	π	sampi[*]
50	ν	nu			

[*]Taken from the Phoenician alphabet.

Since the Greek alphabet contains 24 letters but 27 symbols were needed, the Greeks borrowed the symbols ζ, Q, and π from the Phoenician alphabet.

The number 24 = 20 + 4. When 24 is written as a Greek numeral, the plus sign is omitted:

$$24 = \kappa\delta$$

The number 996 written as a Greek numeral is π Q ζ .

When a prime (′) is placed above a number, it multiplies that number by 1000. For example,

$$\beta' = 2 \times 1000 = 2000$$
$$\sigma' = 200 \times 1000 = 200,000$$

EXAMPLE 8   *The Ionic Greek System: A Ciphered System*

Write $\phi \, \nu \, \gamma$ as a Hindu–Arabic numeral.

SOLUTION: $\phi = 500$, $\nu = 50$, and $\gamma = 3$. Adding these numbers gives 553. ▲

EXAMPLE 9 *Writing an Ionic Greek Numeral*

Write 9432 as an Ionic Greek numeral.

SOLUTION:

$$9432 = 9000 + 400 + 30 + 2$$
$$= (9 \times 1000) + 400 + 30 + 2$$
$$= \theta' \qquad\qquad \upsilon \qquad \lambda \qquad \beta$$
$$= \theta' \upsilon \lambda \beta$$

SECTION 4.1 EXERCISES

Concept/Writing Exercises

1. What is the difference between a number and a numeral?
2. List four numerals given in this section that may be used to represent the number ten.
3. What is a system of numeration?
4. List four numerals given in this section that may be used to represent the number one hundred.
5. What is the name of the system of numeration that we presently use?
6. Explain how numbers are represented in an additive numeration system.
7. Explain how numbers are represented in a multiplicative numeration system.
8. Explain how numbers are represented in a ciphered numeration system.

Practice the Skills

In Exercises 9–14, write the numeral as a Hindu–Arabic numeral.

9. ꓴꓴꓴII

10. ꝿꝿꓴII

11. ꭍꭍꝿꝿꝿꝿꝿꓴꓴIII

12. ꟿꟿꟿꭍꝿꝿꓴ

13. ⋈⋈ꟿꟿꟿꭍꭍꭍꭍꝿꝿꓴIIIII

14. ✶✶✶✶⋈ꝿꝿꝿꝿꓴꓴꓴI

In Exercises 15–20, write the numeral as an Egyptian numeral.

15. 634
16. 752
17. 2045
18. 1812
19. 173,845
20. 3,235,614

In Exercises 21–32, write the numeral as a Hindu–Arabic numeral.

21. XIX
22. XVI
23. DXLVII
24. DLXXV
25. MCDXCII
26. MCMXVIII
27. MMCMXLVI
28. MDCCXLVI
29. $\overline{\text{X}}$MMDCLXVI
30. $\overline{\text{L}}$MCMXLIV
31. $\overline{\text{IX}}$CDLXIV
32. $\overline{\text{V}}$MCCCXXXIII

In Exercises 33–44, write the numeral as a Roman numeral.

33. 59
34. 94
35. 134
36. 269
37. 2005
38. 4285
39. 4793
40. 6274
41. 9999
42. 14,315
43. 20,644
44. 99,999

In Exercises 45–52, write the numeral as a Hindu–Arabic numeral.

45. 七十四

46. 六十二

47. 四千零八十一

48. 三千零二十九

49. 八千五百五十

50. 三千四百八十七

51. 四千零三

52. 五千六百零二

In Exercises 53–60, write the numeral as a traditional Chinese numeral.

53. 53

54. 178

55. 378

56. 2001

57. 4260

58. 6905

59. 7056

60. 3009

In Exercises 61–66, write the numeral as a Hindu–Arabic numeral.

61. $\tau \, \mu \, \alpha$

62. $\psi \, \lambda \, \zeta$

63. $\kappa' \beta' \phi \epsilon$

64. $\rho' \nu' \omega \, \iota \, \gamma$

65. $\theta' \chi \, \zeta$

66. $\delta' \, \mathbb{T} \, Q \, \theta$

In Exercises 67–72, write the numeral as an Ionic Greek numeral.

67. 59

68. 178

69. 726

70. 2001

71. 82,704

72. 690,540

In Exercises 73–75, compare the advantages and disadvantages of a ciphered system of numeration with those of the named system.

73. An additive system

74. A multiplicative system

75. The Hindu–Arabic system

In Exercises 76–79, write the numeral as numerals in the indicated systems of numeration.

76. $\zeta \cap \cap |$ in Hindu–Arabic, Roman, traditional Chinese, and Greek

77. MCMXXXVI in Hindu–Arabic, Egyptian, Greek, and traditional Chinese

78. 五百二十七 in Hindu–Arabic, Egyptian, Roman, and Greek

79. $\nu \kappa \beta$ in Hindu–Arabic, Egyptian, Roman, and traditional Chinese

Challenge Problems/Group Activities

80. Write the Roman numeral for 999,999.

81. Write the Ionic Greek numeral for 999,999.

82. Make up your own additive system of numeration and indicate the symbols and rules used to represent numbers. Using your system of numeration, write
    a) your age.
    b) the year you were born.
    c) the current year.

Recreational Mathematics

83. Without using any type of writing instrument, what can you do to make the following incorrect statement a correct statement?

$$XI + I = X$$

84. Words and numbers that read the same both backward and forward are called *palindromes*. Some examples are the words CIVIC and RACECAR, and the numbers 121 and 32523. Using Roman numerals, list the last year that was a palindrome.

85. Which year in the past 2000 years required the most Roman numerals to write? Write out the year in Roman numerals.

Internet/Research Activity

86. In this section we discussed Egyptian hieroglyphics, Ionic Greek numerals, and other numeration systems. Select either Egypt or Greece.
    a) Give the current numerals used in that country.
    b) Explain how their current system of numeration works.

    If more than one numeration system is used in the country you selected, discuss the system most commonly used.

4.2   PLACE-VALUE OR POSITIONAL-VALUE NUMERATION SYSTEMS

Eighteenth-century mathematician Pierre Simon, Marquis de Laplace, speaking of the positional principle, said: "The idea is so simple that this very simplicity is the reason for our not being sufficiently aware of how much attention it deserves."

Today the most common type of numeration system is the place-value system. The Hindu–Arabic numeration system, used in the United States and many other countries, is an example of a place-value system. In a *place-value system*, which is also called a *positional value system*, the value of the symbol depends on its position in the representation of the number. For example, the 2 in 20 represents 2 tens, and the 2 in 200 represents 2 hundreds. A true positional-value system requires a *base* and a set of symbols, including a symbol for zero and one for each counting number less than the base. Although any number can be written in any base, the most common positional system is the base 10 system which is called the *decimal number system*.

The Hindus in India are credited with the invention of zero and the other symbols used in our system. The Arabs, who traded regularly with the Hindus, also adopted the system, thus the name Hindu–Arabic. Not until the middle of the fifteenth century, however, did the Hindu–Arabic numerals take the form we know today.

The Hindu–Arabic numerals and the positional system of numeration revolutionized mathematics by making addition, subtraction, multiplication, and division much easier to learn and very practical to use. Merchants and traders no longer had to depend on the counting board or abacus. The first group of mathematicians, who computed with the Hindu–Arabic system rather than with pebbles or beads on a wire, were known as the "algorists."

In the Hindu–Arabic system, the symbols 0, 1, 2, 3, 4, 5, 6, 7, 8, and 9 are called *digits*. The base 10 system was developed from counting on fingers, and the word *digit* comes from the Latin word for fingers.

The positional values in the Hindu–Arabic system are

$$\ldots, (10)^5, (10)^4, (10)^3, (10)^2, 10, 1$$

To evaluate a number in the Hindu–Arabic system, we multiply the first digit on the right by 1. We multiply the second digit from the right by the base, 10. We multiply the third digit from the right by the base squared, 10^2 or 100. We multiply the fourth digit from the right by the base cubed, 10^3 or 1000, and so on. In general, we multiply the digit n places from the right by 10^{n-1}. Therefore, we multiply the digit eight places from the right by 10^7. Using the place-value rule, we can write a number in *expanded form*. The number 1234 written in expanded form is

$$1234 = (1 \times 10^3) + (2 \times 10^2) + (3 \times 10) + (4 \times 1)$$

or

$$(1 \times 1000) + (2 \times 100) + (3 \times 10) + 4$$

The oldest known numeration system that resembled a place-value system was developed by the Babylonians in about 2500 B.C. Their system resembled a place-value system with a base of 60, a sexagesimal system. It was not a true place-value system because it lacked a symbol for zero. The lack of a symbol for zero led to a great deal of ambiguity and confusion. Table 4.5 gives the Babylonian numerals.

The positional values in the Babylonian system are

$$\ldots, (60)^3, (60)^2, 60, 1$$

TABLE 4.5   Babylonian Numerals

Babylonian Numerals	$\mathbf{I}$	$\blacktriangleleft$
Hindu–Arabic numerals	1	10

One of the earliest counting devices, used in most ancient civilizations, was the counting board. On such a board, each column represents a positional value. The number of times a value occurs is represented by markers (beads, stones, sticks) in the column. An empty column signifies "no value." The widespread use of counting boards meant that Europeans were already long accustomed to working with positional values when they were introduced to Hindu–Arabic numerals in the fifteenth century. Some people in China, Japan, Russia, Eastern Europe, and the United States still commonly use a type of counting board known as the abacus to perform routine computations.

In a Babylonian numeral, a gap is left between the characters to distinguish between the various place values. From right to left, the sum of the first group of numerals is multiplied by 1. The sum of the second group is multiplied by 60. The sum of the third group is multiplied by $(60)^2$, and so on.

EXAMPLE 1   The Babylonian System: A Positional Value System

Write ⟪   ⟪⟨𝖳𝖳𝖳𝖳 as a Hindu–Arabic numeral.

SOLUTION:

$$\underbrace{≪}_{60\text{'s}} \qquad \underbrace{≪⟨𝖳𝖳𝖳𝖳}_{\text{units}}$$

$$\underbrace{10 + 10}_{60\text{'s}} \quad \underbrace{10 + 10 + 1 + 1 + 1 + 1}_{\text{units}}$$

$$(20 \times 60) + (24 \times 1)$$
$$1200 + 24 = 1224$$

The Babylonians used the symbol $\overset{\frown}{𝖳}$ to indicate subtraction. The numeral ⟨$\overset{\frown}{𝖳}$𝖳𝖳 represents $10 - 2$, or 8. The numeral ⟪⟪ $\overset{\frown}{𝖳}$𝖳𝖳𝖳 represents $40 - 3$, or 37 in base 10 or decimal notation.

EXAMPLE 2   From Babylonian to Hindu–Arabic Numerals

Write 𝖳𝖳   ⟨𝖳   ⟪$\overset{\frown}{𝖳}$𝖳𝖳 as a Hindu–Arabic numeral.

SOLUTION: The place value of these three groups of numerals from left to right is

$$(60)^2, \quad 60, \quad 1$$
or
$$3600, \quad 60, \quad 1$$

The numeral in the group on the right has a value of $20 - 2$, or 18. The numeral in the center group has a value of $10 + 1$, or 11. The numeral on the left represents $1 + 1$, or 2. Multiplying each group by its positional value gives

$$(2 \times 60^2) + (11 \times 60) + (18 \times 1)$$
$$= (2 \times 3600) + (11 \times 60) + (18 \times 1)$$
$$= 7200 + 660 + 18$$
$$= 7878$$

To explain the procedure used to convert from a Hindu–Arabic numeral to a Babylonian numeral, we will consider a length of time. How can we change 9820 seconds into hours, minutes, and seconds? Since there are 3600 seconds in an hour

(60 seconds to a minute and 60 minutes to an hour), we can find the number of hours in 9820 seconds by dividing 9820 by 60^2, or 3600.

$$
\begin{array}{r}
2 \\
3600\overline{)9820} \\
7200 \\
\hline
2620
\end{array}
$$

← Hours

← Remaining seconds

Now we can determine the number of minutes by dividing the remaining seconds by 60, the number of seconds in a minute.

$$
\begin{array}{r}
43 \\
60\overline{)2620} \\
2400 \\
\hline
220 \\
180 \\
\hline
40
\end{array}
$$

← Minutes

← Remaining seconds

Since the remaining number of seconds, 40, is less than the number of seconds in a minute, our task is complete.

$$9820 \text{ sec} = 2 \text{ hr, } 43 \text{ min, and } 40 \text{ sec}$$

The same procedure is used to convert a decimal (base 10) number to a Babylonian number or any number in a different base.

EXAMPLE 3   *From Hindu–Arabic to Babylonian Numerals*

Write 2519 as a Babylonian numeral.

SOLUTION: The Babylonian numeration system has positional values of

$$\ldots, 60^3, 60^2, 60, 1$$

which can be expressed as

$$\ldots, 216000, 3600, 60, 1$$

The largest positional value less than or equal to 2519 is 60. To determine how many groups of 60 are in 2519, divide 2519 by 60.

$$
\begin{array}{r}
41 \\
60\overline{)2519} \\
240 \\
\hline
119 \\
60 \\
\hline
59
\end{array}
$$

← Groups of 60

← Units remaining

Thus, $2519 \div 60 = 41$ with remainder 59. There are 41 groups of 60 and 59 units remaining. Because the remainder, 59, is less than the base, 60, no further division is necessary. The remainder represents the number of units when the number is

Sacred Mayan Glyphs

3

4

In addition to their base 20 numerals the Mayans had a holy numeration system used by priests to create and maintain calendars. They used a special set of hieroglyphs that consisted of pictograms of Mayan gods. For example, the number 3 was represented by the god of wind and rain, the number 4 by the god of sun.

written in expanded form. Therefore, $2519 = (41 \times 60) + (59 \times 1)$. When written as a Babylonian numeral, 2519 is

$$\text{《《《《। 《《《《《《॑।१}$$

EXAMPLE 4   *Using Division to Determine a Babylonian Numeral*

Write 6270 as a Babylonian numeral.

SOLUTION: Divide 6270 by the largest positional value less than or equal to 6270. That value is 3600.

$$6270 \div 3600 = 1 \text{ with remainder } 2670$$

There is one group of 3600 in 6270. Next divide the remainder 2670 by 60 to determine the number of groups of 60 in 2670.

$$2670 \div 60 = 44 \text{ with remainder } 30$$

There are 44 groups of 60 and 30 units remaining.

$$6270 = (1 \times 60^2) + (44 \times 60) + (30 \times 1)$$

Thus, 6270 written as a Babylonian numeral is

$$\text{१ 《《《《।।।। 《《《}$$

Another place-value system is the Mayan numeration system. The Mayans, who lived on the Yucatan Peninsula in present day Mexico, developed a sophisticated numeration system based on their religious and agricultural calendar. The numbers in this system are written vertically rather than horizontally, with the units position on the bottom. In the Mayan system, the number in the bottom row is to be multiplied by 1. The number in the second row from the bottom is to be multiplied by 20. The number in the third row is to be multiplied by 18×20, or 360. You probably expected the number in the third row to be multiplied by 20^2 rather than 18×20. It is believed that the Mayans used 18×20 so that their numeration system would conform to their calendar of 360 days. The positional values above 18×20 are 18×20^2, 18×20^3, and so on.

Positional values in the Mayan system

$\dots 18 \times (20)^3,$	$18 \times (20)^2,$	$18 \times 20,$	20,	1
or $\dots 144{,}000,$	7200,	360,	20,	1

The digits $0, 1, 2, 3, \dots, 19$ of the Mayan systems are formed by a simple grouping of dots and lines, as shown in Table 4.6.

TABLE 4.6   Mayan Numerals

0	1	2	3	4	5	6	7	8	9
⊙	•	••	•••	••••	—	˙—	˙˙—	˙˙˙—	˙˙˙˙—

10	11	12	13	14	15	16	17	18	19
=	˙=	˙˙=	˙˙˙=	˙˙˙˙=	≡	˙≡	˙˙≡	˙˙˙≡	˙˙˙˙≡

	0	1	2	3	4	5	6	7	8	9
LATIN		I	II	III	IV	V	VI	VII	VIII	IX
GREEK		A	B	Γ	Δ	E	F	Z	H	Θ
GEORGIAN		პ	ბ	გ	ი	ე	ვ	ზ	ჱ	თ
ARMENIAN		Ա	Բ	Գ	Դ	Ե	Զ	Է	Ը	Թ
HEBREW		א	ב	ג	ד	ה	ו	ז	ח	ט
ARABIC	·	١	٢	٣	٤	٥	٦	٧	٨	٩
URDU	·	١	٢	٣	٤	٥	٦	٧	٨	٩
MALDIVIAN	·	١	٢	٣	٤	٥	٦	٧	٨	٩
DEVANAGARI	٥	१	२	३	४	५	६	७	८	९
GURMUKHI	٥	੧	੨	੩	੪	੫	੬	੭	੮	੯
GUJARATI	٥	૧	૨	૩	૪	૫	૬	૭	૮	૯
ORIYA	୦	୧	୨	୩	୪	୫	୬	୭	୮	୯
BENGALI	০	১	২	৩	৪	৫	৬	৭	৮	৯
TAMIL		௧	௨	௩	௪	௫	௬	௭	௮	௯
TELUGU	౦	౧	౨	౩	౪	౫	౬	౭	౮	౯
KANNADA	೦	೧	೨	೩	೪	೫	೬	೭	೮	೯
MALAYALAM	൦	൧	൨	൩	൪	൫	൬	൭	൮	൯
SINHALESE										
BURMESE	၀	၁	၂	၃	၄	၅	၆	၇	၈	၉
KHMER	០	១	២	៣	៤	៥	៦	៧	៨	៩
THAI	๐	๑	๒	๓	๔	๕	๖	๗	๘	๙
LAO	໐	໑	໒	໓	໔	໕	໖	໗	໘	໙
CHINESE		一	二	三	四	五	六	七	八	九
TIBETAN	༠	༡	༢	༣	༤	༥	༦	༧	༨	༩
MONGOLIAN	᠐	᠑	᠒	᠓	᠔	᠕	᠖	᠗	᠘	᠙
AMHARIC		፩	፪	፫	፬	፭	፮	፯	፰	፱

Although most countries presently use a place value (or positional value) numeration system with base 10, the numerals used for the digits differ by country. The photo of the artwork entitled *Numbers* by Jan Fleck shows numerals currently used in many countries of the world. For example, in Burmese, the numeral ၃ has a value of 3.

EXAMPLE 5   *The Mayan System: A Positional Value System*

Write •• as a Hindu–Arabic numeral.

SOLUTION: In the Mayan numeration system, the first three positional values are

$$18 \times 20$$
$$20$$
$$1$$

$$•••• \ = \ 9 \times (18 \times 20) = 3240$$
$$•• \ = \ 2 \times 20 \quad\quad = \quad 40$$
$$••• \ = 13 \times 1 \quad\quad = \quad \underline{13}$$
$$3293$$

EXAMPLE 6   *From Mayan to Hindu–Arabic Numerals*

Write as a Hindu–Arabic numeral.

SOLUTION:

$$••• \ = \ 8 \times (18 \times 20) = 2880$$
$$\overset{•}{=} \ = 11 \times 20 \quad\quad = \quad 220$$
$$•••• \ = \ 4 \times 1 \quad\quad = \quad \underline{4}$$
$$3104$$

EXAMPLE 7   *From Hindu–Arabic to Mayan Numerals*

Write 4025 as a Mayan numeral.

SOLUTION: To convert from a Hindu–Arabic to a Mayan numeral, we use a procedure similar to the one used to convert to a Babylonian numeral. The Mayan positional values are . . . , 7200, 360, 20, 1. The greatest positional value less than or equal to 4025 is 360. Divide 4025 by 360.

$$4025 \div 360 = 11 \text{ with remainder } 65$$

There are 11 groups of 360 in 4025. Next, divide the remainder, 65, by 20.

$$65 \div 20 = 3 \text{ with remainder } 5$$

There are 3 groups of 20 with five units remaining.

$$4025 = (11 \times 360) + (3 \times 20) + (5 \times 1)$$

4025 written as a Mayan numeral is

$$\left. \begin{array}{c} 11 \times 360 \\ 3 \times 20 \\ 5 \times 1 \end{array} \right\} =$$

> **TIMELY TIP** Notice that changing a number from the Babylonian or Mayan numeration System *to the Hindu–Arabic* (or decimal or base 10) system involves *multiplication*. Changing a number *from the Hindu–Arabic system* to the Babylonian or Mayan numeration system involves *division*.

SECTION 4.2   EXERCISES

Concept/Writing Exercises

1. What is the most common type of numeration system used in the world today?

2. What is another name for a place-value system?

3. Consider the numbers 40 and 400 in the Hindu–Arabic numeration system. What does the 4 represent in each number?

4. What is the most common base used for a positional value system? Explain why you believe the base you named is the most common base.

5. In a true positional-value system, what symbols are required?

6. **a)** What is the base in the Hindu–Arabic numeration system?
   b) What are the digits in the Hindu–Arabic numeration system?

7. Explain how to write a number in expanded form in a positional-value numeration system.

8. Why was the Babylonian system not a true place-value system?

9. **a)** The Babylonian system did not have a symbol for zero. Why did this lead to some confusion?
   b) Write the numbers 133 and 7980 as Babylonian numerals.

10. Consider the Babylonian number represented by ❬❙. Give two numbers in Hindu–Arabic numerals this number may represent. Explain your answer.

11. List the first five positional values, starting with the units position, for the Mayan numeration system.

12. Describe two ways that the Mayan place-value system differs from the Hindu–Arabic place-value system.

Practice the Skills

In Exercises 13–24, write the Hindu–Arabic numeral in expanded form.

13. 63
14. 75
15. 359
16. 562
17. 897
18. 3769

19. 4387
20. 23,468
21. 16,402
22. 125,678
23. 346,861
24. 3,765,934

In Exercises 25–30, write the Babylonian numeral as a Hindu–Arabic numeral.

25. ❬❬❬❬❬❙❙

26. ❬❬❬❬❙❙❙❙❙

27. ❬❙❙❙ ❙❙❙❙

28. ❬❙ ❬❬❙❙❙❙

29. ❙ ❬❬❬❙ ❬❙❙❙

30. ❬ ❬❬❙❙❙❙ ❙❙

In Exercises 31–36, write the numeral as a Babylonian numeral.

31. 88
32. 97
33. 295
34. 512
35. 3685
36. 3030

In Exercises 37–42, write the Mayan numeral as a Hindu–Arabic numeral.

37. ••••
    ≡

38. ═
    ─

39. ••
    ⬭
    •

40. ••
    ••••
    ••

41. •
    ••
    ⬭

42. ••
    ≡
    ≡

In Exercises 43–48, write the numeral as a Mayan numeral.

43. 17
44. 257
45. 297
46. 406
47. 2163
48. 1978

49. *Comparisons of Systems* Compare the advantages and disadvantages of a place-value system with those of
   a) additive numeration systems.
   b) multiplicative numeration systems.
   c) ciphered numeration systems.

50. *Your Own System* Create your own place-value system. Write 2005 in your system.

In Exercises 51 and 52, write the numeral in the indicated systems of numeration.

51. ◄◄◄▮▮▮ in Hindu–Arabic and Mayan

52. ▬ in Hindu–Arabic and Babylonian
     ••
     ••••

In Exercises 53 and 54, suppose a place-value numeration system has base ◯, with digits represented by the symbols △, ◌, □, and ◌̇. Write each expression in expanded form.

53. △ □ ◌   54. ◌̇ △ ◌ □

Challenge Problems/Group Activities

55. **a)** Is there a largest number in the Babylonian numeration system? Explain.
    b) Write the Babylonian numeral for 999,999.

56. **a)** Is there a largest number in the Mayan numeration system? Explain.
    b) Write the Mayan numeral for 999,999.

In Exercises 57–60, first convert each numeral to a Hindu–Arabic numeral and then perform the indicated operation. Finally, convert the answer back to a numeral in the original numeration system.

57. ▮▮ ◄◄ ▮▮▮ + ◄◄▮▮▮   58. ▮▮▮ ◄◄◄▮▮▮ – ◄◄◄▮▮

59. ••   •   60. ••   •
     ⎯   ••   ⎯   ••
     •   ⎯   •   ⎯
     ⎯   •••   ⎯   •••
      +   –

Recreational Mathematics

61. Hidden in the box are the names of the four different types of systems of numeration we discussed in this chapter: ADDITIVE, MULTIPLICATIVE, CIPHERED, and PLACE-VALUE (without the hyphen). You find them by going box by box, but the boxes you move between must touch vertically, horizontally, or diagonally. You can use the same box more than once when spelling out a word. Find the names of the numeration systems. Make sure you understand how each system of numeration works.

M	L	P	R	E
A	I	A	D	H
V	C	T	D	P
E	A	L	I	C
A	M	U	E	V

Internet/Research Activities

62. Investigate and write a report on the development of the Hindu–Arabic system of numeration. Start with the earliest records of this system in India.

63. The Arabic numeration system currently in use is a base 10 positional-value system, which uses different symbols than the Hindu–Arabic numeration system. Write the symbols used in the Arabic system of numeration and their equivalent symbols in the Hindu–Arabic numeration system. Write 54, 607, and 2000 in Arabic numerals.

4.3 OTHER BASES

The positional values in the Hindu–Arabic numeration system are

$$\ldots, (10)^4, (10)^3, (10)^2, 10, 1$$

The positional values in the Babylonian numeration system are

$$\ldots, (60)^4, (60)^3, (60)^2, 60, 1$$

The numbers 10 and 60 are called the *bases* of the Hindu–Arabic and Babylonian systems, respectively.

DID YOU KNOW

Beyond Their Fingers

The Kewa people of Papua, New Guinea, have gone well beyond counting on their fingers: They use the entire upper body. Going from the little finger of one hand, down the elbow, to shoulder to head to shoulder, down the other elbow, to the little finger of the opposite hand provides them with a count of 68.

Any counting number greater than 1 may be used as a base for a positional-value numeration system. If a positional-value system has a base b, then its positional values will be

$$\ldots, b^4, b^3, b^2, b, 1$$

The positional values in a base 8 system are

$$\ldots, 8^4, 8^3, 8^2, 8, 1$$

and the positional values in a base 2 system are

$$\ldots, 2^4, 2^3, 2^2, 2, 1$$

As we indicated earlier, the Mayan numeration system is based on the number 20. It is not, however, a true base 20 positional-value system. Why not?

The reason for the almost universal acceptance of base 10 numeration systems is that most human beings have 10 fingers. Even so, there are still some positional-value numeration systems that use bases other than 10. Some societies are still using a base 2 numeration system. They include some groups of people in Australia, New Guinea, Africa, and South America. Bases 3 and 4 are also used in some areas of South America. Base 5 systems were used by some primitive tribes in Bolivia, but the tribes are now extinct. The pure base 6 system occurs only sparsely in Northwest Africa. Base 6 also occurs in other systems in combination with base 12, the *duodecimal system*.

We continue to see remains of other base systems in many countries. For example, there are 12 inches in a foot, 12 months in a year. Base 12 is also evident in the dozen, the 24-hour day, and the gross (12×12). English uses the word *score* to mean 20, as in "Four score and seven years ago." Remains of base 60 are found in measurements of time (60 seconds to a minute, 60 minutes to an hour) and angles (60 seconds to one minute, 60 minutes to one degree).

The base 2, or *binary system*, has become very important because it is the internal language of the computer. For example, when a grocery store's cash register computer records the price of your groceries by using a scanning device, the bar codes it scans on the packages are in binary form. Computers use a two-digit "alphabet" that consists of the numerals 0 and 1. Every character on a standard keyboard can be represented by a combination of those two numerals. A single numeral such as 0 or 1 is called a *bit*. Other bases that computers make use of are base 8 and base 16. A group of eight bits is called a *byte*. In the American Standard Code for Information Interchange (ASCII) code, used in most computers, the byte 01000001 represents the character A, 01100001 represents the character a, 00110000 represents the character 0, and 00110001 represents the character 1.

A place-value system with base b must have b distinct symbols, one for zero and one for each number less than the base. A base 6 system must have symbols for the numbers 0, 1, 2, 3, 4, and 5. All numbers in base 6 are constructed from these 6 symbols. A base 8 system must have symbols for 0, 1, 2, 3, 4, 5, 6, and 7. All numbers in base 8 are constructed from these 8 symbols, and so on.

A number in a base other than base 10 will be indicated by a subscript to the right of the number. Thus, 123_5 represents a number in base 5. The number 123_6 represents a number in base 6. The value of 123_5 is not the same as the value of 123_{10}, and the value of 123_6 is not the same as the value 123_{10}. A base 10 number may be written without a subscript. For example 123 means 123_{10} and 456 means 456_{10}. For clarity in certain problems, we will use the subscript 10 to indicate a number in base 10.

Remember the symbols that represent the base itself, in any base b, are 10_b. For example, in base 5, the symbols 10_5 represent the number 5. Note that $10_5 = 1 \times 5 + 0 \times 1 = 5 + 0 = 5_{10}$, or the number 5 in base 10. The symbols 10_5 mean one group of 5 and no units. In base 6, the symbols 10_6 represent the number 6. The symbols 10_6 represent one group of 6 and no units, and so on.

To change a number in a base other than 10 to a base 10 number, we follow the same procedure we used in Section 4.2 to change the Babylonian and Mayan numbers to base 10 numbers. Multiply each digit in the number by its respective positional value. Then find the sum of the products.

EXAMPLE 1   *Converting from Base 6 to Base 10*

Convert 453_6 to base 10.

SOLUTION: In base 6, the positional values are ..., $6^3, 6^2, 6, 1$. In expanded form,

$$
\begin{aligned}
453_6 &= (4 \times 6^2) + (5 \times 6) + (3 \times 1) \\
&= (4 \times 36) + (5 \times 6) + (3 \times 1) \\
&= \quad 144 \quad + \quad 30 \quad + \quad 3 \\
&= 177
\end{aligned}
$$

In Example 1, the units digit in 453_6 is 3. Notice that 3_6 has the same value as 3_{10} since both are equal to 3 units. That is, $3_6 = 3_{10}$. If n is a digit less than the base b, and the base b is less than or equal to 10, then $n_b = n_{10}$.

EXAMPLE 2   *Converting from Base 8 to Base 10*

Convert 3615_8 to base 10.

SOLUTION:

$$
\begin{aligned}
3615_8 &= (3 \times 8^3) \ + (6 \times 8^2) + (1 \times 8) + (5 \times 1) \\
&= (3 \times 512) + (6 \times 64) + (1 \times 8) + (5 \times 1) \\
&= \quad 1536 \quad + \quad 384 \quad + \quad 8 \quad + \quad 5 \\
&= 1933
\end{aligned}
$$

A base 12 system must have 12 distinct symbols. In this text, we use the symbols 0, 1, 2, 3, 4, 5, 6, 7, 8, 9, T, and E, where T represents ten and E represents eleven. Why will the numerals 10_{12} and 11_{12} have different meanings than 10 and 11? The number 10_{12} represents 1 group of twelve plus 0 units, or twelve. The number 11_{12} represents 1 group of twelve plus 1 unit, or 13.

EXAMPLE 3   *Converting from Base 12 to Base 10*

Convert $12T6_{12}$ to base 10.

SOLUTION:

$$
\begin{aligned}
12T6_{12} &= (1 \times 12^3) \ + (2 \times 12^2) + (T \times 12) \ + (6 \times 1) \\
&= (1 \times 1728) + (2 \times 144) + (10 \times 12) + (6 \times 1) \\
&= \quad 1728 \quad + \quad 288 \quad + \quad 120 \quad + \quad 6 \\
&= 2142
\end{aligned}
$$

┌─ EXAMPLE 4   *Converting from Base 2*

Convert 101101_2 to base 10.

SOLUTION:

$$101101_2 = (1 \times 2^5) + (0 \times 2^4) + (1 \times 2^3) + (1 \times 2^2) + (0 \times 2) + (1 \times 1)$$
$$= \quad 32 \quad + \quad 0 \quad + \quad 8 \quad + \quad 4 \quad + \quad 0 \quad + \quad 1$$
$$= 45$$

▲

To change a number from a base 10 system to a different base, we will use a procedure similar to the one we used to convert base 10 numbers to Babylonian and Mayan numbers, as was explained in Section 4.2. Divide the base 10 number by the highest power of the new base that is less than or equal to the given number. Record this quotient. Then divide the remainder by the next smaller power of the new base and record this quotient. Repeat this procedure until the remainder is a number less than the new base. The answer is the set of quotients listed from left to right, with the remainder on the far right. This procedure is illustrated in Examples 5 through 7.

┌─ EXAMPLE 5   *Convert to Base 8*

Convert 486 to base 8.

SOLUTION: We are converting a number in base 10 to a number in base 8. The positional values in the base 8 system are . . . , 8^3, 8^2, 8, 1, or . . . , 512, 64, 8, 1. The highest power of 8 that is less than or equal to 486 is 8^2, or 64. Divide 486 by 64.

First digit in answer
↓
$$486 \div 64 = 7 \text{ with remainder } 38$$

Therefore, there are 7 groups of 8^2 in 486. Next divide the remainder, 38, by 8.

Second digit in answer
↓
$$38 \div 8 = 4 \text{ with remainder } 6$$
↑
Third digit in answer

There are 4 groups of 8 in 38 and 6 units remaining. Since the remainder, 6, is less than the base, 8, no further division is required.

$$= (7 \times 64) + (4 \times 8) + (6 \times 1)$$
$$= (7 \times 8^2) + (4 \times 8) + (6 \times 1)$$
$$= 746_8$$

Notice that we placed the subscript 8 to the right of 746 to show that it is a base 8 number.

▲

EXAMPLE 6   *Convert to Base 3*

Convert 273 to base 3.

SOLUTION: The place values in the base 3 system are ... , $3^6, 3^5, 3^4, 3^3, 3^2, 3, 1$, or ... , 729, 243, 81, 27, 9, 3, 1. The highest power of the base that is less than or equal to 273 is 3^5, or 243. Successive divisions by the powers of the base give the following result.

$$273 \div 243 = \boxed{1} \text{ with remainder } 30$$
$$30 \div 81 = \boxed{0} \text{ with remainder } 30$$
$$30 \div 27 = \boxed{1} \text{ with remainder } 3$$
$$3 \div 9 = \boxed{0} \text{ with remainder } 3$$
$$3 \div 3 = \boxed{1} \text{ with remainder } 0$$

The remainder, 0, is less than the base, 3, so no further division is necessary. To obtain the answer, list the quotients from top to bottom followed by the remainder in the last division.

The number 273 can be represented as one group of 243, no groups of 81, one group of 27, no groups of 9, one group of 3, and no units.

$$273 = (1 \times 243) + (0 \times 81) + (1 \times 27) + (0 \times 9) + (1 \times 3) + (0 \times 1)$$
$$= (1 \times 3^5) + (0 \times 3^4) + (1 \times 3^3) + (0 \times 3^2) + (1 \times 3) + (0 \times 1)$$
$$= 101010_3$$

EXAMPLE 7   *Convert to Base 12*

Convert 558 to base 12.

SOLUTION: The place values in base 12 are ... , $12^3, 12^2, 12, 1$, or ... , 1728, 144, 12, 1. The highest power of the base that is less than or equal to 558 is 12^2, or 144.

$$558 \div 144 = \boxed{3} \text{ with remainder } 126$$
$$126 \div 12 = \boxed{T} \text{ with remainder } 6$$

(Remember that T is used to represent 10 in base 12.)

$$558 = (3 \times 12^2) + (T \times 12) + (6 \times 1) = 3T6_{12}$$

TIMELY TIP It is important to remember the following items presented in this section.

- If a number is shown without a base, we assume the number is a base 10 number, and
- When converting a base 10 number to a different base, your answer should never contain a digit greater than or equal to that different base.

You should also remember that changing a number given in a base other than 10 to a number in base 10 involves multiplication. Changing a base 10 number to a number in a different base involves division.

MATHEMATICS
Everywhere

We use our place-value system daily without thinking of its complexity. The place-value system has come a long way from the first and oldest type of numeration system, the additive numeration system. The changes in numeration systems evolved slowly. Most countries now use a place-value system. For example, the numeration system used in China today is different from the traditional system discussed in this chapter. The present-day system in China is a positional-value system rather than a multiplicative system, and in some areas of China, 0 is used as the numeral for zero. Often when you travel to ethnic areas of cities or to foreign countries, numbers are indicated using both that country's numerals and Hindu–Arabic numerals, as shown in the photo.

It is likely that when new numeration systems are presented they appear abstract to the public. Abstract mathematics often becomes the basis for important discoveries and inventions in the future. That is the case with the binary numeration system. When the binary numeration system was first introduced, nobody could have dreamed that it would form the basis for our computers. Today, computers are found everywhere: in our cars, cameras, watches, calculators, sewing machines; at checkout counters; and in hundreds of other places. When a number or letter is entered into a computer it is converted internally into a binary number. The computations within a computer are made using binary arithmetic, and the binary answer is converted back to a decimal number for us to read. Computers also use octal (base 8) and hexadecimal (base 16) numeration systems.

Computers make use of three numeration systems: the *binary* (base 2), *octal* (base 8), and *hexadecimal* (base 16) numeration systems. Computers and calculators use the binary system to perform their internal computations. The binary number system contains only two digits, 0 and 1. All numbers we enter into a computer are converted internally into a series of 0's and 1's. When a computer performs a calculation it treats 0 as an "off" switch and 1 as an "on" switch. Using these electronic switches, the computer performs calculations using binary numbers, and then the internal result is converted back to a decimal number for us to view.

The octal system is used by computer programmers who work with internal computer codes. In a computer, the central processing unit (CPU) often uses the hexadecimal system to convey information to the printer and other output devices.

We have already given examples of converting numbers given in the binary system and the octal system to numbers in the decimal system, and vice versa. Now let's work an example using the hexadecimal system. Since a hexadecimal system contains 16 symbols, it is treated similarly to a base 12 system in that we need to use additional symbols for numerals. See Examples 3 and 7.

EXAMPLE 8   *Convert to and from Base 16*

In this example, let the numerals 0, 1, 2, 3, 4, 5, 6, 7, 8, 9, A, B, C, D, E, and F represent the numerals in a base 16 system where A through F represent ten through fifteen, respectively.

a) Convert $7DE_{16}$ to base 10.   **b)** Convert 6713 to base 16.

SOLUTION:

a) In a base 16 system the positional values are . . . , 16^3, 16^2, 16, 1 or . . . 4096, 256, 16, 1. Since D has a value of 13 and E has a value of 14, we perform the following calculation.

$$7DE_{16} = (7 \times 16^2) + (D \times 16) + (E \times 1)$$
$$= (7 \times 256) + (13 \times 16) + (14 \times 1)$$
$$= 1792 + 208 + 14$$
$$= 2014$$

b) The highest power of base 16 less than or equal to 6713 is 16^3, or 4096. If we obtain a quotient greater than nine but less than sixteen, we will use the corresponding letter A through F.

$$6713 \div 4096 = 1 \text{ with remainder } 2617$$
$$2617 \div 256 = A \text{ with remainder } 57 \qquad \text{Note that A has a value of ten}$$
$$57 \div 16 = 3 \text{ with remainder } 9$$

Thus, $6713 = 1A39_{16}$.

SECTION 4.3 EXERCISES

Concept/Writing Exercises

1. In your own words, explain how to change a number in a base other than base 10 to base 10.

2. In your own words, explain how to change a number in base 10 to a base other than base 10.

Practice the Skills

In Exercises 3–20, convert the numeral to a numeral in base 10.

3. 5_6	**4.** 60_7	**5.** 42_5
6. 101_2	**7.** 1011_2	**8.** 1101_2
9. 84_{12}	**10.** 21021_3	**11.** 565_8
12. 654_7	**13.** 20432_5	**14.** 101111_2
15. 4003_6	**16.** $123E_{12}$	**17.** 123_8
18. 2043_8	**19.** 14705_8	**20.** 67342_9

In Exercises 21–36, convert the base 10 numeral to a numeral in the base indicated.

21. 8 to base 2	**22.** 16 to base 2
23. 23 to base 2	**24.** 243 to base 6
25. 635 to base 6	**26.** 908 to base 4
27. 2061 to base 12	**28.** 200 to base 4
29. 529 to base 8	**30.** 81 to base 3
31. 2867 to base 12	**32.** 4312 to base 6
33. 1011 to base 2	**34.** 1589 to base 7
35. 2307 to base 8	**36.** 13,469 to base 8

In Exercises 37–40, assume that a base 16 positional-value system uses the numerals 0, 1, 2, 3, 4, 5, 6, 7, 8, 9, A, B, C, D, E, and F, where A through F represent ten through fifteen, respectively. Convert the numeral to a numeral in base 10. See Example 8.

37. 735_{16}	**38.** 581_{16}
39. $6D3B7_{16}$	**40.** $24FEA_{16}$

In Exercises 41–44, convert the numeral to a numeral in base 16. See Example 8.

41. 573	**42.** 349
43. 5478	**44.** 34,721

In Exercises 45–50, convert 2005 to a numeral in the base indicated.

45. 2	**46.** 3	**47.** 5
48. 7	**49.** 12	**50.** 16

In Exercises 51–56, if any numerals are written incorrectly, explain why.

51. 5013_5	**52.** 1203_3
53. 674_8	**54.** 1206_{12}
55. 4086_7	**56.** 3004_5

Problem Solving

In Exercises 57–60, assume the numerals given are in a base 5 numeration system. The numerals in this system and their equivalent Hindu–Arabic numerals are

$\bigcirc = 0$ $\ominus = 1$ $\ovee = 2$ $\oslash = 3$ $\oslash = 4$

Write the Hindu–Arabic numerals equivalent to each of the following.

57. $\ovee\,\ominus_5$ **58.** $\oslash\ominus_5$ **59.** $\oslash\oslash\ominus_5$ **60.** $\ominus\bigcirc\ominus_5$

In Exercises 61–64, write the Hindu–Arabic numerals in the numeration system discussed in Exercises 57–60.

61. 19	**62.** 23	**63.** 74	**64.** 85

In Exercises 65–68, suppose colors as indicated below represent numerals in a base 4 numeration system.

● = 0   ● = 1   ◉ = 2   ● = 3

Write the Hindu–Arabic numerals equivalent to each of the following.

65. ●●$_4$	**66.** ●●$_4$	**67.** ●●●$_4$	**68.** ●●●$_4$

In Exercises 69–72, write the Hindu–Arabic numerals in the base 4 numeration system discussed in Exercises 65–68. You will need to use the colors indicated above to write the answer.

69. 10	**70.** 15	**71.** 60	**72.** 56

73. *Another Conversion Method* There is an alternative method for changing a number in base 10 to a different base. This method will be used to convert 328 to base 5.

Dividing 328 by 5 gives a quotient of 65 and a remainder of 3. Write the quotient below the dividend and the remainder on the right, as shown.

$$5\overline{)328} \quad \text{remainder}$$
$$65 \qquad 3$$

Continue this process of division by 5.

$$
\begin{array}{r|l}
5\overline{)328} & \text{remainder} \\
5\overline{)65} & 3 \\
5\overline{)13} & 0 \\
5\overline{)2} & 3 \\
0 & 2 \\
\end{array}
$$

(In the last division, since the dividend, 2, is smaller than the divisor, 5, the quotient is 0 and the remainder is 2.)

Note that the division continues until the quotient is zero. The answer is read from the bottom number to the top number in the remainder column. Thus, $328 = 2303_5$.

a) Explain why this procedure results in the proper answer.
b) Convert 683 to base 5 by this method.
c) Convert 763 to base 8 by this method.

Challenge Problems/Group Activities

74. a) Use the numerals 0, 1, and 2 to write the first 20 numbers in the base 3 numeration system.
   b) What is the next number after 222_3?

75. a) *Your Own Numeration System* Make up your own base 20 positional-value numeration system. Indicate the 20 numerals you will use to represent the 20 numbers less than the base.
   b) Write the numbers 523 and 5293 in your base 20 numeration system.

76. *Computer Code* The ASCII code used by most computers uses the last seven positions of an eight-bit byte to represent all the characters on a standard keyboard. How many different orderings of 0's and 1's (or how many different characters) can be made by using the last seven positions of an eight-bit byte?

Recreational Mathematics

77. Find b if $111_b = 43$.   **78.** Find d if $ddd_5 = 124$.

79. Suppose a base 4 place-value system has its digits represented by colors as follows:

● $= 0$ ● $= 1$ ● $= 2$ ● $= 3$

a) Determine the value of ●●●●●●$_4$ in base 10.
b) Write 177 in the base 4 system using only the four colors given in the exercise.

Internet/Research Activities

80. Write a report on how digital computers use the binary number system.

81. We mention at the beginning of this section that some societies still use a base 2 and base 3 numeration system. These societies are in Australia, New Guinea, Africa, and South America. Write a report on these societies, covering the symbols they use and how they combine these symbols to represent numbers in their numeration system.

4.4 COMPUTATION IN OTHER BASES

Addition

When computers perform calculations, they do so in base 2, the binary system. In this section, we explain how to perform calculations in base 2 and other bases.

In a base 2 system, the only digits are 0 and 1, and the place values are

$$\ldots, \ 2^4, 2^3, 2^2, 2, 1$$
$$\text{or} \quad \ldots, 16, \ 8, \ 4, \ 2, 1$$

Suppose we want to add $1_2 + 1_2$. The subscript 2 indicates that we are adding in base 2. Remember the answer to $1_2 + 1_2$ must be written using only the digits 0 and 1. The sum of $1_2 + 1_2$ is 10_2, which represents 1 group of two and 0 units in base 2. Recall that 10_2 means $1(2) + 0(1)$.

If we wanted to find the sum of $10_2 + 1_2$, we would add the digits in the right-hand, or units, column. Since $0_2 + 1_2 = 1_2$, the sum of $10_2 + 1_2 = 11_2$.

We are going to work additional examples and exercises in base 2, so rather than performing individual calculations in every problem, we can construct and use an addition table, Table 4.7, for base 2 (just as we used an addition table in base 10 when we first learned to add in base 10).

TABLE 4.7   Base 2 Addition Table

+	0	1
0	0	1
1	1	10

EXAMPLE 1   *Adding in Base 2*

Add 1101_2
$\underline{\quad 111_2}$

SOLUTION: Begin by adding the numbers in the right-hand, or units, column. From previous discussion, and as can be seen in Table 4.7, $1_2 + 1_2 = 10_2$. Place the 0 under the units column and carry the 1 to the 2's column, the second column from the right.

Place value of columns

$$2^3 \; 2^2 \; 2 \; 1$$
$$\downarrow \; \downarrow \; \downarrow \; \downarrow$$
$$1 \;\; 1 \;\; {}^1 0 \;\; 1$$
$$\underline{\quad\;\; 1 \;\; 1 \;\; 1}$$
$$0_2$$

Now add the three digits in the 2's column, $1_2 + 0_2 + 1_2$. Treat this as $(1_2 + 0_2) + 1_2$. Therefore, add $1_2 + 0_2$ to get 1_2, then add $1_2 + 1_2$ to get 10_2. Place the 0 under the 2's column and carry the 1 to the 2^2 column (the third column from the right).

$$1 \;\; {}^1 1 \;\; {}^1 0 \;\; 1$$
$$\underline{\quad\;\; 1 \;\; 1 \;\; 1}$$
$$0 \;\; 0_2$$

Now add the three 1's in the 2^2 column to get $(1_2 + 1_2) + 1_2 = 10_2 + 1_2 = 11_2$. Place the 1 under the 2^2 column and carry the 1 to the 2^3 column (the fourth column from the right).

$${}^1 1 \;\; {}^1 1 \;\; {}^1 0 \;\; 1$$
$$\underline{\quad\;\; 1 \;\; 1 \;\; 1}$$
$$1 \;\; 0 \;\; 0_2$$

Now add the two 1's in the 2^3 column, $1_2 + 1_2 = 10_2$. Place the 10 as follows.

$${}^1 1 \;\; {}^1 1 \;\; {}^1 0 \;\; 1$$
$$\underline{\quad\;\; 1 \;\; 1 \;\; 1}$$
$$1 \;\; 0 \;\; 1 \;\; 0 \;\; 0_2$$

Therefore, the sum is 10100_2.

TABLE 4.8   Base 5 Addition Table

+	0	1	2	3	4
0	0	1	2	3	4
1	1	2	3	4	10
2	2	3	4	10	11
3	3	4	10	11	12
4	4	10	11	⑫	13

Let's now look at addition in a base 5 system. In base 5, the only digits are 0, 1, 2, 3, and 4, and the positional values are

$$\ldots, \quad 5^4, \quad 5^3, 5^2, 5, 1$$

or $\ldots, 625, 125, 25, 5, 1$

What is the sum of $4_5 + 3_5$? We can consider this to mean $(1 + 1 + 1 + 1) + (1 + 1 + 1)$. We can regroup the seven 1's into one group of five and two units as $(1 + 1 + 1 + 1 + 1) + (1 + 1)$. Thus, the sum of $4_5 + 3_5 = 12_5$ (circled in Table 4.8). Recall that 12_5 means $1(5) + 2(1)$. We can use this same procedure in obtaining the remaining values in the base 5 addition table.

─EXAMPLE 2   *Use the Base 5 Addition Table*

Add 42_5
    33_5

SOLUTION: First determine that $2_5 + 3_5$ is 10_5 from Table 4.8. Record the 0 and carry the 1 to the 5's column.

$$\begin{array}{r} {}^1 4 \ 2_5 \\ 3 \ 3_5 \\ \hline 0_5 \end{array}$$

Add the numbers in the second column, $(1_5 + 4_5) + 3_5 = 10_5 + 3_5 = 13_5$. Record the 13.

$$\begin{array}{r} {}^1 4 \ 2_5 \\ 3 \ 3_5 \\ \hline 1 \ 3 \ 0_5 \end{array}$$

The sum is 130_5.   ▲

─EXAMPLE 3   *Add in Base 5*

Add 1234_5
    2042_5

SOLUTION:

$$\begin{array}{r} 1 \ {}^1 2 \ {}^1 3 \ 4_5 \\ 2 \ 0 \ 4 \ 2_5 \\ \hline 3 \ 3 \ 3 \ 1_5 \end{array}$$

▲

You can develop an addition table for any base and use it to add in that base. As you get more comfortable with addition in other bases, however, you may prefer to add numbers in other bases by using mental arithmetic. To do so, convert the sum of the numbers being added from the given base to base 10 and then convert the base 10 number back into the given base. You must clearly understand how to convert from base 10 to the given base, as discussed in Section 4.3. For example, to add $7_9 + 8_9$, add $7 + 8$ in base 10 to get 15_{10} and then mentally convert 15_{10} to 16_9 using the procedure given earlier. Remember, 16_9 when converted to base 10 becomes $1(9) + 6(1)$, or 15. Addition using this procedure is illustrated in Examples 4 and 5.

speaking to Machines

For the past 600 years, we have used the Hindu–Arabic system of numeration without change. Our base 10 numeration system seems so obvious to us, perhaps because of our 10 fingers and 10 toes, but it would be rash to think that numbers in other bases are not useful. In fact, one of the most significant numeration systems is the binary system, or base 2. This system, with its elemental simplicity, is what is used by computers to process information and "talk" to one another. When a computer receives a command or data, every character in the command or data must first be converted into a binary number for the computer to understand and use it. Because of the ever-expanding number of computers in use, the users of the binary number system may soon outnumber the users of base 10.

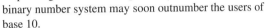

1/2 GALLON (1.89L)

Almost all packaged goods we buy today are marked with a universal product code (UPC), a black-and-white bar code. An optical scanner "reads" the pattern of black and white, thick and thin, and converts it to a binary code that is sent to the scanner's computer, which then calls up the appropriate price and records the sale for inventory purposes.

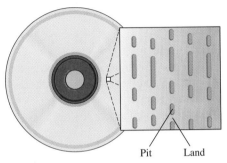

Pit   Land

On digital video discs (DVDs) and compact discs (CDs), video and sound are digitally encoded on the underside of the disc in a binary system of pits and "lands" (nonpits). To play the disc, a laser beam tracks along the spiral and is reflected when it hits a land (signal sent = 1), but it is not reflected by the pits (no signal = 0). The binary sequence is then converted into video images and music.

EXAMPLE 4   Adding in Base 10; Converting to Base 3

Add 1022_3
    2121_3

SOLUTION: To solve this problem, make the necessary conversions by using mental arithmetic. $2 + 1 = 3_{10} = 10_3$. Record the 0 and carry the 1.

$$\begin{array}{r} 1 \; 0 \; {}^{1}2 \; 2_3 \\ 2 \; 1 \;\; 2 \; 1_3 \\ \hline 0_3 \end{array}$$

$1 + 2 + 2 = 5_{10} = 12_3$. Record the 2 and carry the 1.

$$\begin{array}{r} 1 \; {}^{1}0 \; {}^{1}2 \; 2_3 \\ 2 \;\; 1 \;\; 2 \; 1_3 \\ \hline 2 \; 0_3 \end{array}$$

$1 + 0 + 1 = 2_{10} = 2_3$. Record the 2.

$$\begin{array}{r} 1 \; {}^{1}0 \; {}^{1}2 \; 2_3 \\ 2 \;\; 1 \;\; 2 \; 1_3 \\ \hline 2 \; 2 \; 0_3 \end{array}$$

$1 + 2 = 3_{10} = 10_3$. Record the 10.

$$\begin{array}{r} 1022_3 \\ 2121_3 \\ \hline 10220_3 \end{array}$$

The sum is 10220_3.

▲

EXAMPLE 5   *Adding in Base 10; Converting to Base 5*

Add 332_5
     344_5
     443_5
     314_5

SOLUTION: Adding the digits in the right-hand column gives $2 + 4 + 3 + 4 = 13_{10} = 23_5$. Record the 3 and carry the 2. Adding the 2 with the digits in the next column yields $2 + 3 + 4 + 4 + 1 = 14_{10} = 24_5$. Record the 4 and carry the 2. Adding the 2 with the digits in the left-hand column gives $2 + 3 + 3 + 4 + 3 = 15_{10} = 30_5$. Record both digits. The sum of these four numbers is 3043_5.

$$\begin{array}{r} {}^2 3\ {}^2 3\ 2_5 \\ 3\ \ 4\ 4_5 \\ 4\ \ 4\ 3_5 \\ 3\ \ 1\ 4_5 \\ \hline 3\ 0\ 4\ 3_5 \end{array}$$

▲

Subtraction

Subtraction can also be performed in other bases. Always remember that when you "borrow," you borrow the amount of the base given in the subtraction problem. For example, if subtracting in base 5, when you borrow, you borrow 5. If subtracting in base 12, when you borrow, you borrow 12.

EXAMPLE 6   *Subtracting in Base 5*

Subtract 3032_5
           -1004_5

SOLUTION: We will perform the subtraction in base 10 and convert the results to base 5. Since 4 is greater than 2, we must borrow one group of 5 from the preceding column. This action gives a sum of $5 + 2$, or 7 in base 10. Now we subtract 4 from 7; the difference is 3. We complete the problem in the usual manner. The 3 in the second column becomes a 2, $2 - 0 = 2$, $0 - 0 = 0$, and $3 - 1 = 2$.

$$\begin{array}{r} 3032_5 \\ -1004_5 \\ \hline 2023_5 \end{array}$$

▲

EXAMPLE 7   *Subtracting in Base 12*

Subtract 468_{12}
            -295_{12}

SOLUTION: $8 - 5 = 3$. Next we must subtract 9 from 6. Since 9 is greater than 6, borrowing is necessary. We must borrow one group of 12 from the preceding column. We then have a sum of $12 + 6 = 18$ in base 10. Now we subtract 9 from 18, and the difference is 9. The 4 in the left column becomes 3, and $3 - 2 = 1$.

$$\begin{array}{r} 468_{12} \\ -295_{12} \\ \hline 193_{12} \end{array}$$

Multiplication

Multiplication can also be performed in other bases. Doing so is helped by forming a multiplication table for the base desired. Suppose we want to determine the product of $4_5 \times 3_5$. In base 10, 4×3 means there are four groups of three units. Similarly, in a base 5 system, $4_5 \times 3_5$ means there are four groups of three units, or

$$(1 + 1 + 1) + (1 + 1 + 1) + (1 + 1 + 1) + (1 + 1 + 1)$$

Regrouping the 12 units above into groups of five gives

$$(1 + 1 + 1 + 1 + 1) + (1 + 1 + 1 + 1 + 1) + (1 + 1)$$

or two groups of five, and two units. Thus, $4_5 \times 3_5 = 22_5$.

We can construct other values in the base 5 multiplication table in the same way. You may, however, find it easier to multiply the values in the base 10 system and then change the product to base 5 by using the procedure discussed in Section 4.3. Multiplying 4×3 in base 10 gives 12, and converting 12 from base 10 to base 5 gives 22_5.

The product of $4_5 \times 3_5$ is circled in Table 4.9, the base 5 multiplication table. The other values in the table may be found by either method discussed.

TABLE 4.9 Base 5 Multiplication Table

×	0	1	2	3	4
0	0	0	0	0	0
1	0	1	2	3	4
2	0	2	4	11	13
3	0	3	11	14	22
4	0	4	13	(22)	31

EXAMPLE 8   *Using the Base 5 Multiplication Table*

Multiply 13_5
            $\times\ 3_5$

SOLUTION: Multiply as you would in base 10, but use the base 5 multiplication table to find the products. When the product consists of two digits, record the right digit and carry the left digit. Multiplying gives $3_5 \times 3_5 = 14_5$. Record the 4 and carry the 1.

$$\begin{array}{r} {}^{1}13_5 \\ \times\ \ 3_5 \\ \hline 4 \end{array}$$

$(3_5 \times 1_5) + 1_5 = 4_5$. Record the 4.

$$\begin{array}{r} {}^1 13_5 \\ \times \ 3_5 \\ \hline 44_5 \end{array}$$

The product is 44_5.

Constructing a multiplication table is often tedious, especially when the base is large. To multiply in a given base without the use of a table, multiply in base 10 and convert the products to the appropriate base number before recording them. This procedure is illustrated in Example 9.

EXAMPLE 9   Multiplying in Base 7

Multiply 43_7
          $\times\ 25_7$

SOLUTION: $5 \times 3 = 15_{10} = 2(7) + 1(1) = 21_7$. Record the 1 and carry the 2.

$$\begin{array}{r} {}^2 43_7 \\ \times\ 25_7 \\ \hline 1 \end{array}$$

$(5 \times 4) + 2 = 20 + 2 = 22_{10} = 3(7) + 1(1) = 31_7$. Record the 31.

$$\begin{array}{r} {}^2 43_7 \\ \times\ 25_7 \\ \hline 311 \end{array}$$

$2 \times 3 = 6_{10} = 6_7$. Record the 6.

$$\begin{array}{r} {}^2 43_7 \\ \times\ 25_7 \\ \hline 311 \\ 6 \end{array}$$

$2 \times 4 = 8_{10} = 1(7) + 1(1) = 11_7$. Record the 11. Now add in base 7 to determine the answer. Remember, in base 7, there are no digits greater than 6.

$$\begin{array}{r} {}^2 43_7 \\ \times\ 25_7 \\ \hline 311 \\ 116 \\ \hline 1501_7 \end{array}$$

Division

Division is performed in much the same manner as long division in base 10. A detailed example of a division in base 5 is illustrated in Example 10. The same procedure is used for division in any other base.

EXAMPLE 10   *Dividing in Base 5*

Divide $2_5)\overline{143}_5$.

SOLUTION: Using the multiplication table for base 5, Table 4.9 on page 193, we list the multiples of the divisor, 2.

$$2_5 \times 1_5 = \ 2_5$$
$$2_5 \times 2_5 = \ 4_5$$
$$2_5 \times 3_5 = 11_5$$
$$2_5 \times 4_5 = 13_5$$

Since $2_5 \times 4_5 = 13_5$, which is the largest product less than 14_5, 2_5 divides into 14_5 four times.

$$
\begin{array}{r}
4 \\
2_5)\overline{143}_5 \\
\underline{13} \\
1
\end{array}
$$

Subtract 13_5 from 14_5. The difference is 1_5. Record the 1. Now bring down the 3 as when dividing in base 10.

$$
\begin{array}{r}
4 \\
2_5)\overline{143}_5 \\
\underline{13} \\
13
\end{array}
$$

We see that $2_5 \times 4_5 = 13_5$. Use this information to complete the problem.

$$
\begin{array}{r}
44_5 \\
2_5)\overline{143}_5 \\
\underline{13} \\
13 \\
\underline{13} \\
0
\end{array}
$$

Therefore, $143_5 \div 2_5 = 44_5$ with remainder 0_5.

A division problem can be checked by multiplication. If the division was performed correctly, (quotient $\times$ divisor) + remainder = dividend. We can check Example 10 as follows.

$$(44_5 \times 2_5) + 0_5 = 143_5$$

$$
\begin{array}{r}
44_5 \\
\times\ \ 2_5 \\
\hline
143_5 \quad \text{Check}
\end{array}
$$

EXAMPLE 11   *Dividing in Base 6*

Divide $4_6 \overline{)2430_6}$.

SOLUTION: The multiples of 4 in base 6 are

$$4_6 \times 1_6 = 4_6$$
$$4_6 \times 2_6 = 12_6$$
$$4_6 \times 3_6 = 20_6$$
$$4_6 \times 4_6 = 24_6$$
$$4_6 \times 5_6 = 32_6$$

$$
\begin{array}{r}
404_6 \\
4_6 \overline{)2430_6} \\
\underline{24} \\
03 \\
\underline{00} \\
30 \\
\underline{24} \\
2
\end{array}
$$

Thus, the quotient is 404_6, with remainder 2_6.

Be careful when subtracting! When subtracting 4 from 0, you will need to borrow. Remember that you borow 10_6, which is the same as 6 in base 10.

Check: Does $(404_6 \times 4_6) + 2_6 = 2430_6$?

$$
\begin{array}{r}
404_6 \\
\times\ \ \ \ 4_6 \\
\hline
2424_6 + 2_6 = 2430_6 \quad \text{True}
\end{array}
$$

SECTION 4.4   EXERCISES

Concept/Writing Exercises

1. a) What are the first five positional values, from right to left, in base b?
   b) What are the first five positional values, from right to left, in base 6?

2. In the addition

$$367_8$$
$$+24_8$$

what are the positional values of the first column on the right, the second column from the right, and the third column from the right? Explain how you determined your answer.

3. Suppose you add two base 5 numbers and you obtain an answer of 463_5. Can your answer be correct? Explain.

4. Suppose you add two base 3 numbers and you obtain an answer of 2032_3. Can your answer be correct? Explain.

5. In your own words, explain how to add two numbers in a given base. In your explanation, answer the question, "What happens when the sum of the numbers in a column is greater than the base?"

6. In your own words, explain how to subtract two numbers in a given base. Include in your explanation what you do when, in one column, you must subtract a larger number from a smaller number.

Practice the Skills

In Exercises 7–18, add in the indicated base.

7. 43_5
41_5

8. 33_8
65_8

9. 2303_4
232_4

10. 101_2
11_2

11. 799_{12}
218_{12}

12. 222_3
22_3

13. 1112_3
1011_3

14. 470_{12}
347_{12}

15. 14631_7
6040_7

16. 1341_8
341_8

17. 1110_2
110_2

18.* $43A_{16}$
496_{16}

In Exercises 19–30, subtract in the indicated base.

19. 322_4
-103_4

20. 526_7
-145_7

21. 2342_5
-1442_5

22. 1011_2
-101_2

23. 782_{12}
$-13T_{12}$

24. 1221_3
-202_3

25. 1001_2
-110_2

26. $2T34_{12}$
-345_{12}

27. 4223_7
-304_7

28. 4232_5
-2341_5

29. 2100_3
-1012_3

30.* $4E7_{16}$
-189_{16}

In Exercises 31–42, multiply in the indicated base.

31. 33_5
$\times\ 2_5$

32. 323_6
$\times\ 4_6$

33. 342_7
$\times\ 5_7$

34. 101_2
$\times\ 11_2$

35. 512_6
$\times\ 23_6$

36. 124_{12}
$\times\ 6_{12}$

37. 436_9
$\times\ 25_9$

38. $6T3_{12}$
$\times\ 24_{12}$

39. 111_2
$\times\ 101_2$

40. 584_9
$\times\ 24_9$

41. 316_7
$\times\ 16_7$

42. $8T_{12}$
$\times\ 2T_{12}$

In Exercises 43–54, divide in the indicated base.

43. $1_2)\overline{110_2}$

44. $4_6)\overline{231_6}$

45. $3_5)\overline{143_5}$

46. $7_8)\overline{335_8}$

47. $2_4)\overline{312_4}$

48. $6_{12})\overline{431_{12}}$

49. $2_4)\overline{213_4}$

50. $5_6)\overline{214_6}$

51. $3_5)\overline{224_5}$

52. $4_6)\overline{210_6}$

53. $6_7)\overline{404_7}$

54. $3_7)\overline{2101_7}$

Problem Solving

In Exercises 55–58, the numerals in a base 5 numeration system are as illustrated with their equivalent Hindu–Arabic numerals.

$\bigcirc = 0$ $\ominus = 1$ $\bigcirc\!\!| = 2$ $\ominus = 3$ $\bigcirc\!\!| = 4$

Add the following base 5 numbers.

55.

56.

57.

58.

---

*For Exercises 18 and 30, see Exercises 37–40 in Section 4.3.

In Exercises 59–66, assume the numerals given are in a base 4 numeration system. In this system, suppose colors are used as numerals, as indicated below.

● = 0,   ● = 1,   ● = 2,   ● = 3

Add the following base 4 numbers. Your answers will contain a variety of the colors indicated.

59. ●₄   60. ●●₄   61. ●●₄   62. ●●●₄
    ●₄   ●●₄   ●●₄   ●●●₄

Subtract the following in base 4. Your answer will contain a variety of the colors indicated.

63. ●●₄ 64. ●●₄ 65. ●●●₄ 66. ●●●₄
   − ●●₄   − ●●₄   − ●●●₄   − ●●●₄

For Exercises 67 and 68, study the pattern in the boxes. The number in the bottom row of each box represents the value of each dot in the box directly above it. For example, the following box represents $(3 \times 7^2) + (2 \times 7) + (4 \times 1)$, *or the number* 324_7. *This number in base 10 is 165.*

•••	••	••••
7^2	7	1

67. Determine the base 5 number represented by the dots in the top row of the boxes. Then convert the base 5 number to a number in base 10.

••	••••		••
5^3	5^2	5	1

68. Fill in the correct amount of dots in the columns above the base values if the number represented by the dots is to equal 327 in base 10.

9^2	9	1

Challenge Problems/Group Activities

Divide in the indicated base.

69. $14_5 \overline{)242_5}$ 70. $20_4 \overline{)223_4}$

71. Consider the multiplication

$$\begin{array}{r} 462_8 \\ \times\ 35_8 \end{array}$$

a) Multiply the numbers in base 8.
b) Convert 462_8 and 35_8 to base 10.
c) Multiply the base 10 numbers determined in part (b).
d) Convert the answer obtained in base 8 in part (a) to base 10.
e) Are the answers obtained in parts (c) and (d) the same? Why or why not?

Recreational Mathematics

72. Determine b, by trial and error, if $1304_b = 204$.

73. In a base 4 system, each of the four numerals is represented by one of the following colors:

● ● ● ●

Determine the value of each color if the following addition is true in base 4.

$$\begin{array}{r} ●●●_4 \\ +\ ●●●_4 \\ \hline ●●●●_4 \end{array}$$

Internet/Research Activities

74. Investigate and write a report on the use of the duodecimal (base 12) system as a system of numeration. You might contact the Dozenal Society (formerly the Duodecimal Society), Nassau Community College, Garden City, NY 11530 or use their website www.polar.sunynassau.edu/~dozenal/ for information.

75. One method used by computers to perform subtraction is the "end around carry method." Do research and write a report explaining, with specific examples, how a computer performs subtraction by using the end around carry method.

4.5 EARLY COMPUTATIONAL METHODS

Our present procedures for multiplying and dividing numbers are the most recent to be developed. Early civilizations used various methods for multiplying and dividing. Multiplication was performed by *duplation and mediation*, by the *galley method*, and by *Napier rods*. Following is an explanation of each method.

Duplation and Mediation

EXAMPLE 1   *A Pairing Technique for Multiplying*

Multiply 17 × 30 using duplation and mediation.

SOLUTION: Write 17 and 30 with a dash between to separate them. Divide the number on the left, 17, in half, drop the remainder, and place the quotient, 8, under the 17. Double the number on the right, 30, obtaining 60, and place it under the 30. You will then have the following paired lines.

$$17—30$$
$$8—60$$

Continue this process, taking one-half the number in the left-hand column, disregarding the remainder, and doubling the number in the right-hand column, as shown below. When a 1 appears in the left-hand column, stop.

$$17—30$$
$$8—60$$
$$4—120$$
$$2—240$$
$$1—480$$

Cross out all the even numbers in the left-hand column and the corresponding numbers in the right-hand column.

$$17—30$$
$$8—60$$
$$4—120$$
$$2—240$$
$$1—480$$

Now add the remaining numbers in the right-hand column, obtaining 30 + 480 = 510, which is the product you want. If you check, you will find that 17 × 30 = 510. ▲

The Galley Method

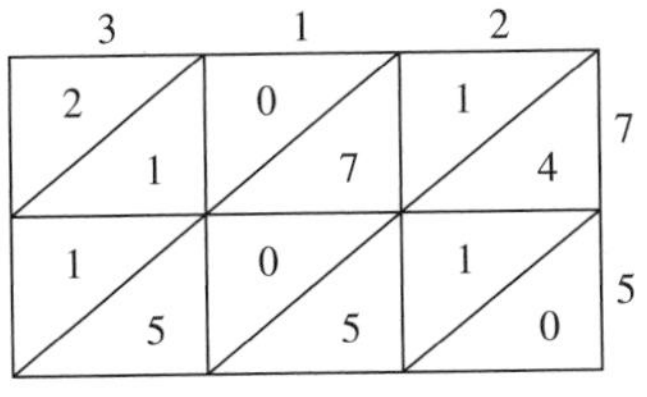

The galley method (sometimes referred to as the Gelosia method) was developed after duplation and mediation. To multiply 312 × 75 using the galley method, you construct a rectangle consisting of three columns (one for each digit of 312) and two rows (one for each digit of 75).

   Place the digits 3, 1, 2 above the boxes and the digits 7, 5 on the right of the boxes, as shown in Fig. 4.1. Then place a diagonal in each box.

   Complete each box by multiplying the number on top of the box by the number to the right of the box (Fig. 4.2). Place the units digit of the product below the diagonal and the tens digit of the product above the diagonal.

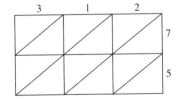

Figure 4.1

Figure 4.2

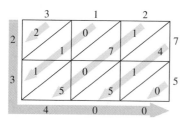

Figure 4.3

Add the numbers along the diagonals, as shown with the blue shaded arrows in Fig. 4.3, starting with the bottom right diagonal. If the sum in a diagonal is 10 or greater, record the units digit below the rectangle and carry the tens digit to the next diagonal to the left.

For example, when adding 4, 1, and 5 (along the second blue diagonal from the right), the sum is 10. Record the 0 below the rectangle and carry the 1 to the next blue diagonal. The sum of $1 + 1 + 7 + 0 + 5$ is 14. Record the 4 and carry the 1. The sum of the numbers in the next blue diagonal is $1 + 0 + 1 + 1$ or 3.

The answer is read down the left-hand column and along the bottom, as shown by the purple arrow in Fig. 4.3. The answer is 23,400.

Napier Rods

The third method used to multiply numbers was developed from the galley method by John Napier in the seventeenth century. His method of multiplication, known as Napier rods, proved to be one of the forerunners of the modern-day computer. Napier developed a system of separate rods numbered from 0 through 9 and an additional strip for an index, numbered vertically 1 through 9 (Fig. 4.4). Each rod is divided into 10 blocks. Each block below the first block contains a multiple of the number in the first block, with a diagonal separating the digits. The units digits are placed to the right of the diagonals and the tens digits to the left. Example 2 explains how Napier rods are used to multiply numbers.

Figure 4.4

┌EXAMPLE 2   *Using Napier Rods*

Multiply 8×365, using Napier rods.

SOLUTION: To multiply 8×365, line up the rods 3, 6, and 5 to the right of the index, as shown in Fig. 4.5 on page 201. Below the 3, 6, and 5 place the blocks that

INDEX	3	6	5
1	0/3	0/6	0/5
2	0/6	1/2	1/0
3	0/9	1/8	1/5
4	1/2	2/4	2/0
5	1/5	3/0	2/5
6	1/8	3/6	3/0
7	2/1	4/2	3/5
8	2/4	4/8	4/0
9	2/7	5/4	4/5

Figure 4.5

contain the products of 8×3, 8×6, and 8×5, respectively. To obtain the answer, add along the diagonals as in the galley method.

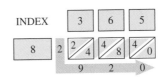

Thus, $8 \times 365 = 2920$.

Example 3 illustrates the procedure to follow to multiply numbers containing more than one digit, using Napier rods.

EXAMPLE 3 *Using Napier Rods to Multiply Two- and Three-Digit Numbers*

Multiply 48×365, using Napier rods.

SOLUTION: $48 \times 365 = (40 + 8) \times 365$

Write $(40 + 8) \times 365 = (40 \times 365) + (8 \times 365)$. To find 40×365, determine 4×365 and multiply the product by 10. To evaluate 4×365, set up Napier rods for 3, 6, and 5 with index 4, and then evaluate along the diagonals, as indicated.

INDEX	3	6	5
4	1/2	2/4	2/0
	4	6	0

Therefore, $4 \times 365 = 1460$. Then $40 \times 365 = 1460 \times 10 = 14,600$.

$$48 \times 365 = (40 \times 365) + (8 \times 365)$$
$$= 14,600 + 2920$$
$$= 17,520$$

$8 \times 365 = 2920$ from Example 2

SECTION 4.5 EXERCISES

Concept/Writing Exercises

1. What are the three early computational methods discussed in this section?

2. **a)** Explain in your own words how multiplication by duplation and mediation is performed.
   b) Using the procedure given in part (a), multiply 267×193.

3. **a)** Explain in your own words how multiplication by the galley method is performed.
   b) Using the procedure given in part (a), multiply 362×29.

4. **a)** Explain in your own words how multiplication using Napier rods is performed.
   b) Using the procedure given in part (a), multiply 25×6.

Practice the Skills

In Exercises 5–12, multiply using duplation and mediation.

5. 23×31

6. 35×23

7. 9×162

8. 175×86

9. 35×236

10. 96×53

11. 93×93

12. 49×124

In Exercises 13–20, multiply using the galley method.

13. 6 × 375
14. 8 × 365
15. 4 × 583
16. 7 × 125
17. 75 × 12
18. 47 × 259
19. 314 × 652
20. 634 × 832

In Exercises 21–28, multiply using Napier rods.

21. 8 × 63
22. 7 × 63
23. 7 × 58
24. 7 × 125
25. 5 × 125
26. 75 × 125
27. 9 × 6742
28. 7 × 3456

Problem Solving

In Exercises 29 and 30, we show multiplications using the galley method. (a) Determine the numbers being multiplied. Explain how you determined your answer. (b) Find the product.

29.

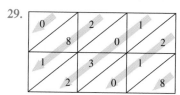

30.

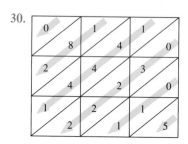

In Exercises 31 and 32, we solve a multiplication problem using Napier rods. (a) Determine the numbers being multiplied. Each empty box contains a single digit. Explain how you determined your answer. (b) Find the product.

31.

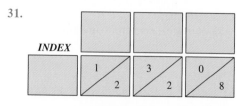

32.

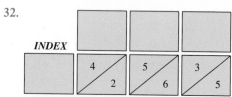

Challenge Problems/Group Activities

In Exercises 33 and 34, use the method of duplation and mediation to perform the multiplication. Write the answer in the numeration system in which the exercise is given.

33. (∩III) • (∩∩II)
34. (XXVI) · (LXVII)

35. Develop a set of Napier rods that can be used to multiply numbers in base 5. Illustrate how your rods can be used to multiply $3_5 \times 21_5$.

In Exercises 36 and 37, (a) use the galley method to perform the multiplication. (Hint: Be sure not to list any number greater than or equal to the base within the box). Write the answer in the base in which the exercise is given. (b) Multiply the numbers as explained in Section 4.4. If you do not obtain the results obtained in part (a), explain why.

36. $21_3 \times 21_3$
37. $24_5 \times 234_5$

Recreational Mathematics

38. Obtain a clean U.S. $1 bill. On the back side of the bill is a circle containing a pyramid. On the base of the pyramid is a Roman numeral. a) Determine the value of that Roman numeral in our Hindu–Arabic system.

While you have that bill out, let's consider something else. For many people the number 13 is considered an unlucky number. In fact, many hotels do not have a thirteenth floor because many guests refuse to stay on the thirteenth floor of a hotel. Yet, if you look at the back of a $1 bill, you will find

13 steps on the pyramid.
13 letters in the Latin words *Annuit Coeptis*.
13 letters in "E Pluribus Unum".
13 stars above the eagle.
13 plum feathers on each span of the eagle's wing.
13 bars on the eagle's shield.
13 leaves on the olive branch.
13 fruits.
13 arrows.

In addition, the U.S. flag has 13 stripes, there were 13 signers of the Declaration of Independence, there were 13 original colonies, and don't forget the important Thirteenth Amendment that abolished slavery. b) So why, in your opinion, do we as a society fear the number 13? By the way, the official name for the fear of the number 13 is *triskaidekaphobia*.

Internet/Research Activities

39. In addition to Napier rods, John Napier is credited with making other important contributions to mathematics. Write a report on John Napier and his contributions to mathematics.

40. Write a paper explaining why the duplation and mediation method works.

CHAPTER 4   SUMMARY

IMPORTANT FACTS

Types of Numeration Systems

Additive (Egyptian hieroglyphics, Roman)

Multiplicative (traditional Chinese)

Ciphered (Ionic Greek)

Place-value (Babylonian, Mayan, Hindu–Arabic)

Early Computational Methods

Duplation and mediation

The galley method

Napier rods

CHAPTER 4   REVIEW EXERCISES

4.1, 4.2

In Exercises 1–6, assume an additive numeration system in which $a = 1$, $b = 10$, $c = 100$, and $d = 1000$. Find the value of the numeral.

1. *dddcaaa*   **2.** *ccbda*   **3.** *bcccad*

4. *cbdadaaa*   **5.** *ddcccbaaaa*   **6.** *ccbaddac*

In Exercises 7–12, assume the same additive numeration system as in Exercises 1–6. Write the numeral in terms of a, b, c, and d.

7. 56   **8.** 125   **9.** 293

10. 2005   **11.** 6851   **12.** 2314

In Exercises 13–18, assume a multiplicative numeration system in which $a = 1$, $b = 2$, $c = 3$, $d = 4$, $e = 5$, $f = 6$, $g = 7$, $h = 8$, $i = 9$, $x = 10$, $y = 100$, and $z = 1000$. Find the value of the numeral.

13. *dxc*   **14.** *bxg*

15. *gydxi*   **16.** *dzfxh*

17. *ezfydxh*   **18.** *fziye*

In Exercises 19–24, assume the same multiplicative numeration system as in Exercises 13–18. Write the Hindu–Arabic numeral in that system.

19. 82   **20.** 295   **21.** 862

22. 3094   **23.** 6004   **24.** 2001

In Exercises 25–36, use the following ciphered numeration system.

Decimal	1	2	3	4	5	6	7	8	9
Units	a	b	c	d	e	f	g	h	i
Tens	j	k	l	m	n	o	p	q	r
Hundreds	s	t	u	v	w	x	y	z	A
Thousands	B	C	D	E	F	G	H	I	J
Ten thousands	K	L	M	N	O	P	Q	R	S

Convert the numeral to a Hindu–Arabic numeral.

25. me   **26.** uh   **27.** woh

28. NGzqc   **29.** PEvqa   **30.** Pwki

Write the numeral in the ciphered numeration system.

31. 85   **32.** 372   **33.** 493

34. 1997   **35.** 53,467   **36.** 75,496

In Exercises 37–42, convert 1462 to a numeral in the indicated numeration system.

37. Egyptian   **38. Roman**   **39. Chinese**

40. Ionic Greek   **41. Babylonian**   **42. Mayan**

In Exercises 43–48, convert the numeral to a Hindu–Arabic numeral.

43. ⌒◁◁𝕸𝄽𝄽∩∩∩|||||

44. 八千二百五十四

45. $\chi \pi \epsilon$

46. MCMXCI

47. ◄◄▎ ◄◄▎̃▎▎▎▎

48. $\overset{\bullet\bullet}{\underset{=}{\bullet\bullet\bullet}}$

4.3

In Exercises 49–54, convert the numeral to a Hindu–Arabic numeral.

49. 47_8
50. 101_2
51. 130_4
52. 3425_7
53. $T0E_{12}$
54. 202200_3

In Exercises 55–60, convert 463 to a numeral in the base indicated.

55. base 4
56. base 3
57. base 2
58. base 5
59. base 12
60. base 8

4.4

In Exercises 61–66, add in the base indicated.

61. $\begin{array}{r} 52_7 \\ 55_7 \end{array}$
62. $\begin{array}{r} 10110_2 \\ 11001_2 \end{array}$
63. $\begin{array}{r} TE_{12} \\ 87_{12} \end{array}$

64. $\begin{array}{r} 234_7 \\ 456_7 \end{array}$
65. $\begin{array}{r} 3024_5 \\ 4023_5 \end{array}$
66. $\begin{array}{r} 3407_8 \\ 7014_8 \end{array}$

In Exercises 67–72, subtract in the base indicated.

67. $\begin{array}{r} 4032_7 \\ -\ 321_7 \end{array}$
68. $\begin{array}{r} 1001_2 \\ -\ 101_2 \end{array}$
69. $\begin{array}{r} 3TT_{12} \\ -\ E7_{12} \end{array}$

70. $\begin{array}{r} 4321_5 \\ -\ 442_5 \end{array}$
71. $\begin{array}{r} 1713_8 \\ -1243_8 \end{array}$
72. $\begin{array}{r} 2021_3 \\ -\ 212_3 \end{array}$

In Exercises 73–78, multiply in the base indicated.

73. $\begin{array}{r} 32_6 \\ \times\ 4_6 \end{array}$
74. $\begin{array}{r} 34_5 \\ \times\ 21_5 \end{array}$
75. $\begin{array}{r} 126_{12} \\ \times\ 47_{12} \end{array}$

76. $\begin{array}{r} 221_3 \\ \times\ 22_3 \end{array}$
77. $\begin{array}{r} 1011_2 \\ \times\ 101_2 \end{array}$
78. $\begin{array}{r} 476_8 \\ \times\ 23_8 \end{array}$

In Exercises 79–84, divide in the base indicated.

79. $1_2 \overline{)1011_2}$
80. $2_4 \overline{)320_4}$
81. $3_5 \overline{)130_5}$
82. $4_6 \overline{)3020_6}$
83. $3_6 \overline{)2034_6}$
84. $6_8 \overline{)5072_8}$

4.5

85. Multiply 142×24, using the duplation and mediation method.

86. Multiply 142×24, using the galley method.

87. Multiply 142×24, using Napier rods.

CHAPTER 4 TEST

1. Explain the difference between a numeral and a number.

In Exercises 2–7, convert the numeral to a Hindu–Arabic numeral.

2. MMMDCXLVI

3. ◄◄▎ ◄▎▎▎▎▎

4. 八
千
零
九
十

5. $\overset{\bullet\bullet}{\underset{\bullet\bullet\bullet\bullet}{\bullet\bullet}}$

6. ∝𝕄𝔰𝔰Ꝺ∩∩∩‖

7. $\theta' \pi \, Q \, \theta$

In Exercises 8–12, convert the number written in base 10 to a numeral in the numeration system indicated.

8. 463 to Egyptian

9. 2476 to Ionic Greek

10. 1434 to Mayan

11. 1596 to Babylonian

12. 2378 to Roman

In Exercises 13–16, describe briefly each of the systems of numeration. Explain how each type of numeration system is used to represent numbers.

13. Additive system
14. Multiplicative system
15. Ciphered system
16. Place-value system

In Exercises 17–20, convert the numeral to a numeral in base 10.

17. 56_7

18. 403_5

19. 101101_2

20. 368_9

In Exercises 21–24, convert the base 10 numeral to a numeral in the base indicated.

21. 36 to base 2

22. 93 to base 5

23. 2356 to base 12

24. 2938 to base 7

In Exercises 25–28, perform the indicated operations.

25.
$$\begin{array}{r} 133_5 \\ + 434_5 \end{array}$$

26.
$$\begin{array}{r} 324_6 \\ - 142_6 \end{array}$$

27.
$$\begin{array}{r} 45_6 \\ \times 23_6 \end{array}$$

28. $3_5)\overline{1210_5}$

29. Multiply 35×28, using duplation and mediation.

30. Multiply 43×196, using the galley method.

GROUP PROJECTS

U.S. Postal Service Bar Codes

Wherever we look nowadays, we see bar codes. We find them on items we buy at grocery stores and department stores and on many pieces of mail we receive. There are various types of bar codes, but each can be considered a type of numeration system. Although bar codes may vary in design, most are made up of a series of long and short bars. (New bar codes now being developed use a variety of shapes.) In this group project, we explain how postal codes are used.

The U.S. Postal Service introduced a bar coding system for zip codes in 1976. The system became known as Postnet (*post*al *n*umeric *e*ncoding *t*echniqe), and it has been refined over the years. Our basic zip code consists of five digits. The post office would like us to use the basic zip code followed by a hyphen and four additional digits. The post office refers to this nine-digit zip code as "zip + 4."

The Postnet bar code uses a series of long and short bars. A bar code may contain either 52 or 62 bars. The code designates the location to which the letter is being sent. The following bar code, with 52 bars, is for an address in Pittsburgh, Pennsylvania.

||..|||.|..||.|.|.|.||..|..|.||.|||..||.|..|

15250-7406 (Pittsburgh, PA)

In bar codes, each short bar represents 0 and each long bar represents 1. Each code starts and ends with a long bar that is *not* used in determining the zip + 4. If the code contains 52 bars, the code represents the zip + 4 and an extra digit referred to as a check digit. If the code contains 62 bars, it contains the zip + 4, the last two digits of the address number, and a check digit. If the code contains 52 bars, the sum of the zip + 4 and the check digit must equal a number that is divisible by 10. If the code contains 62 bars, the sum of the zip + 4, the last two digits of the address number, and the check digit must equal a number that is divisible by 10. The check digit is added to make each sum divisible by 10.

In a postal bar code, each of the digits 0 through 9 is represented by a series of five digits containing zeros and ones:

11000 (0)	00011 (1)	00101 (2)	00110 (3)	01001 (4)
01010 (5)	01100 (6)	10001 (7)	10010 (8)	10100 (9)

Consider the postal code from Pittsburgh given earlier. If you disregard the bar on the left, the next five bars are ..||. Since each small bar represents a 0 and each large bar represents a 1, these five bars can be represented as 00011. From the chart, we see that this represents the number 1. The first five bars (after the bar on the far left has been excluded) tell the region of the country in which the address is located on the map shown on the next page.

Notice that Pennsylvania is located, along with New York, in the region marked 1 on the map.

National zip code areas

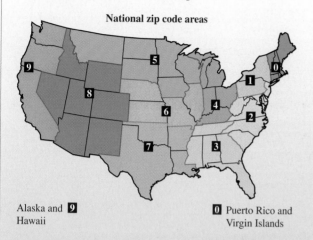

Alaska and **9**
Hawaii

0 Puerto Rico and
Virgin Islands

The second five lines in the bar code, ılılı, represent 01010 and have a value of 5. The other digits in the zip + 4 are determined in a similar manner. This code has 52 bars. The 45 bars, after the first bar, give the zip + 4. If you add the digits in the zip + 4, you get $1 + 5 + 2 + 5 + 0 + 7 + 4 + 0 + 6 = 30$. Since 30 is divisible by 10, the five bars to the left of the bar on the very right should be 0. Note that ‖ııı is represented as

11000 and has a value of 0. If, for example, the sum of the nine digits in the zip + 4 were 36, then the last five digits would need to represent the number 4, to make the sum of the digits divisible by 10. The five bars to the left of the last bar on the right are always used as a check.

Now let's work some problems.

a) For the Postnet code

‖ııı‖ıılıılıı‖ııılılılılılıılılıılıı‖

   determine the zip + 4 and the check digit. Then check by adding the zip + 4 and the check digit. Is the sum divisible by 10?

b) For each of the following Postnet codes, determine the zip + 4, the last two numbers of the address number (if applicable), and the check digit.

   i) lılıııllılılıllıılılıllılılılılıllılılılıl

   ii) lıllılılılıılılıllıllılılılılılılılılılıllılılıllılıl

c) Construct the Postnet code of long and short bars for each of the numbers. The numbers represent the zip + 4 and the last two digits of the address number. Do not forget the check digit.

   i) 32226-8600-34   ii) 20794-1063-50

d) Construct the 52-bar Postnet code for your college's zip + 4. Don't forget to include the check digit.

Number Theory plays an important role in computer science, medical research, and satellite technology.

NUMBER THEORY AND THE REAL NUMBER SYSTEM

I t is impossible to live in our modern world without encountering numbers on a regular basis. In addition to playing a role in our everyday lives, numbers are used to describe the natural world, to communicate vast quantities of information, and to model problems facing scientists and researchers. *Number theory,* the study of numbers and their properties, makes all these roles possible. Mathematicians and computer scientists use number theory extensively to improve the speed of computers in our homes, businesses, and schools. Research scientists use number theory along with another branch of mathematics known as *knot theory* to conduct DNA research, research new drugs, and study how infectious diseases spread. Engineers use number theory in satellite technology which is used in virtually every modern means of communication.

5.1 NUMBER THEORY

This chapter introduces *number theory*, the study of numbers and their properties. The numbers we use to count are called the *counting numbers* or *natural numbers*. Since we begin counting with the number 1, the set of natural numbers begins with 1. The set of natural numbers is frequently denoted by N:

$$N = \{1, 2, 3, 4, 5, \dots\}$$

Any natural number can be expressed as a product of two or more natural numbers. For example, $8 = 2 \times 4$, $16 = 4 \times 4$, and $19 = 1 \times 19$. The natural numbers that are multiplied together are called factors of the product. For example,

$$2 \times 4 = 8$$
$$\uparrow \quad \uparrow$$
$$\text{Factors}$$

A natural number may have many factors. For example, what pairs of numbers have a product of 18?

$$1 \cdot 18 = 18$$
$$2 \cdot 9 = 18$$
$$3 \cdot 6 = 18$$

The numbers 1, 2, 3, 6, 9, and 18 are all factors of 18. Each of these numbers divides 18 without a remainder.

If a and b are natural numbers, we say that a is a *divisor* of b or a *divides* b, symbolized $a \mid b$, if the quotient of b divided by a has a remainder of 0. If a divides b, then b is *divisible* by a. For example, 4 divides 12, symbolized $4 \mid 12$, since the quotient of 12 divided by 4 has a remainder of 0. Note that 12 is divisible by 4. The notation $7 \nmid 12$ means that 7 does not divide 12. Note that every factor of a natural number is also a divisor of the natural number. *Caution:* Do not confuse the symbols $a \mid b$ and a / b; $a \mid b$ means "a divides b" and a / b means "a divided by b" ($a \div b$). The symbols a / b and $a \div b$ indicate that the operation of division is to be performed, and b may or may not be a divisor of a.

Prime and Composite Numbers

Every natural number greater than 1 can be classified as either a prime number or a composite number.

> A **prime number** is a natural number greater than 1 that has exactly two factors (or divisors), itself and 1.

The number 5 is a prime number because it is divisible only by the factors 1 and 5. The first eight prime numbers are 2, 3, 5, 7, 11, 13, 17, and 19. The number 2 is the

PROFILE IN
MATHEMATICS

ERATOSTHENES
OF CYRENE

Eratosthenes of Cyrene (275–195 B.C.) was born in northern Africa near the present-day city of Shahhat, Libya. Eratosthenes is best known for being the first to estimate accurately the diameter of Earth. He is also credited for developing a method of finding prime numbers known as the **sieve of Eratosthenes**. Although he is most known for his work in mathematics, Eratosthenes also was influential in the fields of history, geography, and astronomy. In addition, Eratosthenes served for many years as the director of the famous library in Alexandria, Egypt. Although Eratosthenes was a highly regarded scholar throughout the ancient world, only fragments of his writing remain today. Eratosthenes was near 80 years old when, after going blind, he died from voluntary starvation.

only even prime number. All other even numbers have at least three divisors: 1, 2, and the number itself.

A **composite number** is a natural number that is divisible by a number other than itself and 1.

Any natural number greater than 1 that is not prime is composite. The first eight composite numbers are 4, 6, 8, 9, 10, 12, 14, and 15.

The number 1 is neither prime nor composite; it is called a *unit*. The number 38 has at least three divisors, 1, 2, and 38, and hence is a composite number. In contrast, the number 23 is a prime number since its only divisors are 1 and 23.

More than 2000 years ago, the ancient Greeks developed a technique for determining which numbers are prime numbers and which are not. This technique is named the *sieve of Eratosthenes*, for the Greek mathematician Eratosthenes of Cyrene who first used it.

Figure 5.1

To find the prime numbers less than or equal to any natural number, say, 50, using this method, list the first 50 counting numbers (Fig. 5.1). Cross out 1 since it is not a prime number. Circle 2, the first prime number. Then cross out all the multiples of 2: 4, 6, 8, . . . , 50. Circle the next prime number, 3. Cross out all multiples of 3 that are not already crossed out. Continue this process until you reach the prime number p, such that $p \cdot p$, or p^2, is greater than the last number listed, in this case 50. Therefore, we next circle 5 and cross out its multiples. Then circle 7 and cross out its multiples. The next prime number is 11, and $11 \cdot 11$, or 121, is greater than 50, so you are done. At this point, circle all the remaining numbers to obtain the prime numbers less than or equal to 50. The prime numbers less than or equal to 50 are 2, 3, 5, 7, 11, 13, 17, 19, 23, 29, 31, 37, 41, 43, and 47.

Now we turn our attention to composite numbers and their factors. The rules of divisibility given in the chart on page 210 are helpful in finding divisors (or factors) of composite numbers.

The test for divisibility by 6 is a particular case of the general statement that the product of two prime divisors of a number is a divisor of the number. Thus, for example, if both 3 and 7 divide a number, then 21 will also divide the number.

Note that the chart does not list rules of divisibility for the number 7. There is a rule for 7, but it is difficult to remember. The easiest way to check divisibility by 7 is just to perform the division.

The date November 19, 1999, was a very special day. It was a rare "odd day." The numerical format is 11-19-1999 (or some may write it as 19-11-1999), which contains only odd digits. The next odd day will be January 1, 3111, which would be written 1-1-3111, and is over a thousand years away—a date we certainly will never see.

Days such as 8-27-2002 have both odd and even digits. Thus, it is neither an odd day nor an even day. The first of many even days in the year 2000 was 2-2-2000, the first one since 8-28-888.

So now you have a reason to celebrate, since you have seen your last odd day on Earth!

Rules of Divisibility

Divisible by	Test	Example
2	The number is even.	924 is divisible by 2 since 924 is even.
3	The sum of the digits of the number is divisible by 3.	924 is divisible by 3 since the sum of the digits, $9 + 2 + 4 = 15$, and 15 is divisible by 3.
4	The number formed by the last two digits of the number is divisible by 4.	924 is divisible by 4 since the number formed by the last two digits, 24, is divisible by 4.
5	The number ends in 0 or 5.	265 is divisible by 5 since the number ends in 5.
6	The number is divisible by both 2 and 3.	924 is divisible by 6 since it is divisible by both 2 and 3.
8	The number formed by the last three digits of the number is divisible by 8.	5824 is divisible by 8 since the number formed by the last three digits, 824, is divisible by 8.
9	The sum of the digits of the number is divisible by 9.	837 is divisible by 9 since the sum of the digits, 18, is divisible by 9.
10	The number ends in 0.	290 is divisible by 10 since the number ends in 0.

EXAMPLE 1   *Using the Divisibility Rules*

Determine whether 145,860 is divisible by

a) 2   b) 3   c) 4   d) 5   e) 6   f) 8   g) 9   h) 10

SOLUTION:

a) Since 145,860 is even, it is divisible by 2.

b) The sum of the digits of 145,860 is $1 + 4 + 5 + 8 + 6 + 0 = 24$. Since 24 is divisible by 3, the number 145,860 is divisible by 3.

c) The number formed by the last two digits is 60. Since 60 is divisible by 4, the number 145,860 is divisible by 4.

d) Since 145,860 has 0 as the last digit, 145,860 is divisible by 5.

e) Since 145,860 is divisible by both 2 and 3, 145,860 is divisible by 6.

f) The number formed by the last three digits is 860. Since 860 is not divisible by 8, the number 145,860 is not divisible by 8.

g) The sum of the digits of 145,860 is 24. Since 24 is not divisible by 9, the number 145,860 is not divisible by 9.

h) Since 145,860 has 0 as the last digit, 145,860 is divisible by 10.   ▲

Every composite number can be expressed as a product of prime numbers. The process of breaking a given number down into a product of prime numbers is called *prime factorization*. The prime factorization of 18 is $3 \times 3 \times 2$. No other natural number listed as a product of primes will have the same prime factorization as 18. The *fundamental theorem of arithmetic* states this concept formally. (A *theorem* is a statement or proposition that can be proven true.)

> **The Fundamental Theorem of Arithmetic**
> Every composite number can be expressed as a *unique* product of prime numbers.

In writing the prime factorization of a number, the order of the factors is immaterial. For example, we may write the prime factors of 18 as $3 \times 3 \times 2$ or $2 \times 3 \times 3$ or $3 \times 2 \times 3$.

A number of techniques can be used to find the prime factorization of a number. Two methods are illustrated.

Method 1: Branching

To find the prime factorization of a number, select any two numbers whose product is the number to be factored. If the factors are not prime numbers, then continue factoring each composite number until all numbers are prime.

EXAMPLE 2   *Prime Factorization by Branching*

Write 2100 as a product of primes.

SOLUTION: Select any two numbers whose product is 2100. Among the many choices, two possibilities are $21 \cdot 100$ and $30 \cdot 70$. Let us consider $21 \cdot 100$. Since neither 21 nor 100 are prime numbers, find any two numbers whose product is 21 and any two numbers whose product is 100. Continue branching as shown in Fig. 5.2 until the numbers in the last row are all prime numbers. To determine the answer, write the product of all the prime factors. The branching diagram is sometimes called a *factor tree*.

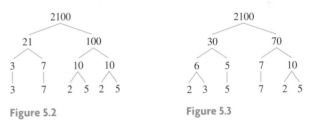

Figure 5.2   Figure 5.3

We see that the numbers in the last row of factors in Fig. 5.2 are all prime numbers. Thus, the prime factorization of 2100 is $3 \cdot 7 \cdot 2 \cdot 5 \cdot 2 \cdot 5 = 2 \cdot 2 \cdot 3 \cdot 5 \cdot 5 \cdot 7 = 2^2 \cdot 3 \cdot 5^2 \cdot 7$. Note from Fig. 5.3 that had we chosen 30 and 70 as the first pair of factors, the prime factorization would still be $2^2 \cdot 3 \cdot 5^2 \cdot 7$. ▲

Method 2: Division

To obtain the prime factorization of a number by this method, divide the given number by the smallest prime number by which it is divisible. Place the quotient under the given number. Then divide the quotient by the smallest prime number by which it is divisible and again record the quotient. Repeat this process until the quotient is a prime number. The prime factorization is the product of all the prime divisors and the prime (or last) quotient. This procedure is illustrated in Example 3.

EXAMPLE 3   *Prime Factorization by Division*

Write 2100 as a product of prime numbers.

SOLUTION: Because 2100 is an even number, the smallest prime number that divides it is 2. Divide 2100 by 2. Place the quotient, 1050, below the 2100. Repeat this process of dividing each quotient by the smallest prime number that divides it.

2	2100
2	1050
3	525
5	175
5	35
	7

The final quotient, 7, is a prime number, so we stop. The prime factorization of 2100 is

$$2 \cdot 2 \cdot 3 \cdot 5 \cdot 5 \cdot 7 = 2^2 \cdot 3 \cdot 5^2 \cdot 7.$$

Note that, despite the different methods used in Examples 2 and 3, the answer is the same.

Greatest Common Divisor

The discussion in Section 5.3 of how to reduce fractions makes use of the greatest common divisor (GCD). One technique of finding the GCD is to use prime factorization.

> The **greatest common divisor (GCD)** of a set of natural numbers is the largest natural number that divides (without remainder) every number in that set.

What is the GCD of 12 and 18? One way to determine it is to make a list of the divisors (or factors) of 12 and 18:

Divisors of 12 $\{$**1**, **2**, **3**, 4, **6**, 12$\}$

Divisors of 18 $\{$**1**, **2**, **3**, **6**, 9, 18$\}$

The common divisors are 1, 2, 3, and 6. Therefore, the greatest common divisor is 6.

If the numbers are large, this method of finding the GCD is not practical. The GCD can be found more efficiently by using prime factorization.

> ### To Find the Greatest Common Divisor of Two or More Numbers
>
> 1. Determine the prime factorization of each number.
> 2. Find each prime factor with the smallest exponent that appears in each of the prime factorizations.
> 3. Determine the product of the factors found in step 2.

Example 4 illustrates this procedure.

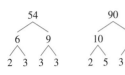

Figure 5.4

EXAMPLE 4 *Using Prime Factorization to Find the GCD*

Find the GCD of 54 and 90.

SOLUTION: The branching method of finding the prime factors of 54 and 90 is illustrated in Fig. 5.4.

a) The prime factorization of 54 is $2 \cdot 3^3$, and the prime factorization of 90 is $2 \cdot 3^2 \cdot 5$.

b) The prime factors with the smallest exponents that appear in each of the factorizations of 54 and 90 are 2 and 3^2.

c) The product of the factors found in step 2 is $2 \cdot 3^2 = 2 \cdot 9 = 18$. The GCD of 54 and 90 is 18. Eighteen is the largest number that divides both 54 and 90. ▲

DID YOU KNOW

Friendly Numbers

The ancient Greeks often thought of numbers as having human qualities. For example, the numbers 220 and 284 were considered "friendly" or "amicable" numbers because each number was the sum of the other number's proper factors. (A proper factor is any factor of a number other than the number itself.) If you sum all the proper factors of 284 $(1 + 2 + 4 + 71 + 142)$, you get the number 220, and if you sum all the proper factors of 220 $(1 + 2 + 4 + 5 + 10 + 11 + 20 + 22 + 44 + 55 + 110)$, you get 284.

EXAMPLE 5 *Finding the GCD*

Find the GCD of 225 and 525.

SOLUTION:

a) The prime factorization of 225 is $3^2 \cdot 5^2$, and the prime factorization of 525 is $3 \cdot 5^2 \cdot 7$ (you should verify these using the branching method or the division method).

b) The prime factors with the smallest exponents that appear in each of the factorizations of 225 and 525 are 3 and 5^2.

c) The product of the factors found in step 2 is $3 \cdot 5^2 = 3 \cdot 25 = 75$. The GCD of 225 and 525 is 75. ▲

Two numbers with a GCD of 1 are said to be ***relatively prime***. The numbers 9 and 14 are relatively prime, since the GCD is 1.

Least Common Multiple

To perform addition and subtraction of fractions (Section 5.3), we use the least common multiple (LCM). One technique of finding the LCM is to use prime factorization.

> The **least common multiple (LCM)** of a set of natural numbers is the smallest natural number that is divisible (without remainder) by each element of the set.

What is the least common multiple of 12 and 18? One way to determine the LCM is to make a list of the multiples of each number:

Multiples of 12	{12, 24, **36**, 48, 60, **72**, 84, 96, **108**, 120, 132, **144**, . . .}
Multiples of 18	{18, **36**, 54, **72**, 90, **108**, 126, **144**, 162, . . .}

Some common multiples of 12 and 18 are 36, 72, 108, and 144. The least common multiple, 36, is the smallest number that is divisible by both 12 and 18. Usually, the most efficient method of finding the LCM is to use prime factorization.

To Find the Least Common Multiple of Two or More Numbers

1. Determine the prime factorization of each number.
2. List each prime factor with the greatest exponent that appears in any of the prime factorizations.
3. Determine the product of the factors found in step 2.

Example 6 illustrates this procedure.

EXAMPLE 6   *Using Prime Factorization to Find the LCM*

Find the LCM of 54 and 90.

SOLUTION:

a) Find the prime factors of each number. In Example 4, we determined that

$$54 = 2 \cdot 3^3 \quad \text{and} \quad 90 = 2 \cdot 3^2 \cdot 5$$

b) List each prime factor with the greatest exponent that appears in either of the prime factorizations: 2, 3^3, 5.

c) Determine the product of the factors found in step 2:

$$2 \cdot 3^3 \cdot 5 = 2 \cdot 27 \cdot 5 = 270$$

Thus, 270 is the LCM of 54 and 90. It is the smallest number that is divisible by both 54 and 90.

EXAMPLE 7   *Finding the LCM*

Find the LCM of 225 and 525.

SOLUTION:

a) Find the prime factors of each number. In Example 5, we determined that

$$225 = 3^2 \cdot 5^2 \quad \text{and} \quad 525 = 3 \cdot 5^2 \cdot 7$$

b) List each prime factor with the greatest exponent that appears in either of the prime factorizations: 3^2, 5^2, 7.

c) Determine the product of the factors found in step 2:

$$3^2 \cdot 5^2 \cdot 7 = 9 \cdot 25 \cdot 7 = 1575$$

Thus, 1575 is the least common multiple of 225 and 525. It is the smallest number divisible by both 225 and 525.

Gimps

George Woltman

The Great Internet Mersenne Prime Search (GIMPS) was started by George Woltman to provide free software and access to a large database to coordinate the efforts of thousands of people interested in seeking new Mersenne prime numbers. Scott Kurowski provided the technology and services needed to make it simple for anyone to join the project via the Internet. GIMPS allows participants to use their computers to search for prime numbers while their computers are idle. A computer communicates, via the specialized software, with the database. Currently, there are over 130,000 worldwide participants in GIMPS. As of July 2003, the largest Mersenne prime was found by the 20-year-old Michael Cameron on November 14, 2001 in conjunction with GIMPS. The number, $2^{13,466,917} - 1$, which is over 4 million digits long, is the 39th Mersenne prime ever found and the fifth discovered by GIMPS participants. Michael's home computer, an AMD T-Bird 880 MHz with 512 Megs of RAM, took 42 days of idle time to conclude that this number was prime.

The Search For Larger Prime Numbers

More than 2000 years ago, the Greek mathematician Euclid proved that there is no largest prime number. Mathematicians, however, continue to strive to find larger and larger prime numbers.

Marin Mersenne (1588–1648), a seventeenth-century monk, found that numbers of the form $2^n - 1$ are often prime numbers when n is a prime number. For example,

$$2^2 - 1 = 4 - 1 = 3 \qquad 2^3 - 1 = 8 - 1 = 7$$
$$2^5 - 1 = 32 - 1 = 31 \qquad 2^7 - 1 = 128 - 1 = 127$$

Numbers of the form $2^n - 1$ that are prime are referred to as *Mersenne primes*. The first 10 Mersenne primes occur when $n = 2, 3, 5, 7, 13, 17, 19, 31, 61, 89$. The first time the expression $2^n - 1$ does not generate a prime number, for prime number n, is when n is 11. The number $2^{11} - 1$ is a composite number (see Exercise 90).

Scientists frequently use Mersenne primes in their search for larger and larger primes. The largest prime number found to date was discovered on November 14, 2001, by 20-year-old Michael Cameron of Owen Sound, Ontario, Canada in conjunction with the Great Internet Mersenne Prime Search (GIMPS). The number is the Mersenne prime $2^{13,466,917} - 1$. This record prime is the 39th known Mersenne prime, and when written out, it is 4,053,946 digits long—over 11 miles long if written using the same size font as this textbook!

More About Prime Numbers

Another mathematician who studied prime numbers was Pierre de Fermat (1601–1665). A lawyer by profession, Fermat became interested in mathematics as a hobby. He became one of the finest mathematicians of the seventeenth century. Fermat conjectured that each number of the form $2^{2^n} + 1$, now referred to as a *Fermat number*, was prime for each natural number n. Recall that a *conjecture* is a supposition that has not been proved nor disproved. In 1732, Leonhard Euler proved that for $n = 5$, $2^{32} + 1$ was a composite number, thus disproving Fermat's conjecture.

Since Euler's time, mathematicians have only been able to evaluate the sixth, seventh, eighth, ninth, tenth, and eleventh Fermat numbers to determine whether they are prime or composite. Each of these numbers has been shown to be composite. The eleventh Fermat number was factored by Richard Brent and François Morain in 1988. The sheer magnitude of the numbers involved makes it difficult to test these numbers, even with supercomputers.

In 1742, Christian Goldbach conjectured in a letter to Euler that every even number greater than or equal to 4 can be represented as the sum of two (not necessarily distinct) prime numbers (for example, $4 = 2 + 2$, $6 = 3 + 3$, $8 = 3 + 5$, $10 = 5 + 5$, $12 = 5 + 7$). This conjecture became known as *Goldbach's conjecture*, and it remains unproven to this day. The *twin prime conjecture* is another famous long-standing conjecture. *Twin primes* are primes of the form p and $p + 2$ (for example, 3 and 5, 5 and 7, 11 and 13). This conjecture states that there are an infinite number of pairs of twin primes. At the time of this writing the largest twin primes are of the form $665,551,035 \cdot 2^{80,025}$ plus or minus 1, which were found by David Underbakke and Phil Carmody on November 28, 2000.

SECTION 5.1   EXERCISES

Concept/Writing Exercises

1. What is number theory?
2. What does "*a* and *b* are factors of *c*" mean?
3. **a)** What does "*a* divides *b*" mean?
   b) What does "*a* is divisible by *b*" mean?
4. What is a prime number?
5. What is a composite number?
6. What does the fundamental theorem of arithmetic state?
7. **a)** What is the least common multiple of a set of natural numbers?
   b) In your own words, explain how to find the LCM of a set of natural numbers by using prime factorization.
   c) Find the LCM of 16 and 40 by using the procedure given in part (b).
8. **a)** What is the greatest common divisor of a set of natural numbers?
   b) In your own words, explain how to find the GCD of a set of natural numbers by using prime factorization.
   c) Find the GCD of 16 and 40 by using the procedure given in part (b).
9. What are Mersenne primes?
10. What is a conjecture?
11. What is Goldbach's conjecture?
12. What are twin primes?

Practice the Skills

13. Use the sieve of Eratosthenes to find the prime numbers up to 100.
14. Use the sieve of Eratosthenes to find the prime numbers up to 150.

In Exercises 15–26, determine whether the statement is true or false. Modify each false statement to make it a true statement.

15. 9 is a factor of 54.
16. 4|36.
17. 7 is a multiple of 21.
18. 35 is a divisor of 5.
19. 8 is divisible by 56.
20. 15 is a factor of 45.
21. If a number is not divisible by 5, then it is not divisible by 10.

22. If a number is not divisible by 10, then it is not divisible by 5.
23. If a number is divisible by 3, then every digit of the number is divisible by 3.
24. If every digit of a number is divisible by 3, then the number itself is divisible by 3.
25. If a number is divisible by 2 and 3, then the number is divisible by 6.
26. If a number is divisible by 3 and 4, then the number is divisible by 12.

In Exercises 27–32, determine whether the number is divisible by each of the following numbers: 2, 3, 4, 5, 6, 8, 9, and 10.

27. 10,368
28. 19,200
29. 2,763,105
30. 3,126,120
31. 1,882,320
32. 3,941,221
33. Determine a number that is divisible by 2, 3, 4, 5, and 6.
34. Determine a number that is divisible by 3, 4, 5, 9, and 10.

In Exercises 35–46, find the prime factorization of the number.

35. 45
36. 52
37. 196
38. 198
39. 303
40. 400
41. 513
42. 663
43. 1336
44. 1313
45. 2001
46. 3190

In Exercises 47–56, find (a) the greatest common divisor (GCD) and (b) the least common multiple (LCM).

47. 6 and 15
48. 20 and 36
49. 48 and 54
50. 22 and 231
51. 40 and 900
52. 120 and 240
53. 96 and 212
54. 240 and 285
55. 24, 48, and 128
56. 18, 78, and 198

Problem Solving

57. Find the next two sets of twin primes that follow the set 11, 13.
58. The primes 2 and 3 are consecutive natural numbers. Is there another pair of consecutive natural numbers both of which are prime? Explain.

59. For each pair of numbers, determine whether the numbers are relatively prime. Write yes or no as your answer.
   a) 14, 15
   b) 21, 30
   c) 24, 25
   d) 119, 143

60. Find the first three Fermat numbers and determine whether they are prime or composite.

61. Show that Goldbach's conjecture is true for the even numbers 4 through 20.

62. Find the first five Mersenne prime numbers.

63. *Barbie and Ken* Mary Lois King collects Barbie dolls and Ken dolls. She has 350 Barbie dolls and 140 Ken dolls. Mary Lois wishes to display the dolls in groups so that the same number of dolls are in each group and that each doll belongs to one group. If each group is to consist only of Barbie dolls or only of Ken dolls, what is the largest number of dolls Mary Lois can have in each group?

64. *Toy Car Collection* Martha Goshaw collects Matchbox® and HotWheels® toy cars. She has 288 red cars and 192 blue cars. She wants to line up her cars in groups so that each group has the same number of cars and each group contains only red cars or only blue cars. What is the largest number of cars she can have in a group?

65. *Stacking Trading Cards* Desmond Freeman collects trading cards. He has 432 baseball cards and 360 football cards. He wants to make stacks of cards on a table so that each stack contains the same number of cards and each card belongs to one stack. If the baseball and football cards must not be mixed in the stacks, what is the largest number of cards that he can have in a stack?

66. *Tree Rows* Elizabeth Dwyer is the manager at Queen Palm Nursery and is in charge of displaying potted trees in rows. Elizabeth has 150 citrus trees and 180 palm trees. She wants to make rows of trees so that each row has the same number of trees and each tree is in a row. If the citrus trees and the palm trees must not be mixed in the rows, what is the largest number of trees that she can have in a row?

67. *Airport Activity* O'Hare International Airport in Chicago has a flight leaving for New York City every 45 minutes and a flight leaving for Atlanta every 60 minutes. If a flight to New York City and a flight to Atlanta leave at the same time, how many minutes will it be before a flight to New York City and a flight to Atlanta again leave at the same time?

O'Hare International Airport

68. *Car Maintenance* For many sport utility vehicles, it is recommended that the oil be changed every 3500 miles and that the tires be rotated every 6000 miles. If Carmella Gonzalez just had the oil changed and tires rotated on her SUV during the same visit to her mechanic, how many miles will she drive before she has the oil changed and tires rotated again during the same visit?

69. *Work Schedules* Sara Pappas and Harry Kinnan both work the 3:00 P.M. to 11:00 P.M. shift. Sara has every fifth night off and Harry has every sixth night off. If they both have tonight off, how many days will pass before they have the same night off again?

70. *Restaurant Service* Peter Theodus runs a professional accounting service for restaurants. Peter goes to Arturo's Family Restaurant every 15 days, and he goes to Xang's Great Wall Restaurant every 18 days. If on October 1 Peter visits both restaurants, how many days would it be before he visited both restaurants on the same day again?

71. *U.S. Senate Committees* The U.S. Senate consists of 100 members. Senate committees are to be formed so that each of the committees contains the same number of senators and each senator is a member of exactly one committee. The committees are to have more than 2 members but fewer than 50 members. There are various ways that these committees can be formed.
   a) What size committees are possible?
   b) How many committees are there for each size?

72. *Prime Numbers* Consider the first eight prime numbers greater than 3. The numbers are 5, 7, 11, 13, 17, 19, 23, and 29.
   a) Determine which of these prime numbers differs by 1 from a multiple of the number 6.
   b) Use inductive reasoning and the results obtained in part (a) to make a conjecture regarding prime numbers.
   c) Select a few more prime numbers and determine whether your conjecture appears to be correct.

73. State a procedure that defines a divisibility test for 15.

74. State a procedure that defines a divisibility test for 22.

Euclidean Algorithm Another method that can be used to find the greatest common divisor is known as the Euclidean algorithm. We illustrate this procedure by finding the GCD of 60 and 220.

First divide 220 by 60 as shown below. Disregard the quotient 3 and then divide 60 by the remainder 40. Continue this process of dividing the divisors by the remainders until you obtain a remainder of 0. The divisor in the last division, in which the remainder is 0, is the GCD.

$$
\begin{array}{r} 3 \\ 60\overline{)220} \\ \underline{180} \\ 40 \end{array}
\qquad
\begin{array}{r} 1 \\ 40\overline{)60} \\ \underline{40} \\ 20 \end{array}
\qquad
\begin{array}{r} 2 \\ 20\overline{)40} \\ \underline{40} \\ 0 \end{array}
$$

Since 40/20 had a remainder of 0, the GCD is 20.

In Exercises 75–80, use the Euclidean algorithm to find the GCD.

75. 15, 35

76. 16, 28

77. 36, 108

78. 76, 240

79. 150, 180

80. 210, 560

Perfect Numbers A number whose proper factors (factors other than the number itself) add up to the number is called a perfect number. For example, 6 is a perfect number because its proper factors are 1, 2, and 3, and $1 + 2 + 3 = 6$. Determine which, if any, of the following numbers are perfect.

81. 12

82. 28

83. 496

84. 48

Challenge Problems/Group Activities

85. *Number of Factors* The following procedure can be used to determine the *number of factors* (or *divisors*) of a composite number. Write the number in prime factorization form. Examine the exponents on the prime numbers in the prime factorization. Add 1 to each exponent and then find the product of these numbers. This product gives the number of positive divisors of the composite number.
   a) Use this procedure to determine the number of divisors of 60.
   b) To check your answer, list all the divisors of 60. You should obtain the same number of divisors found in part (a).

86. Recall that if a number is divisible by both 2 and 3, then the number is divisible by 6. If a number is divisible by both 2 and 4, is the number necessarily divisible by 8? Explain your answer.

87. The product of any three consecutive natural numbers is divisible by 6. Explain why.

88. A number in which each digit except 0 appears exactly three times is divisible by 3. For example, 888,444,555 and 714,714,714 are both divisible by 3. Explain why this outcome must be true.

89. Use the fact that if $a|b$ and $a|c$, then $a|(b + c)$ to determine whether 36,018 is divisible by 18. (*Hint:* Write 36,018 as $36,000 + 18$.)

90. Show that the $2^n - 1$ is a (Mersenne) prime for $n = 2, 3, 5,$ and 7 but composite for $n = 11$.

91. Goldbach also conjectured in his letter to Euler that *every* integer greater than 5 is the sum of three prime numbers. For example, $6 = 2 + 2 + 2$ and $7 = 2 + 2 + 3$. Show that this conjecture is true for integers 8 through 20.

Recreational Mathematics

92. *Country, Animal, Fruit* Select a number from 1 to 10. Multiply your selected number by 9. Add the digits of the product together (if the product has more than one digit). Now subtract 5. Determine which letter of the alphabet corresponds to the number you ended with (for example, $1 = A, 2 = B, 3 = C,$ and so on). Think of a country whose name begins with that letter. Remember the last letter of the name of that country. Think of an animal whose name begins with that letter. Remember the last letter in the name of that animal. Think of a fruit whose name begins with that letter. a) What country, animal, and fruit did you select? Turn to the answer section to see if your response matches the responses of over 90% of the people who attempt this activity. b) Can you explain why most people select the given answer?

Research Activities

93. Do research and explain what *deficient numbers* and *abundant numbers* are. Give an example of each type of number. References include history of mathematics books, encyclopedias, and the Internet.

94. Conduct an Internet search on the GIMPS project. Write a report describing the history and development of the project. Include a current update of the project's findings.

5.2 THE INTEGERS

In Section 5.1, we introduced the natural or counting numbers:

$$N = \{1, 2, 3, 4, \ldots\}$$

Another important set of numbers, the *whole numbers*, help to answer the question "How many?"

$$\text{Whole numbers} = \{0, 1, 2, 3, 4, \ldots\}$$

Note that the set of whole numbers contains the number 0 but that the set of counting numbers does not. If a farmer were asked how many chickens were in a coop, the answer would be a whole number. If the farmer had no chickens, he or she would answer zero. Although we use the number 0 daily and take it for granted, the number 0 as we know it was not used and accepted until the sixteenth century.

If the temperature is 12°F and drops 20°, the resulting temperature is −8°F. This type of problem shows the need for negative numbers. The set of *integers* consists of the negative integers, 0, and the positive integers.

$$\text{Integers} = \{\ldots, -4, -3, -2, -1, 0, 1, 2, 3, \ldots\}$$

Negative integers   Positive integers

The term *positive integers* is yet another name for the natural numbers or counting numbers.

An understanding of addition, subtraction, multiplication, and division of the integers is essential in understanding algebra (Chapter 6). To aid in our explanation of addition and subtraction of integers, we introduce the real number line (Fig. 5.5). To construct the real number line, arbitrarily select a point for zero to serve as the starting point. Place the positive integers to the right of 0, equally spaced from one another. Place the negative integers to the left of 0, using the same spacing. The real number line contains the integers and all the other real numbers that are not integers. Some examples of real numbers that are not integers are indicated in Fig. 5.5, namely $-\frac{5}{2}, \frac{1}{2}, \sqrt{2}$, and π. We discuss real numbers that are not integers in the next two sections.

Figure 5.5

The arrows at the ends of the real number line indicate that the line continues indefinitely in both directions. Note that for any natural number, n, on the number line, the *opposite of* that number, $-n$, is also on the number line. This real number line was drawn horizontally, but it could just as well have been drawn vertically. In fact, in the next chapter, we show that the axes of a graph are the union of two number lines, one horizontal and the other vertical.

The number line can be used to determine the greater (or lesser) of two integers. Two *inequality symbols* that we will use in this chapter are > and <. The symbol > is read "is greater than," and the symbol < is read "is less than." Expressions that contain an inequality symbol are called *inequalities*. On the number line, the numbers increase from left to right. The number 3 is greater than 2, written $3 > 2$. Observe that 3 is to the right of 2. Similarly, we can see that $0 > -1$ by observing that 0 is to the right of -1 on the number line.

Instead of stating that 3 is greater than 2, we could state that 2 is less than 3, written $2 < 3$. Note that 2 is to the left of 3 on the number line. We can also see that $-1 < 0$ by observing that -1 is to the left of 0. The inequality symbol always points to the smaller of the two numbers when the inequality is true.

┌─ **EXAMPLE 1**   *Writing an Inequality*

Insert either $>$ or $<$ in the shaded area between the paired numbers to make the statement correct.

a) $-3 \blacksquare 1$ b) $-3 \blacksquare -5$ c) $-6 \blacksquare -4$ d) $0 \blacksquare -7$

SOLUTION:

a) $-3 < 1$ since -3 is to the left of 1 on the number line.

b) $-3 > -5$ since -3 is to the right of -5 on the number line.

c) $-6 < -4$ since -6 is to the left of -4 on the number line.

d) $0 > -7$ since 0 is to the right of -7 on the number line.   ▲

Addition of Integers

Addition of integers can be represented geometrically with a number line. To do so, begin at 0 on the number line. Represent the first addend (the first number to be added) by an arrow starting at 0. Draw the arrow to the right if the addend is positive. If the addend is negative, draw the arrow to the left. From the tip of the first arrow, draw a second arrow to represent the second addend. Draw the second arrow to the right or left, as just explained. The sum of the two integers is found at the tip of the second arrow.

┌─ **EXAMPLE 2**   *Adding Integers*

Evaluate the following using the number line.

a) $3 + (-5)$ b) $-1 + (-4)$ c) $-6 + 4$ d) $3 + (-3)$

SOLUTION:

a)

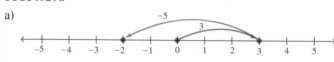

Thus, $3 + (-5) = -2$

b)

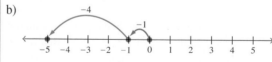

Thus, $-1 + (-4) = -5$

c)

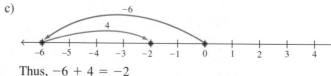

Thus, $-6 + 4 = -2$

d)

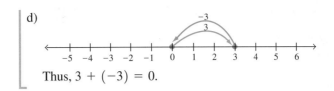

Thus, $3 + (-3) = 0$.   ▲

In Example 2(d), the number -3 is said to be the additive inverse of 3 and 3 is the additive inverse of -3, because their sum is 0. In general, the *additive inverse* of the number n is $-n$, since $n + (-n) = 0$. Inverses are discussed more formally in Chapter 10.

Subtraction of Integers

Any subtraction problem can be rewritten as an addition problem. To do so, we use the following definition of subtraction.

Subtraction

$$a - b = a + (-b)$$

The rule for subtraction indicates that to subtract b from a, *add* the additive inverse of b to a. For example,

$$3 - 5 = 3 + (-5)$$

Subtraction   Addition   Additive inverse of 5

Now we can determine the value of $3 + (-5)$.

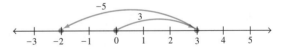

Thus, $3 - 5 = 3 + (-5) = -2$.

EXAMPLE 3   *Subtracting Integers*

Evaluate $-4 - (-3)$ using the number line.

SOLUTION: We are subtracting -3 from -4. The additive inverse of -3 is 3; therefore, we add 3 to -4. We now add $-4 + 3$ on the number line to obtain the answer -1.

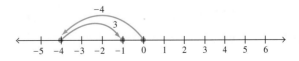

Thus, $-4 - (-3) = -4 + 3 = -1$.   ▲

In Example 3, we found that $-4 - (-3) = -4 + 3$. In general, $a - (-b) = a + b$. As you get more proficient in working with integers, you should be able to answer questions involving them without drawing a number line.

EXAMPLE 4   *Subtracting: Adding the Inverse*

Evaluate

a) $-5 - 2$ b) $-5 - (-2)$ c) $5 - (-2)$ d) $5 - 2$

SOLUTION:

a) $-5 - 2 = -5 + (-2) = -7$ b) $-5 - (-2) = -5 + 2 = -3$
c) $5 - (-2) = 5 + 2 = 7$ d) $5 - 2 = 5 + (-2) = 3$

EXAMPLE 5   *Elevation Difference*

The highest point on Earth is Mount Everest, in the Himalayas, at a height of 29,035 ft above sea level. The lowest point on Earth is the Mariana Trench, in the Pacific Ocean, at a depth of 36,198 ft below sea level ($-36,198$ ft). Find the vertical height difference between Mount Everest and the Mariana Trench.

SOLUTION: We obtain the vertical difference by subtracting the lower elevation from the higher elevation.

$$29,035 - (-36,198) = 29,035 + 36,198 = 65,233$$

The vertical difference is 65,233 ft.

Multiplication of Integers

The multiplication property of zero is important in our discussion of multiplication of integers. It indicates that the product of 0 and any number is 0.

> **Multiplication Property of Zero**
> $$a \cdot 0 = 0 \cdot a = 0$$

We will develop the rules for multiplication of integers using number patterns. The four possible cases are

1. positive integer $\times$ positive integer,
2. positive integer $\times$ negative integer,
3. negative integer $\times$ positive integer, and
4. negative integer $\times$ negative integer.

CASE 1: *POSITIVE INTEGER $\times$ POSITIVE INTEGER* The product of two positive integers can be defined as repeated addition of a positive integer. Thus, $3 \cdot 2$ means $2 + 2 + 2$. This sum will always be positive. Thus, a positive integer times a positive integer is a positive integer.

CASE 2: *POSITIVE INTEGER × NEGATIVE INTEGER* Consider the following patterns:

$$3(3) = 9$$
$$3(2) = 6$$
$$3(1) = 3$$

Note that each time the second factor is reduced by 1, the product is reduced by 3. Continuing the process gives

$$3(0) = 0$$

What comes next?

$$3(-1) = -3$$
$$3(-2) = -6$$

The pattern indicates that a positive integer times a negative integer is a negative integer.

We can confirm this result by using the number line. The expression $3(-2)$ means $(-2) + (-2) + (-2)$. Adding $(-2) + (-2) + (-2)$ on the number line, we obtain a sum of -6.

CASE 3: *NEGATIVE INTEGER × POSITIVE INTEGER* A procedure similar to that used in case 2 will indicate that a negative integer times a positive integer is a negative integer.

CASE 4: *NEGATIVE INTEGER × NEGATIVE INTEGER* We have illustrated that a positive integer times a negative integer is a negative integer. We make use of this fact in the following pattern:

$$4(-4) = -16$$
$$3(-4) = -12$$
$$2(-4) = -8$$
$$1(-4) = -4$$

In this pattern, each time the first term is decreased by 1, the product is increased by 4. Continuing this process gives

$$0(-4) = 0$$
$$(-1)(-4) = 4$$
$$(-2)(-4) = 8$$

This pattern illustrates that a negative integer times a negative integer is a positive integer.

The examples were restricted to integers. The rules for multiplication, however, can be used for any numbers. We summarize them as follows.

Rules for Multiplication

1. The product of two numbers with *like signs* (positive $\times$ positive or negative $\times$ negative) is a *positive number.*
2. The product of two numbers with *unlike signs* (positive $\times$ negative or negative $\times$ positive) is a *negative number.*

EXAMPLE 6   *Multiplying Integers*

Evaluate

a) $5 \cdot 9$ b) $5 \cdot (-9)$ c) $(-5) \cdot 9$ d) $(-5)(-9)$

SOLUTION:

a) $5 \cdot 9 = 45$ b) $5 \cdot (-9) = -45$ c) $(-5) \cdot 9 = -45$

d) $(-5)(-9) = 45$ ▲

Division of Integers

You may already realize that a relationship exists between multiplication and division.

$$6 \div 2 = 3 \quad \text{means that} \quad 3 \cdot 2 = 6$$

$$\frac{20}{10} = 2 \quad \text{means that} \quad 2 \cdot 10 = 20$$

These examples demonstrate that division is the reverse process of multiplication.

Division

For any a, b, and c where $b \neq 0$, $\dfrac{a}{b} = c$ means that $c \cdot b = a$.

We discuss the four possible cases for division, which are similar to those for multiplication.

CASE 1: *POSITIVE INTEGER $\div$ POSITIVE INTEGER* A positive integer divided by a positive integer is positive.

$$\frac{6}{2} = 3 \quad \text{since} \quad 3(2) = 6$$

CASE 2: *POSITIVE INTEGER $\div$ NEGATIVE INTEGER* A positive integer divided by a negative integer is negative.

$$\frac{6}{-2} = -3 \quad \text{since} \quad (-3)(-2) = 6$$

CASE 3: *NEGATIVE INTEGER ÷ POSITIVE INTEGER* A negative integer divided by a positive integer is negative.

$$\frac{-6}{2} = -3 \qquad \text{since} \qquad (-3)(2) = -6$$

CASE 4: *NEGATIVE INTEGER ÷ NEGATIVE INTEGER* A negative integer divided by a negative integer is positive.

$$\frac{-6}{-2} = 3 \qquad \text{since} \qquad 3(-2) = -6$$

The examples were restricted to integers. The rules for division, however, can be used for any numbers. You should realize that division of integers does not always result in an integer. The rules for division are summarized as follows.

Rules for Division

1. The quotient of two numbers with *like signs* (positive ÷ positive or negative ÷ negative) is a *positive number.*
2. The quotient of two numbers with *unlike signs* (positive ÷ negative or negative ÷ positive) is a *negative number.*

┌ **EXAMPLE 7** *Dividing Integers*

Evaluate

a) $\dfrac{56}{8}$ b) $\dfrac{-56}{8}$ c) $\dfrac{56}{-8}$ d) $\dfrac{-56}{-8}$

SOLUTION:

a) $\dfrac{56}{8} = 7$ b) $\dfrac{-56}{8} = -7$ c) $\dfrac{56}{-8} = -7$ d) $\dfrac{-56}{-8} = 7$ ▲

In the definition of division, we stated that the denominator could not be 0. Why not? Suppose we are trying to find the quotient $\frac{5}{0}$. Let's say that this quotient is equal to some number x. Then we would have $\frac{5}{0} = x$. If true, this would mean that $5 = x \cdot 0$. The right side of the equation is $x \cdot 0$, which is equal to 0 for any real value of x. This leads us to conclude that $5 = 0$, which is false. Thus, there is no number that can replace x that makes the equation $\frac{5}{0} = x$ true. Therefore, in mathematics, division by 0 is not allowed and we say that a quotient of any number divided by zero is *undefined.*

SECTION 5.2 EXERCISES

Concept/Writing Exercises

1. Explain how to add numbers using a number line.

2. What is the additive inverse of a number n?

3. Explain how to rewrite a subtraction problem as an addition problem.

4. Explain the rule for multiplication of real numbers.

5. Explain the rule for division of real numbers.

6. Explain why the quotient of a number divided by 0 is undefined.

Practice the Skills

In Exercises 7–16, evaluate the expression.

7. $-6 + 9$

8. $4 + (-5)$

9. $(-7) + 9$

10. $(-3) + (-3)$

11. $[6 + (-11)] + 0$

12. $(2 + 5) + (-4)$

13. $[(-3) + (-4)] + 9$

14. $[8 + (-3)] + (-2)$

15. $[(-23) + (-9)] + 11$

16. $[5 + (-13)] + 18$

In Exercises 17–26, evaluate the expression.

17. $3 - 6$

18. $-3 - 7$

19. $-4 - 6$

20. $7 - (-1)$

21. $-5 - (-3)$

22. $-4 - 4$

23. $14 - 20$

24. $8 - (-3)$

25. $[5 + (-3)] - 4$

26. $6 - (8 + 6)$

In Exercises 27–36, evaluate the expression.

27. $-4 \cdot 5$

28. $4(-3)$

29. $(-12)(-12)$

30. $5(-5)$

31. $[(-8)(-2)] \cdot 6$

32. $4(-5)(-6)$

33. $(5 \cdot 6)(-2)$

34. $(-9)(-1)(-2)$

35. $[(-3)(-6)] \cdot [(-5)(8)]$

36. $[(-8 \cdot 4) \cdot 5](-2)$

In Exercises 37–46, evaluate the expression.

37. $-26 \div (-13)$

38. $-56 \div 8$

39. $23 \div (-23)$

40. $-64 \div 16$

41. $56/-8$

42. $-75/15$

43. $-210/14$

44. $186/-6$

45. $144 \div (-3)$

46. $(-900) \div (-4)$

In Exercises 47–56, determine whether the statement is true or false. Modify each false statement to make it a true statement.

47. Every whole number is an integer.

48. Every integer is a whole number.

49. The difference of any two negative integers is a negative integer.

50. The sum of any two negative integers is a negative integer.

51. The product of any two positive integers is a positive integer.

52. The difference of a positive integer and a negative integer is always a negative integer.

53. The quotient of a negative integer and a positive integer is always a negative number.

54. The quotient of any two negative integers is a negative number.

55. The sum of a positive integer and a negative integer is always a positive integer.

56. The product of a positive integer and a negative integer is always a positive integer.

In Exercises 57–66, evaluate the expression.

57. $(5 + 7) \div 2$

58. $(-4) \div [14 \div (-7)]$

59. $[6(-2)] - 5$

60. $[(-5)(-6)] - 3$

61. $(4 - 8)(3)$

62. $[18 \div (-2)](-3)$

63. $[2 + (-17)] \div 3$

64. $(5 - 9) \div (-4)$

65. $[(-22)(-3)] \div (2 - 13)$

66. $[15(-4)] \div (-6)$

In Exercises 67–70, write the numbers in increasing order from left to right.

67. $0, -5, -10, 10, 5, -15$

68. $-20, 30, -40, 10, 0, -10$

69. $-5, -2, -3, -1, -4, -6$

70. $106, 33, -47, -108, 72, -76$

Problem Solving

71. *Extreme Temperatures* The hottest temperature ever recorded in the United States was 134°F, which occurred at Greenland Ranch, California, in Death Valley on July 10, 1913. The coldest temperature ever recorded in the United States was −79.8°F, which occurred at Prospect Creek Camp, Alaska, in the Endicott Mountains on January 23, 1971. Determine the difference between these two temperatures.

72. *NASDAQ Average* On August 28, 2002, the NASDAQ composite average opened at 1347 points. During that day it lost 33 points. On August 29 it gained 22 points, and on August 30 it lost 21 points. What was the closing NASDAQ composite average on August 30, 2002?

73. *Pit Score* While playing the game of Pit, John Pearse began with a score of zero points. He then gained 100 points, lost 40 points, gained 90 points, lost 20 points, and gained 80 points on his next five rounds. What is John's score after five rounds?

74. *Elevation Difference* Mount Whitney, in the Sierra Nevada mountains of California, is the highest point in the

contiguous United States. It is 14,495 ft above sea level. Death Valley, in California and Nevada, is the lowest point in the United States, 282 ft below sea level. Find the vertical height difference between Mount Whitney and Death Valley.

75. *Vertical Distance Traveled* A helicopter drops a package from a height of 842 ft above sea level. The package lands in the ocean and settles at a point 927 ft below sea level. What was the vertical distance the package traveled?

76. *Football Yardage* In the first four plays of the game, the Texans gained 8 yd, lost 5 yd, gained 3 yd, and gained 4 yd. What is the total number of yards gained in the first four plays? Did the Texans make a first down? (Ten yards are needed for a first down.)

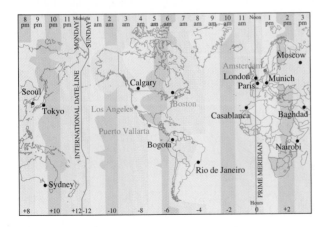

77. *Time Zone Calculations* Part of a World Standard Time Zones chart used by airlines and the United States Navy is shown. The scale along the bottom is just like a number line with the integers $-12, -11, \ldots, 11, 12$ on it.
   a) Find the difference in time between Amsterdam (zone $+1$) and Los Angeles (zone -8).
   b) Find the difference in time between Boston (zone -5) and Puerto Vallarta (zone -7).

78. Explain why $\dfrac{a}{b} = \dfrac{-a}{-b}$.

Challenge Problems/Group Activities

79. Find the quotient:

$$\frac{-1 + 2 - 3 + 4 - 5 + \cdots - 99 + 100}{1 - 2 + 3 - 4 + 5 - \cdots + 99 - 100}$$

80. *Pentagonal Numbers* Triangular numbers and square numbers were introduced in the Section 1.1 Exercises. There are also **pentagonal numbers**, which were also studied by the Greeks. Four pentagonal numbers are 1, 5, 12, and 22.

  1 5 12 22

   a) Determine the next three pentagonal numbers.
   b) Describe a procedure to determine the next five pentagonal numbers without drawing the figures.
   c) Is 72 a pentagonal number? Explain how you determined your answer.

81. Place the appropriate plus or minus signs between each digit so that the total will equal 1.

  0 1 2 3 4 5 6 7 8 9 = 1

Recreational Mathematics

82. *Four 4's* The game of *Four 4's* is a challenging way to learn about some of the operations on integers. In this game you must use exactly four 4's along with one or more of the operations of addition, subtraction, multiplication, and division* to write and evaluate expressions. The object of the game is to write expressions that when evaluated will give each whole number from 0 through 9. You may use as many grouping symbols as you wish, but you must use exactly four 4's. For example, one way to obtain 1 is as follows: $(4 + 4) \div (4 + 4) = 8 \div 8 = 1$. One way to obtain 2 is as follows:
$(4 \div 4) + (4 \div 4) = 1 + 1 = 2$.
   a) Use the rules as defined above to obtain each whole number 0 through 9.
   b) Use the rules as defined above to obtain the following whole numbers: 12, 15, 16, 17, 20.
   c) We will now change our rules to allow the number 44 to count as two of the four 4's. Use the number 44 and two other fours to obtain the whole number 10.

Research Activity

83. Do research and write a report on the history of the number 0 in the Hindu–Arabic numeration system.

---

*This game will be expanded in future exercise sets to include other operations such as exponents and square roots.

5.3 THE RATIONAL NUMBERS

"When you can measure what you are talking about and express it in numbers, you know something about it."
                    Lord Kelvin

We introduced the number line in Section 5.1 and discussed the integers in Section 5.2. The numbers that fall between the integers on the number line are either rational or irrational numbers. In this section, we discuss the rational numbers, and in Section 5.4, we discuss the irrational numbers.

Any number that can be expressed as a quotient of two integers (denominator not 0) is a rational number.

> The set of **rational numbers**, denoted by Q, is the set of all numbers of the form p/q, where p and q are integers and $q \neq 0$.

The following numbers are examples of rational numbers:

$$\frac{1}{3}, \quad \frac{3}{4}, \quad -\frac{7}{8}, \quad 1\frac{2}{3}, \quad 2, \quad 0, \quad \frac{15}{7}$$

The integers 2 and 0 are rational numbers because each can be expressed as the quotient of two integers: $2 = \frac{2}{1}$ and $0 = \frac{0}{1}$. In fact, every integer n is a rational number, since it can be written in the form of $\frac{n}{1}$.

Numbers such as $\frac{1}{3}$ and $-\frac{7}{8}$ are also called *fractions*. The number above the fraction line is called the *numerator*, and the number below the fraction line is called the *denominator*.

Reducing Fractions

Sometimes the numerator and denominator in a fraction have a common divisor (or common factor). For example, both the numerator and denominator of the fraction $\frac{6}{10}$ have the common divisor 2. When a numerator and denominator have a common divisor, we can *reduce the fraction to its lowest terms*.

A fraction is said to be in its lowest terms (or reduced) when the numerator and denominator are relatively prime (that is, have no common divisors other than 1). To reduce a fraction to its lowest terms, divide both the numerator and the denominator by the greatest common divisor. Recall that a procedure for finding the greatest common divisor was discussed in Section 5.1.

The fraction $\frac{6}{10}$ is reduced to its lowest terms as follows.

$$\frac{6}{10} = \frac{6 \div 2}{10 \div 2} = \frac{3}{5}$$

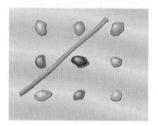
EXAMPLE 1   *Reducing a Fraction to Lowest Terms*

Reduce $\dfrac{54}{90}$ to its lowest terms.

SOLUTION: On page 213 in Example 4 of Section 5.1, we determined that the GCD of 54 and 90 is 18. Divide the numerator and the denominator by GCD, 18.

$$\frac{54}{90} = \frac{54 \div 18}{90 \div 18} = \frac{3}{5}$$

Since there are no common divisors of 3 and 5 other than 1, this fraction is in its lowest terms.   ▲

Mixed Numbers and Improper Fractions

Consider the number $2\frac{3}{4}$. It is an example of a *mixed number*. It is called a mixed number because it consists of an integer, 2, and a fraction, $\frac{3}{4}$. The mixed number $2\frac{3}{4}$ means $2 + \frac{3}{4}$. The mixed number $-4\frac{1}{4}$ means $-(4 + \frac{1}{4})$. Rational numbers greater than 1 or less than -1 that are not integers may be represented as mixed numbers, or as *improper fractions*. An improper fraction is a fraction whose numerator is greater than its denominator. An example of an improper fraction is $\frac{8}{5}$. Figure 5.6 shows both mixed numbers and improper fractions indicated on a number line. In this section, we show how to convert mixed numbers to improper fractions and vice versa.

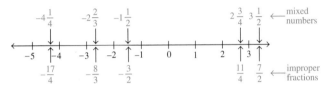

Figure 5.6

We begin by limiting our discussion to positive mixed numbers and positive improper fractions.

Converting a Positive Mixed Number to an Improper Fraction

1. Multiply the denominator of the fraction in the mixed number by the integer preceding it.
2. Add the product obtained in step 1 to the numerator of the fraction in the mixed number. This sum is the numerator of the improper fraction we are seeking. The denominator of the improper fraction we are seeking is the same as the denominator of the fraction in the mixed number.

EXAMPLE 2   *From Mixed Number to Improper Fraction*

Convert the following mixed numbers to improper fractions.

a) $1\frac{7}{8}$ b) $3\frac{5}{6}$

SOLUTION:

a) $1\dfrac{7}{8} = \dfrac{8 \cdot 1 + 7}{8} = \dfrac{8 + 7}{8} = \dfrac{15}{8}$

b) $3\dfrac{5}{6} = \dfrac{6 \cdot 3 + 5}{6} = \dfrac{18 + 5}{6} = \dfrac{23}{6}$

Notice that both $\frac{15}{8}$ and $\frac{23}{6}$ have numerators larger than their denominators and that both are improper fractions.   ▲

> **Converting a Positive Improper Fraction to a Mixed Number**
>
> 1. Divide the numerator by the denominator. Identify the quotient and the remainder.
> 2. The quotient obtained in step 1 is the integer part of the mixed number. The remainder is the numerator of the fraction in the mixed number. The denominator in the fraction of the mixed number will be the same as the denominator in the original fraction.

EXAMPLE 3   *From Improper Fraction to Mixed Number*

Convert the following improper fractions to mixed numbers.

a) $\dfrac{8}{5}$ b) $\dfrac{225}{8}$

SOLUTION:

a) Divide the numerator, 8, by the denominator, 5.

$$
\begin{array}{r}
1 \leftarrow \text{Quotient} \\
\text{Divisor} \rightarrow \quad 5\overline{)8} \leftarrow \text{Dividend} \\
5 \\
\hline
3 \leftarrow \text{Remainder}
\end{array}
$$

Therefore,

$$
\overset{\text{Quotient}}{\underset{\downarrow}{}}
$$

$$
\frac{8}{5} = 1\frac{3}{5} \quad \begin{array}{l} \leftarrow \text{Remainder} \\ \leftarrow \text{Divisor} \end{array}
$$

The mixed number is $1\frac{3}{5}$.

b) Divide the numerator, 225, by the denominator, 8.

$$
\begin{array}{r}
28 \leftarrow \text{Quotient} \\
\text{Divisor} \rightarrow \quad 8\overline{)225} \leftarrow \text{Dividend} \\
16 \\
\hline
65 \\
64 \\
\hline
1 \leftarrow \text{Remainder}
\end{array}
$$

Therefore,

$$
\overset{\text{Quotient}}{\underset{\downarrow}{}}
$$

$$
\frac{225}{8} = 28\frac{1}{8} \quad \begin{array}{l} \leftarrow \text{Remainder} \\ \leftarrow \text{Divisor} \end{array}
$$

The mixed number is $28\frac{1}{8}$.   ▲

Up to this point, we have only worked with positive mixed numbers and positive improper fractions. When converting a negative mixed number to an improper fraction, or a negative improper fraction to a mixed number, it is best to ignore the negative sign temporarily. Perform the calculation as described earlier and then reattach the negative sign.

┌ EXAMPLE 4   *Negative Mixed Numbers and Improper Fractions*

a) Convert $-1\frac{7}{8}$ to an improper fraction.
b) Convert $-\frac{8}{5}$ to a mixed number.

SOLUTION:
a) First, ignore the negative sign and examine $1\frac{7}{8}$. We learned in Example 2(a) that $1\frac{7}{8} = \frac{15}{8}$. Now to convert $-1\frac{7}{8}$ to an improper fraction, we reattach the negative sign. Thus, $-1\frac{7}{8} = -\frac{15}{8}$.
b) We learned in Example 3(a) that $\frac{8}{5} = 1\frac{3}{5}$. Therefore, $-\frac{8}{5} = -1\frac{3}{5}$.   ▲

Terminating or Repeating Decimal Numbers

Note the following important property of the rational numbers.

Every *rational number* when expressed as a decimal number will be either a terminating or a repeating decimal number.

Examples of terminating decimal numbers are 0.5, 0.75, and 4.65. Examples of repeating decimal numbers are 0.333..., 0.2323..., and 8.13456456.... One way to indicate that a number or group of numbers repeat is to place a bar above the number or group of numbers that repeat. Thus, 0.333... may be written $0.\overline{3}$, 0.2323... may be written $0.\overline{23}$, and 8.13456456... may be written $8.13\overline{456}$.

┌ EXAMPLE 5   *Terminating Decimal Numbers*

Show that the following rational numbers are terminating decimal numbers.

a) $\frac{2}{5}$ b) $-\frac{7}{8}$ c) $\frac{17}{16}$

SOLUTION: To express the rational number in decimal form, divide the numerator by the denominator. If you use a calculator, or use long division, you will obtain the following results.

a) $\frac{2}{5} = 0.4$ b) $-\frac{7}{8} = -0.875$ c) $\frac{17}{16} = 1.0625$ ▲

┌ EXAMPLE 6   *Repeating Decimal Numbers*

Show that the following rational numbers are repeating decimal numbers.

a) $\frac{2}{3}$ b) $\frac{14}{99}$ c) $1\frac{4}{33}$

SOLUTION: If you use a calculator, or use long division, you will see that each fraction results in a repeating decimal number.

a) $2 \div 3 = 0.6666\ldots$ or $0.\overline{6}$

b) $14 \div 99 = 0.141414\ldots$ or $0.\overline{14}$

c) $1\frac{4}{33} = \frac{37}{33} = 1.121212\ldots$ or $1.\overline{12}$ ▲

Note that in each part of Example 6, the quotient has no final digit and continues indefinitely. Each number is a repeating decimal number.

When a fraction is converted to a decimal number, the maximum number of digits that can repeat is $n - 1$, where n is the denominator of the fraction. For example, when $\frac{2}{7}$ is converted to a decimal number, the maximum number of digits that can repeat is $7 - 1$, or 6.

Converting Decimal Numbers to Fractions

We can convert a terminating or repeating decimal number into a quotient of integers. The explanation of the procedure will refer to the positional values to the right of the decimal point, as illustrated here:

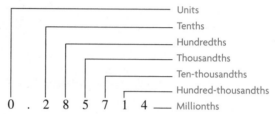

Example 7 demonstrates how to convert from a decimal number to a fraction.

┌ **EXAMPLE 7** *Converting a Decimal Number into a Fraction*

Convert the following terminating decimal numbers to a quotient of integers.

a) 0.4   b) 0.62   c) 0.062   d) 1.37

SOLUTION: When converting a terminating decimal number to a quotient of integers, we observe the last digit to the right of the decimal point. The position of this digit will indicate the denominator of the quotient of integers.

a) $0.4 = \frac{4}{10}$ because the 4 is in the tenths position.

b) $0.62 = \frac{62}{100}$ because the last digit on the right, 2, is in the hundredths position.

c) $0.062 = \frac{62}{1000}$ because the last digit on the right, 2, is in the thousandths position.

d) $1.37 = \frac{137}{100}$ because the last digit on the right, 7, is in the ten-thousandths position.
Notice the numerator is the decimal number with the decimal point removed.
When the decimal number is larger than 1, the numerator of the resulting fraction will be greater than the denominator or an improper fraction. ▲

Converting a repeating decimal number to a quotient of integers is more difficult. To do so, we must "create" another repeating decimal number with the same repeating digits so that when one repeating decimal number is subtracted from the other repeating decimal number, the difference will be a whole number. To create a number with the same repeating digits, multiply the original repeating decimal number by 10 if one digit repeats, by 100 if two digits repeat, by 1000 if three digits repeat, and so on. Examples 8 through 10 demonstrate this procedure.

EXAMPLE 8   Converting a Repeating Decimal Number into a Fraction

Convert $0.\overline{3}$ to a quotient of integers.

SOLUTION: $0.\overline{3} = 0.3\overline{3} = 0.33\overline{3}$, and so on.

Let the original repeating decimal number be n; thus, $n = 0.\overline{3}$. Because one digit repeats, we multiply both sides of the equation by 10, which gives $10n = 3.\overline{3}$. Then we subtract.

$$\begin{aligned} 10n &= 3.\overline{3} \\ - \quad n &= 0.\overline{3} \\ \hline 9n &= 3.0 \end{aligned}$$

Note that $10n - n = 9n$ and $3.\overline{3} - 0.\overline{3} = 3.0$.

Next, we solve for n by dividing both sides of the equation by 9.

$$\frac{9n}{9} = \frac{3.0}{9}$$

$$n = \frac{3}{9} = \frac{1}{3}$$

Therefore, $0.\overline{3} = \frac{1}{3}$. Evaluate $1 \div 3$ on a calculator now and see what value you get.   ▲

EXAMPLE 9   Converting a Repeating Decimal Number into a Fraction

Convert $0.\overline{35}$ to a quotient of integers.

SOLUTION: Let $n = 0.\overline{35}$. Since two digits repeat, multiply both sides of the equation by 100. Thus, $100n = 35.\overline{35}$. Now we subtract n from $100n$.

$$\begin{aligned} 100n &= 35.\overline{35} \\ - \quad n &= 0.\overline{35} \\ \hline 99n &= 35 \end{aligned}$$

Finally, we divide both sides of the equation by 99.

$$\frac{99n}{99} = \frac{35}{99}$$

$$n = \frac{35}{99}$$

Therefore, $0.\overline{35} = \frac{35}{99}$. Evaluate $35 \div 99$ on a calculator now and see what value you get.   ▲

EXAMPLE 10   Converting a Repeating Decimal Number into a Fraction

Convert $12.14\overline{2}$ to a quotient of integers.

SOLUTION: This problem is different from the two preceding examples in that the repeating digit, 2, is not directly to the right of the decimal point. When this situation arises, move the decimal point to the right until the repeating terms are directly to its right. For each place the decimal point is moved, the number is multiplied by 10. In this example, the decimal point must be moved two places to the right. Thus, the number must be multiplied by 100.

$$n = 12.14\overline{2}$$
$$100n = 100 \times 12.14\overline{2} = 1214.\overline{2}$$

Now proceed as in the previous two examples. Since one digit repeats, multiply both sides by 10.

$$100n = 1214.\overline{2}$$
$$10 \times 100n = 10 \times 1214.\overline{2}$$
$$1000n = 12142.\overline{2}$$

Now subtract $100n$ from $1000n$ so that the repeating part will drop out.

$$
\begin{array}{r}
1000n = 12142.\overline{2} \\
-\ 100n = \ \ 1214.\overline{2} \\
\hline
900n = 10928
\end{array}
$$

$$n = \frac{10{,}928}{900} = \frac{2732}{225}$$

Therefore, $12.14\overline{2} = \frac{2732}{225}$. Evaluate $2732 \div 225$ on a calculator now and see what value you get.   ▲

Multiplication and Division of Fractions

The product of two fractions is found by multiplying the numerators together and multiplying the denominators together.

Multiplication of Fractions

$$\frac{a}{b} \cdot \frac{c}{d} = \frac{a \cdot c}{b \cdot d} = \frac{ac}{bd}, \quad b \neq 0, \quad d \neq 0$$

┌─ **EXAMPLE 11**   *Multiplying Fractions*

Evaluate the following.

a) $\dfrac{3}{5} \cdot \dfrac{7}{8}$ b) $\left(\dfrac{-2}{3}\right)\left(\dfrac{-4}{9}\right)$ c) $\left(1\dfrac{7}{8}\right)\left(2\dfrac{1}{4}\right)$

SOLUTION:

a) $\dfrac{3}{5} \cdot \dfrac{7}{8} = \dfrac{3 \cdot 7}{5 \cdot 8} = \dfrac{21}{40}$

b) $\left(\dfrac{-2}{3}\right)\left(\dfrac{-4}{9}\right) = \dfrac{(-2)(-4)}{(3)(9)} = \dfrac{8}{27}$

c) $\left(1\dfrac{7}{8}\right)\left(2\dfrac{1}{4}\right) = \dfrac{15}{8} \cdot \dfrac{9}{4} = \dfrac{135}{32} = 4\dfrac{7}{32}$ ▲

The *reciprocal* of any number is 1 divided by that number. The product of a number and its reciprocal must equal 1. Examples of some numbers and their reciprocals follow.

Number		Reciprocal		Product
3	$\cdot$	$\dfrac{1}{3}$	$=$	1
$\dfrac{3}{5}$	$\cdot$	$\dfrac{5}{3}$	$=$	1
-6	$\cdot$	$-\dfrac{1}{6}$	$=$	1

To find the quotient of two fractions, multiply the first fraction by the reciprocal of the second fraction.

Division of Fractions

$$\frac{a}{b} \div \frac{c}{d} = \frac{a}{b} \cdot \frac{d}{c} = \frac{ad}{bc}, \quad b \neq 0, \quad d \neq 0, \quad c \neq 0$$

EXAMPLE 12　*Dividing Fractions*

Evaluate the following.

a) $\dfrac{2}{3} \div \dfrac{5}{7}$　　b) $\dfrac{-3}{5} \div \dfrac{5}{7}$

SOLUTION:

a) $\dfrac{2}{3} \div \dfrac{5}{7} = \dfrac{2}{3} \cdot \dfrac{7}{5} = \dfrac{2 \cdot 7}{3 \cdot 5} = \dfrac{14}{15}$

b) $\dfrac{-3}{5} \div \dfrac{5}{7} = \dfrac{-3}{5} \cdot \dfrac{7}{5} = \dfrac{-3 \cdot 7}{5 \cdot 5} = \dfrac{-21}{25}$ or $-\dfrac{21}{25}$

Addition and Subtraction of Fractions

Before we can add or subtract fractions, the fractions must have a common denominator. A common denominator is another name for a common multiple of the denominators. The *lowest common denominator (LCD)* is the least common multiple of the denominators.

To add or subtract two fractions with a common denominator, we add or subtract their numerators and retain the common denominator.

Addition and Subtraction of Fractions

$$\frac{a}{c} + \frac{b}{c} = \frac{a + b}{c}, \quad c \neq 0; \qquad \frac{a}{c} - \frac{b}{c} = \frac{a - b}{c}, \quad c \neq 0$$

Mathematical Music

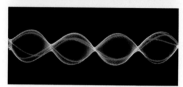

When the string of a musical instrument is plucked or bowed, it moves in a wave-like pattern like the strings shown here. The vibration this creates in the surrounding air is what your eardrums detect as sound.

The ancient Greeks believed that in nature, all harmony and everything of beauty could be explained with rational numbers. This belief was reinforced by the discovery that the sound of plucked strings could be quite pleasing if the strings plucked were in the ratio of 1 to 2 (an octave), 2 to 3 (a fifth), 3 to 4 (a fourth), and so on. Thus, the secret of harmony lies in the rational numbers such as $\frac{1}{2}$, $\frac{2}{3}$, and $\frac{3}{4}$.

The theory of vibrating strings has applications today that go well beyond music. How materials vibrate, and hence the stress they can absorb, is a vital matter in the construction of rockets, buildings, and bridges.

EXAMPLE 13   Adding and Subtracting Fractions with a Common Denominator

Evaluate the following.

a) $\dfrac{3}{8} + \dfrac{2}{8}$

b) $\dfrac{15}{16} - \dfrac{7}{16}$

SOLUTION:

a) $\dfrac{3}{8} + \dfrac{2}{8} = \dfrac{3+2}{8} = \dfrac{5}{8}$

b) $\dfrac{15}{16} - \dfrac{7}{16} = \dfrac{15-7}{16} = \dfrac{8}{16} = \dfrac{1}{2}$

Note that in Example 13, the denominators of the fractions being added or subtracted were the same; that is, they have a common denominator. *When adding or subtracting two fractions with unlike denominators, first rewrite each fraction with a common denominator. Then add or subtract the fractions.*

Writing fractions with a common denominator is accomplished with the *fundamental law of rational numbers.*

Fundamental Law of Rational Numbers

If a, b, and c are integers, with $b \neq 0$ and $c \neq 0$, then

$$\frac{a}{b} = \frac{a}{b} \cdot \frac{c}{c} = \frac{a \cdot c}{b \cdot c}$$

The terms $\dfrac{a}{b}$ and $\dfrac{a \cdot c}{b \cdot c}$ are called *equivalent fractions*. For example, since $\dfrac{5}{12} = \dfrac{5 \cdot 5}{12 \cdot 5} = \dfrac{25}{60}$, the fractions $\dfrac{5}{12}$ and $\dfrac{25}{60}$ are equivalent fractions. We will see the importance of equivalent fractions in the next two examples.

EXAMPLE 14   Subtracting Fractions with Unlike Denominators

Evaluate $\dfrac{5}{12} - \dfrac{3}{10}$.

SOLUTION: Using prime factorization (Section 5.1), we find that the LCM of 12 and 10 is 60. We will therefore express each fraction as an equivalent fraction with a denominator of 60. Sixty divided by 12 is 5. Therefore, the denominator, 12, must be multiplied by 5 to get 60. If the denominator is multiplied by 5, the numerator must also be multiplied by 5 so that the value of the fraction remains unchanged. Multiplying both numerator and denominator by 5 is the same as multiplying by 1.

We follow the same procedure for the other fraction, $\frac{3}{10}$. Sixty divided by 10 is 6. Therefore, we multiply both the denominator, 10, and the numerator, 3, by 6 to obtain an equivalent fraction with a denominator of 60.

$$\frac{5}{12} - \frac{3}{10} = \left(\frac{5}{12} \cdot \frac{5}{5}\right) - \left(\frac{3}{10} \cdot \frac{6}{6}\right)$$

$$= \frac{25}{60} - \frac{18}{60}$$

$$= \frac{7}{60}$$

▲

EXAMPLE 15   *Adding Fractions with Unlike Denominators*

Evaluate $\dfrac{1}{54} + \dfrac{1}{90}$.

SOLUTION: On page 214, in Example 6 of Section 5.1, we determined that the LCM of 54 and 90 is 270. Rewrite each fraction as an equivalent fraction using the LCM as the common denominator.

$$\frac{1}{54} + \frac{1}{90} = \left(\frac{1}{54} \cdot \frac{5}{5}\right) + \left(\frac{1}{90} \cdot \frac{3}{3}\right)$$

$$= \frac{5}{270} + \frac{3}{270}$$

$$= \frac{8}{270}$$

Now we reduce $\frac{8}{270}$ by dividing both 8 and 270 by 2, their greatest common factor.

$$\frac{8}{270} = \frac{8 \div 2}{270 \div 2} = \frac{4}{135}$$

▲

EXAMPLE 16   *Rice Preparation*

Following are the instructions given on a box of Minute Rice. Determine the amount of (a) rice and water, (b) salt, and (c) butter or margarine needed to make 3 servings of rice.

Directions

1. Bring water, salt, and butter (or margarine) to a boil.

2. Stir in rice. Cover; remove from heat. Let stand 5 minutes. Fluff with fork.

To Make	Rice & Water (Equal Measures)	Salt	Butter or Margarine (If Desired)
2 servings	$\frac{2}{3}$ cup	$\frac{1}{4}$ tsp	1 tsp
4 servings	$1\frac{1}{3}$ cups	$\frac{1}{2}$ tsp	2 tsp

SOLUTION: Since 3 is halfway between 2 and 4, we can find the amount of each ingredient by finding the average of the amount for 2 and 4 servings. To do so, we add the amounts for 2 servings and 4 servings and divide the sum by 2.

a) Rice and water: $\dfrac{\frac{2}{3} + 1\frac{1}{3}}{2} = \dfrac{\frac{2}{3} + \frac{4}{3}}{2} = \dfrac{\frac{6}{3}}{2} = \dfrac{2}{2} = 1$ cup

b) Salt: $\dfrac{\frac{1}{4} + \frac{1}{2}}{2} = \dfrac{\frac{1}{4} + \frac{2}{4}}{2} = \dfrac{\frac{3}{4}}{2} = \dfrac{3}{4} \cdot \dfrac{1}{2} = \dfrac{3}{8}$ tsp

c) Butter or margarine: $\dfrac{1 + 2}{2} = \dfrac{3}{2}$, or $1\frac{1}{2}$ tsp

The solution to Example 16 can be found in other ways. Suggest two other procedures for solving the same problem.

SECTION 5.3   EXERCISES

Concept/Writing Exercises

1. Describe the set of rational numbers.

2. **a)** Explain how to write a terminating decimal number as a fraction.
   b) Write 0.397 as a fraction.

3. **a)** Explain how to reduce a fraction to lowest terms.
   b) Reduce $\frac{15}{27}$ to lowest terms by using the procedure in part (a).

4. Explain how to convert an improper fraction into a mixed number.

5. Explain how to convert a mixed number into an improper fraction.

6. **a)** Explain how to multiply two fractions.
   b) Multiply $\frac{15}{16} \cdot \frac{24}{25}$ by using the procedure in part (a).

7. **a)** Explain how to determine the reciprocal of a number.
   b) Using the procedure in part (a), determine the reciprocal of -2.

8. **a)** Explain how to divide two fractions.
   b) Divide $\frac{4}{15} \div \frac{16}{55}$ by using the procedure in part (a).

9. **a)** Explain how to add or subtract two fractions having a common denominator.
   b) Add $\frac{11}{36} + \frac{13}{36}$ by using the procedure in part (a).
   c) Subtract $\frac{37}{48} - \frac{13}{48}$ using the procedure in part (a).

10. **a)** Explain how to add or subtract two fractions having unlike denominators.
    b) Using the procedure in part (a), add $\frac{5}{12} + \frac{4}{9}$.
    c) Subtract $\frac{5}{6} - \frac{2}{15}$ using the procedure in part (a).

11. In your own words, state the fundamental law of rational numbers.

12. Are $\frac{4}{7}$ and $\frac{20}{35}$ equivalent fractions? Explain your answer.

Practice the Skills

In Exercises 13–22, reduce each fraction to lowest terms.

13. $\dfrac{4}{6}$ 14. $\dfrac{21}{35}$ 15. $\dfrac{26}{91}$

16. $\dfrac{36}{56}$ 17. $\dfrac{525}{800}$ 18. $\dfrac{13}{221}$

19. $\dfrac{112}{176}$ 20. $\dfrac{120}{135}$ 21. $\dfrac{45}{495}$

22. $\dfrac{124}{148}$

In Exercises 23–28, convert each mixed number into an improper fraction.

23. $3\dfrac{4}{7}$ 24. $4\dfrac{5}{6}$ 25. $-1\dfrac{15}{16}$

26. $-7\dfrac{1}{5}$ 27. $-4\dfrac{15}{16}$ 28. $11\dfrac{9}{16}$

In Exercises 29–32, write the number of inches indicated by the arrows as an improper fraction.

29.

30.

31.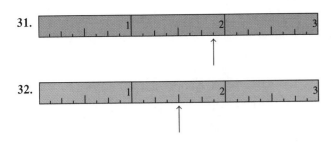

32.

In Exercises 33–38, convert each improper fraction into a mixed number.

33. $\dfrac{11}{8}$

34. $\dfrac{23}{4}$

35. $-\dfrac{73}{6}$

36. $-\dfrac{457}{11}$

37. $-\dfrac{878}{15}$

38. $\dfrac{1028}{21}$

In Exercises 39–48, express each rational number as terminating or repeating decimal number.

39. $\dfrac{3}{5}$

40. $\dfrac{15}{16}$

41. $\dfrac{2}{9}$

42. $\dfrac{5}{6}$

43. $\dfrac{3}{8}$

44. $\dfrac{23}{7}$

45. $\dfrac{13}{3}$

46. $\dfrac{115}{15}$

47. $\dfrac{85}{15}$

48. $\dfrac{1002}{11}$

In Exercises 49–58, express each terminating decimal number as a quotient of two integers.

49. 0.25

50. 0.29

51. 0.045

52. 0.0125

53. 0.2

54. 0.251

55. 0.452

56. 0.2345

57. 0.0001

58. 0.2535

In Exercises 59–68, express each repeating decimal number as a quotient of two integers.

59. $0.\overline{6}$

60. $0.\overline{5}$

61. $1.\overline{9}$

62. $0.\overline{51}$

63. $1.\overline{36}$

64. $0.\overline{135}$

65. $1.0\overline{2}$

66. $2.4\overline{9}$

67. $3.4\overline{78}$

68. $5.2\overline{39}$

In Exercises 69–78, perform the indicated operation and reduce your answer to lowest terms.

69. $\dfrac{4}{11} \cdot \dfrac{3}{8}$

70. $\dfrac{3}{5} \div \dfrac{6}{7}$

71. $\left(\dfrac{-3}{8}\right)\left(\dfrac{-16}{15}\right)$

72. $\left(-\dfrac{3}{5}\right) \div \dfrac{10}{21}$

73. $\dfrac{7}{8} \div \dfrac{8}{7}$

74. $\dfrac{3}{7} \div \dfrac{3}{7}$

75. $\left(\dfrac{3}{5} \cdot \dfrac{4}{7}\right) \div \dfrac{1}{3}$

76. $\left(\dfrac{4}{7} \div \dfrac{4}{5}\right) \cdot \dfrac{1}{7}$

77. $\left[\left(\dfrac{-3}{4}\right)\left(\dfrac{-2}{7}\right)\right] \div \dfrac{3}{5}$

78. $\left(\dfrac{3}{8} \cdot \dfrac{5}{9}\right) \cdot \left(\dfrac{4}{7} \div \dfrac{5}{8}\right)$

In Exercises 79–88, perform the indicated operation and reduce your answer to lowest terms.

79. $\dfrac{2}{3} + \dfrac{1}{5}$

80. $\dfrac{5}{6} - \dfrac{1}{8}$

81. $\dfrac{5}{13} + \dfrac{11}{26}$

82. $\dfrac{5}{12} + \dfrac{7}{36}$

83. $\dfrac{5}{9} - \dfrac{7}{54}$

84. $\dfrac{13}{30} - \dfrac{17}{120}$

85. $\dfrac{1}{12} + \dfrac{1}{48} + \dfrac{1}{72}$

86. $\dfrac{3}{5} + \dfrac{7}{15} + \dfrac{9}{75}$

87. $\dfrac{1}{30} - \dfrac{3}{40} - \dfrac{7}{50}$

88. $\dfrac{4}{25} - \dfrac{9}{100} - \dfrac{7}{40}$

Problem Solving

Alternative methods for adding and subtracting two fractions are shown. These methods may not result in a solution in its lowest terms.

$$\dfrac{a}{b} + \dfrac{c}{d} = \dfrac{ad + bc}{bd} \quad \text{and} \quad \dfrac{a}{b} - \dfrac{c}{d} = \dfrac{ad - bc}{bd}$$

In Exercises 89–94, use one of the two formulas to evaluate the expression.

89. $\dfrac{2}{5} + \dfrac{7}{8}$

90. $\dfrac{3}{4} + \dfrac{2}{9}$

91. $\dfrac{5}{6} - \dfrac{7}{8}$

92. $\dfrac{7}{3} - \dfrac{5}{12}$

93. $\dfrac{3}{8} + \dfrac{5}{12}$

94. $\left(\dfrac{2}{3} + \dfrac{1}{4}\right) - \dfrac{3}{5}$

In Exercises 95–100, evaluate each expression.

95. $\left(\dfrac{2}{3} \cdot \dfrac{9}{10}\right) + \dfrac{2}{5}$

96. $\left(\dfrac{7}{6} \div \dfrac{4}{3}\right) - \dfrac{11}{12}$

97. $\left(\dfrac{1}{2} + \dfrac{3}{10}\right) \div \left(\dfrac{1}{5} + 2\right)$

98. $\left(\dfrac{1}{9} \cdot \dfrac{3}{5}\right) + \left(\dfrac{2}{3} \cdot \dfrac{1}{5}\right)$

99. $\left(3 - \dfrac{4}{9}\right) \div \left(4 + \dfrac{2}{3}\right)$

100. $\left(\dfrac{2}{5} \div \dfrac{4}{9}\right)\left(\dfrac{3}{5} \cdot 6\right)$

In Exercises 101–114, write an expression that will solve the problem and then evaluate the expression.

101. *Thistles* Diane Helbing has four different varieties of thistles invading her pasture. She estimates that of these thistles, $\frac{1}{2}$ are Canada thistles, $\frac{1}{4}$ are bull thistles, $\frac{1}{6}$ are plumeless thistles, and the rest are musk thistles. What fraction of the thistles are musk thistles?

Bull Thistle Flower

102. *Height Increase* When David Conway finished his freshman year of high school, his height was $69\frac{7}{8}$ inches. When he returned to school after the summer, David's height was $71\frac{5}{8}$ inches. How much did David's height increase over the summer?

103. *Stairway Height* A stairway consists of 14 stairs, each $8\frac{5}{8}$ inches high. What is the vertical height of the stairway?

104. *Math Team* Julie Cholet is hosting the math team after school and wants to share a $67\frac{5}{8}$ oz bottle of soda. How much soda should she pour into each of six glasses so that each glass contains the same amount of soda?

105. *Alphabet Soup* Margaret Cannata's recipe for alphabet soup calls for (among other items) $\frac{1}{4}$ cup snipped parsley, $\frac{1}{8}$ teaspoon pepper, and $\frac{1}{2}$ cup sliced carrots. Margaret is expecting company and needs to multiply the amounts of the ingredients by $1\frac{1}{2}$ times. Determine the amount of (a) snipped parsley, (b) pepper, and (c) sliced carrots she needs for the soup.

106. *Sprinkler System* To repair his sprinkler system, Tony Gambino needs a total of $20\frac{5}{16}$ inches of PVC pipe. He has on hand pieces that measure $2\frac{1}{4}$ inches, $3\frac{7}{8}$ inches, and $4\frac{1}{4}$ inches in length. If he can combine these pieces and use them in the repair, how long of a piece of PVC pipe will Tony need to purchase to repair his sprinkler system?

107. *Crop Storage* Todd Schroeder has a silo on his farm in which he can store silage made from his various crops.

He currently has a silo that is $\frac{1}{4}$ full of corn silage, $\frac{2}{5}$ full of hay silage, and $\frac{1}{3}$ full of oats silage. What fraction of Todd's silo is currently in use?

108. *Department Budget* Jaime Bailey is chair of the humanities department at Santa Fe Community College. Jaime has a budget in which $\frac{1}{2}$ of the money is for photocopying, $\frac{2}{5}$ of the money is for computer-related expenses, and the rest of the money is for student tutors in the foreign languages lab. What fraction of Jaime's budget is for student tutors?

109. *Proofreading a Textbook* To help proofread her new textbook, Chris Mishke assigns three students to proofread $\frac{1}{4}$, $\frac{1}{5}$, and $\frac{1}{2}$ of the book, respectively. She decides to proofread the rest of the book herself. If the book has 540 pages, how many pages must Chris proofread herself?

110. *Art Supplies* Denise Viale teaches kindergarten and is buying supplies for her class to make papier-mâché piggy banks. Each piggy bank to be made requires $1\frac{1}{4}$ cups of flour. If Denise has 15 students who are going to make piggy banks, how much flour does Denise need to purchase?

111. *Height of a Computer Stand* The instructions for assembling a computer stand include a diagram illustrating its dimensions. Find the total height of the stand.

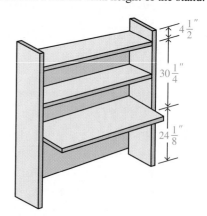

112. *Cutting Lumber* A piece of wood measures $15\frac{3}{8}$ in.
  a) How far from one end should you cut the wood if you want to cut the length in half?
  b) What is the length of each piece after the cut? You must allow $\frac{1}{8}$ in. for the saw cut.

113. *Width of a Picture* The width of a picture is $24\frac{7}{8}$ in., as shown in the diagram. Find x, the distance from the edge of the frame to the center.

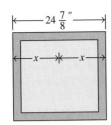

114. *Floor Molding* Rafela Weiss wants to place $\frac{1}{2}$ in. molding along the floor around the perimeter of her room (excluding door openings). She finds that she needs lengths of $26\frac{1}{2}$ in., $105\frac{1}{4}$ in., $53\frac{1}{4}$ in., and $106\frac{5}{16}$ in. How much molding will she need?

Challenge Problems/Group Activities

115. *Cutting Lumber* If a piece of wood $8\frac{3}{4}$ ft long is to be cut into four equal pieces, find the length of each piece. (Allow $\frac{1}{8}$ in. for each saw cut.)

116. *Increasing a Book Size* The dimensions of the cover of a book have been increased from $8\frac{1}{2}$ in. by $9\frac{1}{4}$ in. to $8\frac{1}{2}$ in. by $10\frac{1}{4}$ in. By how many square inches has the surface area increased? Use area = length × width.

117. *Dimensions of a Room* A rectangular room measures 8 ft 3 in. by 10 ft 8 in. by 9 ft 2 in. high.
   a) Determine the perimeter of the room in feet.
   b) Calculate the area of the floor of the room in square feet.
   c) Calculate the volume of the room in cubic feet.

118. *Hanging a Picture* The back of a framed picture that is to be hung is shown. A nail is to be hammered into the wall, and the picture will be hung by the wire on the nail.

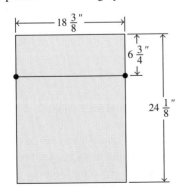

   a) If the center of the wire is to rest on the nail and a side of the picture is to be 20 in. from the window, how far from the window should the nail be placed?
   b) If the top of the frame is to be $26\frac{1}{4}$ in. from the ceiling, how far from the ceiling should the nail be placed? (Assume the wire will not stretch.)
   c) Repeat part (b) if the wire will stretch $\frac{1}{4}$ in. when the picture is hung.

Dense Set of Numbers A set of numbers is said to be a *dense set* if between any two distinct members of the set there exists a third distinct member of the set. The set of integers is not dense, since between any two consecutive integers, there is not another integer. For example, between 1 and 2 there are no other integers. The set of rational numbers is dense because between any two distinct rational numbers there exists a third distinct rational number. For example, we can find a rational number between 0.243 and 0.244. The number 0.243 can be written as 0.2430, and 0.244 can be written as 0.2440. There are many numbers between these two. Some of them are 0.2431, 0.2435, and 0.243912. In Exercises 119–126, find a rational number between the two numbers in each pair.

119. 0.10 and 0.11
120. 5.03 and 5.003
121. −2.176 and −2.175
122. 1.3457 and 1.34571
123. 3.12345 and 3.123451
124. 0.4105 and 0.4106
125. 4.872 and 4.873
126. −3.7896 and −3.7895

Halfway Between Two Numbers To find a rational number halfway between any two rational numbers given in fraction form, add the two numbers together and divide their sum by 2. In Exercises 127–134, find a rational number halfway between the two fractions in each pair.

127. $\frac{1}{3}$ and $\frac{2}{3}$
128. $\frac{2}{7}$ and $\frac{3}{7}$
129. $\frac{1}{100}$ and $\frac{1}{10}$
130. $\frac{7}{13}$ and $\frac{8}{13}$
131. $\frac{1}{4}$ and $\frac{1}{5}$
132. $\frac{1}{3}$ and $\frac{2}{3}$
133. $\frac{1}{10}$ and $\frac{1}{100}$
134. $\frac{1}{2}$ and $\frac{2}{3}$

135. *Cooking Oatmeal* Following are the instructions given on a box of oatmeal. Determine the amount of water (or milk) and oats needed to make $1\frac{1}{2}$ servings by:
   a) Adding the amount of each ingredient needed for 1 serving to the amount needed for 2 servings and dividing by 2.
   b) Adding the amount of each ingredient needed for 1 serving to half the amount needed for 1 serving.

Directions	Servings	1	2
1. Boil water or milk and salt (if desired).	Water (or milk)	1 cup	$1\frac{3}{4}$ cup
2. Stir in oats.	Oats	$\frac{1}{2}$ cup	1 cup
3. Stirring occasionally, cook over medium heat for 5 minutes.	Salt (optional)	dash	$\frac{1}{8}$ tsp

136. Consider the rational number $0.\overline{9}$.
  a) Use the method from Example 8 on page 233 to convert $0.\overline{9}$ to a quotient of integers.
  b) Find a number halfway between $0.\overline{9}$ and 1 by adding the two numbers and dividing by 2.
  c) Find $\frac{1}{3} + \frac{2}{3}$. Express $\frac{1}{3}$ and $\frac{2}{3}$ as repeating decimals. Now find the same sum using the repeating decimal representation of $\frac{1}{3}$ and $\frac{2}{3}$.
  d) What conclusion can you draw from parts (a), (b), and (c)?

Recreational Mathematics

137. *Paper Folding* Fold a sheet of paper in half. Now unfold the paper. You will see that this one crease divided the paper into two equal regions. Each of these regions represents $\frac{1}{2}$ of the area of the entire sheet of paper. Next, fold a sheet of paper in half and then fold it in half again. Now unfold this piece of paper. You will see that these two creases divided the paper into four equal regions. Each of

these regions can be considered $\frac{1}{4}$ of the area of the sheet of paper. Continue this process and answer the following questions.
  a) If you fold the paper in half three times, each region will be what fraction of the area of the sheet of paper?
  b) If you fold the paper in half four times, each region will be what fraction of the area of the sheet of paper?
  c) How many creases will you need to form regions that are $\frac{1}{32}$ of the area of the sheet of paper?
  d) How many creases will you need to form regions that are $\frac{1}{64}$ of the area of the sheet of paper?

Internet/Research Activity

138. The ancient Greeks are often considered the first true mathematicians. Write a report summarizing the ancient Greeks' contributions to rational numbers. Include in your report what they learned and believed about the rational numbers. References include encyclopedias, history of mathematics books, and Internet websites.

5.4 THE IRRATIONAL NUMBERS AND THE REAL NUMBER SYSTEM

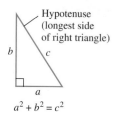

Hypotenuse (longest side of right triangle)

$a^2 + b^2 = c^2$

Figure 5.7

Pythagoras (ca. 585–500 B.C.), a Greek mathematician, is credited with providing a written proof that in any *right triangle* (a triangle with a 90° angle; see Fig. 5.7), the square of the length of one side (a^2) added to the square of the length of the other side (b^2) equals the square of the length of the hypotenuse (c^2). The formula $a^2 + b^2 = c^2$ is now known as the *Pythagorean theorem*.* Pythagoras found that the solution of the formula, where $a = 1$ and $b = 1$, is not a rational number.

$$a^2 + b^2 = c^2$$
$$1^2 + 1^2 = c^2$$
$$1 + 1 = c^2$$
$$2 = c^2$$

There is no rational number that when squared will equal 2. This prompted a need for a new set of numbers, the irrational numbers.

In Section 5.2, we introduced the real number line. The points on the real number line that are not rational numbers are referred to as irrational numbers. Recall that every rational number is either a terminating or a repeating decimal number. Therefore, irrational numbers, when represented as decimal numbers, will be nonterminating, nonrepeating decimal numbers.

An **irrational number** is a real number whose decimal representation is a nonterminating, nonrepeating decimal number.

---

*The Pythagorean theorem is discussed in more detail in Section 9.3.

PYTHAGORAS
OF SAMOS

Pythagoras of Samos founded a philosophical and religious school in southern Italy in the sixth century B.C. The scholars at the school, known as Pythagoreans, produced important works of mathematics, astronomy, and theory of music. Although the Pythagoreans are credited with proving the Pythagorean theorem, it was known to the ancient Babylonians 1000 years earlier. The Pythagoreans were a secret society that formed a model for many secret societies in existence today. One practice was that students were to spend their first three years of study in silence, while their master, Pythagoras, spoke to them from behind a curtain. Among other philosophical beliefs was "that at its deepest level, reality is mathematical in nature."

A nonrepeating decimal number such as 5.12639537 . . . can be used to indicate an irrational number. Notice that no number or set of numbers repeat on a continuous basis, and the three dots at the end of the number indicate that the number continues indefinitely. Nonrepeating number patterns can be used to indicate irrational numbers. For example, 6.1011011101111 . . . and 0.525225222 . . . are both irrational numbers.

The expression $\sqrt{2}$ is read "the square root of 2" or "radical 2." The symbol $\sqrt{}$ is called the *radical sign*, and the number or expression inside the radical sign is called the *radicand*. In $\sqrt{2}$, 2 is the radicand.

The square roots of some numbers are rational, whereas the square roots of other numbers are irrational. The *principal* (or *positive*) *square root* of a number n, written $\sqrt{n}$, is the positive number that when multiplied by itself, gives n. Whenever we mention the term "square root" in this text, we mean the principal square root. For example,

$$\sqrt{9} = 3 \quad \text{since} \quad 3 \cdot 3 = 9$$
$$\sqrt{36} = 6 \quad \text{since} \quad 6 \cdot 6 = 36$$

Both $\sqrt{9}$ and $\sqrt{36}$ are examples of numbers that are rational numbers because their square roots, 3 and 6 respectively, are terminating decimal numbers.

Returning to the problem faced by Pythagoras: If $c^2 = 2$, then c has a value of $\sqrt{2}$, but what is $\sqrt{2}$ equal to? The $\sqrt{2}$ is an irrational number, and it cannot be expressed as a terminating or repeating decimal number. It can only be approximated by a decimal number: $\sqrt{2}$ is approximately 1.4142135 (to seven decimal places). Later in this section, we will discuss using a calculator to approximate irrational numbers.

Other irrational numbers include $\sqrt{3}$, $\sqrt{5}$, and $\sqrt{37}$. Another important irrational number used to represent the ratio of a circle's circumference to its diameter is pi, symbolized π. Pi is approximately 3.1415926.

We have discussed procedures for performing the arithmetic operations of addition, subtraction, multiplication, and division with rational numbers. We can perform the same operations with the irrational numbers. Before we can proceed, however, we must understand the numbers called perfect squares. Any number that is the square of a natural number is said to be a *perfect square*.

Natural numbers		1,	2,	3,	4,	5,	6, . . .
Squares of the natural numbers		1^2,	2^2,	3^2,	4^2,	5^2,	6^2, . . .
or perfect squares		1,	4,	9,	16,	25,	36, . . .

The numbers 1, 4, 9, 16, 25, and 36 are some of the perfect square numbers. Can you determine the next two perfect square numbers? How many perfect square numbers are there? The square root of a perfect square number will be a natural number. For example, $\sqrt{1} = 1$, $\sqrt{4} = 2$, $\sqrt{9} = 3$, $\sqrt{16} = 4$, $\sqrt{25} = 5$, and so on.

The number that multiplies a radical is called the radical's *coefficient*. For example, in $3\sqrt{5}$, the 3 is the coefficient of the radical.

Some irrational numbers can be simplified by determining whether there are any perfect square factors in the radicand. If there are, the following rule can be used to simplify the radical.

Product Rule for Radicals

$$\sqrt{a \cdot b} = \sqrt{a} \cdot \sqrt{b}, \quad a \geq 0, \quad b \geq 0$$

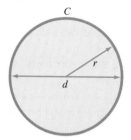
To simplify a radical, write the radical as a product of two radicals. One of the radicals should contain the greatest perfect square that is a factor of the radicand in the original expression. Then simplify the radical containing the perfect square factor. For example,

$$\sqrt{18} = \sqrt{9 \cdot 2} = \sqrt{9} \cdot \sqrt{2} = 3 \cdot \sqrt{2} = 3\sqrt{2}$$

and

$$\sqrt{75} = \sqrt{25 \cdot 3} = \sqrt{25} \cdot \sqrt{3} = 5 \cdot \sqrt{3} = 5\sqrt{3}$$

EXAMPLE 1   *Simplifying Radicals*

Simplify
a) $\sqrt{28}$ b) $\sqrt{48}$

SOLUTION:

a) Since 4 is a perfect square factor of 28, we write

$$\sqrt{28} = \sqrt{4 \cdot 7} = \sqrt{4} \cdot \sqrt{7} = 2 \cdot \sqrt{7} = 2\sqrt{7}$$

Since 7 has no perfect square factors, $\sqrt{7}$ cannot be simplified.

b) Since 16 is a perfect square factor of 48, we write

$$\sqrt{48} = \sqrt{16 \cdot 3} = \sqrt{16} \cdot \sqrt{3} = 4 \cdot \sqrt{3} = 4\sqrt{3}$$

In Example 1(b), you can obtain the correct answer if you start out factoring differently:

$$\sqrt{48} = \sqrt{4 \cdot 12} = \sqrt{4} \cdot \sqrt{12} = 2\sqrt{12}$$

Note that 12 has 4 as a perfect square factor.

$$2\sqrt{12} = 2\sqrt{4 \cdot 3} = 2 \cdot \sqrt{4} \cdot \sqrt{3} = 2 \cdot 2 \cdot \sqrt{3} = 4\sqrt{3}$$

The second method will eventually give the same answer, but it requires more work. It is best to try to factor out the *largest* perfect square factor from the radicand.

Addition and Subtraction of Irrational Numbers

To add or subtract two or more square roots with the same radicand, add or subtract their coefficients. The answer is the sum or difference of the coefficients multiplied by the common radical.

EXAMPLE 2   *Adding and Subtracting Radicals with the Same Radicand*

Simplify
a) $3\sqrt{2} + 6\sqrt{2}$ b) $4\sqrt{7} + \sqrt{7} - 8\sqrt{7}$

SOLUTION:
a) $3\sqrt{2} + 6\sqrt{2} = (3 + 6)\sqrt{2} = 9\sqrt{2}$
b) $4\sqrt{7} + \sqrt{7} - 8\sqrt{7} = (4 + 1 - 8)\sqrt{7} = -3\sqrt{7}$

Note that $\sqrt{7} = 1\sqrt{7}$.

EXAMPLE 3   *Adding and Subtracting Radicals with Different Radicands*

Simplify $5\sqrt{3} - \sqrt{12}$.

SOLUTION: These radicals cannot be added in their present form because they contain different radicands. When this occurs, determine whether one or more of the radicals can be simplified so that they have the same radicand.

$$
\begin{aligned}
5\sqrt{3} - \sqrt{12} &= 5\sqrt{3} - \sqrt{4 \cdot 3} \\
&= 5\sqrt{3} - \sqrt{4} \cdot \sqrt{3} \\
&= 5\sqrt{3} - 2\sqrt{3} \\
&= (5 - 2)\sqrt{3} = 3\sqrt{3} \qquad \blacktriangle
\end{aligned}
$$

Multiplication of Irrational Numbers

When multiplying irrational numbers, we again make use of the product rule for radicals. After the radicands are multiplied, simplify the remaining radical when possible.

EXAMPLE 4   *Multiplying Radicals*

Simplify
a) $\sqrt{3} \cdot \sqrt{27}$ b) $\sqrt{3} \cdot \sqrt{7}$ c) $\sqrt{6} \cdot \sqrt{10}$

SOLUTION:
a) $\sqrt{3} \cdot \sqrt{27} = \sqrt{3 \cdot 27} = \sqrt{81} = 9$
b) $\sqrt{3} \cdot \sqrt{7} = \sqrt{3 \cdot 7} = \sqrt{21}$
c) $\sqrt{6} \cdot \sqrt{10} = \sqrt{6 \cdot 10} = \sqrt{60} = \sqrt{4 \cdot 15} = \sqrt{4} \cdot \sqrt{15} = 2\sqrt{15}$ $\qquad \blacktriangle$

Division of Irrational Numbers

To divide irrational numbers, use the following rule. After performing the division, simplify when possible.

> **Quotient Rule for Radicals**
>
> $$\frac{\sqrt{a}}{\sqrt{b}} = \sqrt{\frac{a}{b}}, \qquad a \geq 0, \qquad b > 0$$

EXAMPLE 5   *Dividing Radicals*

Divide
a) $\dfrac{\sqrt{8}}{\sqrt{2}}$ b) $\dfrac{\sqrt{96}}{\sqrt{2}}$

SOLUTION:

a) $\dfrac{\sqrt{8}}{\sqrt{2}} = \sqrt{\dfrac{8}{2}} = \sqrt{4} = 2$

b) $\dfrac{\sqrt{96}}{\sqrt{2}} = \sqrt{\dfrac{96}{2}} = \sqrt{48} = \sqrt{16 \cdot 3} = \sqrt{16} \cdot \sqrt{3} = 4\sqrt{3}$ $\qquad \blacktriangle$

Rationalizing the Denominator

A denominator is *rationalized* when it contains no radical expressions. To rationalize a denominator that contains only a square root, multiply both the numerator and denominator of the fraction by a number that will result in the radicand in the denominator becoming a perfect square. (This action is the equivalent of multiplying the fraction by 1 because the value of the fraction does not change.) Then simplify the fractions when possible.

EXAMPLE 6   *Rationalizing the Denominator*

Rationalize the denominator of

a) $\dfrac{5}{\sqrt{2}}$ b) $\dfrac{5}{\sqrt{12}}$ c) $\dfrac{\sqrt{5}}{\sqrt{10}}$

SOLUTION:

a) Multiply the numerator and denominator by a number that will make the radicand a perfect square.

$$\frac{5}{\sqrt{2}} = \frac{5}{\sqrt{2}} \cdot \frac{\sqrt{2}}{\sqrt{2}} = \frac{5\sqrt{2}}{\sqrt{4}} = \frac{5\sqrt{2}}{2}$$

Note that the 2's in the answer cannot be divided out because one 2 is a radicand and the other is not.

b) $\dfrac{5}{\sqrt{12}} = \dfrac{5}{\sqrt{12}} \cdot \dfrac{\sqrt{3}}{\sqrt{3}} = \dfrac{5\sqrt{3}}{\sqrt{36}} = \dfrac{5\sqrt{3}}{6}$

You could have obtained the same answer to this problem by multiplying both the numerator and denominator by $\sqrt{12}$ and then simplifying. Try to do so now.

c) Write $\dfrac{\sqrt{5}}{\sqrt{10}}$ as $\sqrt{\dfrac{5}{10}}$ and reduce the fraction to obtain $\sqrt{\dfrac{1}{2}}$. By the quotient rule for radicals, $\sqrt{\dfrac{1}{2}} = \dfrac{\sqrt{1}}{\sqrt{2}}$ or $\dfrac{1}{\sqrt{2}}$. Now rationalize $\dfrac{1}{\sqrt{2}}$.

$$\frac{1}{\sqrt{2}} = \frac{1}{\sqrt{2}} \cdot \frac{\sqrt{2}}{\sqrt{2}} = \frac{\sqrt{2}}{2}$$

▲

Approximating Square Roots on a Scientific Calculator

Consider the irrational number the square root of two. We use the symbol $\sqrt{2}$ to represent the *exact value* of this number. Although exact values are important, approximations are also important, especially when working with application problems. We can use a scientific calculator to obtain approximations for square roots. Scientific calculators generally have one of the following square root keys:*

$$\boxed{\sqrt{}} \quad \text{or} \quad \boxed{\sqrt{x}}$$

*If your calculator has the $\sqrt{}$ symbol printed *above* the key instead of on the face of the key, you can access the square root function by first pressing the "2nd" or the "inverse" key.

For simplicity, we will refer to the square root key with the $\boxed{\sqrt{}}$ symbol. To approximate $\sqrt{2}$, perform the following keystrokes:

$$2 \quad \boxed{\sqrt{}}$$

or, depending on your model of calculator, you may have to do the following:

$$\boxed{\sqrt{}} \quad \boxed{2} \quad \boxed{\text{ENTER}}$$

The display on your calculator may read 1.414213562. Your calculator may display more or fewer digits. It is important to realize that 1.414213562 is a rational number *approximation* for the irrational number $\sqrt{2}$. The symbol $\approx$ means *is approximately equal to,* and we write

$$\sqrt{2} \approx 1.414213562$$

Exact value (irrational number)   Approximation (rational number)

EXAMPLE 7 *Approximating Square Roots*

Use a scientific calculator to approximate the following square roots. Round your answers to two decimal places.

a) $\sqrt{5}$ b) $\sqrt{17}$ c) $\sqrt{91}$ d) $\sqrt{237}$

SOLUTION:

a) $\sqrt{5} \approx 2.24$ b) $\sqrt{17} \approx 4.12$ c) $\sqrt{91} \approx 9.54$ d) $\sqrt{237} \approx 15.39$

▲

SECTION 5.4   EXERCISES

Concept/Writing Exercises

1. Explain the difference between a rational number and an irrational number.

2. What is the principal square root of a number?

3. What is a perfect square?

4. a) State the product rule for radicals.
   b) State the quotient rule for radicals.

5. a) Explain how to add or subtract square roots that have the same radicand.
   b) Using the procedure in part (a), add $3\sqrt{6} + 5\sqrt{6} - 9\sqrt{6}$.

6. What does it mean to rationalize the denominator?

7. a) Explain how to rationalize a denominator that contains a square root.
   b) Using the procedure in part (a), rationalize $\dfrac{7}{\sqrt{3}}$.

8. a) Explain how to approximate square roots on your calculator.
   b) Using the procedure in part (a), approximate $\sqrt{7}$. Round your answer to the nearest hundredth.

Practice the Skills

In Exercises 9–18, determine whether the number is rational or irrational.

9. $\sqrt{36}$

10. $\sqrt{18}$

11. $\dfrac{2}{3}$

12. 0.212112111...

13. 3.575775777...

14. π

15. $\dfrac{22}{7}$

16. 3.14159

17. 3.14159...

18. $\dfrac{\sqrt{5}}{\sqrt{5}}$

In Exercises 19–28, evaluate the expression.

19. $\sqrt{64}$ 20. $\sqrt{144}$ 21. $\sqrt{100}$

22. $-\sqrt{144}$ 23. $-\sqrt{169}$ 24. $\sqrt{25}$

25. $-\sqrt{225}$ 26. $-\sqrt{36}$ 27. $-\sqrt{100}$

28. $\sqrt{256}$

In Exercises 29–38, classify the number as a member of one or more of the following sets: the rational numbers, the integers, the natural numbers, the irrational numbers.

29. 1

30. -4

31. $\sqrt{49}$

32. $\dfrac{4}{5}$

33. 0.040040004

34. 2.718

35. $-\dfrac{7}{8}$

36. 0.123123123

37. $0.\overline{123}$

38. $0.123112311123\ldots$

In Exercises 39–48, simplify the radical.

39. $\sqrt{18}$ 40. $\sqrt{20}$ 41. $\sqrt{48}$

42. $\sqrt{60}$ 43. $\sqrt{63}$ 44. $\sqrt{75}$

45. $\sqrt{80}$ 46. $\sqrt{90}$ 47. $\sqrt{162}$

48. $\sqrt{300}$

In Exercises 49–58, perform the indicated operation.

49. $2\sqrt{6} + 5\sqrt{6}$ 50. $3\sqrt{17} + \sqrt{17}$

51. $5\sqrt{12} - \sqrt{75}$ 52. $2\sqrt{5} + 3\sqrt{20}$

53. $4\sqrt{12} - 7\sqrt{27}$ 54. $2\sqrt{7} + 5\sqrt{28}$

55. $5\sqrt{3} + 7\sqrt{12} - 3\sqrt{75}$

56. $13\sqrt{2} + 2\sqrt{18} - 5\sqrt{32}$

57. $\sqrt{8} - 3\sqrt{50} + 9\sqrt{32}$

58. $\sqrt{63} + 13\sqrt{98} - 5\sqrt{112}$

In Exercises 59–68, perform the indicated operation. Simplify the answer when possible.

59. $\sqrt{2}\sqrt{8}$ 60. $\sqrt{5}\sqrt{15}$ 61. $\sqrt{6}\sqrt{10}$

62. $\sqrt{3}\sqrt{6}$ 63. $\sqrt{10}\sqrt{20}$ 64. $\sqrt{11}\sqrt{33}$

65. $\dfrac{\sqrt{8}}{\sqrt{4}}$ 66. $\dfrac{\sqrt{125}}{\sqrt{5}}$ 67. $\dfrac{\sqrt{72}}{\sqrt{8}}$

68. $\dfrac{\sqrt{136}}{\sqrt{8}}$

In Exercises 69–78, rationalize the denominator.

69. $\dfrac{1}{\sqrt{2}}$ 70. $\dfrac{3}{\sqrt{3}}$ 71. $\dfrac{\sqrt{3}}{\sqrt{7}}$

72. $\dfrac{\sqrt{3}}{\sqrt{10}}$ 73. $\dfrac{\sqrt{20}}{\sqrt{3}}$ 74. $\dfrac{\sqrt{50}}{\sqrt{14}}$

75. $\dfrac{\sqrt{9}}{\sqrt{2}}$ 76. $\dfrac{\sqrt{15}}{\sqrt{3}}$ 77. $\dfrac{\sqrt{10}}{\sqrt{6}}$

78. $\dfrac{8}{\sqrt{8}}$

Problem Solving

Approximating Radicals *The following diagram shows a 16 in. ruler marked using $\frac{1}{2}$ inches.*

In Exercises 79–84, without using a calculator, indicate between which two adjacent markers each of the following irrational numbers will fall. Explain how you obtained your answer. Support your answer by obtaining an approximation with a calculator.

79. $\sqrt{7}$ in.   80. $\sqrt{37}$ in.

81. $\sqrt{107}$ in.   82. $\sqrt{135}$ in.

83. $\sqrt{170}$ in.   84. $\sqrt{200}$ in.

In Exercises 85–90, determine whether the statement is true or false. Rewrite each false statement to make it a true statement. A false statement can be modified in more than one way to be made a true statement.

85. $\sqrt{p}$ is a rational number for any prime number p.

86. $\sqrt{c}$ is a rational number for any composite number c.

87. The sum of any two rational numbers is always a rational number.

88. The product of any two rational numbers is always a rational number.

89. The product of an irrational and a rational number is always an irrational number.

90. The product of any two irrational numbers is always an irrational number.

In Exercises 91–94, give an example to show that the stated case can occur.

91. The sum of two irrational numbers may be a rational number.

92. The sum of two irrational numbers may be an irrational number.

93. The product of two irrational numbers may be an irrational number.

94. The product of two irrational numbers may be a rational number.

95. Without doing any calculations, determine whether $\sqrt{5} = 2.236$. Explain your answer.

96. Without doing any calculations, determine whether $\sqrt{14} = 3.742$. Explain your answer.

97. The number π is an irrational number. Often the values 3.14 or $\frac{22}{7}$ are used for π. Does π equal either 3.14 or $\frac{22}{7}$? Explain your answer.

98. Give an example to show that $\sqrt{a + b} \neq \sqrt{a} + \sqrt{b}$.

99. Give an example to show that $\sqrt{a \cdot b} = \sqrt{a} \cdot \sqrt{b}$.

100. *A Swinging Pendulum* The time T required for a pendulum to swing back and forth may be found by the formula

$$T = 2\pi\sqrt{\frac{l}{g}}$$

where l is the length of the pendulum and g is the acceleration of gravity. Find the time in seconds if $l = 35$ cm and $g = 980$ cm/sec^2. Round answer to the nearest tenth of a second.

101. *Estimating Speed of a Vehicle* The speed a vehicle was traveling, s, in miles per hour, when the brakes were first applied, can be estimated using the formula $s = \sqrt{\dfrac{d}{0.04}}$

where d is the length of the vehicle's skid marks, in feet.

a) Determine the speed of a car that made skid marks 4 ft long.

b) Determine the speed of a car that made skid marks 16 ft long.

c) Determine the speed of a car that made skid marks 64 ft long.

d) Determine the speed of a car that made skid marks 256 ft long.

102. *Dropping an Object* The formula $t = \dfrac{\sqrt{d}}{4}$ can be used to

estimate the time, t, in seconds it takes for an object dropped to travel d feet.

a) Determine the time it takes for an object to drop 100 ft.

b) Determine the time it takes for an object to drop 400 ft.

c) Determine the time it takes for an object to drop 900 ft.

d) Determine the time it takes for an object to drop 1600 ft.

Challenge Problems/Group Activities

103. a) If a radical expression is evaluated on a calculator, explain how you can determine whether the expression is a rational or irrational number.

b) Is $\sqrt{0.04}$ rational or irrational? Explain.

c) Is $\sqrt{0.7}$ rational or irrational? Explain.

104. One way to find a rational number between two distinct rational numbers is to add the two distinct rational numbers and divide by 2. Do you think that this method will work for finding an irrational number between two distinct irrational numbers? Explain.

Recreational Mathematics

105. *More Four 4's* In Exercise 82 on page 227, we introduced some of the basic rules of the game Four 4's. We now expand our operations to include square roots. For example, one way to obtain the whole number 8 is $\sqrt{4} + \sqrt{4} + \sqrt{4} + \sqrt{4} = 2 + 2 + 2 + 2 = 8$. Using the rules given on page 227, and using at least one square root of 4, $\sqrt{4}$, play Four 4's to obtain the following whole numbers:

a) 11

b) 13

c) 14

d) 18

Internet/Research Activities

In Exercises 106 and 107, references include history of mathematics books, encyclopedias, and Internet web sites.

106. Write a report on the history of the development of the irrational numbers.

107. Write a report on the history of pi. In your report, indicate when the symbol π was first used and list the first 10 digits of π.

5.5 REAL NUMBERS AND THEIR PROPERTIES

Now that we have discussed both the rational and irrational numbers, we can discuss the real numbers and the properties of the real number system. The union of the rational numbers and the irrational numbers is the *set of real numbers*, symbolized by $\mathbb{R}$.

Figure 5.8 illustrates the relationship among various sets of numbers. It shows that the natural numbers are a subset of the whole numbers, the integers, the rational numbers, and the real numbers. For example, since the number 3 is a natural or counting number, it is also a whole number, an integer, a rational number, and a real number. Since the rational number $\frac{1}{4}$ is outside the set of integers, it is not an integer, a whole number, or a natural number. The number $\frac{1}{4}$ is a real number, however, as is the irrational number $\sqrt{2}$. Note that the real numbers are the union of the rational numbers and the irrational numbers.

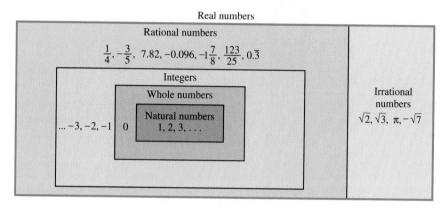

Figure 5.8

The relationship between the various sets of numbers in the real number system can also be illustrated with a tree diagram, as in Fig. 5.9.

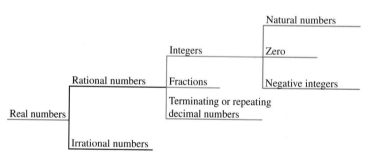

Figure 5.9

Figure 5.9 shows that, for example, the natural numbers are a subset of the integers, the rational numbers, and the real numbers. We can also see, for example, the natural numbers, zero, and the negative integers together form the integers.

Properties of the Real Number System

We are now prepared to consider the properties of the real number system. The first property that we will discuss is *closure*.

If an operation is performed on any two elements of a set and the result is an element of the set, we say that the set is **closed** under that given operation.

Is the sum of any two natural numbers a natural number? The answer is yes. Thus, we say that the natural numbers are closed under the operation of addition.

Are the natural numbers closed under the operation of subtraction? If we subtract one natural number from another natural number, must the difference always be a natural number? The answer is no. For example, $3 - 5 = -2$, which is not a natural number. Therefore, the natural numbers are not closed under the operation of subtraction.

EXAMPLE 1 Closure of Sets

Determine whether the integers are closed under the operations of (a) multiplication and (b) division.

SOLUTION:

a) If we multiply any two integers, will the product always be an integer? The answer is yes. Thus, the integers are closed under the operation of multiplication.

b) If we divide any two integers, will the quotient always be an integer? The answer is no. For example, $6 \div 5 = \frac{6}{5}$, which is not an integer. Therefore, the integers are not closed under the operation of division. ▲

Next we will discuss three important properties: the commutative property, the associative property, and the distributive property. A knowledge of these properties is essential for the understanding of algebra. We begin with the commutative property.

Commutative Property

ADDITION	MULTIPLICATION
$a + b = b + a$	$a \cdot b = b \cdot a$

for any real numbers a and b.

The commutative property states that the *order* in which two numbers are added or multiplied is not important. For example, $4 + 5 = 5 + 4 = 9$ and $3 \cdot 6 = 6 \cdot 3 = 18$. Note that the commutative property does not hold for the operations of subtraction or division. For example,

$$4 - 7 \neq 7 - 4 \quad \text{and} \quad 9 \div 3 \neq 3 \div 9$$

Now we introduce the associative property.

Associative Property

ADDITION	MULTIPLICATION
$(a + b) + c = a + (b + c)$	$(a \cdot b) \cdot c = a \cdot (b \cdot c)$

for any real numbers a, b, and c.

The associative property states that when adding or multiplying three real numbers, we may place parentheses around any two adjacent numbers. For example,

$$(3 + 4) + 5 = 3 + (4 + 5) \qquad (3 \cdot 4) \cdot 5 = 3 \cdot (4 \cdot 5)$$
$$7 + 5 = 3 + 9 \qquad 12 \cdot 5 = 3 \cdot 20$$
$$12 = 12 \qquad 60 = 60$$

The associative property does not hold for the operations of subtraction and division. For example,

$$(10 - 6) - 2 \neq 10 - (6 - 2) \qquad \text{and} \qquad (27 \div 9) \div 3 \neq 27 \div (9 \div 3)$$

Note the difference between the commutative property and the associative property. The commutative property involves a change in *order*, whereas the associative property involves a change in *grouping* (or the *association* of numbers that are grouped together).

Another property of the real numbers is the distributive property of multiplication over addition.

Distributive Property of Multiplication over Addition

$$a \cdot (b + c) = a \cdot b + a \cdot c$$

for any real numbers a, b, and c.

For example, if $a = 3$, $b = 4$, and $c = 5$, then

$$3 \cdot (4 + 5) = (3 \cdot 4) + (3 \cdot 5)$$
$$3 \cdot 9 = 12 + 15$$
$$27 = 27$$

This result indicates that, when using the distributive property, you may either add first and then multiply or multiply first and then add. Note that the distributive property involves two operations, addition and multiplication. Although positive integers were used in the example, any real numbers could have been used.

We frequently use the commutative, associative, and distributive properties without realizing that we are doing so. To add $13 + 4 + 6$, we may add the $4 + 6$ first to get 10. To this sum we then add 13 to get 23. Here we have done the equivalent of placing parentheses around the $4 + 6$. We can do so because of the associative property of addition.

To multiply 102×11 in our heads, we might multiply $100 \times 11 = 1100$ and $2 \times 11 = 22$ and add these two products to get 1122. We are permitted to do so because of the distributive property.

$$102 \times 11 = (100 + 2) \times 11 = (100 \times 11) + (2 \times 11)$$
$$= 1100 + 22 = 1122$$

EXAMPLE 2 *Identifying Properties of Real Numbers*

Name the property illustrated.

a) $2 + 5 = 5 + 2$

b) $(x + 3) + 5 = x + (3 + 5)$

c) $4 \cdot (3 \cdot y) = (4 \cdot 3) \cdot y$

d) $9(w + 3) = 9 \cdot w + 9 \cdot 3$

e) $5 + (z + 3) = 5 + (3 + z)$

f) $(2p) \cdot 5 = 5 \cdot (2p)$

SOLUTION:

a) Commutative property of addition

b) Associative property of addition

c) Associative property of multiplication

d) Distributive property of multiplication over addition

e) The only change between the left and right sides of the equal sign is the order of the z and 3 within the parentheses. The order is changed from $z + 3$ to $3 + z$ using the commutative property of addition.

f) The order of 5 and $(2p)$ is changed by using the commutative property of multiplication.

EXAMPLE 3   *Simplifying by Using the Distributive Property*

Use the distributive property to simplify

a) $2(3 + \sqrt{5})$ b) $\sqrt{2}(7 + \sqrt{3})$

SOLUTION:

a) $2(3 + \sqrt{5}) = (2 \cdot 3) + (2 \cdot \sqrt{5})$
$$= 6 + 2\sqrt{5}$$

b) $\sqrt{2}(7 + \sqrt{3}) = (\sqrt{2} \cdot 7) + (\sqrt{2} \cdot \sqrt{3})$
$$= 7\sqrt{2} + \sqrt{6}$$

Note that $\sqrt{2} \cdot 7$ is written $7\sqrt{2}$.

EXAMPLE 4   *Distributive Property*

Use the distributive property to multiply $5(q + 7)$. Then simplify the result.

SOLUTION:

$$5(q + 7) = 5 \cdot q + 5 \cdot 7$$
$$= 5q + 35$$

We summarize the properties mentioned in this section as follows, where a, b, and c are any real numbers.

Commutative property of addition	$a + b = b + a$
Commutative property of multiplication	$a \cdot b = b \cdot a$
Associative property of addition	$(a + b) + c = a + (b + c)$
Associative property of multiplication	$(a \cdot b) \cdot c = a \cdot (b \cdot c)$
Distributive property of multiplication over addition	$a \cdot (b + c) = a \cdot b + a \cdot c$

SECTION 5.5   EXERCISES

Concept/Writing Exercises

1. What are the real numbers?

2. What symbol is used to represent the set of real numbers?

3. What does it mean if a set is closed under a given operation?

4. Give the commutative property of multiplication, explain what it means, and give an example illustrating it.

5. Give the commutative property of addition, explain what it means, and give an example illustrating it.

6. Give the associative property of addition, explain what it means, and give an example illustrating it.

7. Give the associative property of multiplication, explain what it means, and give an example illustrating it.

8. Give the distributive property of multiplication over addition, explain what it means, and give an example illustrating it.

Practice the Skills

In Exercises 9–12, determine whether the natural numbers are closed under the given operation.

9. Addition

10. Subtraction

11. Division

12. Multiplication

In Exercises 13–16, determine whether the integers are closed under the given operation.

13. Subtraction

14. Addition

15. Division

16. Multiplication

In Exercises 17–20, determine whether the rational numbers are closed under the given operation.

17. Addition

18. Subtraction

19. Multiplication

20. Division

In Exercises 21–24, determine whether the irrational numbers are closed under the given operation.

21. Addition

22. Subtraction

23. Multiplication

24. Division

In Exercises 25–28, determine whether the real numbers are closed under the given operation.

25. Addition

26. Subtraction

27. Division

28. Multiplication

29. Does $x + (3 + 4) = (3 + 4) + x$ illustrate the commutative property or the associative property? Explain your answer.

30. Does $4 + (5 + 6) = 4 + (6 + 5)$ illustrate the commutative property or the associative property? Explain your answer.

31. Give an example to show that the commutative property of multiplication may be true for the negative integers.

32. Give an example to show that the commutative property of addition may be true for the negative integers.

33. Does the commutative property hold for the rational numbers under the operation of division? Give an example to support your answer.

34. Does the commutative property hold for the integers under the operation of subtraction? Give an example to support your answer.

35. Give an example to show that the associative property of multiplication may be true for the negative integers.

36. Give an example to show that the associative property of addition may be true for the negative integers.

37. Does the associative property hold for the integers under the operation of division? Give an example to support your answer.

38. Does the associative property hold for the integers under the operation of subtraction? Give an example to support your answer.

39. Does the associative property hold for the real numbers under the operation of division? Give an example to support your answer.

40. Does $a + (b \cdot c) = (a + b) \cdot (a + c)$? Give an example to support your answer.

In Exercises 41–56, state the name of the property illustrated.

41. $24 + 7 = 7 + 24$

42. $5(x + 3) = 5 \cdot x + 5 \cdot 3$

43. $(7 \cdot 4) \cdot 5 = 7 \cdot (4 \cdot 5)$

44. $v + w = w + v$

45. $(24 + 7) + 3 = 24 + (7 + 3)$

46. $4 \cdot (11 \cdot x) = (4 \cdot 11) \cdot x$

47. $\sqrt{3} \cdot 7 = 7 \cdot \sqrt{3}$

48. $\dfrac{3}{8} + \left(\dfrac{1}{8} + \dfrac{3}{2} \right) = \left(\dfrac{3}{8} + \dfrac{1}{8} \right) + \dfrac{3}{2}$

49. $8 \cdot (7 + \sqrt{2}) = 8 \cdot 7 + 8 \cdot \sqrt{2}$

50. $\sqrt{5} \cdot \dfrac{2}{3} = \dfrac{2}{3} \cdot \sqrt{5}$

51. $(1 + 10) + 100 = (10 + 1) + 100$

52. $(r + s) + t = t + (r + s)$

53. $(r + s) \cdot t = (r \cdot t) + (s \cdot t)$

54. $g \cdot (h + i) = (h + i) \cdot g$

55. $(p + q) + (r + s) = (r + s) + (p + q)$

56. $(a \cdot b) + (c \cdot d) = (b \cdot a) + (c \cdot d)$

In Exercises 57–68, use the distributive property to multiply. Then, if possible, simplify the resulting expression.

57. $2(c + 7)$

58. $-3(d - 1)$

59. $\dfrac{2}{3}(x - 6)$

60. $-\dfrac{5}{8}(k + 8)$

61. $6\left(\dfrac{x}{2} + \dfrac{2}{3}\right)$

62. $24\left(\dfrac{x}{3} - \dfrac{1}{8}\right)$

63. $32\left(\dfrac{1}{16}x - \dfrac{1}{32}\right)$

64. $15\left(\dfrac{2}{3}x - \dfrac{4}{5}\right)$

65. $3(5 - \sqrt{5})$

66. $-7(2 + \sqrt{11})$

67. $\sqrt{2}(\sqrt{2} + \sqrt{3})$

68. $\sqrt{3}(\sqrt{15} + \sqrt{21})$

In Exercises 69–74, name the property used to go from step to step. You only need to name the properties indicated by an a), b), c), or d). For example, in Exercise 69, you need to supply an answer for part a), and an answer to go from the second step of part a) to part b).

69. a) $7(x + 2) + 3 = (7 \cdot x + 7 \cdot 2) + 3$
$\qquad\qquad\qquad = (7x + 14) + 3$
b) $\qquad\qquad\quad = 7x + (14 + 3)$
$\qquad\qquad\qquad = 7x + 17$

70. a) $3(n + 5) + 6 = (3 \cdot n + 3 \cdot 5) + 6$
$\qquad\qquad\qquad = (3n + 15) + 6$
b) $\qquad\qquad\quad = 3n + (15 + 6)$
$\qquad\qquad\qquad = 3n + 21$

71. a) $7(k + 1) + 2k = (7 \cdot k + 7 \cdot 1) + 2k$
$\qquad\qquad\qquad = (7k + 7) + 2k$
b) $\qquad\qquad\quad = 7k + (7 + 2k)$
c) $\qquad\qquad\quad = 7k + (2k + 7)$
d) $\qquad\qquad\quad = (7k + 2k) + 7$
$\qquad\qquad\qquad = 9k + 7$

72. a) $11(h + 6) + 5h = (11 \cdot h + 11 \cdot 6) + 5h$
$\qquad\qquad\qquad = (11h + 66) + 5h$
b) $\qquad\qquad\quad = 11h + (66 + 5h)$
c) $\qquad\qquad\quad = 11h + (5h + 66)$
d) $\qquad\qquad\quad = (11h + 5h) + 66$
$\qquad\qquad\qquad = 16h + 66$

73. a) $9 + 2(t + 3) + 7t = 9 + (2 \cdot t + 2 \cdot 3) + 7t$
$\qquad\qquad\qquad = 9 + (2t + 6) + 7t$
b) $\qquad\qquad\quad = 9 + (6 + 2t) + 7t$
c) $\qquad\qquad\quad = (9 + 6) + 2t + 7t$
$\qquad\qquad\qquad = 15 + 9t$
d) $\qquad\qquad\quad = 9t + 15$

74. a) $7 + 5(s + 4) + 3s = 7 + (5 \cdot s + 5 \cdot 4) + 3s$
$\qquad\qquad\qquad = 7 + (5s + 20) + 3s$
b) $\qquad\qquad\quad = 7 + (20 + 5s) + 3s$
c) $\qquad\qquad\quad = (7 + 20) + 5s + 3s$
$\qquad\qquad\qquad = 27 + 8s$
d) $\qquad\qquad\quad = 8s + 27$

In Exercises 75–80, determine whether the activity can be used to illustrate the commutative property. For the property to hold, the end result must be identical, regardless of the order in which the actions are performed.

75. Putting on your seat belt and locking your car door

76. Putting on your left shoe and putting on your right shoe

77. Washing clothes and drying clothes

78. Turning on a computer and typing a term paper on the computer

79. Filling your car with gasoline and washing the windshield

80. Turning on a lamp and reading a book

In Exercises 81–88, determine whether the activity can be used to illustrate the associative property. For the property to hold, doing the first two actions followed by the third would produce the same end result as doing the second and third actions followed by the first.

81. Washing the exterior of your car, vacuuming out the interior, and checking the oil

82. Reading a novel, writing a book report on the novel, and making a presentation to your class about your book report

83. Sending a holiday card to your grandmother, sending one to your parents, and sending one to your teacher

84. Mowing the lawn, trimming the bushes, and removing dead limbs from trees

85. Brushing your teeth, washing your face, and combing your hair

86. Cracking an egg, pouring out the egg, and cooking the egg

87. Taking a bath, brushing your teeth, and taking your vitamins

88. While making meatloaf, mixing in the milk, mixing in the spices, and mixing in the bread crumbs

Challenge Problems/Group Activities

89. Describe two other activities that can be used to illustrate the commutative property (see Exercises 75–80).

90. Describe three other activities that can be used to illustrate the associative property (see Exercises 81–88).

91. Does $0 \div a = a \div 0$ (assume $a \neq 0$)? Explain.

Recreational Mathematics

92. a) Consider the three words *man eating tiger*. Does (*man eating*) *tiger* mean the same as *man* (*eating tiger*)?
   b) Does (*horse riding*) *monkey* mean the same as *horse* (*riding monkey*)?
   c) Can you find three other nonassociative word triples?

Internet/Research Activity

93. A set of numbers that was not discussed in this chapter is the set of *complex numbers*. Write a report on complex numbers. Include their relationship to the real numbers.

5.6 RULES OF EXPONENTS AND SCIENTIFIC NOTATION

An understanding of exponents is important in solving problems in algebra. In the expression 5^2, the 2 is referred to as the *exponent* and the 5 is referred to as the *base*. We read 5^2 as 5 to the second power, or 5 squared, which means

$$5^2 = \underbrace{5 \cdot 5}_{2 \text{ factors of } 5}$$

The number 5 to the third power, or 5 cubed, written 5^3, means

$$5^3 = \underbrace{5 \cdot 5 \cdot 5}_{3 \text{ factors of } 5}$$

In general, the number b to the nth power, written b^n, means

$$b^n = \underbrace{b \cdot b \cdot b \cdot \,\cdots\, \cdot b}_{n \text{ factors of } b}$$

EXAMPLE 1   *Evaluating the Power of a Number*

Evaluate the following.

a) 4^2 b) $(-5)^2$ c) 5^3 d) 1^{1000} e) 7^1

A Very Large Number

170,141,183,460,469,231,731,687, 303,715,884,105,727 is a very large number. How would you read this number? Take a breath.

170 undecillion, 141 decillion, 183 nonillion, 460 octillion, 469 septillion, 231 sextillion, 731 quintillion, 687 quadrillion, 303 trillion, 715 billion, 884 million, 105 thousand, 727.

Often numbers this large can be represented with an approximation involving scientific notation. This number, however, is a prime number, and its *exact* representation is very important. Mathematicians frequently represent such large numbers by using exponents. Here, another exact, and more efficient, representation of this number is $2^{127} - 1$.

SOLUTION:

a) $4^2 = 4 \cdot 4 = 16$

b) $(-5)^2 = (-5)(-5) = 25$

c) $5^3 = 5 \cdot 5 \cdot 5 = 125$

d) $1^{1000} = 1$. (The number 1 times itself any number of times equals 1.)

e) $7^1 = 7$. (Any number with an exponent of 1 equals the number itself.)

EXAMPLE 2   The Importance of Parentheses

Evaluate the following.

a) $(-2)^4$ b) -2^4 c) $(-2)^5$ d) -2^5

SOLUTION:

a) $(-2)^4 = (-2)(-2)(-2)(-2) = 4(-2)(-2) = -8(-2) = 16$

b) -2^4 means take the opposite of 2^4 or $-1 \cdot 2^4$.

$-1 \cdot 2^4 = -1 \cdot 2 \cdot 2 \cdot 2 \cdot 2 = -1 \cdot 16 = -16$

c) $(-2)^5 = (-2)(-2)(-2)(-2)(-2) = 4(-2)(-2)(-2) = -8(-2)(-2)$
$= 16(-2) = -32$

d) $-2^5 = -1 \cdot 2^5 = -1 \cdot 32 = -32$

From Example 2, we can see that $(-x)^n \neq -x^n$, where n is an even natural number.

Rules of Exponents

Now that we know how to evaluate powers of numbers we can discuss the rules of exponents. Consider

$$2^2 \cdot 2^3 = \underbrace{2 \cdot 2}_{2\,\text{factors}} \cdot \underbrace{2 \cdot 2 \cdot 2}_{3\,\text{factors}} = 2^5$$

This example illustrates the product rule for exponents.

Product Rule for Exponents

$$a^m \cdot a^n = a^{m+n}$$

Therefore, by using the product rule, $2^2 \cdot 2^3 = 2^{2+3} = 2^5$.

EXAMPLE 3   Using the Product Rule for Exponents

Use the product rule to simplify.

a) $3^4 \cdot 3^5$ b) $7^2 \cdot 7^6$

SOLUTION:

a) $3^4 \cdot 3^5 = 3^{4+5} = 3^9$ b) $7^2 \cdot 7^6 = 7^{2+6} = 7^8$

Consider

$$\frac{2^5}{2^2} = \frac{2 \cdot 2 \cdot 2 \cdot 2 \cdot 2}{2 \cdot 2} = 2 \cdot 2 \cdot 2 = 2^3$$

This example illustrates the quotient rule for exponents.

Quotient Rule for Exponents

$$\frac{a^m}{a^n} = a^{m-n}, \qquad a \neq 0$$

Therefore, $\dfrac{2^5}{2^2} = 2^{5-2} = 2^3$.

EXAMPLE 4   *Using the Quotient Rule for Exponents*

Use the quotient rule to simplify.

a) $\dfrac{5^8}{5^5}$ b) $\dfrac{8^{12}}{8^5}$

SOLUTION:

a) $\dfrac{5^8}{5^5} = 5^{8-5} = 5^3$ b) $\dfrac{8^{12}}{8^5} = 8^{12-5} = 8^7$ ▲

Consider $2^3 \div 2^3$. The quotient rule gives

$$\frac{2^3}{2^3} = 2^{3-3} = 2^0$$

But $\dfrac{2^3}{2^3} = \dfrac{8}{8} = 1$. Therefore, 2^0 must equal 1. This example illustrates the zero exponent rule.

Zero Exponent Rule

$$a^0 = 1, \qquad a \neq 0$$

Note that 0^0 is not defined by the zero exponent rule.

EXAMPLE 5   *The Zero Power*

Use the zero exponent rule to simplify.

a) 2^0 b) $(-2)^0$ c) -2^0 d) $(5x)^0$ e) $5x^0$

SOLUTION:

a) $2^0 = 1$ b) $(-2)^0 = 1$ c) $-2^0 = -1 \cdot 2^0 = -1 \cdot 1 = -1$

d) $(5x)^0 = 1$ e) $5x^0 = 5 \cdot x^0 = 5 \cdot 1 = 5$ ▲

Consider $2^3 \div 2^5$. The quotient rule yields

$$\frac{2^3}{2^5} = 2^{3-5} = 2^{-2}$$

But $\dfrac{2^3}{2^5} = \dfrac{2 \cdot 2 \cdot 2}{2 \cdot 2 \cdot 2 \cdot 2 \cdot 2} = \dfrac{1}{2^2}$. Since $\dfrac{2^3}{2^5}$ equals both 2^{-2} and $\dfrac{1}{2^2}$, then 2^{-2} must equal

$\dfrac{1}{2^2}$. This example illustrates the negative exponent rule.

Negative Exponent Rule

$$a^{-m} = \frac{1}{a^m}, \qquad a \neq 0$$

EXAMPLE 6   *Using the Negative Exponent Rule*

Use the negative exponent rule to simplify.
a) 5^{-2} b) 8^{-1}

SOLUTION:

a) $5^{-2} = \dfrac{1}{5^2} = \dfrac{1}{25}$ b) $8^{-1} = \dfrac{1}{8^1} = \dfrac{1}{8}$ ▲

Consider $(2^3)^2$.

$$(2^3)^2 = (2^3)(2^3) = 2^{3+3} = 2^6$$

This example illustrates the power rule for exponents.

Power Rule for Exponents

$$(a^m)^n = a^{m \cdot n}$$

Thus, $(2^3)^2 = 2^{3 \cdot 2} = 2^6$.

EXAMPLE 7   *Evaluating a Power Raised to Another Power*

Use the power rule to simplify.
a) $(5^4)^3$ b) $(7^2)^5$

SOLUTION:

a) $(5^4)^3 = 5^{4 \cdot 3} = 5^{12}$ b) $(7^2)^5 = 7^{2 \cdot 5} = 7^{10}$ ▲

Large and Small Numbers

Diameter of a galaxy may be 1×10^5 light-years

Diameter of an atom may be 1×10^{-10} meter

Our everyday activities don't require us to deal with quantities much above those in the thousands: $6.95 for lunch, 100 meters to a lap, a $15,000 car loan, and so on. Yet as modern technology has developed, so has our ability to study all aspects of the universe we live in, from the very large to the very small. Modern technology can be used with the rules of exponents and scientific notation to study everything from the diameter of a galaxy to the diameter of an atom.

Summary of the Rules of Exponents

$a^m \cdot a^n = a^{m+n}$ Product rule for exponents

$\dfrac{a^m}{a^n} = a^{m-n}, \quad a \neq 0$ Quotient rule for exponents

$a^0 = 1, \quad a \neq 0$ Zero exponent rule

$a^{-m} = \dfrac{1}{a^m}, \quad a \neq 0$ Negative exponent rule

$(a^m)^n = a^{m \cdot n}$ Power rule for exponents

Scientific Notation

Often scientific problems deal with very large and very small numbers. For example, the distance from Earth to the sun is about 93,000,000 miles. The wavelength of a yellow color of light is about 0.0000006 meter. Because working with many zeros is difficult, scientists developed a notation that expresses such numbers with exponents. For example, consider the distance from Earth to the sun, 93,000,000 miles.

$$93,000,000 = 9.3 \times 10,000,000$$
$$= 9.3 \times 10^7$$

The wavelength of a yellow color of light is about 0.0000006 meter.

$$0.0000006 = 6.0 \times 0.0000001$$
$$= 6.0 \times 10^{-7}$$

The numbers 9.3×10^7 and 6.0×10^{-7} are written in a form called *scientific notation*. Each number written in scientific notation is written as a number greater than or equal to 1 and less than 10 multiplied by some power of 10.

Some examples of numbers in scientific notation are

$$3.7 \times 10^3, \qquad 2.05 \times 10^{-3}, \qquad 5.6 \times 10^8, \qquad \text{and} \qquad 1.00 \times 10^{-5}$$

The following is a procedure for writing a number in scientific notation.

To Write a Number in Scientific Notation

1. Move the decimal point in the original number to the right or left until you obtain a number greater than or equal to 1 and less than 10.
2. Count the number of places you have moved the decimal point to obtain the number in step 1. If the decimal point was moved to the left, the count is to be considered positive. If the decimal point was moved to the right, the count is to be considered negative.
3. Multiply the number obtained in step 1 by 10 raised to the count found in step 2. (Note that the count determined in step 2 is the exponent on the base 10.)

EXAMPLE 8   *Converting from Decimal Notation to Scientific Notation*

Write each number in scientific notation.

a) In 2002, the population of the United States was about 288,000,000.
b) In 2002, the population of China was about 1,283,000,000.
c) In 2002, the population of the world was about 6,251,000,000.
d) The diameter of a hydrogen atom nucleus is about 0.0000000000011 millimeter.
e) The wavelength of an x-ray is about 0.000000000492 meter.

SOLUTION

a) $288,000,000 = 2.88 \times 10^8$
b) $1,283,000,000 = 1.283 \times 10^9$
c) $6,251,000,000 = 6.251 \times 10^9$
d) $0.0000000000011 = 1.1 \times 10^{-12}$
e) $0.000000000492 = 4.92 \times 10^{-10}$

▲

To convert from a number given in scientific notation to decimal notation we reverse the procedure.

To Change a Number in Scientific Notation to Decimal Notation

1. Observe the exponent on the 10.
2. a) If the exponent is positive, move the decimal point in the number to the right the same number of places as the exponent. Adding zeros to the number might be necessary.
   b) If the exponent is negative, move the decimal point in the number to the left the same number of places as the exponent. Adding zeros might be necessary.

EXAMPLE 9   *Converting from Scientific Notation to Decimal Notation*

Write each number in decimal notation.

a) The average distance from Earth to the sun is about 9.3×10^7 miles.
b) The half-life of uranium 235 is about 4.5×10^9 years.
c) The average grain size in siltstone is 1.35×10^{-3} inch.
d) A *millimicron* is a unit of measure used for very small distances. One millimicron is about 3.94×10^{-8} inch.

SOLUTION:

a) $9.3 \times 10^7 = 93,000,000$
b) $4.5 \times 10^9 = 4,500,000,000$
c) $1.35 \times 10^{-3} = 0.00135$
d) $3.94 \times 10^{-8} = 0.0000000394$

▲

In scientific journals and books, we occasionally see numbers like 10^{15} and 10^{-6}. We interpret these numbers as 1×10^{15} and 1×10^{-6}, respectively, when converting the numbers to decimal form.

┌─ **EXAMPLE 10**   *Multiplying Numbers in Scientific Notation*

Multiply $(2.1 \times 10^5)(9 \times 10^{-3})$. Write the answer in scientific notation and in decimal notation.

SOLUTION:

$$
\begin{aligned}
(2.1 \times 10^5)(9 \times 10^{-3}) &= (2.1 \times 9)(10^5 \times 10^{-3}) \\
&= 18.9 \times 10^2 \\
&= 1.89 \times 10^3 \qquad \text{Scientific notation} \\
&= 1.890 \qquad\qquad \text{Decimal notation} \qquad ▲
\end{aligned}
$$

┌─ **EXAMPLE 11**   *Dividing Numbers Using Scientific Notation*

Divide $\dfrac{0.000000000048}{24,000,000,000}$. Write the answer in scientific notation.

SOLUTION: First write each number in scientific notation.

$$
\begin{aligned}
\frac{0.000000000048}{24,000,000,000} = \frac{4.8 \times 10^{-11}}{2.4 \times 10^{10}} &= \left(\frac{4.8}{2.4}\right)\left(\frac{10^{-11}}{10^{10}}\right) \\
&= 2.0 \times 10^{-11-10} \\
&= 2.0 \times 10^{-21} \qquad ▲
\end{aligned}
$$

Scientific Notation on the Scientific Calculator

One of the advantages of using scientific notation when working with very large and very small numbers is the ease with which you can perform operations. Performing these operations is even easier with the use of a scientific calculator. Most scientific calculators have a scientific notation key labeled "Exp," "EXP," or "EE." We will refer to the scientific notation key as $\boxed{\text{EXP}}$. The following keystrokes can be used to enter the number 4.3×10^6

Keystroke(s)	Calculator display
4.3	4.3
$\boxed{\text{EXP}}$	4.3^{00}
6	4.3^{06}

Your calculator may have some slight variations to the display shown here. The display 4.3^{06} means 4.3×10^6. We now will use our calculators to perform some computations using scientific notation.

┌─ **EXAMPLE 12**   *Use Scientific Notation on a Calculator to Find a Product*

Multiply $(4.3 \times 10^6)(2 \times 10^{-4})$ using a scientific calculator. Write the answer in decimal notation.

SOLUTION: Our sequence of keystrokes is as follows:

Keystroke(s)	Display
4.3	4.3
EXP	4.3^{00}
6	4.3^{06}
$\times$	4300000

4.3×10^6 is now entered in the calculator. Most calculators will convert to decimal notation (if the display can show the number)

2	2.
EXP	$2.^{00}$
4	$2.^{04}$
+/−	$2.^{-04}$
=	860.

Enter the positive form of the exponent
Make the exponent negative*
Press = to obtain the answer of 860[†]   ▲

EXAMPLE 13   *Use Scientific Notation on a Calculator to Find a Quotient*

Divide $\dfrac{0.000000000048}{24,000,000,000}$ using a scientific calculator. Write the answer in scientific notation.

SOLUTION: We first rewrite the numerator and denominator using scientific notation. See Example 11.

$$\frac{0.000000000048}{24,000,000,000} = \frac{4.8 \times 10^{-11}}{2.4 \times 10^{10}}$$

Next we use a scientific calculator to perform the computation. The keystrokes are as follows

4.8 [EXP] 11 [+/−] [÷] 2.4 [EXP] 10 [=]

The display on the calculator is $2.^{-21}$, which means 2.0×10^{-21}.   ▲

EXAMPLE 14   *U.S. Debt per Person*

On July 30, 2003, the U.S. Department of the Treasury estimated the U.S. federal debt to be about $6.74 trillion. On this same day, the U.S. Bureau of the Census estimated the U.S. population to be about 292 million people. Determine the average debt, per person, by dividing the U.S. federal debt by the U.S. population.

---

*Some calculators will require you to enter the negative sign before entering the exponent.
[†]Some calculators will display the answer in scientific notation. In this case, the display will show $8.6^{\,02}$, which means 8.6×10^2 and equals 860.

SOLUTION: First, we will write the numbers involved using decimal notation and then convert them to scientific notation.

$$6.74 \text{ trillion} = 6,740,000,000,000 = 6.74 \times 10^{12}$$
$$292 \text{ million} = 292,000,000 = 2.92 \times 10^{8}$$

Now we will divide 6.74×10^{12} by 2.92×10^{8} using a scientific calculator. The keystrokes are

6.74 [EXP] 12 [÷] 2.92 [EXP] 8 [=]

The display shows 23,082.1918. This number indicates that on July 30, 2003, the U.S. government owed about $23,082.19 per man, woman, and child living in the United States. ▲

SECTION 5.6   EXERCISES

Concept/Writing Exercises

1. In the expression 2^3, what is the name given to the 2, and what is the name given to the 3?

2. Explain the meaning of b^n.

3. **a)** Explain the product rule for exponents.
   b) Use the product rule to simplify $2^3 \cdot 2^4$.

4. **a)** Explain the quotient rule for exponents.
   b) Use the quotient rule to simplify $\dfrac{5^6}{5^4}$.

5. **a)** Explain the zero exponent rule.
   b) Use the zero exponent rule to simplify 7^0.

6. **a)** Explain the negative exponent rule.
   b) Use the negative exponent rule to simplify 2^{-3}.

7. **a)** Explain the power rule for exponents.
   b) Use the power rule to simplify $(3^2)^4$.

8. Explain how you can simplify the expression 1^{500}.

9. Explain how you can simplify the following expressions and then simplify the expression.
   a) -1^{500}
   b) $(-1)^{500}$
   c) -1^{501}
   d) $(-1)^{501}$

10. **a)** In your own words, explain how to change a number in decimal notation to scientific notation.
    b) Using the procedure in part (a), change 0.000426 to scientific notation.

11. **a)** In your own words, explain how to change a number in scientific notation to decimal notation.
    b) Using the procedure in part (a), change 5.76×10^{-4} to decimal notation.

12. A number is given in scientific notation. What does it indicate about the number when the exponent on the 10 is (a) positive, (b) zero, and (c) negative?

Practice the Skills

In Exercises 13–44, evaluate the expression.

13. 5^2

14. 3^4

15. $(-2)^4$

16. -2^4

17. -3^2

18. $(-3)^2$

19. $\left(\dfrac{2}{3}\right)^2$

20. $\left(-\dfrac{7}{8}\right)^2$

21. $(-5)^2$

22. -5^2

23. $2^3 \cdot 3^2$

24. $\dfrac{15^2}{3^2}$

25. $\dfrac{5^7}{5^5}$

26. $3^3 \cdot 3^4$

27. $\dfrac{7}{7^3}$

28. $3^4 \cdot 7^0$

29. $(-13)^0$

30. $(-3)^4$

31. 3^4

32. -3^4

33. 3^{-2}

34. 3^{-3}

35. $(2^3)^4$

36. $(1^{12})^{13}$

37. $\dfrac{11^{25}}{11^{23}}$

38. $5^2 \cdot 5$

39. $(-4)^2$

40. 4^{-2}

41. -4^2

42. $(4^3)^2$

43. $(2^2)^{-3}$

44. $3^{-3} \cdot 3$

In Exercises 45–60, express the number in scientific notation.

45. 231,000

46. 297,000,000

47. 15

48. 0.000034

49. 0.56

50. 0.00467

51. 19,000   **52.** 1,260,000,000   **53.** 0.000186
54. 0.0003   **55.** 0.00000423   **56.** 54,000
57. 711   **58.** 0.02   **59.** 0.153
60. 416,000

In Exercises 61–76, express the number in decimal notation.

61. 2.3×10^3 **62.** 4.78×10^5 **63.** 3.901×10^{-3}
64. 1.764×10^7 **65.** 8.62×10^{-5} **66.** 2.19×10^{-4}
67. 3.12×10^{-1} **68.** 4.6×10^1 **69.** 9×10^6
70. 7.3×10^4 **71.** 2.31×10^2 **72.** 1.04×10^{-2}
73. 3.5×10^4 **74.** 2.17×10^{-6} **75.** 1×10^4
76. 1×10^{-3}

In Exercises 77–86, (a) perform the indicated operation without the use of a calculator and express each answer in decimal notation. (b) Confirm your answer from part (a) by using a scientific calculator to perform the operations. If the calculator displays the answer in scientific notation, convert the answer to decimal notation.

77. $(2 \times 10^3)(4 \times 10^2)$ **78.** $(4.1 \times 10^{-3})(2 \times 10^3)$
79. $(5.1 \times 10^1)(3 \times 10^{-4})$
80. $(1.6 \times 10^{-2})(4 \times 10^{-3})$
81. $\dfrac{6.4 \times 10^5}{2 \times 10^3}$ **82.** $\dfrac{8 \times 10^{-3}}{2 \times 10^1}$
83. $\dfrac{8.4 \times 10^{-6}}{4 \times 10^{-3}}$ **84.** $\dfrac{25 \times 10^3}{5 \times 10^{-2}}$
85. $\dfrac{4 \times 10^5}{2 \times 10^4}$ **86.** $\dfrac{16 \times 10^3}{8 \times 10^{-3}}$

In Exercises 87–96, (a) perform the indicated operation without the use of a calculator and express each answer in scientific notation. (b) Confirm your answer from part (a) by using a scientific calculator to perform the operations. If the calculator displays the answer in decimal notation, convert the answer to scientific notation.

87. (300,000)(2,000,000)   **88.** (0.000041)(3000)
89. (0.003)(0.00015)   **90.** (230,000)(3000)
91. $\dfrac{1,400,000}{700}$ **92.** $\dfrac{20,000}{0.0005}$
93. $\dfrac{0.00004}{200}$ **94.** $\dfrac{0.0012}{0.000006}$
95. $\dfrac{150,000}{0.0005}$ **96.** $\dfrac{24,000}{8,000,000}$

Problem Solving

In Exercises 97–100, list the numbers from smallest to largest.

97. 5.8×10^5; 3.2×10^{-1}; 4.6; 8.3×10^{-4}
98. 8.5×10^{-5}; 8.2×10^3; 1.3×10^{-1}; 6.2×10^4
99. $40,000$; 4.1×10^3; 0.00079; 8.3×10^{-5}
100. $267,000,000$; 3.14×10^7; $1,962,000$; 4.79×10^6

In Exercises 101–107, express your answer (a) using decimal notation and (b) using scientific notation. You may use a scientific calculator to perform the necessary operations.

101. *Gross Domestic Product* The gross domestic product (GDP) of a country is the total national output of goods and services produced within that country. In 2001, the GDP of the United States was about \$10.1432 trillion and the U.S. population was about 285 million people. Determine the U.S. GDP per person by dividing the GDP by the population.

102. *Japan's GDP* In 2001, the GDP (see Exercise 101) of Japan was about \$4.1468 trillion and the population of Japan was about 127 million people. Determine Japan's GDP per person by dividing the GDP by the population.

103. *Computer Speed* On April 20, 2002, the NEC Earth Simulator computer—located in Yokohama, Japan—broke the world's record for being the fastest supercomputer. This computer is capable of performing 36.6 trillion calculations per second. At this rate, how long would it take to perform a task requiring 7.69×10^{33} calculations?

104. *World Population* According to the U.S. Bureau of the Census, the population of the world in 2002 was approximately 6.251×10^9 and the population of China was about 1.283×10^9. How many people lived outside China?

105. *Traveling to Jupiter* The distance from Earth to the planet Jupiter is approximately 4.5×10^8 mi. If a spacecraft traveled at a speed of 25,000 mph, how many hours would the spacecraft need to travel from Earth to Jupiter? Use distance = rate × time.

106. *Traveling to the Moon* The distance from Earth to the moon is approximately 239,000 mi. If a spacecraft travels at a speed of 20,000 mph, how many hours would the spacecraft need to travel from Earth to the moon? Use distance = rate × time.

107. *Bucket Full of Molecules* A drop of water contains about 40 billion molecules. If a bucket has half a million drops of water in it, how many molecules of water are in the bucket?

108. *Blood Cells in a Cubic Millimeter* If a cubic millimeter of blood contains 5,800,000 red blood cells, how many red blood cells are contained in 50 cubic millimeters of blood?

109. *Radioactive Isotopes* The half-life of a radioactive isotope is the time required for half the quantity of the isotope to decompose. The half-life of uranium 238 is 4.5×10^9 years, and the half-life of uranium 234 is 2.5×10^5 years. How many times greater is the half-life of uranium 238 than uranium 234?

110. *1950 Niagara Treaty* The 1950 Niagara Treaty between the United States and Canada requires that during the tourist season a minimum of 100,000 cubic feet of water per second (ft^3/sec) flow over Niagara Falls (another 130,000–160,000 ft^3/sec are diverted for power generation). Find the minimum amount of water that will flow over the falls in a 24-hour period during the tourist season.

111. *U.S. Debt per Person: 1993 versus 2003* In Example 14, the U.S. government debt was discussed. It was found that the debt in 2003 was $23,082.19 per person. In 1993, the U.S. government debt was about $4.41 trillion, and the population of the United States was about 258 million people.

a) Determine the amount of debt per person in the United States in 1993.

b) How much more per person did the U.S. government owe in 2003 than in 1993?

112. *Disposable Diaper Quantity* Laid end to end, the 18 billion disposable diapers thrown away in the United States each year would reach the moon and back seven times.

a) Write 18 billion in scientific notation.

b) If the distance from Earth to the moon is 2.38×10^5 miles, what is the length of all these diapers placed end to end? Write the answer in decimal notation.

113. *Mutual Fund Manager* Lauri Mackey is the fund manager for the Mackey Mutual Fund. This mutual fund has total assets of $1.2 billion. Lauri wants to maintain the investments in this fund according to the following pie chart.

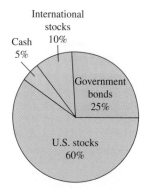

Source: Ibbotson Associates

a) How much of the $1.2 billion should be invested in U.S. stocks?

b) How much should be invested in government bonds?

c) How much should be invested in international stocks?

d) How much should remain in cash?

114. *Another Mutual Fund Manager* Susan Dratch is the fund manager for the Dratch Mutual Fund. This mutual fund has total assets of $3.4 billion. Susan wants to maintain the investments in this fund according to the following pie chart.

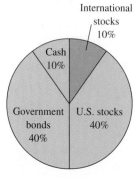

Source: Ibbotson Associates

a) How much of the $3.4 billion should be invested in U.S. stocks?

b) How much should be invested in government bonds?

c) How much should be invested in international stocks?

d) How much should remain in cash?

115. *Metric System Comparison* In the metric system, 1 meter $= 10^3$ millimeters. How many times greater is a meter than a millimeter? Explain how you determined your answer.

116. In the metric system, 1 gram $= 10^3$ millimeters and 1 gram $= 10^{-3}$ kilogram. What is the relationship between milligrams and kilograms? Explain how you determined your answer.

117. *Earth to Sun Comparison* The mass of the sun is approximately 2×10^{30} kilograms, and the mass of Earth is approximately 6×10^{24} kilograms. How many times greater is the mass of the sun than the mass of Earth? Write your answer in decimal notation.

118. *The Day of Six Billion* The United Nations declared October 12, 1999, the *Day of Six Billion*. On this day, Earth's population was estimated to reach 6 billion. Currently, Earth's population is doubling about every 35 years.

a) Using this figure, estimate the world's population in the year 2034.

b) Assuming 365 days in a year, estimate the average number of additional people added to Earth's population each day between 1999 and 2034.

119. *Computer Calculation Speed* The IBM Blue Pacific computer is capable of operating at a peak speed of about 3.9 trillion (3,900,000,000,000) calculations per second. At this rate, how long would it take to perform a task requiring 897 quadrillion (897,000,000,000,000,000) calculations?

Challenge Problems/Group Activities

120. *Comparing a Million to a Billion* Many people have no idea of the difference in size between a million (1,000,000), a billion (1,000,000,000), and a trillion (1,000,000,000,000).

a) Write a million, a billion, and a trillion in scientific notation.

b) Determine how long it would take to spend a million dollars if you spent $1000 a day.

c) Repeat part (b) for a billion dollars.

d) Repeat part (b) for a trillion dollars.

e) How many times greater is a billion dollars than a million dollars?

121. *Speed of Light*

a) Light travels at a speed of 1.86×10^5 mi/sec. A *light-year* is the distance that light travels in 1 year. Determine the number of miles in a light year.

b) Earth is approximately 93,000,000 mi from the sun. How long does it take light from the sun to reach Earth?

122. *Bacteria in a Culture* The exponential function $E(t) = 2^{10} \cdot 2^t$ approximates the number of bacteria in a certain culture after t hours.

a) The initial number of bacteria is determined when $t = 0$. What is the initial number of bacteria?

b) How many bacteria are there after $\frac{1}{2}$ hour?

Internet/Research Activities

123. John Allen Paulos of Temple University has written many entertaining books about mathematics for nonmathematicians. Included among these are *Mathematics and Humor* (1980); *I Think, Therefore I Laugh* (1985); *Innumeracy— Mathematical Illiteracy and Its Consequences* (1989); *Beyond Numeracy—Ruminations of a Numbers Man* (1991); *A Mathematician Reads the Newspaper* (1995); *Once Upon a Number* (1998); *A Mathematician Plays the Stock Market* (2003); and *Music and Gender* (2003). Read one of Paulos's books and write a 500-word report on it.

John Allen Paulos

124. Obtain data from the U.S. Department of the Treasury and from the U.S. Bureau of the Census Internet web sites to calculate the current U.S. government debt per person. Write a report in which you compare your figure with those obtained in Exercise 111 and Example 14. Include in your report definitions of the following terms: revenues, expenditures, deficit, and surplus.

125. Find an article in a newspaper or magazine that contains scientific notation. Write a paragraph explaining how scientific notation was used. Attach a copy of the article to your report.

5.7 ARITHMETIC AND GEOMETRIC SEQUENCES

Now that you can recognize the various sets of real numbers and know how to add, subtract, multiply, and divide real numbers, we can discuss sequences. A *sequence* is a list of numbers that are related to each other by a rule. The numbers that form the sequence are called its *terms*. If your salary increases or decreases by a fixed amount over a period of time, the listing of the amounts, over time, would form an arithmetic sequence. When interest in a savings account is compounded at regular intervals, the listing of the amounts in the account over time will be a geometric sequence.

Arithmetic Sequences

A sequence in which each term after the first term differs from the preceding term by a constant amount is called an *arithmetic sequence*. The amount by which each pair of successive terms differs is called the *common difference, d*. The common difference can be found by subtracting any term from the term that directly follows it.

Examples of arithmetic sequences	Common differences
$1, 5, 9, 13, 17, \ldots$	$d = 5 - 1 = 4$
$-7, -5, -3, -1, 1, \ldots$	$d = -5 - (-7) = -5 + 7 = 2$
$\dfrac{5}{2}, \dfrac{3}{2}, \dfrac{1}{2}, -\dfrac{1}{2}, \ldots$	$d = \dfrac{3}{2} - \dfrac{5}{2} = -\dfrac{2}{2} = -1$

┌─ **EXAMPLE 1**   *The First Five Terms of an Arithmetic Sequence*

Write the first five terms of the arithmetic sequence with first term 5 and a common difference of 4.

SOLUTION: The first term is 5. The second term is $5 + 4$ or 9. The third term is $9 + 4$ or 13. The fourth term is $13 + 4$ or 17. The fifth term is $17 + 4$ or 21. Thus, the first five terms of the sequence are 5, 9, 13, 17, 21.   ▲

┌─ **EXAMPLE 2**   *An Arithmetic Sequence with a Negative Difference*

Write the first five terms of the arithmetic sequence with first term 10 and common difference of -3.

SOLUTION: The sequence is

$$10, 7, 4, 1, -2$$

   ▲

When discussing a sequence, we often represent the first term as a_1 (read "a sub 1"), the second term as a_2, the fifteenth term as a_{15}, and so on. We use the notation a_n to represent the general or *n*th term of a sequence. Thus a sequence may be symbolized as

$$a_1, a_2, a_3, a_4, \ldots, a_n, \ldots$$

For example, in the sequence 2, 5, 8, 11, 14, $\ldots$, we have

$$a_1 = 2, a_2 = 5, a_3 = 8, a_4 = 11, a_5 = 14, \ldots.$$

Carl Friedrich Gauss (1777–1855), often called the "Prince of Mathematicians," made significant contributions to the fields of algebra, geometry, and number theory. Gauss was only 22 years old when he proved the fundamental theorem of algebra for his doctoral dissertation.

When Gauss was only 10, his mathematics teacher gave him the problem of finding the sum of the first 100 natural numbers, thinking that this would keep him busy for a while. Gauss recognized a pattern in the sequence of numbers when he considered the sum of the following numbers.

$$\begin{array}{rrrrrr} 1 + & 2 + & 3 + & \cdots + & 99 + & 100 \\ 100 + & 99 + & 98 + & \cdots + & 2 + & 1 \\ \hline 101 + & 101 + & 101 + & \cdots + & 101 + & 101 \end{array}$$

He had the required answer in no time at all. When he added, he had one hundred 101's. Therefore, the sum is $\frac{1}{2}(100)(101) = 5050$.

When we know the first term of an arithmetic sequence and the common difference, we can use the following formula to find the value of any specific term.

General or nth Term of an Arithmetic Sequence

$$a_n = a_1 + (n - 1)d$$

EXAMPLE 3   *Finding the Seventh Term of an Arithmetic Sequence*

Find the seventh term of the arithmetic sequence whose first term is 3 and whose common difference is -6.

SOLUTION: To find the seventh term, or a_7, replace n in the formula with 7, a_1 with 3, and d with -6.

$$\begin{aligned} a_n &= a_1 + (n - 1)d \\ a_7 &= 3 + (7 - 1)(-6) \\ &= 3 + (6)(-6) \\ &= 3 - 36 \\ &= -33 \end{aligned}$$

The seventh term is -33. As a check, we have listed the first seven terms of the sequence: $3, -3, -9, -15, -21, -27, -33$.   ▲

EXAMPLE 4   *Finding the nth Term of an Arithmetic Sequence*

Write an expression for the general or nth term, a_n, for the sequence $1, 6, 11, 16, \ldots$.

SOLUTION: In this sequence, the first term a_1, is 1, and the common difference, d, is 5. We substitute these values into $a_n = a_1 + (n - 1)d$ to obtain an expression for the nth term, a_n.

$$\begin{aligned} a_n &= a_1 + (n - 1)d \\ &= 1 + (n - 1)5 \\ &= 1 + 5n - 5 \\ &= 5n - 4 \end{aligned}$$

Note that when $n = 1$, the first term is $5(1) - 4 = 1$. When $n = 2$, the second term is $5(2) - 4 = 6$, and so on.   ▲

We can use the following formula to find the sum of the first n terms in an arithmetic sequence.

Sum of the First n Terms in an Arithmetic Sequence

$$s_n = \frac{n(a_1 + a_n)}{2}$$

In this formula, s_n represents the sum of the first n terms, a_1 is the first term, a_n is the nth term, and n is the number of terms in the sequence from a_1 to a_n.

EXAMPLE 5   *Finding the Sum of a Sequence*

Find the sum of the first 25 natural numbers.

SOLUTION: The sequence we are discussing is

$$1, 2, 3, 4, 5, \ldots, 25$$

In this sequence, $a_1 = 1$, $a_{25} = 25$, and $n = 25$. Thus, the sum of the first 25 terms is

$$s_n = \frac{n(a_1 + a_n)}{2}$$

$$s_{25} = \frac{25(1 + 25)}{2}$$

$$= \frac{25(26)}{2} = 325$$

Thus, the sum of the terms $1 + 2 + 3 + 4 + \cdots + 25$ is 325.

Geometric Sequences

The next type of sequence we will discuss is the geometric sequence. A *geometric sequence* is one in which the ratio of any term to the term that directly precedes it is a constant. This constant is called the *common ratio*. The common ratio, r, can be found by taking any term except the first and dividing that term by the preceding term.

Examples of geometric sequences	Common ratios
$2, 4, 8, 16, 32, \ldots$	$r = 4 \div 2 = 2$
$-3, 6, -12, 24, -48, \ldots$	$r = 6 \div (-3) = -2$
$\frac{2}{3}, \frac{2}{9}, \frac{2}{27}, \frac{2}{81}, \ldots$	$r = \frac{2}{9} \div \frac{2}{3} = \left(\frac{2}{9}\right)\left(\frac{3}{2}\right) = \frac{1}{3}$

To construct a geometric sequence when the first term, a_1, and common ratio are known, multiply the first term by the common ratio to get the second term. Then multiply the second term by the common ratio to get the third term, and so on.

EXAMPLE 6   *The First Five Terms of a Geometric Sequence*

Write the first five terms of the geometric sequence whose first term, a_1, is 3 and whose common ratio, r, is 4.

SOLUTION: The first term is 3. The second term, found by multiplying the first term by 4, is $3 \cdot 4$ or 12. The third term is $12 \cdot 4$ or 48. The fourth term is $48 \cdot 4$ or 192. The fifth term is $192 \cdot 4$ or 768. Thus, the first five terms of the sequence are 3, 12, 48, 192, 768.

When we know the first term of a geometric sequence and the common ratio, we can use the following formula to find the value of the general or nth term, a_n.

General or nth Term of a Geometric Sequence

$$a_n = a_1 r^{n-1}$$

EXAMPLE 7   *Finding the Seventh Term of a Geometric Sequence*

Find the seventh term of the geometric sequence whose first term is -3 and whose common ratio is -2.

SOLUTION: In this sequence, $a_1 = -3$, $r = -2$, and $n = 7$. Substituting the values, we obtain

$$a_n = a_1 r^{n-1}$$
$$a_7 = -3(-2)^{7-1}$$
$$= -3(-2)^6$$
$$= -3(64)$$
$$= -192$$

As a check, we have listed the first seven terms of the sequence: $-3, 6, -12, 24,$ $-48, 96, -192$.

EXAMPLE 8   *Finding the nth Term of a Geometric Sequence*

Write an expression for the general or nth term, a_n, of the sequence 2, 6, 18, 54, ...

SOLUTION: In this sequence, $a_1 = 2$ and $r = 3$. We substitute these values into $a_n = a_1 r^{n-1}$ to obtain an expression for the nth term, a_n.

$$a_n = a_1 r^{n-1}$$
$$= 2(3)^{n-1}$$

Note than when $n = 1$, $a_1 = 2(3)^0 = 2(1) = 2$. When $n = 2$, $a_2 = 2(3)^1 = 6$, and so on.

We can use the following formula to find the sum of the first n terms of a geometric sequence.

Sum of the First n Terms of a Geometric Sequence

$$s_n = \frac{a_1(1 - r^n)}{1 - r}, \qquad r \neq 1$$

EXAMPLE 9   *Adding the First n Terms of a Geometric Sequence*

Find the sum of the first five terms in the geometric sequence whose first term is 4 and whose common ratio is 2.

SOLUTION: In this sequence, $a_1 = 4$, $r = 2$, and $n = 5$. Substituting these values into the formula, we get

$$s_n = \frac{a_1(1 - r^n)}{1 - r}$$

$$s_5 = \frac{4[1 - (2)^5]}{1 - 2}$$

$$= \frac{4(1 - 32)}{-1}$$

$$= \frac{4(-31)}{-1} = \frac{-124}{-1} = 124$$

The sum of the first five terms of the sequence is 124. The first five terms of the sequence are 4, 8, 16, 32, 64. If you add these five numbers, you will obtain the sum 124. ▲

EXAMPLE 10   *Pounds and Pounds of Silver*

As a reward for saving his kingdom from a band of thieves, a king offered a knight one of two options. The knight's first option was to be paid 100,000 pounds of silver all at once. The second option was to be paid over the course of a month. On the first day, he would receive one pound of silver. On the second day, he would receive two pounds of silver. On the third day, he would receive four pounds of silver, and so on, each day receiving double the amount given on the previous day. Assuming the month is 30 days, which option would pay the knight more silver?

SOLUTION: The first option pays the knight 100,000 pounds of silver. The second option pays according to the geometric sequence 1, 2, 4, 8, 16, ... In this sequence, $a_1 = 1$, $r = 2$, and $n = 30$. The sum of this sequence can be found by substituting these values into the formula to obtain

$$s_n = \frac{a_1(1 - r^n)}{1 - r}$$

$$s_{30} = \frac{1(1 - 2^{30})}{1 - 2}$$

$$= \frac{1 - 1{,}073{,}741{,}824}{-1}$$

$$= \frac{-1{,}073{,}741{,}823}{-1}$$

$$= 1{,}073{,}741{,}823$$

Thus, the knight would get paid 1,073,741,823 pounds of silver with the second option. The second option pays 1,073,641,823 more pounds of silver than the first option. ▲

SECTION 5.7 EXERCISES

Concept/Writing Exercises

1. State the definition of *sequence* and give an example.

2. What are the numbers that make up a sequence called?

3. **a)** State the definition of *arithmetic sequence* and give an example.
   b) State the definition of *geometric sequence* and give an example.

4. **a)** In the arithmetic sequence $2, 5, 8, 11, 14, \ldots$, state the common difference, d.
   b) In the geometric sequence $3, 6, 12, 24, 48, \ldots$, state the common ratio, r.

5. For an arithmetic sequence, state the meaning of each of the following symbols.
   a) a_n **b)** a_1 **c)** d **d)** s_n

6. For a geometric sequence, state the meaning of each of the following symbols.
   a) a_n **b)** a_1 **c)** r **d)** s_n

Practice the Skills

In Exercises 7–14, write the first five terms of the arithmetic sequence with the first term, a_1, and common difference, d.

7. $a_1 = 3, d = 2$ 8. $a_1 = 1, d = 3$

9. $a_1 = -5, d = 3$ 10. $a_1 = -11, d = 5$

11. $a_1 = 5, d = -2$ 12. $a_1 = -3, d = -4$

13. $a_1 = \frac{1}{2}, d = \frac{1}{2}$ 14. $a_1 = \frac{5}{2}, d = -\frac{3}{2}$

In Exercises 15–22, find the indicated term for the arithmetic sequence with the first term, a_1, and common difference, d.

15. Find a_6 when $a_1 = 2, d = 3$.

16. Find a_9 when $a_1 = 3$ and $d = -2$.

17. Find a_{10} when $a_1 = -5, d = 2$.

18. Find a_{12} when $a_1 = 7, d = -3$.

19. Find a_{20} when $a_1 = \frac{4}{5}, d = -1$.

20. Find a_{15} when $a_1 = -\frac{1}{2}, d = -2$.

21. Find a_{11} when $a_1 = 4, d = \frac{1}{2}$.

22. Find a_{15} when $a_1 = \frac{4}{3}, d = \frac{1}{3}$.

In Exercises 23–30, write an expression for the general or nth term, a_n, for the arithmetic sequence.

23. $1, 2, 3, 4, \ldots$ 24. $1, 3, 5, 7, \ldots$

25. $2, 4, 6, 8, \ldots$ 26. $3, 1, -1, -3, \ldots$

27. $-\frac{5}{3}, -\frac{4}{3}, -1, -\frac{2}{3}, \ldots$ 28. $-15, -10, -5, 0, \ldots$

29. $-3, -\frac{3}{2}, 0, \frac{3}{2}, \ldots$ 30. $-5, -2, 1, 4, \ldots$

In Exercises 31–38, find the sum of the terms of the arithmetic sequence. The number of terms, n, is given.

31. $1, 2, 3, 4, \ldots, 50; n = 50$

32. $2, 4, 6, 8, \ldots, 100; n = 50$

33. $1, 3, 5, 7, \ldots, 99; n = 50$

34. $-4, -7, -10, -13, \ldots, -28; n = 9$

35. $11, 6, 1, -4, \ldots, -24; n = 8$

36. $-9, -\frac{17}{2}, -8, -\frac{15}{2}, \ldots, -\frac{1}{2}; n = 18$

37. $\frac{1}{2}, \frac{5}{2}, \frac{9}{2}, \frac{13}{2}, \ldots, \frac{29}{2}; n = 8$

38. $\frac{3}{5}, \frac{4}{5}, 1, \frac{6}{5}, \ldots, 4; n = 18$

In Exercises 39–46, write the first five terms of the geometric sequence with the first term, a_1, and common ratio, r.

39. $a_1 = 3, r = 2$ 40. $a_1 = 6, r = 3$

41. $a_1 = 2, r = -2$ 42. $a_1 = 8, r = \frac{1}{2}$

43. $a_1 = -3, r = -1$ 44. $a_1 = -6, r = -2$

45. $a_1 = -16, r = -\frac{1}{2}$ 46. $a_1 = 5, r = \frac{3}{5}$

In Exercises 47–54, find the indicated term for the geometric sequence with the first term, a_1, and common ratio, r.

47. Find a_6 when $a_1 = 3, r = 4$.

48. Find a_5 when $a_1 = 2, r = 2$.

49. Find a_3 when $a_1 = 3, r = \frac{1}{2}$.

50. Find a_7 when $a_1 = -3, r = -3$.

51. Find a_5 when $a_1 = \frac{1}{2}, r = 2$.

52. Find a_{25} when $a_1 = 1, r = 2$.

53. Find a_{10} when $a_1 = -2, r = 3$.

54. Find a_{18} when $a_1 = -5, r = -2$.

In Exercises 55–62, write an expression for the general or nth term, a_n, for the geometric sequence.

55. $1, 2, 4, 8, \ldots$ 56. $3, 6, 12, 24, \ldots$

57. $3, -3, 3, -3, \ldots$ 58. $-16, -8, -4, -2, \ldots$

59. $\frac{1}{4}, \frac{1}{2}, 1, 2, \ldots$ 60. $-3, 6, -12, 24, \ldots$

61. $9, 3, 1, \frac{1}{3}, \frac{1}{9}, \ldots$ 62. $-4, -\frac{8}{3}, -\frac{16}{9}, -\frac{32}{27}, \ldots$

In Exercises 63–70, find the sum of the first n terms of the geometric sequence for the values of a_1 and r.

63. $n = 4, a_1 = 3, r = 2$

64. $n = 5, a_1 = 2, r = 3$

65. $n = 7, a_1 = 5, r = 4$

66. $n = 9, a_1 = -3, r = 5$

67. $n = 11, a_1 = -7, r = 3$

68. $n = 15, a_1 = -1, r = 2$

69. $n = 15, a_1 = -1, r = -2$

70. $n = 10, a_1 = 512, r = \dfrac{1}{2}$

Problem Solving

71. Find the sum of the first 100 natural numbers.

72. Find the sum of the first 100 even natural numbers.

73. Find the sum of the first 100 odd natural numbers.

74. Find the sum of the first 50 multiples of 3.

75. *Annual Pay Raises* Rita Fernandez is given a starting salary of $20,200 and promised a $1200 raise per year after each of the next eight years.
a) Determine her salary during her eighth year of work.
b) Determine the total salary she received over the 8 years.

76. *Pendulum Movement* Each swing of a pendulum (from far left to far right) is 3 in. shorter than the preceding swing. The first swing is 8 ft.
a) Find the length of the twelfth swing.
b) Determine the total distance traveled by the pendulum during the first 12 swings.

77. *A Bouncing Ball* Each time a ball bounces, the height attained by the ball is 6 in. less than the previous height attained. If on the first bounce the ball reaches a height of 6 ft, find the height attained on the eleventh bounce.

78. *Clock Strikes* A clock strikes once at 1 o'clock, twice at 2 o'clock, and so on. How many times does it strike over a 12 hr period?

79. *Squirrels and Pinecones* A tree squirrel cut down 1 pinecone on the first day of October, 2 pinecones on the second day, 3 pinecones on the third day, and so on. How many pinecones did this squirrel cut down during the month of October, which contains 31 days?

80. *Enrollment Increase* The enrollment at Loras College in 2001 was 8000 students. If the enrollment increases by 8% per year, determine the enrollment 10 years later.

81. *Decomposing Substance* A certain substance decomposes and loses 20% of its weight each hour. If there are originally 200 g of the substance, how much remains after 6 hr?

82. *Samurai Sword Construction* While making a traditional Japanese samurai sword, the master sword maker prepares the blade by heating a bar of iron until it is white hot. He then folds it over and pounds it smooth. Therefore, after each folding, the number of layers of steel is doubled. Assuming the sword maker starts with a bar of one layer and folds it 15 times, how many layers of steel will the finished sword contain?

83. *Salary Increase* If your salary were to increase at a rate of 6% per year, find your salary during your 15th year if your original salary is $20,000.

84. *A Bouncing Ball* When dropped, a ball rebounds to four-fifths of its original height. How high will the ball rebound after the fourth bounce if it is dropped from a height of 30 ft?

85. *Value of a Stock* Ten years ago, Nancy Hart purchased $2,000 worth of shares in RCF, Inc. Since then, the price of the stock has roughly tripled every two years. Approximately how much are Nancy's shares worth today?

86. *A Baseball Game* During a baseball game, the visiting team scored 1 run in the first inning, 2 runs in the second inning, 3 runs in the third inning, 4 runs in the fourth inning, and so on. The home team scored 1 run in the first inning, 2 runs in the second inning, 4 runs in the third inning, 8 runs in the fourth inning, and so on. What is the score of the game after eight innings?

Inning	1	2	3	4	5	6	7	8	9
Visitors	1	2	3	4					
Home	1	2	4	8					

Challenge Problems/Group Activities

87. A geometric sequence has $a_1 = 82$ and $r = \frac{1}{2}$; find s_6.

88. *Sums of Interior Angles* The sums of the interior angles of a triangle, a quadrilateral, a pentagon, and a sextagon are 180°, 360°, 540°, and 720°, respectively. Use this pattern to find a formula for the general term, a_n, where a_n represents the sum of the interior angles of an n-sided quadrilateral.

89. *Divisibility by 6* Determine how many numbers between 7 and 1610 are divisible by 6.

90. Find r and a_1 for the geometric sequence with $a_2 = 24$ and $a_5 = 648$.

91. *Total Distance Traveled by a Bouncing Ball* A ball is dropped from a height of 30 ft. On each bounce it attains a height four-fifths of its original height (or of the previous bounce). Find the total vertical distance traveled by the ball after it has completed its fifth bounce (therefore has hit the ground six times).

Recreational Mathematics

92. *A Wagering Strategy* The following is a strategy used by some people involved in games of chance. A player begins by betting a standard bet, say $1. If the player wins, the player again bets $1 in the next round. If the player loses, the player bets $2 in the next round. Next, if the player wins, the player again bets $1; if the player loses, the player now bets $4 in the next round. The process continues as long as the player keeps playing, betting $1 after a win or doubling the previous bet after a loss.

a) Assume a player is using a $1 standard bet and loses five times in a row. How much money should the player bet in the sixth round? How much money has the player lost at the end of the fifth round?

b) Assume a player is using a $10 standard bet and loses five times in a row. How much money should the player bet in the sixth round? How much money has the player lost at the end of the fifth round?

c) Assume a player is using a $1 standard bet and loses 10 times in a row. How much money should the player bet in the 11th round? How much money has the player lost at the end of the 10th round?

d) Assume a player is using a $10 standard bet and loses 10 times in a row. How much money should the player bet in the 11th round? How much money has the player lost at the end of the 10th round?

e) Why is this a dangerous strategy?

Internet/Research Activity

93. A topic generally associated with sequences is *series*.

a) Research *series* and explain what a series is and how it differs from a sequence. Also write a formal definition of series. Give examples of different kinds of series.

b) Write the arithmetic series associated with the arithmetic sequence 1, 4, 7, 10, 13, ...

c) Write the geometric series associated with the geometric sequence 3, 6, 12, 24, 48, ...

d) What is an infinite geometric series?

e) Find the sum of the terms of the infinite geometric series $1 + \dfrac{1}{2} + \dfrac{1}{4} + \dfrac{1}{8} + \dfrac{1}{16} + \cdots$.

5.8 FIBONACCI SEQUENCE

Our discussion of sequences would not be complete without mentioning a sequence known as the *Fibonacci sequence*. The sequence is named after Leonardo of Pisa, also known as Fibonacci. He was one of the most distinguished mathematicians of the Middle Ages. This sequence is first mentioned in his book *Liber Abacci* (Book of the Abacus), which contained many interesting problems, such as: "A certain man put a pair of rabbits in a place surrounded on all sides by a wall. How many pairs of rabbits can be produced from that pair in a year if it is assumed that every month each pair begets a new pair which from the second month becomes productive?"

The solution to this problem (Fig. 5.10 on page 276) led to the development of the sequence that bears its author's name: the Fibonacci sequence. The sequence is shown in Table 5.1 on page 276. The numbers in the columns titled *Pairs of Adults* form the Fibonacci sequence.

PROFILE IN MATHEMATICS

FIBONACCI

Leonardo of Pisa (1170–1250) is considered one of the most distinguished mathematicians of the Middle Ages. He was born in Italy and was sent by his father to study mathematics with an Arab master. When he began writing, he referred to himself as Fibonacci, or "son of Bonacci," the name by which he is known today. In addition to the famous sequence bearing his name, Fibonacci is also credited with introducing the Hindu–Arabic number system into Europe. His 1202 book, *Liber Abacci* (Book of the Abacus), explained the use of this number system and emphasized the importance of the number zero.

The head of a sunflower

TABLE 5.1

Month	Pairs of Adults	Pairs of Babies	Total Pairs
1	1	0	1
2	1	1	2
3	2	1	3
4	3	2	5
5	5	3	8
6	8	5	13
7	13	8	21
8	21	13	34
9	34	21	55
10	55	34	89
11	89	55	144
12	144	89	233

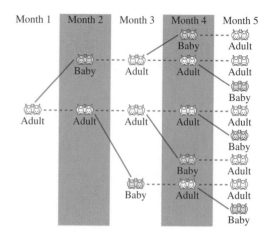

Figure 5.10

Fibonacci Sequence

$$1, 1, 2, 3, 5, 8, 13, 21, \ldots$$

In the Fibonacci sequence, the first and second terms are 1. The sum of these two terms is the third term. The sum of the second and third terms is the fourth term, and so on.

In the middle of the nineteenth century, mathematicians made a serious study of this sequence and found strong similarities between it and many natural phenomena. Fibonacci numbers appear in the seed arrangement of many species of plants and in the petal counts of various flowers. For example, when the flowering head of the sunflower matures to seed, the seeds' spiral arrangement becomes clearly visible. A typical count of these spirals may give 89 steeply curving to the right, 55 curving more shallowly to the left, and 34 again shallowly to the right. The largest known specimen to be examined had spiral counts of 144 right, 89 left, and 55 right. These numbers, like the other three mentioned, are consecutive terms of the Fibonacci sequence.

On the heads of many flowers, petals surrounding the central disk generally yield a Fibonacci number. For example, some daisies contain 21 petals, and others contain 34, 55, or 89 petals. (People who use a daisy to play the "love me, love me not" game will likely pluck 21, 34, 55, or 89 petals before arriving at an answer.)

Fibonacci numbers are also observed in the structure of pinecones and pineapples. The tablike or scalelike structures called bracts that make up the main body of the pinecone form a set of spirals that start from the cone's attachment to the branch. Two sets of oppositely directed spirals can be observed, one steep and the other more gradual. A count on the steep spiral will reveal a Fibonacci number, and a count on the gradual one will be the adjacent smaller Fibonacci number, or if not, the next smaller

TABLE 5.2

Numbers	Ratio
1, 1	$\dfrac{1}{1} = 1$
1, 2	$\dfrac{2}{1} = 2$
2, 3	$\dfrac{3}{2} = 1.5$
3, 5	$\dfrac{5}{3} = 1.666\ldots$
5, 8	$\dfrac{8}{5} = 1.6$
8, 13	$\dfrac{13}{8} = 1.625$
13, 21	$\dfrac{21}{13} \approx 1.615$
21, 34	$\dfrac{34}{21} \approx 1.619$
34, 55	$\dfrac{55}{34} \approx 1.618$
55, 89	$\dfrac{89}{55} \approx 1.618$

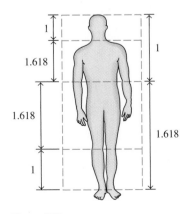

The Great Pyramid of Gizeh

Figure 5.12

Fibonacci number. One investigation of 4290 pinecones from 10 species of pine trees found in California revealed that only 74 cones, or 1.7%, deviated from this Fibonacci pattern.

Like pinecone bracts, pineapple scales are patterned into spirals, and because they are roughly hexagonal in shape, three distinct sets of spirals can be counted.

Fibonacci Numbers and Divine Proportions

In 1753, while studying the Fibonacci sequence, Robert Simson, a mathematician at the University of Glasgow, noticed that when he took the ratio of any term to the term that immediately preceded it, the value he obtained remained in the vicinity of one specific number. To illustrate this, we indicate in Table 5.2 the ratio of various pairs of sequential Fibonacci numbers.

The ratio of the 50th term to the 49th term is 1.6180. Simson proved that the ratio of the $(n + 1)$ term to the nth term as n gets larger and larger is the irrational number $(\sqrt{5} + 1)/2$, which begins $1.61803\ldots$. This number was already well known to mathematicians at that time as the *golden number*.

Many years earlier, the Bavarian astronomer and mathematician Johannes Kepler wrote that for him the golden number symbolized the Creator's intention "to create like from like." The golden number $(\sqrt{5} + 1)/2$ is frequently referred to as "phi," symbolized by the Greek letter Φ.

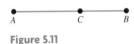

Figure 5.11

The ancient Greeks, in about the sixth century B.C., sought unifying principles of beauty and perfection, which they believed could be described by using mathematics. In their study of beauty, the Greeks used the term *golden ratio*. To understand the golden ratio, let's consider the line segment AB in Fig. 5.11. When this line segment is divided at a point C, such that the ratio of the whole, AB, to the larger part, AC, is equal to the ratio of the larger part, AC, to the smaller part, CB, then each ratio AB/AC and AC/CB is referred to as a *golden ratio*. The proportion they form, $AB/AC = AC/CB$, is called the *golden proportion*. Furthermore, each ratio in the proportion will have a value equal to the golden number, $(\sqrt{5} + 1)/2$.

$$\frac{AB}{AC} = \frac{AC}{CB} = \frac{\sqrt{5} + 1}{2} \approx 1.618$$

The Great Pyramid of Gizeh in Egypt, built about 2600 B.C., is the earliest known example of use of the golden ratio in architecture. The ratio of any of its sides of the square base (775.75 ft) to its altitude (481.4 ft) is about 1.611. Other evidence of the use of the golden ratio appears in other Egyptian buildings and tombs.

In medieval times, people referred to the golden proportion as the *divine proportion*, reflecting their belief in its relationship to the will of God.

The twentieth-century architect Le Corbusier developed a scale of proportions for the human body that he called the Modulor (Fig. 5.12). Note that the navel separates the entire body into golden proportions, as does the neck and knee.

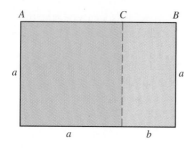

Figure 5.13

From the golden proportion, the *golden rectangle* can be formed, as shown in Fig. 5.13.

$$\frac{\text{Length}}{\text{Width}} = \frac{a + b}{a} = \frac{a}{b} = \frac{\sqrt{5} + 1}{2}$$

Note that when a square is cut off one end of a golden rectangle, as in Fig. 5.13, the remaining rectangle has the same properties as the original golden rectangle (creating "like from like" as Johannes Kepler had written) and is therefore itself a golden rectangle. Interestingly, the curve derived from a succession of diminishing golden rectangles, as shown in Fig. 5.14, is the same as the spiral curve of the chambered nautilus. The same curve appears on the horns of rams and some other animals. It is the same curve that is observed in the plant structures mentioned earlier—sunflowers, other flower heads, pinecones, and pineapples. You will recall that Fibonacci numbers were observed in each of these plant structures. The curve shown in Fig. 5.14 closely approximates what mathematicians call a *logarithmic spiral*.

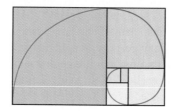 

Figure 5.14

Ancient Greek civilization used the golden rectangle in art and architecture. The main measurements of many buildings of antiquity, including the Parthenon in Athens, are governed by golden ratios and rectangles. Greek statues, vases, urns, and so on also exhibit characteristics of the golden ratio. It is for Phidas, considered the greatest of Greek sculptors, that the golden ratio was named "phi." The proportions can be found abundantly in his work.

The proportions of the golden rectangle can be found in the work of many artists, from the old masters to the moderns. For example, the golden rectangle can be seen in the painting *Invitation to the Sideshow (La Parade de Cirque),* 1887, by George Seurat, a French neoimpressionist artist.

Fibonacci's Garden by Caryl Bryer Fallert (see page 279)

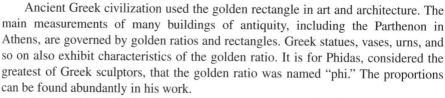

The Parthenon

Invitation to the Sideshow (La Parade de Cirque), 1887, by George Seurat

DID YOU KNOW

Fibonacci and the Male Bee's Ancestors

The most frequent example given to introduce the Fibonacci sequence involves rabbits producing offspring, two at a time. Although this makes for a nice introduction to Fibonacci sequences, it is not at all realistic. A much better example comes from the breeding practices of bees. Female or worker bees are produced when the queen bee mates with a male bee. Male bees are produced from the queen's unfertilized eggs. In essence, then, female bees have two parents, whereas male bees only have one parent. The family tree of a male bee would look like this:

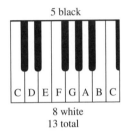

From this tree, we can see that the **1** male bee (circled) has **1** parent, **2** grandparents, **3** great-grandparents, **5** great-great-grandparents, **8** great-great-great-grandparents, and so on. We see the Fibonacci sequence as we move back through the male bees' generations.

In addition to using the golden rectangle in art, several artists have used Fibonacci numbers in art. One contemporary example is the 1995 work by Caryl Bryer Fallert called *Fibonacci's Garden* (see page 278). This artwork is a quilt constructed from two separate fabrics that are put together in a pattern based on the Fibonacci sequence.

Fibonacci numbers are also found in another form of art, namely music. Perhaps the most obvious link between Fibonacci numbers and music can be found on the piano keyboard. An octave (Fig. 5.15) on a keyboard has 13 keys: 8 white keys and 5 black keys (the 5 black keys are in one group of 2 and one group of 3).

```
                    5 black

            C D E F G A B C
                  8 white
                  13 total
```

Figure 5.15

In Western music, the most complete scale, the chromatic scale, consists of 13 notes (from C to the next higher C). Its predecessor, the diatonic scale, contains 8 notes (an octave). The diatonic scale was preceded by a 5-note pentatonic scale (*penta* is Greek for "five"). Each number is a Fibonacci number.

The visual arts deal with what is pleasing to the eye, whereas musical composition deals with what is pleasing to the ear. Whereas art achieves some of its goals by using division of planes and area, music achieves some of its goals by a similar division of time, using notes of various duration and spacing. The musical intervals considered by many to be the most pleasing to the ear are the major sixth and minor sixth. A major sixth, for example, consists of the note C, vibrating at about 264* vibrations per second, and note A, vibrating at about 440 vibrations per second. The ratio of 440 to 264 reduces to 5 to 3, or $\frac{5}{3}$, a ratio of two consecutive Fibonacci numbers. An example of a minor sixth is E (about 330 vibrations per second) and C (about 528 vibrations per second). The ratio 528 to 330 reduces to 8 to 5, or $\frac{8}{5}$, the next ratio of two consecutive Fibonacci numbers. The vibrations of any sixth interval reduce to a similar ratio.

Patterns that can be expressed mathematically in terms of Fibonacci relationships have been found in Gregorian chants and works of many composers, including Bach, Beethoven, and Bartók. A number of twentieth-century musical works, including Ernst Krenek's *Fibonacci Mobile*, have been deliberately structured by using Fibonacci proportions.

A number of studies have tried to explain why the Fibonacci sequence and related items are linked to so many real-life situations. It appears that the Fibonacci numbers are a part of natural harmony that is pleasing to both the eye and the ear. In the nineteenth century, German physicist and psychologist Gustav Fechner tried to determine which dimensions were most pleasing to the eye. Fechner, along with psychologist Wilhelm Wundt, found that most people do unconsciously favor golden dimensions when purchasing greeting cards, mirrors, and other rectangular objects. This discovery has been widely used by commercial manufacturers in their packaging and labeling designs, by retailers in their store displays, and in other areas of business and advertising.

---

*Frequencies of notes vary in different parts of the world and change over time.

SECTION 5.8   EXERCISES

Concept/Writing Exercises

1. Explain how to construct the Fibonacci sequence.

2. **a)** Write out the first ten terms of the Fibonacci sequence.
   b) Divide the ninth term by the eighth term, rounding to the nearest thousandth.
   c) Divide the tenth term by the ninth term, rounding to the nearest thousandth.
   d) Try a few more divisions and then make a conjecture about the result.

3. **a)** What is the value of the golden number?
   b) What is the golden ratio?
   c) What is the golden proportion?
   d) What is the golden rectangle?

4. In your own words, explain the relationship between the golden number, golden ratio, golden proportion, and golden rectangle.

5. Describe three examples of where the golden ratio can be found
   a) in nature.
   b) in manufactured items.

6. Describe three examples of where Fibonacci numbers can be found
   a) in nature.
   b) in manufactured items.

Practice the Skills/Problem Solving

7. **a)** To what decimal value is $(\sqrt{5} + 1)/2$ aproximately equal?
   b) To what decimal value is $(\sqrt{5} - 1)/2$ approximately equal?
   c) By how much do the results in parts (a) and (b) differ?

8. The eleventh Fibonacci number is 89. Examine the first six digits in the decimal expression of its reciprocal, $\frac{1}{89}$. What do you find?

9. Find the ratio of the second to the first term of the Fibonacci sequence. Then find the ratio of the third to the second term of the sequence and determine whether this ratio was an increase or decrease from the first ratio. Continue this process for 10 ratios and then make a conjecture regarding the increasing or decreasing values in consecutive ratios.

10. A musical composition is described as follows. Explain why this piece is based on the golden ratio.

Entire Composition

34 measures	55 measures	21 measures	34 measures
Theme	Fast, Loud	Slow	Repeat of theme

11. The greatest common factor of any two consecutive Fibonacci numbers is 1. Show this is true for the first 15 Fibonacci numbers.

12. The sum of any 10 consecutive Fibonacci numbers is always divisible by 11. Select any 10 consecutive Fibonacci numbers and show that for your selection this is true.

13. Twice any Fibonacci number minus the next Fibonacci number equals the second number preceding the original number. Select a number in the Fibonacci sequence and show that this pattern holds for the number selected.

14. For any four consecutive Fibonacci numbers, the difference of the squares of the middle two numbers equals the product of the smallest and largest numbers. Select four consecutive Fibonacci numbers and show that this pattern holds for the numbers you selected.

15. Determine the ratio of the length to width of various photographs and compare these ratios to Φ.

16. Determine the ratio of the length to the width of a 6 inch by 4 inch standard index card, and compare the ratio to Φ.

17. Determine the ratio of the length to width of several picture frames and compare these ratios to Φ.

18. Determine the ratio of the length to the width of your television screen and compare this ratio to Φ.

19. Determine the ratio of the length to width of a desktop in your classroom and compare this ratio to Φ.

20. Determine the ratio of the length to width of this textbook and compare this ratio to Φ.

21. Determine the ratio of the length to the width of a computer screen and compare this ratio to Φ.

22. Find three physical objects whose dimensions are very close to a golden rectangle.
   a) List the articles and record the dimensions.
   b) Compute the ratios of their lengths to their widths.
   c) Find the difference between the golden ratio and the ratio you obtain in part (b)—to the nearest tenth—for each object.

In Exercises 23–30, determine whether the sequence is a Fibonacci-type sequence (each term is the sum of the two preceding terms). If it is, determine the next two terms of the sequence.

23. $1, 3, 4, 7, 11, 18, \ldots$ 24. $1, 1, 2, 2, 3, 3, \ldots$

25. $1, 4, 9, 16, 25, 36, \ldots$ 26. $-1, 1, 0, 1, 1, 2, \ldots$

27. $5, 10, 15, 25, 40, 65, \ldots$ 28. $\frac{1}{4}, \frac{1}{4}, \frac{1}{2}, \frac{3}{4}, 1\frac{1}{4}, 2, \ldots$

29. $-5, 3, -2, 1, -1, 0, \ldots$ 30. $-4, 5, 1, 6, 7, 13, \ldots$

31. **a)** Select any two nonzero digits and add them to obtain a third digit. Continue adding the two previous terms to get a Fibonacci-type sequence.

b) Form ratios of successive terms to show how they will eventually approach the golden number.

32. Repeat Exercise 31 for two different nonzero numbers.

33. a) Select any three consecutive terms of a Fibonacci sequence. Subtract the product of the terms on each side of the middle term from the square of the middle term. What is the difference?
b) Repeat part (a) with three different consecutive terms of the sequence.
c) Make a conjecture about what will happen when you repeat this process for any three consecutive terms of a Fibonacci sequence.

34. *Pascal's Triangle* One of the most famous number patterns involves *Pascal's triangle*. The Fibonacci sequence can be found by using Pascal's triangle. Can you explain how that can be done? A hint is shown.

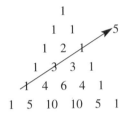

35. *Lucas Sequence* **a)** A sequence related to the Fibonacci sequence is the *Lucas sequence*. The Lucas sequence is formed in a manner similar to the Fibonacci sequence. The first two numbers of the Lucas sequence are 1 and 3. Write the first eight terms of the Lucas sequence.
b) Complete the next two lines of the following chart.

$$1 + 2 = 3$$
$$1 + 3 = 4$$
$$2 + 5 = 7$$
$$3 + 8 = 11$$
$$5 + 13 = 18$$

c) What do you observe about the first column in the chart in part (b)?

Challenge Problems/Group Activities

36. *Fibonacci-Type Sequence* The following sequence represents a Fibonacci-type sequence (each term is the sum of the two preceding terms). Here x represents any natural number from 1 to 10:

$$-10, x, -10 + x, -10 + 2x, -20 + 3x, -30 + 5x, \ldots$$

For example, if $x = 2$, the first 10 terms of the sequence would be $-10, 2, -8, -6, -14, -20, -34, -54, -88, -142$.

Write out the first 10 terms of this Fibonacci-type sequence for x equal to
a) 4. **b)** 5. **c)** 6. **d)** 7. **e)** 8.
f) For values of x of 4, 5, and 6, you should have found that each term after the seventh term in the sequence

was a negative number. For values of x of 7 and 8, you should have found that each term after the seventh term in the sequence was a positive number. Do you believe that for any value of x greater than or equal to 7, each term after the seventh term of the sequence will always be a positive number? Explain.

37. The divine proportion is $(a + b)/a = a/b$ (see Fig. 5.13), which can be written $1 + (b/a) = a/b$. Now let $x = a/b$, which gives $1 + (1/x) = x$. Multiply both sides of this equation by x to get a quadratic equation and then use the quadratic formula (Section 6.8) to show that one answer is $x = (1 + \sqrt{5})/2$ (the golden ratio).

38. Draw a line of length 5 in. Determine and mark the point on the line that will create the golden ratio. Explain how you determined your answer.

39. *Pythagorean Triples* A Pythagorean triple is a set of three whole numbers, $\{a, b, c\}$, such that $a^2 + b^2 = c^2$. For example, since $6^2 + 8^2 = (10)^2$, $\{6, 8, 10\}$ is a Pythagorean triple. The following steps show how to find Pythagorean triples using any four consecutive Fibonacci numbers. Here we will demonstrate the process with the Fibonacci numbers 3, 5, 8, and 13.
  1. Determine the product of 2 and the two inner Fibonacci numbers. We have $2(5)(8) = 80$, which is the first number in the Pythagorean triple. So $a = 80$.
  2. Determine the product of the two outer numbers. We have $3(13) = 39$, which is the second number in the Pythagorean triple. So $b = 39$.
  3. Determine the sum of the squares of the inner two numbers. We have $5^2 + 8^2 = 25 + 64 = 89$, which is the third number in the Pythagorean triple. So $c = 89$.

This process has produced the Pythagorean triple, $\{80, 39, 89\}$. To verify,

$$(80)^2 + (39)^2 = (89)^2$$
$$6400 + 1521 = 7921$$
$$7921 = 7921$$

Use this process to produce four other Pythagorean triples.

40. *Reflections* When two panes of glass are placed face to face, four interior reflective surfaces exist labeled 1, 2, 3, and 4. If light is not reflected, it has just one path through the glass (see the figure below). If it has one reflection, it can be reflected in two ways. If it has two reflections, it can be reflected in three ways. Use this information to answer parts (a) through (c).

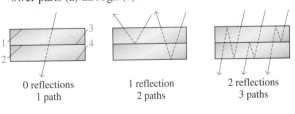

0 reflections   1 reflection   2 reflections
1 path   2 paths   3 paths

a) If a ray is reflected three times, there are five paths it can follow. Show the paths.

b) If a ray is reflected four times, there are eight paths it can follow. Show the paths.

c) How many paths can a ray follow if it is reflected five times? Explain how you determined your answer.

Internet/Research Activities

41. The digits 1 through 9 have evolved considerably since they appeared in Fibonacci's book *Liber Abacci*. Write a report tracing the history of the evolution of the digits 1 through 9 since Fibonacci's time.

42. Write a report on the history and mathematical contributions of Fibonacci.

43. Write a report indicating where the golden ratio and golden rectangle have been used in art and architecture. You may wish to include information on art and architecture related to the golden ratio and Fibonacci sequences.

CHAPTER 5 SUMMARY

IMPORTANT FACTS

Fundamental theorem of arithmetic

Every composite number can be expressed as a unique product of prime numbers.

Sets of numbers

Natural or counting numbers: $\{1, 2, 3, 4, \ldots\}$

Whole numbers: $\{0, 1, 2, 3, 4, \ldots\}$

Integers: $\{\ldots, -3, -2, -1, 0, 1, 2, 3, \ldots\}$

Rational numbers: Numbers of the form p/q, where p and q are integers, $q \neq 0$. Every rational number when expressed as a decimal number will be either a terminating or repeating decimal number.

Irrational number: A real number whose representation is a nonterminating, nonrepeating decimal number (not a rational number).

Definition of subtraction

$$a - b = a + (-b)$$

Fundamental law of rational numbers

$$\frac{a}{b} = \frac{a}{b} \cdot \frac{c}{c} = \frac{ac}{bc}, \quad b \neq 0, \quad c \neq 0$$

Rules of radicals

Product rule for radicals:

$$\sqrt{a \cdot b} = \sqrt{a} \cdot \sqrt{b}, \quad a \geq 0, \quad b \geq 0$$

Quotient rule for radicals:

$$\frac{\sqrt{a}}{\sqrt{b}} = \sqrt{\frac{a}{b}}, \quad a \geq 0, \quad b > 0$$

Properties of real numbers

Commutative property of addition: $a + b = b + a$

Commutative property of multiplication: $a \cdot b = b \cdot a$

Associative property of addition:

$$(a + b) + c = a + (b + c)$$

Associative property of multiplication:

$$(a \cdot b) \cdot c = a \cdot (b \cdot c)$$

Distributive property: $a \cdot (b + c) = ab + ac$

Rules of exponents

Product rule for exponents: $a^m \cdot a^n = a^{m+n}$

Quotient rule for exponents: $\dfrac{a^m}{a^n} = a^{m-n}, \quad a \neq 0$

Zero exponent rule: $a^0 = 1, \quad a \neq 0$

Negative exponent rule: $a^{-m} = \dfrac{1}{a^m}, \quad a \neq 0$

Power rule: $(a^m)^n = a^{m \cdot n}$

Arithmetic sequence

$$a_n = a_1 + (n - 1)d$$

$$s_n = \frac{n(a_1 + a_n)}{2}$$

Geometric sequence

$$a_n = a_1 r^{n-1}$$

$$s_n = \frac{a_1(1 - r^n)}{1 - r}, \quad r \neq 1$$

Fibonacci sequence

$$1, 1, 2, 3, 5, 8, 13, 21, \ldots$$

Golden number

$$\frac{\sqrt{5} + 1}{2} \approx 1.618$$

Golden proportion

$$\frac{a + b}{a} = \frac{a}{b}$$

CHAPTER 5   REVIEW EXERCISES

5.1

In Exercises 1 and 2, determine whether the number is divisible by each of the following numbers: 2, 3, 4, 5, 6, 8, 9, and 10.

1. 894,348   **2.** 400,644

In Exercises 3–7, find the prime factorization of the number.

3. 252   **4.** 385   **5.** 840
6. 882   **7.** 1452

In Exercises 8–13, find the GCD and LCM of the numbers.

8. 15, 60   **9.** 63, 108   **10.** 45, 250
11. 840, 320   **12.** 60, 40, 96   **13.** 36, 108, 144

14. *Train Stops* From 1912 to 1971, the Milwaukee Road Railroad Company had a train stop every 15 days in Dubuque, Iowa. During this same period, the same train also stopped in Des Moines, Iowa, every 9 days. If on April 18, 1964, the train made a stop in Dubuque and a stop in Des Moines, how many days was it until the train again stopped in both cities on the same day?

5.2

In Exercises 15–22, use a number line to evaluate the expression.

15. $-2 + 5$ **16.** $4 + (-7)$
17. $4 - 8$ **18.** $-2 + (-4)$
19. $-5 - 4$ **20.** $-3 - (-6)$
21. $(-3 + 7) - 4$ **22.** $-1 + (9 - 4)$

In Exercises 23–30, evaluate the expression.

23. $(-3)(-11)$ **24.** $-4(9)$

25. $(14)(-4)$ **26.** $\dfrac{-35}{-7}$

27. $\dfrac{12}{-6}$ **28.** $[8 \div (-4)](-3)$

29. $[(-4)(-3)] \div 2$ **30.** $[(-30) \div (10)] \div (-1)$

5.3

In Exercises 31–39, express the fraction as a terminating or repeating decimal.

31. $\dfrac{3}{10}$ **32.** $\dfrac{3}{5}$ **33.** $\dfrac{15}{40}$

34. $\dfrac{13}{4}$ **35.** $\dfrac{3}{7}$ **36.** $\dfrac{7}{12}$

37. $\dfrac{3}{8}$ **38.** $\dfrac{7}{8}$ **39.** $\dfrac{5}{7}$

In Exercises 40–46, express the decimal number as a quotient of two integers.

40. 0.225 **41.** 4.5 **42.** $0.\overline{6}$ **43.** $2.\overline{37}$
44. 0.083 **45.** 0.0042 **46.** $2.3\overline{4}$

In Exercises 47–50, express each mixed number as an improper fraction.

47. $2\frac{5}{7}$ **48.** $4\frac{1}{6}$ **49.** $-3\frac{1}{4}$ **50.** $-35\frac{3}{8}$

In Exercises 51–54, express each improper fraction as a mixed number.

51. $\dfrac{11}{5}$ **52.** $\dfrac{27}{15}$ **53.** $-\dfrac{12}{7}$ **54.** $-\dfrac{136}{5}$

In Exercises 55–63, perform the indicated operation and reduce your answer to lowest terms.

55. $\dfrac{1}{2} + \dfrac{4}{5}$ **56.** $\dfrac{7}{8} - \dfrac{3}{4}$

57. $\dfrac{1}{6} + \dfrac{5}{4}$ **58.** $\dfrac{4}{5} \cdot \dfrac{15}{16}$

59. $\dfrac{5}{9} \div \dfrac{6}{7}$ **60.** $\left(\dfrac{4}{5} + \dfrac{5}{7}\right) \div \dfrac{4}{5}$

61. $\left(\dfrac{2}{3} \cdot \dfrac{1}{7}\right) \div \dfrac{4}{7}$ **62.** $\left(\dfrac{1}{5} + \dfrac{2}{3}\right)\left(\dfrac{3}{8}\right)$

63. $\left(\dfrac{1}{5} \cdot \dfrac{2}{3}\right) + \left(\dfrac{1}{5} \div \dfrac{1}{2}\right)$

64. *Cajun Turkey* A recipe for Roasted Cajun Turkey calls for $\frac{1}{8}$ teaspoon of cayenne pepper per pound of turkey. If

Jennifer Thornton is preparing a turkey that weighs $17\frac{3}{4}$ pounds, how much cayenne pepper does she need?

5.4

In Exercises 65–80, simplify the expression. Rationalize the denominator when necessary.

65. $\sqrt{50}$ 66. $\sqrt{200}$ 67. $\sqrt{5} + 7\sqrt{5}$

68. $\sqrt{3} - 4\sqrt{3}$ 69. $\sqrt{8} + 6\sqrt{2}$ 70. $\sqrt{3} - 7\sqrt{27}$

71. $\sqrt{75} + \sqrt{27}$ 72. $\sqrt{3} \cdot \sqrt{6}$ 73. $\sqrt{8} \cdot \sqrt{6}$

74. $\dfrac{\sqrt{18}}{\sqrt{2}}$ 75. $\dfrac{\sqrt{56}}{\sqrt{2}}$ 76. $\dfrac{4}{\sqrt{3}}$

77. $\dfrac{\sqrt{3}}{\sqrt{5}}$ 78. $3(2 + \sqrt{7})$

79. $\sqrt{3}(4 + \sqrt{6})$ 80. $\sqrt{3}(\sqrt{6} + \sqrt{15})$

5.5

In Exercises 81–90, state the name of the property illustrated.

81. $x + 2 = 2 + x$

82. $5 \cdot m = m \cdot 5$

83. $(1 + 2) + 3 = 1 + (2 + 3)$

84. $4(y + 3) = 4 \cdot y + 4 \cdot 3$

85. $(1 + 2) + 3 = 3 + (1 + 2)$

86. $(3 + 5) + (4 + 3) = (4 + 3) + (3 + 5)$

87. $(3 \cdot a) \cdot b = 3 \cdot (a \cdot b)$

88. $a \cdot (2 + 3) = (2 + 3) \cdot a$

89. $2(x + 3) = (2 \cdot x) + (2 \cdot 3)$

90. $x \cdot 2 + 6 = 2 \cdot x + 6$

In Exercises 91–96, determine whether the set of numbers is closed under the given operation.

91. Natural numbers, addition

92. Whole numbers, subtraction

93. Integers, division

94. Real numbers, subtraction

95. Irrational numbers, multiplication

96. Rational numbers, division

5.6

In Exercises 97–104, evaluate each expression.

97. 3^2 98. 3^{-2} 99. $\dfrac{9^5}{9^3}$ 100. $5^2 \cdot 5$

101. 7^0 102. 4^{-3} 103. $(2^3)^2$ 104. $(3^2)^2$

In Exercises 105–108, write each number in scientific notation.

105. 230,000,000   106. 0.0000158

107. 0.00275   108. 4,950,000

In Exercises 109–112, express each number in decimal notation.

109. 4.3×10^7 110. 1.39×10^{-4}

111. 1.75×10^{-4} 112. 1×10^5

In Exercises 113–116, (a) perform the indicated operation and write your answer in scientific notation. (b) Confirm the result found in part (a) by performing the calculation on a scientific calculator.

113. $(7 \times 10^3)(2 \times 10^{-5})$

114. $(4 \times 10^2)(2.5 \times 10^2)$

115. $\dfrac{8.4 \times 10^3}{4 \times 10^2}$

116. $\dfrac{1.5 \times 10^{-3}}{5 \times 10^{-4}}$

In Exercises 117–121, (a) perform the indicated calculation by first converting each number to scientific notation. Write your answer in decimal notation. (b) Confirm the result found in part (a) by performing the calculation on a scientific calculator.

117. $(4,000,000)(2,000)$ 118. $(35,000)(0.00002)$

119. $\dfrac{9,600,000}{3000}$ 120. $\dfrac{0.000002}{0.0000004}$

121. *Space Distances* The distance from Earth to the sun is about 1.49×10^{11} meters. The distance from Earth to the moon is about 3.84×10^8 meters. The distance from Earth to the sun is how many times larger than the distance from Earth to the moon? Use a scientific calculator and round your answer to the nearest whole number.

See Exercise 121

122. *Outstanding Debt* As a result of a recent water and sewer system improvement, the city of Galena, Illinois, has an outstanding debt of $20,000,000. If the population of Galena is 3600 people, how much would each person have to contribute to pay off the outstanding debt?

5.7

In Exercises 123–128, determine whether the sequence is arithmetic or geometric. Then determine the next two terms of the sequence.

123. $2, 5, 8, 11, \ldots$

124. $\frac{1}{2}, 1, 2, 4, \ldots$

125. $-3, -6, -9, -12, \ldots$

126. $\frac{1}{2}, \frac{1}{4}, \frac{1}{8}, \frac{1}{16}, \ldots$

127. $1, 4, 7, 10, 13, \ldots$

128. $2, -2, 2, -2, 2, \ldots$

In Exercises 129–134, find the indicated term of the sequence with the given first term, a_1, and common difference, d, or common ratio, r.

129. Find a_4 when $a_1 = 3, d = 4$.

130. Find a_8 when $a_1 = -6, d = -4$.

131. Find a_{10} when $a_1 = -20, d = 5$.

132. Find a_5 when $a_1 = 3, r = 2$.

133. Find a_5 when $a_1 = 4, r = \frac{1}{2}$.

134. Find a_4 when $a_1 = -6, r = 2$.

In Exercises 135–138, find the sum of the arithmetic sequence. The number of terms, n, is given.

135. $2, 5, 8, 11, \ldots, 89; n = 30$

136. $-4, -3\frac{3}{4}, -3\frac{1}{2}, -3\frac{1}{4}, \ldots, -2\frac{1}{4}; n = 8$

137. $100, 94, 88, 82, \ldots, 58; n = 8$

138. $0.5, 0.75, 1.00, 1.25, \ldots, 5.25; n = 20$

In Exercises 139–142, find the sum of the first n terms of the geometric sequence for the values of a_1 and r.

139. $n = 4, a_1 = 5, r = 3$

140. $n = 4, a_1 = 2, r = 3$

141. $n = 5, a_1 = 3, r = -2$

142. $n = 6, a_1 = 1, r = -2$

In Exercises 143–148, first determine whether the sequence is arithmetic or geometric; then write an expression for the general or nth term, a_n.

143. $7, 4, 1, -2, \ldots$

144. $3, 6, 9, 12, \ldots$

145. $4, \frac{5}{2}, 1, -\frac{1}{2}, \ldots$

146. $3, 6, 12, 24, \ldots$

147. $2, -2, 2, -2, \ldots$

148. $5, \frac{5}{3}, \frac{5}{9}, \frac{5}{27}, \ldots$

5.8

In Exercises 149–152, determine whether the sequence is a Fibonacci-type sequence. If so, determine the next two terms.

149. $0, 1, 1, 2, 3, 5, 8, \ldots$

150. $-3, 4, 1, 5, 6, 11, \ldots$

151. $1, 4, 3, -1, -4, -5, \ldots$

152. $-10, 10, 0, 10, 20, \ldots$

CHAPTER 5 TEST

1. Which of the numbers 2, 3, 4, 5, 6, 8, 9, and 10 divide 38,610?

2. Find the prime factorization of 840.

3. Evaluate $[(-6) + (-9)] + 8$.

4. Evaluate $-7 - 13$.

5. Evaluate $[(-70)(-5)] \div (8 - 10)$.

6. Convert $4\frac{5}{8}$ to an improper fraction.

7. Convert $\frac{176}{9}$ to a mixed number.

8. Write $\frac{5}{8}$ as a terminating or repeating decimal.

9. Express 6.45 as a quotient of two integers.

10. Evalute $\left(\frac{5}{16} \div 3\right) + \left(\frac{4}{5} \cdot \frac{1}{2}\right)$.

11. Perform the operation and reduce the answer to lowest terms: $\frac{11}{12} - \frac{3}{8}$.

12. Simplify $\sqrt{75} + \sqrt{48}$.

13. Rationalize $\dfrac{\sqrt{2}}{\sqrt{7}}$.

14. Determine whether the integers are closed under the operation of multiplication. Explain your answer.

Name the property illustrated.

15. $(4 + y) + 5 = 4 + (y + 5)$

16. $3(x + y) = 3x + 3y$

Evaluate.

17. $\dfrac{4^5}{4^2}$ **18.** $4^3 \cdot 4^2$ **19.** 3^{-4}

20. Perform the operation by first converting the numerator and denominator to scientific notation. Write the answer in scientific notation.

$$\dfrac{7{,}200{,}000}{0.000009}$$

21. Write an expression for the general or nth term, a_n, of the sequence $-2, -6, -10, -14, \ldots$.

22. Find the sum of the terms of the arithmetic sequence. The number of terms, n, is given.

$$-2, -5, -8, -11, \ldots, -32; n = 11$$

23. Find a_5 when $a_1 = 3$ and $r = 3$.

24. Find the sum of the first five terms of the sequence when $a_1 = 3$ and $r = 4$.

25. Write an expression for the general or nth term, a_n, of the sequence $3, 6, 12, 24, \ldots$.

26. Write the first 10 terms of the Fibonacci sequence.

GROUP PROJECTS

1. *Making Rice* The amount of ingredients needed to make 3 and 5 servings of rice are:

To Make	Rice and Water	Salt	Butter
3 servings	1 cup	$\frac{3}{8}$ tsp	$1\frac{1}{2}$ tsp
5 servings	$1\frac{2}{3}$ cup	$\frac{5}{8}$ tsp	$2\frac{1}{2}$ tsp

Find the amount of each ingredient needed to make (a) 2 servings, (b) 1 serving, and (c) 29 servings. Explain how you determined your answers.

2. *Finding Areas*

a) Determine the area of the trapezoid shown by finding the area of the three parts indicated and finding the sum of the three areas. The necessary geometric formulas are given in Chapter 9.

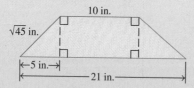

b) Determine the area of the trapezoid by using the formula for the area of a trapezoid given in Chapter 9.

c) Compare your answers from parts (a) and (b). Are they the same? If not, explain why they are different.

3. *Medical Insurance* On a medical insurance policy (such as Blue Cross/Blue Shield), the policyholder may need to make copayments for prescription drugs, office visits, and procedures until the total of all copayments reaches a specified amount. Suppose on the Gattelaro's medical policy that the copayment for prescription drugs is 50% of the cost; the copayment for office visits is $10; and the copayment for all medical tests, x-rays, and other procedures is 20% of the cost. After the family's copayment totals $500 in a calendar year, all medical and prescription bills are paid in full by the insurance company. The Gattelaros had the following medical expenses from January 1 through April 30.

Date	Reason	Cost before Copayment
January 10	Office visit	$40
	Prescription	$44
February 27	Office visit	$40
	Medical tests	$188
April 19	Office visit	$40
	X-rays	$348
	Prescription	$76

a) How much had the Gattelaros paid in copayments from January 1 through April 30?

b) How much had the medical insurance company paid?

c) What is the remaining copayment that must be paid by the Gattelaros before the $500 copayment limit is reached?

4. *A Branching Plant* A plant grows for two months and then adds a new branch. Each new branch grows for two months and then adds another branch. After the second month, each branch adds a new branch every month. Assume the growth begins in January.

a) How many branches will there be in February?

b) How many branches will there be in May?

c) How many branches will there be after 12 months?

d) How is this problem similar to the problem involving rabbits that appeared in Fibonacci's book *Liber Abacci* (see pages 275 and 276)?

GROUP PROJECTS

Supporting a Jacuzzi

1. Samantha Saraniti is thinking of buying a circular hot tub 12 ft in diameter, 4 ft deep, and weighing 475 lb. She wants to place the hot tub on a deck built to support 30,000 lb.
   a) Determine the volume of the water in the hot tub in cubic feet.
   b) Determine the number of gallons of water the hot tub will hold. Note 1 ft^3 ≈ 7.5 gal.
   c) Determine the weight of the water in the hot tub. (*Hint:* Fresh water weighs about 52.4 lb/ft^3.)
   d) Will the deck support the weight of the hot tub and water?
   e) Will the deck support the weight of the hot tub, water, and four people, whose average weight is 115 lb?

Designing a Ramp

2. David and Sandra Jessee are planning to build a ramp so that their front entrance is wheelchair accessible. The ramp will be 36 in. wide. It will rise 2 in. for each foot of length of horizontal distance. Where the ramp meets the porch, the ramp must be 2 ft high. To provide stability for the ramp, the Jessees will install a slab of concrete 4 in. thick and 6 in. longer and wider than the ramp (see accompanying figure). The top of the slab will be level with the ground. The ramp may be constructed of concrete or pressure-treated lumber. You are to estimate the cost of materials for constructing the slab, the ramp of concrete, and the ramp of pressure-treated lumber.

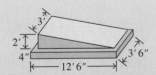

Slab
   a) Determine the length of the base of the ramp.
   b) Determine the dimensions of the concrete slab on which the ramp will set.
   c) Determine the volume of the concrete in cubic yards needed to construct the slab.
   d) If ready-mix concrete costs $45 per cubic yard, determine the cost of the concrete needed to construct the slab.

Concrete Ramp
   e) To build the ramp of concrete a form in the shape of the ramp must be framed. The two sides of the form are triangular, and the shape of the end, which is against the porch is rectangular. The form will be framed from $\frac{3}{4}$ in. plywood, which comes in 4 ft × 8 ft sheets. Determine the number of sheets of plywood needed. Assume that the entire sheet(s) will be used to make the sides and the end of the form and that there is no waste.
   f) If the plywood costs $18.95 for a 4 ft × 8 ft sheet, determine the cost of the plywood.
   g) To brace the form, the Jessees will need two boards 2 in. × 4 in. × 8 ft (referred to as 8 ft 2 × 4's) and six pieces of lumber 2 in. × 4 in. × 3 ft. These six pieces of lumber will be cut from 8 ft 2 × 4 boards. Determine the number of 8 ft 2 × 4 boards needed.
   h) Determine the cost of the 8 ft 2 × 4 boards needed in part (g) if one board costs $2.14.
   i) Determine the volume, in cubic yards, of concrete needed to fill the form.
   j) Determine the cost of the concrete needed to fill the form.
   k) Determine the total cost of materials for building the ramp of concrete by adding the results in parts (d), (f), (h), and (j).

Wooden Ramp
   l) Determine the length of the top of the ramp.
   m) The top of the ramp will be constructed of $\frac{5}{4}$ in. × 6 in. × 10 ft pressure-treated lumber. The boards will be butted end to end to make the necessary length and will be supported from underneath by a wooden frame. Determine the number of boards needed to cover the top of the ramp. The boards are laid lengthwise on the ramp.
   n) Determine the cost of the boards to cover the top of the ramp if the price of a 10 ft length is $6.47.
   o) To support the top of the ramp, the Jessees will need 10 pieces of 8 ft 2 × 4's. The price of a pressure-treated 8 ft 2 × 4 is $2.44. Determine the cost of the supports.
   p) Determine the cost of the materials for building a wooden ramp by adding the amounts from parts (d), (n), and (o).
   q) Are the materials for constructing a concrete ramp or a wooden ramp less expensive?

Despite the seemingly endless variety of patterns the human imagination can devise, group theory can be used to catalog and define patterns by the way in which the design elements are transformed and positioned.

MATHEMATICAL SYSTEMS

In the last 200 years, much of the focus of scientific study of the fundamental laws of nature has shifted from what things are to how they change in space and time. The mathematics used for this purpose belongs to a branch of mathematics known as group theory. A group is a collection of fundamentally basic elements along with an operation that acts upon these elements. The elements in a group could be numbers, or elementary particles of physics, or a pattern of repeating geometric designs. The way in which the elements change or remain the same when acted upon by some operation or transformation defines membership in the group.

To appreciate why group theory is so useful to scientists, consider the physicists who are trying to piece together the history of the universe. They have a clear sense of what the universe is like today, but what about 15 billion years ago when some scientists believe the universe exploded into existence in what is called the Big Bang? Group theory may enable them to derive what the initial conditions of the universe may have been from knowledge of what matter is like today. Group theory can also be used to describe many other items, including number systems, and the basic building blocks of crystalline solids. It can even be used to define the symmetries that appear in the artifacts of a given culture. No wonder the physicist Sir Arthur Stanley Eddington called group theory the "super-mathematics."

10.1 GROUPS

We begin our discussion by introducing a mathematical system. As you will learn shortly, you already know and use many mathematical systems.

> A **mathematical system** consists of a set of elements and at least one binary operation.

In the above definition we mention binary operation. A *binary operation* is an operation, or rule, that can be performed on two and only two elements of a set. The result is a single element. When we add *two* integers, the sum is *one* integer. When we multiply *two* integers, the product is *one* integer. Thus, addition and multiplication are both binary operations. Is finding the reciprocal of a number a binary operation? No, it is an operation on a single element of a set.

When you learned how to add integers, you were introduced to a mathematical system. The set of elements is the set of integers, and the binary operation is addition. When you learned how to multiply integers, you became familiar with a second mathematical system. The set of integers with the operation of subtraction and the set of integers with the operation of division are two other examples of mathematical systems since subtraction and division are also binary operations.

Some systems are used in solving everyday problems, such as planning work schedules. Others are more abstract and are used primarily in research, chemistry, physical structure, matter, the nature of genes, and other scientific fields.

Commutative and Associative Properties

Once a mathematical system is defined, its structure may display certain properties. Consider the set of integers:

$$I = \{\ldots, -3, -2, -1, 0, 1, 2, 3, \ldots\}$$

Recall that the ellipsis, the three dots at each end of the set, indicates that the set continues in the same manner.

The set of integers can be studied with the operations of addition, subtraction, multiplication, and division as separate mathematical systems. For example, when we study the set of integers under the operations of addition or multiplication, we see that the commutative and associative properties hold. The general forms of the properties are shown here.

For Any Elements *a*, *b*, and *c*	Addition	Multiplication
Commutative property	$a + b = b + a$	$a \cdot b = b \cdot a$
Associative property	$(a + b) + c = a + (b + c)$	$(a \cdot b) \cdot c = a \cdot (b \cdot c)$

The integers *are commutative* under the operations of *addition and multiplication*. For example,

Addition		Multiplication
$2 + 4 = 4 + 2$	and	$2 \cdot 4 = 4 \cdot 2$
$6 = 6$		$8 = 8$

The integers, however, *are not commutative* under the operations of *subtraction and division*. For example,

Subtraction		**Division**
$4 - 2 \neq 2 - 4$	and	$4 \div 2 \neq 2 \div 4$
$2 \neq -2$		$2 \neq \frac{1}{2}$

The integers *are associative* under the operations of *addition and multiplication*. For example,

Addition		**Multiplication**
$(1 + 2) + 3 = 1 + (2 + 3)$	and	$(1 \cdot 2) \cdot 3 = 1 \cdot (2 \cdot 3)$
$3 + 3 = 1 + 5$		$2 \cdot 3 = 1 \cdot 6$
$6 = 6$		$6 = 6$

The integers, however, *are not associative* under the operations of *subtraction and division*. See Exercises 21 and 22 at the end of this section.

To say that a set of elements is commutative under a given operation means that the commutative property holds for *any* elements a and b in the set. Similarly, to say that a set of elements is associative under a given operation means that the associative property holds for *any* elements a, b, and c in the set.

Consider the mathematical system consisting of the set of integers under the operation of addition. Because the set of integers is infinite, this mathematical system is an example of an *infinite mathematical system*. We will study certain properties of this mathematical system. The first property that we examine is closure.

Closure

The sum of any two integers is an integer. Therefore, the set of integers is said to be *closed*, or to satisfy the *closure property*, under the operation of addition.

> If a binary operation is performed on any two elements of a set and the result is an element of the set, then that set is **closed** (or has **closure**) under the given binary operation.

Is the set of integers closed under the operation of multiplication? The answer is yes. When any two integers are multiplied, the product will be an integer.

Is the set of integers closed under the operation of subtraction? Again, the answer is yes. The difference of any two integers is an integer.

Is the set of integers closed under the operation of division? The answer is no because two integers may have a quotient that is not an integer. For example, if we select the integers 2 and 3, the quotient of 2 divided by 3 is $\frac{2}{3}$, which is not an integer. Thus, the integers are not closed under the operation of division.

We showed that the set of integers was not closed under the operation of division by finding two integers whose quotient was not an integer. A specific example illustrating that a specific property is not true is called a *counterexample*. Mathematicians and scientists often try to find a counterexample to confirm that a specific property is not always true.

Identity Element

Now we will discuss the identity element for the set of integers under the operation of addition. Is there an element in the set that, when added to any given integer, results in a sum that is the given integer? The answer is yes. The sum of 0 and any integer is the given integer. For example, $1 + 0 = 0 + 1 = 1$, $-4 + 0 = 0 + (-4) = -4$, and so on. For this reason, we call 0 the *additive identity element* for the set of integers. Note that for any integer a, $a + 0 = 0 + a = a$.

> An **identity element** is an element in a set such that when a binary operation is performed on it and any given element in the set, the result is the given element.

Is there an identity element for the set of integers under the operation of multiplication? The answer is yes; it is the number 1. Note that $2 \cdot 1 = 1 \cdot 2 = 2$, $3 \cdot 1 = 1 \cdot 3 = 3$, and so on. For any integer a, $a \cdot 1 = 1 \cdot a = a$. For this reason, 1 is called the *multiplicative identity element* for the set of integers.

Inverses

What integer, when added to 4, gives a sum of 0; that is, $4 + \boxed{} = 0$? The shaded area is to be filled in with the integer -4: $4 + \boxed{(-4)} = 0$. We say that -4 is the additive inverse of 4 and that 4 is the additive inverse of -4. Note that the sum of the element and its additive inverse gives the additive identity element 0. What is the additive inverse of 12? Since $12 + (-12) = 0$, -12 is the additive inverse of 12.

Other examples of integers and their additive inverses are

Element	+	Additive Inverse	=	Identity Element
0	+	0	=	0
2	+	(-2)	=	0
-5	+	5	=	0

Note that for the operation of addition, every integer a has a unique inverse, $-a$, such that $a + (-a) = -a + a = 0$.

> When a binary operation is performed on two elements in a set and the result is the identity element for the binary operation, each element is said to be the **inverse** of the other.

Does every integer have an inverse under the operation of multiplication? For multiplication the product of an integer and its inverse must yield the multiplicative identity element, 1. What is the multiplicative inverse of 2? That is, 2 times what number gives 1?

$$2 \cdot \boxed{?} = 1 \qquad 2 \cdot \tfrac{1}{2} = 1$$

However, since $\frac{1}{2}$ is not an integer, 2 does not have a multiplicative inverse in the set of integers.

Group

Let's review what we have learned about the mathematical system consisting of the set of integers under the operation of addition.

1. The set of integers is *closed* under the operation of addition.
2. The set of integers has an *identity element* under the operation of addition.
3. Each element in the set of integers has an *inverse* under the operation of addition.
4. The *associative property* holds for the set of integers under the operation of addition.

The set of integers under the operation of addition is an example of a *group*. The properties of a group can be summarized as follows.

> **Properties of a Group**
> Any mathematical system that meets the following four requirements is called a **group.**
> 1. The set of elements is *closed* under the given operation.
> 2. An *identity element* exists for the set under the given operation.
> 3. Every element in the set has an *inverse* under the given operation.
> 4. The set of elements is *associative* under the given operation.

> **TIMELY TIP** Note that the set of elements need *not* be commutative for the mathematical system to be a group. Also note that *every* element in the set must have an inverse for the mathematical system to be a group.

It is often very time consuming to show that the associative property holds for all cases. In many of the examples that follow, we will state that the associative property holds for the given set of elements under the given operation.

Commutative Group

The commutative property does not need to hold for a mathematical system to be a group. However, if a mathematical system meets the four requirements of a group and is also commutative under the given operation, the mathematical system is a *commutative* (or *abelian*) *group*. The abelian group is named after Niels Abel (see the Profiles in Mathematics).

> A group that satisfies the commutative property is called a **commutative group** (or **abelian group**)

Because the commutative property holds for the set of integers under the operation of addition, the set of integers under the operation of addition is not only a group, but it is a commutative group.

Properties of a Commutative Group

A mathematical system is a **commutative group** if all five conditions hold.

1. The set of elements is *closed* under the given operation.
2. An *identity element* exists for the set.
3. Every element in the set has an *inverse*.
4. The set of elements is *associative* under the given operation.
5. The set of elements is *commutative* under the given operation.

To determine whether a mathematical system is a group under a given operation, *check, in the following order,* to determine whether (a) the system is closed under the given operation, (b) there is an identity element in the set for the given operation, (c) every element in the set has an inverse under the given operation, and (d) the associative property holds under the given operation. If *any* of these four requirements is *not* met, stop and state the mathematical system is not a group. If asked to determine whether the mathematical system is a commutative group, you also need to check to determine whether the commutative property holds for the given operation.

EXAMPLE 1 Is It a Group?

Determine whether the set of rational numbers under the operation of multiplication forms a group.

SOLUTION: Recall from Chapter 5 that the rational numbers are the set of numbers of the form p/q where p and q are integers and $q \neq 0$. All fractions and integers are rational numbers.

1. *Closure:* The product of any two rational numbers is a rational number. Therefore, the rational numbers are closed under the operation of multiplication.
2. *Identity element:* The multiplicative identity element for the set of rational numbers is 1. Note, for example, that $3 \cdot 1 = 1 \cdot 3 = 3$, and $\frac{3}{8} \cdot 1 = 1 \cdot \frac{3}{8} = \frac{3}{8}$. For any rational number a, $a \cdot 1 = 1 \cdot a = a$.
3. *Inverse elements:* For the mathematical system to be a group under the operation of multiplication, *each and every* rational number must have a multiplicative inverse in the set of rational numbers. Remember that for the operation of multiplication, the product of a number and its inverse must give the multiplicative identity element, 1. Let's check a few rational numbers:

$$\text{Rational number} \cdot \text{Inverse} = \text{Identity element}$$

$$3 \quad \cdot \quad \frac{1}{3} \quad = \quad 1$$

$$\frac{2}{3} \quad \cdot \quad \frac{3}{2} \quad = \quad 1$$

$$-\frac{1}{5} \quad \cdot \quad -5 \quad = \quad 1$$

Looking at these examples you might deduce that each rational number does have an inverse. However, one rational number, 0, does not have an inverse.

$$0 \cdot ? = 1$$

Because there is no rational number that, when multiplied by 0, gives 1, 0 does not have a multiplicative inverse. Since *every* rational number does not have an inverse, this mathematical system is not a group.

There is no need at this point to check the associative property because we have already shown that the mathematical system of rational numbers under the operation of multiplication is not a group.

MATHEMATICS
Everywhere

The Universe

Woody Allen and Diane Keaton in *Annie Hall*

In the chapter opening material, we mentioned that group theory is helpful to scientists in determining what the universe was like 15 billion years ago. Group theory plays an important role in many areas of higher mathematics and science. We often see articles where the information provided comes in part from group theory. For example, the June 25, 2001, issue of *Time* featured an article on space. The article mentions that "the Milky Way is a huge, whirling pinwheel made of 100 billion or more stars; that tens of billions of other galaxies lie beyond its edges; and most astonishing of all, that these galaxies are rushing headlong away from one another in the aftermath of an explosive cataclysm known as the Big Bang."

The article also discusses and illustrates how Albert Einstein believed that the universe is curved. He believed that parts of the universe have a positive curvature, parts are flat, and parts have a negative curvature. The curvature of our universe is discussed briefly in Section 9.7, non-Euclidean Geometry.

How and when will the universe end? In the Woody Allen movie *Annie Hall*, a boy (Woody Allen), having just read that the universe is expanding, becomes so worried that he can't do his homework. "Someday it will break apart," he tells his psychiatrist, "and that will be the end of everything." But his mother snaps, "You're here in Brooklyn! Brooklyn is not expanding!"

The article indicates that Allen may have been on to something. The universe could break apart. However, this will not be for trillions of years, and life as we know it on Earth will cease long before that. Our sun, halfway through its estimated 10-billion-year lifetime, is slowly brightening. In about 1 billion years, its energy output will have increased by at least 10 percent, turning Earth into a Venus-like hothouse incapable of supporting life as we know it. The article goes on to mention that long before that, humans may make plans to escape to Mars, which is farther from the sun and hence cooler. Although quite some time away, scientists are already considering various scenarios to make the surface of Mars a livable habitat.

Doradus Nebula, a satellite galaxy of the Milky Way

SECTION 10.1   EXERCISES

Concept/Writing Exercises

1. What is a binary operation?

2. What does a mathematical system consist of?

3. Explain why each of the following is a binary operation. Give an example to illustrate each binary operation.
   a) Addition   b) Subtraction
   c) Multiplication   d) Division

4. What properties are required for a mathematical system to be a group?

5. What properties are required for a mathematical system to be a commutative group?

6. What is another name for a commutative group?

7. Explain the closure property. Give an example of the property.

8. What is an identity element? Give the additive and multiplicative identity elements for the set of integers.

9. What is an inverse element? Give the additive and multiplicative inverse of the number 2 for the set of rational numbers.

10. What is a counterexample?

11. Is it possible that a mathematical system is a commutative group but not a group? Explain.

12. Is it possible that a mathematical system is a group but not a commutative group? Explain.

13. Which of the following properties is not required for a mathematical system to be a group?
    a) Closure
    b) An identity element
    c) Every element must have an inverse.
    d) The commutative property must apply.
    e) The associative property must apply.

14. For the set of integers, list two operations that are not binary. Explain.

Practice the Skills

15. Give the associative property of addition and illustrate the property with an example.

16. Give the associative property of multiplication and illustrate the property with an example.

17. Give the commutative property of multiplication and illustrate the property with an example.

18. Give the commutative property of addition and illustrate the property with an example.

19. Give an example to show that the commutative property does not hold for the set of integers under the operation of division.

20. Give an example to show that the commutative property does not hold for the set of integers under the operation of subtraction.

21. Give an example to show that the associative property does not hold for the set of integers under the operation of subtraction.

22. Give an example to show that the associative property does not hold for the set of integers under the operation of division.

Problem Solving

In Exercises 23–38, explain your answer.

23. Is the set of positive integers a group under the operation of addition?

24. Is the set of positive integers a commutative group under the operation of addition?

25. Is the set of integers a commutative group under the operation of addition?

26. Is the set of integers a group under the operation of addition?

27. Is the set of positive integers a group under the operation of subtraction?

28. Is the set of negative integers a group under the operation of division?

29. Is the set of negative integers a commutative group under the operation of addition?

30. Is the set of integers a group under the operation of multiplication?

31. Is the set of positive integers a commutative group under the operation of multiplication?

32. Is the set of negative integers a group under the operation of multiplication?

33. Is the set of rational numbers a group under the operation of addition?

34. Is the set of rational numbers a commutative group under the operation of multiplication?

35. Is the set of rational numbers a commutative group under the operation of division?

36. Is the set of rational numbers a group under the operation of subtraction?

37. Is the set of rational numbers a commutative group under the operation of subtraction?

38. Is the set of positive integers a commutative group under the operation of division?

Challenge Problems/Group Activities

In Exercises 39–42, explain your answer.

39. Is the set of irrational numbers a group under the operation of addition?

40. Is the set of irrational numbers a group under the operation of multiplication?

41. Is the set of real numbers a group under the operation of addition?

42. Is the set of real numbers a group under the operation of multiplication?

43. Create a mathematical system with two binary operations. Select a set of elements and two binary operations so that one binary operation with the set of elements meets the requirements for a group and the other binary operation will not. Explain why the one binary operation with the set of elements is a group. For the other binary operation and the set of elements find counterexamples to show that it is not a group.

Recreational Mathematics

44. *The Greatest Number* Find the greatest number that can be written with three digits.

45. *Sign Maker* There are 100 buildings along a street. A sign maker is asked to number the buildings from 1 to 100. How many "9's" will the sign maker need?

Internet/Research Activity

46. There are other classifications of mathematical systems besides groups. For example, there are *rings* and *fields*. Do research to determine the requirements that must be met for a mathematical system to be (a) a ring and (b) a field. (c) Is the set of real numbers, under the operations of addition and multiplication, a field? Ask your instructor for references to use.

10.2   FINITE MATHEMATICAL SYSTEMS

In the preceding section we presented infinite mathematical systems. In this section we present some finite mathematical systems. A *finite mathematical system* is one whose set contains a finite number of elements.

Clock Arithmetic

Figure 10.1

Let's develop a finite mathematical system called *clock arithmetic*. The set of elements in this system will be the hours on a clock: {1, 2, 3, 4, 5, 6, 7, 8, 9, 10, 11, 12}. The binary operation that we will use is addition, which we define as movement of the hour hand in a clockwise direction. Assume that it is 4 o'clock. What time will it be in 9 hours? (See Fig. 10.1.) If we add 9 hours to 4 o'clock, the clock will read 1 o'clock. Thus $4 + 9 = 1$ in clock arithmetic. Would $9 + 4$ be the same as $4 + 9$? Yes, $4 + 9 = 9 + 4 = 1$.

Table 10.1 is the addition table for clock arithmetic. Its elements are based on the definition of addition as previously illustrated. For example, the sum of 4 and 9 is 1, so we put a 1 in the table where the row to the right of the 4 intersects the column below the 9. Likewise, the sum of 11 and 10 is 9, so we put a 9 in the table where the row to the right of the 11 intersects the column below the 10.

The binary operation of this system is defined by the table. It is denoted by the symbol +. To determine the value of $a + b$, where a and b are any two numbers in the set, find a in the left-hand column and find b along the top row. Assume that there is a horizontal line through a and a vertical line through b; the point of intersection of these two lines is where you find the value of $a + b$. For example, $10 + 4 = 2$ has been circled in Table 10.1. Note that $4 + 10$ also equals 2, but this result will not necessarily hold for all examples in this chapter.

TABLE 10.1   Clock 12 Arithmetic

+	1	2	3	4	5	6	7	8	9	10	11	12
1	2	3	4	5	6	7	8	9	10	11	12	1
2	3	4	5	6	7	8	9	10	11	12	1	2
3	4	5	6	7	8	9	10	11	12	1	2	3
4	5	6	7	8	9	10	11	12	1	2	3	4
5	6	7	8	9	10	11	12	1	2	3	4	5
6	7	8	9	10	11	12	1	2	3	4	5	6
7	8	9	10	11	12	1	2	3	4	5	6	7
8	9	10	11	12	1	2	3	4	5	6	7	8
9	10	11	12	1	2	3	4	5	6	7	8	9
10	11	12	1	②	3	4	5	6	7	8	9	10
11	12	1	2	3	4	5	6	7	8	9	10	11
12	1	2	3	4	5	6	7	8	9	10	11	12

EXAMPLE 1   *A Commutative Group?*

Determine whether the clock arithmetic system under the operation of addition is a commutative group.

SOLUTION: Check the five requirements that must be satisfied for a commutative group.

1. *Closure:* Is the set of elements in clock arithmetic closed under the operation of addition? Yes, since Table 10.1 contains only the elements in the set

$\{1, 2, 3, 4, 5, 6, 7, 8, 9, 10, 11, 12\}$. If Table 10.1 had contained an element other than the numbers 1 through 12, the set would not have been closed under addition.

2. *Identity element:* Is there an identity element for clock arithmetic? If the time is currently 4 o'clock, how many hours have to pass before it is 4 o'clock again? Twelve hours: $4 + 12 = 12 + 4 = 4$. In fact, given any hour, in 12 hours the clock will return to the starting point. Therefore, 12 is the additive identity element in clock arithmetic.

   In examining Table 10.1 we see that the row of numbers next to the 12 in the left-hand column is identical to the row of numbers along the top. We also see that the column of numbers under the 12 in the top row is identical to the column of numbers on the left. The search for such a column and row is one technique for determining whether an identity element exists for a system defined by a table.

3. *Inverse elements:* Is there an inverse for the number 4 in clock arithmetic for the operation of addition? Recall that the identity element in clock arithmetic is 12. What number when added to 4 gives 12; that is, $4 + \_\_ = 12$? Table 10.1 shows that $4 + 8 = 12$ and also that $8 + 4 = 12$. Thus, 8 is the additive inverse of 4, and 4 is the additive inverse of 8.

   To find the additive inverse of 7, find 7 in the left-hand column of Table 10.1. Look to the right of the 7 until you come to the identity element 12. Determine the number at the top of this column. The number is 5. Since $7 + 5 = 5 + 7 = 12$, 5 is the inverse of 7, and 7 is the inverse of 5. The other inverses can be found in the same way. Table 10.2 shows each element in clock 12 arithmetic and its inverse. Note that each element in the set has an *inverse*.

TABLE 10.2 Clock 12 Inverses

Element	+	Inverse	=	Identity Element
1	+	11	=	12
2	+	10	=	12
3	+	9	=	12
4	+	8	=	12
5	+	7	=	12
6	+	6	=	12
7	+	5	=	12
8	+	4	=	12
9	+	3	=	12
10	+	2	=	12
11	+	1	=	12
12	+	12	=	12

4. *Associative property:* Now consider the associative property. Does $(a + b) + c = a + (b + c)$ for all values a, b, and c of the set? Remember to always evaluate the values within the parentheses first. Let's select some values for a, b, and c. Let $a = 2$, $b = 6$, and $c = 8$. Then

$$(2 + 6) + 8 = 2 + (6 + 8)$$
$$8 + 8 = 2 + 2$$
$$4 = 4 \quad \text{True}$$

Let $a = 5$, $b = 12$, and $c = 9$. Then

$$(5 + 12) + 9 = 5 + (12 + 9)$$
$$5 + 9 = 5 + 9$$
$$2 = 2 \quad \text{True}$$

Randomly selecting *any* elements a, b, and c of the set reveals $(a + b) + c = a + (b + c)$. Thus, the system of clock arithmetic is associative under the operation of addition. Note that if there is just one set of values a, b, and c such that $(a + b) + c \neq a + (b + c)$, the system is not associative. Normally you will not be asked to check every case to determine whether the associative property holds. *If every element in the set does not appear in every row and column of the table, however, you need to check the associative property carefully.*

5. *Commutative property:* Does the commutative property hold under the given operation? Does $a + b = b + a$ for all elements a and b of the set? Let's randomly select some values for a and b to determine whether the commutative property appears to hold. Let $a = 5$ and $b = 8$; then Table 10.1 shows that

$$5 + 8 = 8 + 5$$
$$1 = 1 \quad \text{True}$$

Let $a = 9$ and $b = 6$; then

$$9 + 6 = 6 + 9$$
$$3 = 3 \quad \text{True}$$

The commutative property holds for these two specific cases. In fact, if we were to select *any* values for a and b, we would find that $a + b = b + a$. Thus, the commutative property of addition is true in clock arithmetic. Note that if there is just one set of values a and b such that $a + b \neq b + a$, the system is not commutative.

This system satisfies the five properties required for a mathematical system to be a commutative group. Thus, clock arithmetic under the operation of addition is a commutative or abelian group. ▲

TABLE 10.3   Symmetry about the Main Diagonal

+	0	1	2	3	4
0	0	1	2	3	4
1	1	2	3	4	0
2	2	3	4	0	1
3	3	4	0	1	2
4	4	0	1	2	3

One method that can be used to determine whether a system defined by a table is commutative under the given operation is to determine whether the elements in the table are symmetric about the main diagonal. The main diagonal is the diagonal from the upper left-hand corner to the lower right-hand corner of the table. In Table 10.3 the main diagonal is shaded in color.

If the elements are symmetric about the main diagonal, then the system is commutative. If the elements are not symmetric about the main diagonal, then the system is not commutative. If you examine the system in Table 10.3, you see that its elements are symmetric about the main diagonal because the same numbers appear in the same relative positions on opposite sides of the main diagonal. Therefore, this mathematical system is commutative.

It is possible to have groups that are not commutative. Such groups are called *noncommutative* or *nonabelian groups*. However, a *noncommutative group defined by a table must be at least a six-element by six-element table.* Nonabelian groups are illustrated in Exercises 83 through 85 at the end of this section.

Now we will look at another finite mathematical system.

TABLE 10.4 Four-Element System

⊙	1	3	5	7
1	5	7	1	3
3	7	1	3	5
5	1	3	5	7
7	3	5	7	1

EXAMPLE 2   *A Finite System*

Consider the mathematical system defined by Table 10.4. Assume that the associative property holds for the given operation.

a) List the elements in the set of this mathematical system.

b) Identify the binary operation.

c) Determine whether this mathematical system is a commutative group.

SOLUTION:

a) The set of elements for this mathematical system consists of the elements found on the top (or left-hand side) of the table: $\{1, 3, 5, 7\}$.

b) The binary operation is $\odot$

c) We must determine whether the five requirements for a commutative group are satisfied.

1. *Closure:* All the elements in the table are in the original set of elements, $\{1, 3, 5, 7\}$, so the system is closed.

2. *Identity element:* The identity element is 5. Note that the row of elements to the right of the 5 is identical to the top row *and* the column of elements under the 5 is identical to the left-hand column.

3. *Inverse elements:* When an element operates on its inverse, the result is the identity element. For this example the identity element is 5. To determine the inverse of 1, find the element to replace the question mark:

$$1 \odot ? = 5$$

Since $1 \odot 1 = 5$, 1 is the inverse of 1. Thus, 1 is its own inverse.

To find the inverse of 3, find the element to replace the question mark:

$$3 \odot ? = 5$$

Since $3 \odot 7 = 7 \odot 3 = 5$, 7 is the inverse of 3 (and 3 is the inverse of 7). The elements and their inverses are shown in Table 10.5. Every element has a unique inverse.

4. *Associative property:* It is given that the associative property holds for this operation. One example of associative property is

$$(7 \odot 3) \odot 1 = 7 \odot (3 \odot 1)$$
$$5 \odot 1 = 7 \odot 7$$
$$1 = 1 \quad \text{True}$$

5. *Commutative property:* The elements in Table 10.4 are symmetric about the main diagonal, so the commutative property holds for the operation of $\odot$. One example of the commutative property is

$$3 \odot 5 = 5 \odot 3$$
$$3 = 3 \quad \text{True}$$

The five necessary properties hold. Thus, the mathematical system is a commutative group. ▲

TABLE 10.5 Inverses under $\odot$

Element	$\odot$	Inverse	=	Identity Element
1	$\odot$	1	=	5
3	$\odot$	7	=	5
5	$\odot$	5	=	5
7	$\odot$	3	=	5

Mathematical Systems Without Numbers

Thus far, all the systems we have discussed have been based on sets of numbers. Example 3 illustrates a mathematical system of symbols rather than numbers.

EXAMPLE 3   *Investigating a System of Symbols*

Use the mathematical system defined by Table 10.6 and determine

TABLE 10.6 A System of Symbols

$\cdot$	@	P	W
@	P	W	@
P	W	@	P
W	@	P	W

a) the set of elements.

b) the binary operation.

c) closure or nonclosure of the system.

d) the identity element.

e) the inverse of @.

f) $W \cdot P$ and $P \cdot$ @.

g) $(@ \cdot P) \cdot P$ and $@ \cdot (P \cdot P)$.

SOLUTION:

a) The set of elements of this mathematical system is $\{@, P, W\}$.

b) The binary operation is $\cdot$.

c) Because the table does not contain any symbols other than @, P, and W, the system is closed under $\cdot$.

d) The identity element is W. Note that the row next to W in the left-hand column is the same as the top row and that the column under W is identical to the left-hand column. We see that

$$@ \cdot W = W \cdot @ = @$$
$$P \cdot W = W \cdot P = P$$
$$W \cdot W = W$$

e) We know that

element $\cdot$ inverse element = identity element,

and since W is the identity element, to find the inverse of @ we write

$$@ \cdot ? = W$$

To find the inverse of @, we must determine the element to replace the question mark. Since $@ \cdot P = W$ and $P \cdot @ = W$, P is the inverse of @.

f) $W \cdot P = P$ and $P \cdot @ = W$

g) We first evaluate the information within parentheses.

$$(@ \cdot P) \cdot P = W \cdot P \qquad \text{and} \qquad @ \cdot (P \cdot P) = @ \cdot @$$
$$= P \qquad\qquad\qquad\qquad\qquad = P$$

EXAMPLE 4   *Is the System a Commutative Group?*

Determine whether the mathematical system in Table 10.7 is a commutative group. Assume that the associative property holds for the given operation.

TABLE 10.7

*	A	B	C	D
A	D	A	B	C
B	A	B	C	D
C	B	C	D	A
D	C	D	A	B

TABLE 10.8

Element	*	Inverse	=	Identity element
A	*	C	=	B
B	*	B	=	B
C	*	A	=	B
D	*	D	=	B

SOLUTION:

1. *Closure:* The system is closed.
2. *Identity element:* The identity element is B.
3. *Inverse elements:* Each element has an inverse as illustrated in Table 10.8.
4. *Associative property:* It is given that the associative property holds. An example illustrating the associative property is

$$(D*A)*C = D*(A*C)$$
$$C*C = D*B$$
$$D = D \quad \text{True}$$

5. *Commutative property:* By examining the table we can see that it is symmetric about the main diagonal. Thus, the system is commutative under the given operation. One example of the commutative property is

$$D*C = C*D$$
$$A = A \quad \text{True}$$

All five properties are satisfied. Thus, the system is a commutative group. ▲

EXAMPLE 5   *Another System to Study*

Determine whether the mathematical system in Table 10.9 is a commutative group under the operation of ☺.

SOLUTION:

1. The system is closed.
2. No row is identical to the top row, so there is no identity element. Therefore, this mathematical system is *not a group*. There is no need to go any further, but for practice, let's look at a few more items.
3. Since there is no identity element, there can be no inverses.
4. The associative property does not hold. The following counterexample illustrates the associative property does not hold for every case.

$$(x ☺ y) ☺ z \neq x ☺ (y ☺ z)$$
$$z ☺ z \neq x ☺ x$$
$$z \neq x$$

TABLE 10.9

☺	x	y	z
x	x	z	y
y	z	y	x
z	y	x	z

5. The table is symmetric about the main diagonal. Therefore, the commutative property does hold for the operation of ☺.

Note that the associative property does not hold even though the commutative property does hold. This outcome can occur when there is no identity element and every element does not have an inverse, as in this example. ▲

EXAMPLE 6   *Is the System a Commutative Group?*

Determine whether the mathematical system in Table 10.10 is a commutative group under the operation of *.

SOLUTION:

1. The system is closed.
2. There is an identity element, □.

TABLE 10.10

*	□	b	c
□	□	b	c
b	b	b	□
c	c	□	c

3. Each element has an inverse; □ is the inverse of □, *b* is the inverse of *c*, and *c* is the inverse of *b*.

4. Every element in the set does not appear in every row and every column of the table, so we need to check the associative property carefully. There are many specific cases where the associative property does hold. However, the following counterexample illustrates that the associative property does not hold for every case.

$$(b*b)*c \neq b*(b*c)$$
$$b*c \neq b*\square$$
$$\square \neq b$$

5. The commutative property holds because there is symmetry about the main diagonal.

Since we have shown that the associative property does not hold under the operation of *, this system is not a group. Therefore, it cannot be a commutative group. ▲

DID YOU KNOW

Creating Patterns by Design

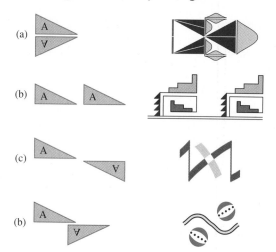

(a)

(b)

(c)

(b)

Patterns from *Symmetries of Culture* by Dorothy K. Washburn and Donald W. Crowe (University of Washington Press, 1988)

What makes group theory such a powerful tool is that it can be used to reveal the underlying structure of just about any physical phenomenon that involves symmetry and patterning, such as wallpaper or quilt patterns. Interest in the formal study of symmetry in design came out of the Industrial Revolution in the late nineteenth century. The new machines of the Industrial Revolution could vary any given pattern almost indefinitely. Designers needed a way to describe and manipulate patterns systematically. At the same time, explorers were discovering artifacts of other cultures, which stimulated interest in categorizing patterns. Shown here are the four geometric motions that generate all two-dimensional patterns: (a) reflection, (b) translation, (c) rotation, and (d) glide reflection. How these motions are applied, or not applied, is the basis of pattern analysis. The geometric motions, called *rigid motions,* were discussed in Section 9.5.

SECTION 10.2   EXERCISES

Concept/Writing Exercises

1. Explain how the clock 12 addition table is formed.

2. What is 12 + 12 in clock 12 arithmetic? Explain how you obtained your answer.

3. **a)** Explain how to add the numbers (4 + 10) + 3 in clock 12 arithmetic using the addition table.
   b) What is (4 + 10) + 3 in clock 12 arithmetic?

4. **a)** Explain how to determine a difference of two numbers in clock arithmetic by using the face of a clock.

   b) Determine 4 − 7 in clock 12 arithmetic using the method explained in part (a).

5. **a)** Explain how to find 5 − 9 in clock 12 arithmetic by adding the number 12 to one of the numbers.
   b) Determine 5 − 9 in clock 12 arithmetic using the method explained in part (a).
   c) Explain why the procedure you give in part (a) works.

6. Explain one method of determining whether a system defined by a table is commutative under the given operation.

7. Is clock 12 arithmetic closed under the operation of addition? Explain.

8. Is there an identity element for addition in clock 12 arithmetic? If so, what is it?

9. Does each element in clock 12 arithmetic have an inverse? If so, give each element and its corresponding inverse.

10. Give an example to illustrate the associative property of addition in clock 12 arithmetic.

11. Is clock 12 arithmetic commutative? Give an example to verify your answer.

12. Is clock 12 arithmetic under the operation of addition a commutative group? Explain.

13. Consider clock 5 arithmetic under the operation of addition. The set of elements in such a mathematical system is $\{1, 2, 3, 4, 5\}$.
    a) Which of these elements is the additive identity element?
    b) What is the additive inverse of 2? Explain your answer.

14. Consider clock 8 arithmetic under the operation of addition. The set of elements in such a mathematical system is $\{1, 2, 3, 4, 5, 6, 7, 8\}$.
    a) Which of these elements is the additive identity element?
    b) What is the additive inverse of 3? Explain your answer.

In Exercises 15 and 16, determine if the system is commutative. Explain how you determined your answer.

15.

$\boxminus$	A	$\otimes$	W
A	$\otimes$	W	A
$\otimes$	W	A	$\otimes$
W	A	$\otimes$	$\otimes$

16.

I	P	A	L
P	L	P	A
A	P	L	A
L	A	L	P

In Exercises 17 and 18, determine if the system has an identity element. If so, list the identity element. Explain how you determined your answer.

17.

W	A	B	C
A	C	B	A
B	B	C	B
C	A	B	C

18.

$\ominus$	$\square$	$\odot$	$\triangle$
$\square$	$\triangle$	$\square$	$\odot$
$\odot$	$\odot$	$\triangle$	$\square$
$\triangle$	$\square$	$\odot$	$\triangle$

In Exercises 19 and 20, the identity element is C. Determine the inverse of A. Explain how you determined your answer.

19.

$\oslash$	A	B	C
A	B	C	A
B	C	A	B
C	A	B	C

20.

$\oslash$	C	A	B
C	C	A	B
A	A	C	B
B	B	B	C

Practice the Skills

In Exercises 21–32, use Table 10.1 on page 568 to determine the sum in clock 12 arithmetic.

21. $4 + 7$

22. $8 + 7$

23. $9 + 8$

24. $10 + 4$

25. $4 + 12$

26. $12 + 12$

27. $3 + (8 + 9)$

28. $(8 + 7) + 6$

29. $(6 + 4) + 8$

30. $(6 + 10) + 12$

31. $(7 + 8) + (9 + 6)$

32. $(7 + 11) + (9 + 5)$

In Exercises 33–44, determine the difference in clock 12 arithmetic by starting at the first number and counting counterclockwise on the clock the number of units given by the second number.

33. $7 - 4$

34. $11 - 8$

35. $4 - 12$

36. $3 - 9$

37. $5 - 10$

38. $3 - 10$

39. $1 - 12$

40. $6 - 10$

41. $5 - 5$

42. $8 - 8$

43. $12 - 12$

44. $5 - 8$

45. Use the following figure to develop an addition table for clock 6 arithmetic. The figure will also be used in Exercises 46–54.

In Exercises 46–54, determine the sum or difference in clock 6 arithmetic.

46. $4 + 5$

47. $1 + 6$

48. $6 + 4$

49. $5 - 2$

50. $4 - 5$

51. $2 - 6$

52. $3 - 4$

53. $(3 - 5) - 6$

54. $2 + (1 - 3)$

55. Use the following figure to develop an addition table for clock 7 arithmetic. The figure will also be used in Exercises 56–64.

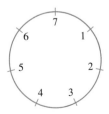

In Exercises 56–64, determine the sum or difference in clock 7 arithmetic.

56. $5 + 4$

57. $6 + 5$

58. $4 + 4$

59. $7 + 6$

60. $2 - 3$

61. $3 - 6$

62. $2 - 4$

63. $(4 - 5) - 6$

64. $3 - (2 - 6)$

65. Determine whether clock 7 arithmetic under the operation of addition is a commutative group. Explain.

66. A mathematical system is defined by a three-element by three-element table where every element in the set appears in each row and each column. Must the mathematical system be a commutative group? Explain.

67. Consider the mathematical system indicated by the following table. Assume that the associative property holds for the given operation.

✈	0	1	2	3
0	0	1	2	3
1	1	2	3	0
2	2	3	0	1
3	3	0	1	2

a) What are the elements of the set in this mathematical system?
b) What is the binary operation?
c) Is the system closed? Explain.
d) Is there an identity element for the system under the given operation? If so, what is it?
e) Does every element in the system have an inverse? If so, give each element and its corresponding inverse.
f) Give an example to illustrate the associative property.
g) Is the system commutative? Give an example to verify your answer.
h) Is the mathematical system a commutative group? Explain.

In Exercises 68–70, repeat parts (a)–(h) of Exercise 67 for the mathematical system in the table. Assume that the associative property holds for the given operation.

68.

🦙	*	5	L
*	5	L	*
5	L	*	5
L	*	5	L

69.

🛸	r	s	t	u
r	t	u	r	s
s	u	r	s	t
t	r	s	t	u
u	s	t	u	r

70.

👤	3	5	8	4
3	5	8	4	3
5	8	4	3	5
8	4	3	5	8
4	3	5	8	4

71. For the mathematical system

⚔	f	r	o	m
f	f	r	o	m
r	r	o	m	f
o	o	m	f	r
m	m	f	r	o

determine
a) the elements in the set.
b) the binary operation.
c) closure or nonclosure of the system.
d) $(r \; ⚔ \; o) \; ⚔ \; f$
e) $(f \; ⚔ \; r) \; ⚔ \; m$
f) the identity element.
g) the inverse of r.
h) the inverse of m.

72. a) Is the following mathematical system a group? Explain your answer.
b) Find an example showing that the associative property does not hold for the given set of elements.

⍵	1	2	3	4
1	2	3	4	1
2	3	4	1	2
3	4	1	2	3
4	1	4	3	2

In Exercises 73–78, for the mathematical system given, determine which of the five properties of a commutative group do not hold.

73.

⊗	⊡	M	🔔
⊡	⊡	M	🔔
M	M	⊡	🔔
🔔	🔔	M	⊡

74.

∧	w	x	y
w	w	y	x
x	y	x	w
y	x	a	y

75.

·	⊙	*	?	T	P
⊙	T	P	⊙	*	*
*	P	⊙	*	⊙	T
?	⊙	*	?	T	P
T	*	⊙	T	P	?
P	*	T	P	?	⊙

76.

☺	a	b	π	0	Δ
a	Δ	a	b	π	0
b	a	b	π	0	Δ
π	b	π	0	Δ	a
0	π	0	Δ	a	b
Δ	0	Δ	π	b	a

77.

⇔	a	b	c	d	e
a	c	d	e	a	b
b	d	e	a	b	c
c	e	a	b	c	d
d	a	b	c	e	d
e	b	c	d	e	a

78.

▽	0	1	2	3	4	5
0	0	0	0	0	0	0
1	0	1	2	3	4	5
2	0	2	4	0	2	4
3	0	3	0	3	0	3
4	0	4	2	0	4	2
5	0	5	4	3	2	1

Problem Solving Exercises

79. a) Consider the set consisting of two elements $\{E, O\}$, where E stands for an even number and O stands for an odd number. For the operation of addition, complete the table.

+	E	O
E		
O		

b) Determine whether this mathematical system forms a commutative group under the operation of addition. Explain your answer.

80. a) Let E and O represent even numbers and odd numbers, respectively, as in Exercise 79. Complete the table for the operation of multiplication.

×	E	O
E		
O		

b) Determine whether this mathematical system forms a commutative group under the operation of multiplication. Explain your answer.

In Exercises 81 and 82, make up your own mathematical system that is a group. List the identity element and the inverses of each element. Do so with sets containing

81. three elements.

82. four elements.

83. The tables in Exercises 83 and 84 are examples of non-commutative or nonabelian groups. For each exercise, do the following.
   a) Show that the system under the given operation is a group. (It would be very time consuming to prove that the associative property holds, but you can give some examples to show that it appears to hold.)
   b) Find a counterexample to show that the commutative property does not hold.

∞	1	2	3	4	5	6
1	5	3	4	2	6	1
2	4	6	5	1	3	2
3	2	1	6	5	4	3
4	3	5	1	6	2	4
5	6	4	2	3	1	5
6	1	2	3	4	5	6

84.

⊖	A	B	C	D	E	F
A	E	C	D	B	F	A
B	D	F	E	A	C	B
C	B	A	F	E	D	C
D	C	E	A	F	B	D
E	F	D	B	C	A	E
F	A	B	C	D	E	F

Challenge Problems/Group Activities

85. *Book Arrangements* Suppose that three books numbered 1, 2, and 3 are placed next to one another on a shelf. If we remove volume 3 and place it before volume 1, the new order of books is 3, 1, 2. Let's call this replacement R. We can write

$$R = \begin{pmatrix} 1 & 2 & 3 \\ 3 & 1 & 2 \end{pmatrix}$$

which indicates the books were switched in order from 1, 2, 3 to 3, 1, 2. Other possible replacements are S, T, U, V, and I, as indicated.

$$S = \begin{pmatrix} 1 & 2 & 3 \\ 2 & 1 & 3 \end{pmatrix} \quad T = \begin{pmatrix} 1 & 2 & 3 \\ 3 & 2 & 1 \end{pmatrix} \quad U = \begin{pmatrix} 1 & 2 & 3 \\ 1 & 3 & 2 \end{pmatrix}$$

$$V = \begin{pmatrix} 1 & 2 & 3 \\ 2 & 3 & 1 \end{pmatrix} \quad I = \begin{pmatrix} 1 & 2 & 3 \\ 1 & 2 & 3 \end{pmatrix}$$

Replacement set I indicates that the books were removed from the shelves and placed back in their original order. Consider the mathematical system with the set of elements, R, S, T, U, V, I, with the operation $*$.

To evaluate $R * S$, write

$$\begin{matrix} R & & S \end{matrix}$$

$$R * S = \begin{pmatrix} 1 & 2 & 3 \\ 3 & 1 & 2 \end{pmatrix} * \begin{pmatrix} 1 & 2 & 3 \\ 2 & 1 & 3 \end{pmatrix}.$$

As shown in Fig. 10.2, R replaces 1 with 3 and S replaces 3 with 3 (no change), so $R * S$ replaces 1 with 3. R replaces 2 with 1 and S replaces 1 with 2, so $R * S$ replaces 2 with 2 (no change). R replaces 3 with 2 and S replaces 2 with 1, so $R * S$ replaces 3 with 1. $R * S$ replaces 1 with 3, 2 with 2, and 3 with 1.

$$\begin{matrix} & R & & S \\ 1 & \longrightarrow & 3 & \longrightarrow & 3 \\ 2 & \longrightarrow & 1 & \longrightarrow & 2 \\ 3 & \longrightarrow & 2 & \longrightarrow & 1 \\ \uparrow & R & * & S & \uparrow \end{matrix}$$

$$R * S = \begin{pmatrix} 1 & 2 & 3 \\ 3 & 2 & 1 \end{pmatrix} = T$$

Figure 10.2

Since this result is the same as replacement set T, we write $R * S = T$.

a) Complete the table for the operation using the procedure outlined.

*	R	S	T	U	V	I
R		T				
S						
T						
U						
V						
I						

b) Is this mathematical system a group? Explain.
c) Is this mathematical system a commutative group? Explain.

86. If a mathematical system is defined by a four-element by four-element table, how many specific cases must be illustrated to prove the set of elements is associative under the given operation?

Recreational Mathematics

The following recreational exercises will help prepare you for the next section.

87. A table is shown below.

+	0	1	2	3	4
0	0		2		4
1	1		3		
2			4		1
3	3		0	1	2
4		0	1		

Fill in the blank areas of the table by performing the following operations.

1. Add the number in the left-hand column and the number in the top row.

2. Divide this sum by 5.

3. Place the *remainder* in the cell where the number in the left-hand column and the number in the top row would meet.

For example, in the table, the number 2 is in red. This 2 is found as follows:

$$(3 + 4) \div 5 = 1, \text{remainder } 2$$

88. Using Exercise 87 as a guide, complete the following table by dividing the sum of the numbers by 6. Place the remainders in the table as explained in Exercise 87.

+	0	1	2	3	4	5
0						
1						
2						
3						
4						
5						

89. Consider the mathematical system defined by the following table.

+	0	1	2	3
0	0	1	2	3
1	1	2	3	0
2	2	3	0	1
3	3	0	1	2

After working Exercises 87 and 88, can you explain how this table was formed?

Internet/Research Activities

90. In section 7.3 we introduced matrices. Show that 2×2 matrices under the operation of addition form a commutative group.

91. Show that 2×2 matrices under the operation of multiplication do not form a commutative group.

10.3 MODULAR ARITHMETIC

Figure 10.3

Figure 10.4

TABLE 10.11   Modular 7 Addition

+	0	1	2	3	4	5	6
0	0	1	2	3	4	5	6
1	1	2	3	4	5	6	0
2	2	3	4	5	6	0	1
3	3	4	5	6	0	1	2
4	4	5	6	0	1	2	③
5	5	6	0	1	2	3	4
6	6	0	1	2	3	4	5

Figure 10.5

The clock arithmetic we discussed in the previous section is similar to modular arithmetic. The set of elements $\{0, 1, 2, 3, 4, 5, 6, 7, 8, 9, 10, 11\}$ together with the operation of addition is called a modulo 12 or mod 12 system. There is one difference in notation between clock 12 arithmetic and modulo 12 arithmetic. In the modulo 12 system the symbol 12 is replaced with the symbol 0.

A *modulo m system* consists of m elements, 0 through $m - 1$, and a binary operation. In this section we will discuss modular arithmetic systems and their properties.

If today is Sunday, what day of the week will it be in 23 days? The answer, Tuesday, is arrived at by dividing 23 by 7 and observing the remainder of 2. Twenty-three days represent 3 weeks plus 2 days. Since we are interested only in the day of the week on which the twenty-third day will fall, the 3-week segment is unimportant to the answer. The remainder of 2 indicates the answer will be 2 days later than Sunday, which is Tuesday.

If we place the days of the week on a clock face as shown in Fig. 10.3, then in 23 days the hand would have made three complete revolutions and end on Tuesday. If we replace the days of the week with numbers, then a modulo 7 arithmetic system will result. See Fig. 10.4: Sunday = 0, Monday = 1, Tuesday = 2, and so on. If we start at 0 and move the hand 23 places, we will end at 2. Table 10.11 shows a modulo 7 addition table.

If we start at 4 and add 6, we end at 3 on the clock in Fig. 10.5. This number is circled in Table 10.11. The other numbers can be obtained in the same way.

A second method of determining the sum of $4 + 6$ in modulo 7 arithmetic is to divide the sum, 10, by 7 and observe the remainder.

$$10 \div 7 = 1, \quad \text{remainder } 3$$

The remainder, 3, is the sum of $4 + 6$ in a modulo 7 arithmetic system.

The concept of congruence is important in modular arithmetic.

> a is **congruent** to b modulo m, written, $a \equiv b \pmod{m}$, if a and b have the same remainder when divided by m.

We can show, for example, that $10 \equiv 3 \pmod 7$ by dividing both 10 and 3 by 7 and observing that we obtain the same remainder in each case.

$$10 \div 7 = 1, \quad \text{remainder } 3 \qquad \text{and} \qquad 3 \div 7 = 0, \quad \text{remainder } 3$$

Since the remainders are the same, 3 in each case, 10 is congruent to 3 modulo 7, and we may write $10 \equiv 3 \pmod 7$.

TABLE 10.12   Modulo 7 Classes

0	1	2	3	4	5	6
0	1	2	3	4	5	6
7	8	9	10	11	12	13
14	15	16	17	18	19	20
21	22	23	24	25	26	27
28	29	30	31	32	33	34
⋮	⋮	⋮	⋮	⋮	⋮	⋮

Now consider $37 \equiv 5 \pmod 8$. If we divide both 37 and 5 by 8, each has the same remainder, 5.

In any modulo system we can develop a set of *modulo classes* by placing all numbers with the same remainder in the appropriate modulo class. In a modulo 7 system every number must have a remainder of either 0, 1, 2, 3, 4, 5, or 6. Thus, a modulo 7 system has seven modulo classes. The seven classes are presented in Table 10.12.

Every number is congruent to a number from 0 to 6 in modulo 7. For example, $24 \equiv 3 \pmod 7$ because 24 is in the same modulo class as 3.

The solution to a problem in modular arithmetic, if it exists, will always be a number from 0 through $m - 1$, where m is the *modulus* of the system. For example, in a modulo 7 system, because 7 is the modulus, the solution will be a number from 0 through 6.

EXAMPLE 1   *Congruence Modulo 7*

Determine which number, from 0 through 6, the following numbers are congruent to in modulo 7.

a) 62   b) 53   c) 105

SOLUTION: We could determine the answer by listing more entries in Table 10.12. Another method of finding the answer is to divide the given number by 7 and observe the remainder. In the solutions we will use a question mark, ?, as a place holder. The ? will represent a number from 0 through 6. When we determine the answer, we will replace the ? with the answer.

a) $62 \equiv ? \pmod 7$

To determine the value that 62 is congruent to in mod 7, divide 62 by 7 and find the remainder.

$$\begin{array}{r} 8 \\ 7\overline{)62} \\ 56 \\ \hline 6 \end{array} \leftarrow \text{remainder}$$

$$62 \div 7 = 8, \quad \text{remainder } 6$$

Thus, $62 \equiv 6 \pmod 7$.

b) $53 \equiv ? \pmod 7$

$$53 \div 7 = 7, \quad \text{remainder } 4$$

Thus, $53 \equiv 4 \pmod 7$.

c) $105 \equiv ? \pmod 7$

$$105 \div 7 = 15, \quad \text{remainder } 0$$

Thus, $105 \equiv 0 \pmod 7$.   ▲

EXAMPLE 2   *Congruence Modulo 5*

Evaluate each of the following in mod 5.

a) $3 + 4$ b) $4 - 3$ c) $4 \cdot 2$

SOLUTION: In each part, because we are working in modulo 5, the answer will be a number from 0 through 4.

a) $3 + 4 \equiv ? \pmod 5$

$\qquad 7 \equiv ? \pmod 5$

$$7 \div 5 = 1, \quad \text{remainder } 2$$

Therefore, $4 + 3 \equiv 2 \pmod 5$.

b) $4 - 3 \equiv ? \pmod 5$

$\qquad 1 \equiv ? \pmod 5$

$\qquad 1 \equiv 1 \pmod 5$

Remember that we want to replace the question mark with a number between 0 and 4, inclusive. Thus, $4 - 3 \equiv 1 \pmod 5$.

c) $4 \cdot 2 \equiv ? \pmod 5$

$\qquad 8 \equiv ? \pmod 5$

Since $8 \div 5 = 1$, remainder 3, $8 \equiv 3 \pmod 5$. Thus, $4 \cdot 2 \equiv 3 \pmod 5$. ▲

Note in Table 10.12 that every number in the same modulo class differs by a multiple of the modulo, in this case a multiple of 7. Adding (or subtracting) a multiple of the modulo number to (or from) a given number does not change the modulo class or congruence of the given number. For example, $3, 3 + 1(7), 3 + 2(7), 3 + 3(7), \ldots,$ $3 + n(7)$ are all in the same modulo class, namely, 3. We use this fact in the solution to Example 3.

EXAMPLE 3 *Using Modulo Classes in Subtraction*

Find the replacement for the question mark that makes each of the following true.

a) $3 - 5 \equiv ? \pmod 7$ b) $? - 4 \equiv 3 \pmod 5$ c) $5 - ? \equiv 7 \pmod 8$

SOLUTION: In each part we wish to replace the question mark with a number less than the modular number. Therefore, in part (a) we wish to replace the ? with a number less than 7. In part (b) we wish to replace the ? with a number less than 5. In part (c) we wish to replace the ? with a number less than 8.

a) In mod 7, adding 7, or a multiple of 7, to a number results in a sum that is in the same modulo class. Thus, if we add $7, 14, 21, \ldots$ to 3, the result will be a number in the same modulo class. We want to replace 3 with an equivalent mod 7 number that is greater than 5. Adding 7 to 3 yields a sum of 10, which is greater than 5.

$$3 - 5 \equiv ? \pmod 7$$
$$(3 + 7) - 5 \equiv ? \pmod 7$$
$$10 - 5 \equiv ? \pmod 7$$
$$5 \equiv ? \pmod 7$$
$$5 \equiv 5 \pmod 7$$

Therefore, $? = 5$ and $3 - 5 \equiv 5 \pmod 7$.

b) We wish to replace the ? with a number less than 5. We know that $7 - 4 \equiv 3 \bmod 5$ because $3 \equiv 3 \bmod 5$. Therefore, we need to determine what number, less than 5, the number 7 is congruent to in mod 5. If we subtract the

modulo, 5, from 7, we obtain 2. Thus, 2 and 7 are in the same modular class. Therefore, $? = 2$.

$$? - 4 \equiv 3 \ (\text{mod } 5)$$
$$7 - 4 \equiv 3 \ (\text{mod } 5)$$
$$2 - 4 \equiv 3 \ (\text{mod } 5)$$

Notice in the last equivalence that if we add 5 to 2, we get $7 - 4 \equiv 3 \ (\text{mod } 5)$, which is a true statement.

c) $5 - ? \equiv 7 \ (\text{mod } 8)$

In mod 8, adding 8, or a multiple of 8, to a number results in a sum that is in the same modulo class. Thus, we can add 8 to 5 so that the statement becomes

$$(8 + 5) - ? \equiv 7 \ (\text{mod } 8)$$
$$13 - ? \equiv 7 \ (\text{mod } 8)$$

We can see that $13 - 6 = 7$. Therefore, $? = 6$ and $5 - 6 \equiv 7 \ (\text{mod } 8)$.   ▲

EXAMPLE 4   *Using Modulo Classes in Multiplication*

Find all replacements for the question mark that make the statements true.

a) $4 \cdot ? \equiv 3 \ (\text{mod } 5)$ b) $3 \cdot ? \equiv 0 \ (\text{mod } 6)$ c) $3 \cdot ? \equiv 2 \ (\text{mod } 6)$

SOLUTION:

a) One method of determining the solution is to replace the question mark with the numbers 0–4 and then find the equivalent modulo class of the product. We use the numbers 0–4 because we are working in modulo 5.

$$4 \cdot ? \equiv 3 \ (\text{mod } 5)$$
$$4 \cdot 0 \equiv 0 \ (\text{mod } 5)$$
$$4 \cdot 1 \equiv 4 \ (\text{mod } 5)$$
$$4 \cdot 2 \equiv 3 \ (\text{mod } 5)$$
$$4 \cdot 3 \equiv 2 \ (\text{mod } 5)$$
$$4 \cdot 4 \equiv 1 \ (\text{mod } 5)$$

Therefore, $? = 2$ since $4 \cdot 2 \equiv 3 \ (\text{mod } 5)$.

b) Since we are working in modulo 6, replace the question mark with the numbers 0–5 and follow the procedure used in part (a).

$$3 \cdot ? \equiv 0 \ (\text{mod } 6)$$
$$3 \cdot 0 \equiv 0 \ (\text{mod } 6)$$
$$3 \cdot 1 \equiv 3 \ (\text{mod } 6)$$
$$3 \cdot 2 \equiv 0 \ (\text{mod } 6)$$
$$3 \cdot 3 \equiv 3 \ (\text{mod } 6)$$
$$3 \cdot 4 \equiv 0 \ (\text{mod } 6)$$
$$3 \cdot 5 \equiv 3 \ (\text{mod } 6)$$

Therefore, replacing the question mark with 0, 2, or 4 results in true statements. The answers are 0, 2, and 4.

c) $3 \cdot ? \equiv 2 \ (\text{mod } 6)$

Examining the products in part (b) shows there are no values that satisfy the statement. The answer is "no solution."   ▲

Modular arithmetic systems under the operation of addition are commutative groups, as illustrated in Example 5.

EXAMPLE 5   *A Commutative Group*

Construct a mod 5 addition table and show that the mathematical system is a commutative group. Assume that the associative property holds for the given operation.

SOLUTION: The set of elements in modulo 5 arithmetic is $\{0, 1, 2, 3, 4\}$; the binary operation is $+$.

+	0	1	2	3	4
0	0	1	2	3	4
1	1	2	3	4	0
2	2	3	4	0	1
3	3	4	0	1	2
4	4	0	1	2	3

For this system to be a commutative group, it must satisfy the five properties of a commutative group.

1. *Closure:* Every entry in the table is a member of the set $\{0, 1, 2, 3, 4\}$, so the system is closed under addition.
2. *Identity element:* An easy way to determine whether there is an identity element is to look for a row in the table that is identical to the elements at the top of the table. Note that the row next to 0 is identical to the top of the table, which indicates that 0 *might be* the identity element. Now look at the column under the 0 at the top of the table. If this column is identical to the left-hand column, then 0 is the identity element. Since the column under 0 is the same as the left-hand column, 0 is the additive identity element in modulo 5 arithmetic.

Element	+	Identity	=	Element
0	+	0	=	0
1	+	0	=	1
2	+	0	=	2
3	+	0	=	3
4	+	0	=	4

3. *Inverse elements:* Does every element have an inverse? Recall an element plus its inverse must equal the identity element. In this example, the identity element is 0. Therefore, for each of the given elements 0, 1, 2, 3, and 4, we must find the element that when added to it results in a sum of zero. These elements will be the inverses.

Element	+	Inverse	=	Identity	
0	+	?	=	0	Since $0 + 0 = 0$, 0 is its own inverse.
1	+	?	=	0	Since $1 + 4 = 0$, 4 is the inverse of 1.
2	+	?	=	0	Since $2 + 3 = 0$, 3 is the inverse of 2.
3	+	?	=	0	Since $3 + 2 = 0$, 2 is the inverse of 3.
4	+	?	=	0	Since $4 + 1 = 0$, 1 is the inverse of 4.

Note that each element has an inverse.

4. *Associative property:* It is given that the associative property holds. One example that illustrates the associative property is

$$(2 + 3) + 4 = 2 + (3 + 4)$$
$$0 + 4 = 2 + 2$$
$$4 = 4 \quad \text{True}$$

5. *Commutative property:* Is $a + b = b + a$ for *all* elements a and b of the given set? The table shows that the system is commutative because the elements are symmetric about the main diagonal. We will give one example to illustrate the commutative property.

$$4 + 2 = 2 + 4$$
$$1 = 1 \quad \text{True}$$

All five properties are satisfied. Thus, modulo 5 arithmetic under the operation of addition is a commutative group. ▲

Whenever a process is repetitive, modular arithmetic may be helpful in answering some questions about the process. Now let's look at an application of modular arithmetic.

EXAMPLE 6   *Work Schedule*

Ellis drives a bus for a living. His working schedule is to drive for 6 days, and then he gets 2 days off. If today is the third day that Ellis has been driving, determine the following.

a) Will he be driving 60 days from today?
b) Will he be driving 82 days from today?
c) Was he driving 124 days ago?

SOLUTION:

a) Since Ellis drives for 6 days and then gets 2 days off, his working schedule may be considered a modular 8 system. That is, 8, 16, 24, ... days from today will be just like today, the third day of the 8-day cycle.

If we divide 60 by 8, we obtain

$$\begin{array}{r} 7 \\ 8\overline{)60} \\ \underline{56} \\ 4 \leftarrow \text{remainder} \end{array}$$

Therefore, in 60 days Ellis will go through 7 complete cycles and be 4 days further into the next cycle. If we let D represent a driving day and N represent a not driving day, then Ellis's cycle may be represented as follows:

$$D\ D\ D\ D\ D\ D\ N\ N$$

↑   ↑
today   4 days
from today

Notice that 4 days from today will be his first nonworking day. Therefore, Ellis will not be driving 60 days from today.

b) We work this part in the same way we worked part (a). Divide 82 by 8 and determine the remainder.

$$
\begin{array}{r}
10 \\
8\overline{)82} \\
\underline{80} \\
2 \leftarrow \text{remainder}
\end{array}
$$

Thus, in 82 days it will be 2 days later in the cycle than it is today. Because he is currently in day 3 of his cycle, Ellis will be in day 5 of his cycle and will be driving the bus.

c) This part is worked in the same way as parts (a) and (b), but once we find the remainders we must move backward in the cycle.

$$
\begin{array}{r}
15 \\
8\overline{)124} \\
\underline{120} \\
4 \leftarrow \text{remainder}
\end{array}
$$

Thus, 124 days ago was 4 days earlier in the cycle. Marking day 3 of the cycle (indicated by word today) and then moving 4 days backwards brings us to the first nondriving day. The two N's shown at the beginning of the letters below are actually the end days of the previous cycle.

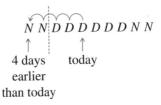

$$
N\ N\ D\ D\ D\ D\ D\ D\ N\ N
$$

4 days   today
earlier
than today

Therefore, 124 days ago Ellis was not driving.

TIMELY TIP A knowledge of modular arithmetic may prove useful throughout life. Answers to problems like those presented in Example 6 and Exercises 67–74 can often be found using modular arithmetic.

SECTION 10.3   EXERCISES

Concept/Writing Exercises

1. What does a *modulo m* system consist of?

2. **a)** Explain the meaning of the statement, "*a* is congruent to *b* modulo *m*."
   b) Explain the meaning of $13 \equiv 3 \pmod 5$.

3. In a modulo 5 system, how many modulo classes will there be? Present a table similar to Table 10.12 on page 580 showing elements from each class.

4. In general, for a modulo *m* system, how are modulo classes developed?

5. In a modulo 12 system, how many modulo classes will there be? Explain.

6. In a modulo n system, how many modulo classes will there be? Explain.

7. Consider $27 \equiv ? \pmod 5$. Which of the following values could replace the question mark and result in a true statement? Explain.
   a) 20   **b)** 2   **c)** 12   **d)** 107

8. Consider $106 \equiv ? \pmod 7$. Which of the following values could replace the question mark and result in a true statement? Explain.
   a) 83   **b)** 71   **c)** 7   **d)** 22

Practice the Skills

In Exercises 9–16, assume that Sunday is represented as day 0, Monday is represented by day 1, and so on. If today is Thursday (day 4), determine the day of the week it will be at the end of each period. Assume no leap years.

9. 30 days   **10.** 161 days   **11.** 365 days

12. 2 years   **13.** 3 years, 34 days   **14.** 463 days

15. 728 days   **16.** 3 years, 27 days

In Exercises 17–24, consider 12 months to be a modulo 12 system. If it is currently October, determine the month it will be in the specified number of months.

17. 9 months   **18.** 36 months

19. 3 years, 5 months   **20.** 4 years, 8 months

21. 83 months   **22.** 7 years

23. 105 months   **24.** 5 years, 9 months

In Exercises 25–36, determine what number the sum, difference, or product is congruent to in mod 5.

25. $8 + 6$ **26.** $5 + 10$

27. $1 + 9 + 12$ **28.** $9 - 3$

29. $5 - 12$ **30.** $7 \cdot 4$

31. $8 \cdot 9$ **32.** $10 - 15$

33. $4 - 8$ **34.** $3 - 7$

35. $(15 \cdot 4) - 8$ **36.** $(4 - 9) \cdot 7$

In Exercises 37–50, find the modulo class to which each number belongs for the indicated modulo system.

37. 15, mod 5   **38.** 23, mod 7   **39.** 84, mod 12

40. 43, mod 6   **41.** 60, mod 9   **42.** 75, mod 8

43. 30, mod 7   **44.** 53, mod 4   **45.** −5, mod 7

46. −7, mod 4   **47.** −13, mod 11   **48.** −11, mod 13

49. 135, mod 10   **50.** −12, mod 4

In Exercises 51–66, find all replacements (less than the modulus) for the question mark that make the statement true.

51. $3 + 4 \equiv ? \pmod 6$ **52.** $? + 5 \equiv 3 \pmod 8$

53. $2 + ? \equiv 4 \pmod 5$ **54.** $4 + ? \equiv 3 \pmod 6$

55. $4 - ? \equiv 5 \pmod 6$ **56.** $4 \cdot 5 \equiv ? \pmod 7$

57. $5 \cdot ? \equiv 7 \pmod 9$ **58.** $3 \cdot ? \equiv 5 \pmod 6$

59. $3 \cdot ? \equiv 1 \pmod 6$ **60.** $3 \cdot ? \equiv 3 \pmod{12}$

61. $4 \cdot ? \equiv 4 \pmod{10}$ **62.** $? - 6 \equiv 4 \pmod 8$

63. $? - 7 \equiv 9 \pmod{12}$ **64.** $6 - ? \equiv 8 \pmod 9$

65. $3 \cdot ? \equiv 0 \pmod{10}$ **66.** $4 \cdot ? \equiv 5 \pmod 8$

Problem Solving

67. *Presidential Elections* The upcoming presidential election years are 2004, 2008, 2012, ...
    a) List the next five presidential election years after 2012.
    b) What will be the first election year after the year 3000?
    c) List the election years between the years 2550 and 2575.

68. *Flight Schedules* A pilot is scheduled to fly for 5 consecutive days and rest for 3 consecutive days. If today is the second day of her rest shift, determine whether she will be flying or resting
    a) 60 days from today.
    b) 90 days from today.
    c) 240 days from today.
    d) Was she flying 6 days ago?
    e) Was she flying 20 days ago?

69. *Workout Schedule* A tennis pro's workout schedule is to have both morning and afternoon practice for 3 days, rest for 1 day, have only morning practice for 2 days, rest for 2 days, and then start the cycle again. If the tennis pro is on her rest for 1 day part of the schedule, determine what she will be doing
    a) 28 days from today.
    b) 60 days from today.
    c) 127 days from today.
    d) Will the tennis pro have a day off 82 days from today?

70. *Physical Therapy* A man has an Achilles' tendon injury and is receiving physical therapy. He must have physical therapy twice a day for 5 days, physical therapy once a day

for 3 days, 2 days off, and then the cycle begins again. If he is in his second day of his twice a day therapy cycle, determine what he will be doing

a) 20 days from today.

b) 49 days from today.

c) 103 days from today.

d) Will the man have a day off 78 days from today?

71. *The Weekend Off* A manager of a theater has both Saturday and Sunday off every 7 weeks. This is week 2 of the 7 weeks.

a) Determine the number of weeks before she will have both Saturday and Sunday off.

b) Will she have both Saturday and Sunday off 25 weeks from this week?

c) What is the first week, after 50 weeks from this week, that she will have both Saturday and Sunday off?

72. *Nursing Shifts* A nurse's work pattern at Community Hospital consists of working the 7 A.M.–3 P.M. shift for 3 weeks and then the 3 P.M.–11 P.M. shift for 2 weeks.

a) If this is the third week of the pattern, what shift will the nurse be working 6 weeks from now?

b) If this is the fourth week of the pattern, what shift will the nurse be working 7 weeks from now?

c) If this is the first week of the pattern, what shift will the nurse be working 11 weeks from now?

73. *Restaurant Rotation* A waiter at a restaurant works both daytime and evening shifts. He works daytime for 5 consecutive days, then evenings for 3 consecutive days, then daytime for 4 consecutive days, then evenings for 2 consecutive days. Then the rotation starts again. If this is day 2 of the 5-day consecutive daytime shift, determine whether he will be working the daytime or evening shift

a) 20 days from today.

b) 52 days from today.

c) 365 days from today.

74. *A Truck Driver's Schedule* A truck driver's routine is as follows: Drive 3 days from New York to Chicago, rest 1 day in Chicago, drive 3 days from Chicago to Los Angeles, rest 2 days in Los Angeles, drive 5 days to return to New York, rest 3 days in New York. Then the cycle begins again. If the truck driver is starting his trip to Chicago today, what will he be doing

a) 30 days from today?

b) 70 days from today?

c) 2 years from today?

75. **a)** Construct a modulo 4 addition table.

b) Is the system closed? Explain.

c) Is there an identity element for the system? If so, what is it?

d) Does every element in the system have an inverse? If so, list the elements and their inverses.

e) The associative property holds for the system. Give an example.

f) Does the commutative property hold for the system? Give an example.

g) Is the system a commutative group?

h) Will every modulo system under the operation of addition be a commutative group? Explain.

76. Construct a modulo 8 addition table. Repeat parts (b)–(h) in Exercise 75.

77. **a)** Construct a modulo 4 multiplication table.

b) Is the system closed under the operation of multiplication?

c) Is there an identity element in the system? If so, what is it?

d) Does every element in the system have an inverse? Make a list showing the elements that have a multiplicative inverse and list the inverses.

e) The associative property holds for the system. Give an example.

f) Does the commutative property hold for the system? Give an example.

g) Is this mathematical system a commutative group? Explain.

78. Construct a modulo 7 multiplication table. Repeat parts (b)–(g) in Exercise 77.

Challenge Problems/Group Activities

We have not discussed division in modular arithmetic. With what number or numbers, if any, can you replace the question marks to make the statement true? The question mark must be a number less than the modulo. Hint: Use the fact that $\frac{a}{b} \equiv c \ (mod\ m)$ means $a \equiv b \cdot c \ (mod\ m)$ and use trial and error to obtain your answer.

79. $5 \div 7 \equiv ? \ (\text{mod } 9)$ **80.** $? \div 5 \equiv 5 \ (\text{mod } 9)$

81. $? \div ? \equiv 1 \ (\text{mod } 4)$ **82.** $1 \div 2 \equiv ? \ (\text{mod } 5)$

In Exercises 83–85, solve for x where k is any counting number.

83. $5k \equiv x \ (\text{mod } 5)$ **84.** $5k + 4 \equiv x \ (\text{mod } 5)$

85. $4k - 2 \equiv x \ (\text{mod } 4)$

86. Find the smallest positive number divisible by 5 to which 2 is congruent in modulo 6.

Recreational Mathematics

87. *Rolling Wheel* The wheel shown below is to be rolled. Before the wheel is rolled, it is resting on number 0. The wheel will be rolled at a uniform rate of one complete roll every 4 minutes. In exactly 1 year (not a leap year), what number will be at the bottom of the wheel?

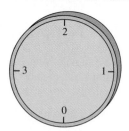

88. *Climbing a Mountain Range* A person climbs a uniform mountain range like the one shown below. Assume that the mountain range continues indefinitely.

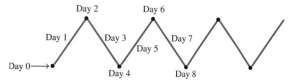

On day 0, the person rests at the bottom of a mountain in the mountain range. On day 1, the person climbs the mountain and reaches halfway up the mountain. On day 2, the person reaches the top and rests for the balance of the day. On day 3, the person starts down the mountain, and reaches halfway down the mountain. On day 4, the person reaches the bottom of the mountain and rests for the balance of the day. Then the process starts again on the next mountain in the mountain range. If today is day 4, where in the mountain range (bottom of a mountain, halfway up a mountain, halfway down a mountain, or the top of a mountain) will the person be after 1 year 21 days?

89. *Deciphering a Code* One important use of modular arithmetic is in coding. One type of coding circle is given in Fig. 10.6. To use it, the person you are sending the message to must know the code key to decipher the code. The code key to this message is *j*. Can you decipher this code? (*Hint:* Subtract the code key from the code numbers.)

23   11   3   18   10   19   2   10   16   4   24

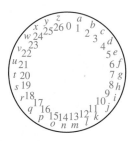

Figure 10.6

Internet/Research Activity

90. The concept and notation for modular systems were introduced by Carl Friedrich Gauss in 1801. Write a paper on Gauss's contribution to modular systems.

CHAPTER 10 SUMMARY

IMPORTANT FACTS

If the elements in a table are symmetric about the main diagonal, then the system is commutative.

	Addition	Multiplication
Commutative property	$a + b = b + a$	$a \cdot b = b \cdot a$
Associative property	$(a + b) + c$ $= a + (b + c)$	$(a \cdot b) \cdot c = a \cdot (b \cdot c)$

a is **congruent** to *b* modulo *m*, written $a \equiv b \pmod{m}$, if *a* and *b* have the same remainder when divided by *m*.

Properties of a group and a commutative group

A mathematical system is a group if the first four conditions hold and a commutative group if all five conditions hold.

Commutative Group / Group

1. The set of elements is *closed* under the given operation.
2. An *identity element* exists for the set.
3. Every element in the set has an *inverse*.
4. The set of elements is *associative* under the given operation.
5. The set of elements is *commutative* under the given operation.

CHAPTER 10   REVIEW EXERCISES

10.1, 10.2

1. List the parts of a mathematical system.

2. What is a binary operation?

3. Are the integers closed under the operation of addition? Explain.

4. Are the natural numbers closed under the operation of subtraction? Explain.

Determine the sum or difference in clock 12 arithmetic.

5. $9 + 10$ **6.** $5 + 12$ **7.** $8 - 10$

8. $4 + 7 + 9$ **9.** $7 - 4 + 6$ **10.** $2 - 8 - 7$

11. List the properties of a group, and explain what each property means.

12. What is an abelian group?

In Exercises 13 and 14, explain your answer.

13. Determine whether the set of positive integers under the operation of addition forms a group.

14. Determine whether the set of integers under the operation of multiplication forms a group.

15. Determine whether the set of rational numbers under the operation of addition forms a group.

16. Determine whether the set of rational numbers under the operation of multiplication forms a group.

In Exercises 17–19, for the mathematical system, determine which of the five properties of a commutative group do not hold.

17.

●	R	S	⊗
R	R	⊗	S
S	⊗	S	R
⊗	S	R	⊗

18.

□	!	?	Δ	*p*
!	?	Δ	!	*p*
?	Δ	*p*	?	!
Δ	!	?	Δ	*p*
p	*p*	!	*p*	Δ

19.

?	4	#	L	P
4	P	4	#	L
#	4	#	L	P
L	#	L	P	4
P	L	P	4	L

20. Consider the following mathematical system in which the operation is associative.

⌐/	⊢	⊙	?	Δ
⊢	⊢	⊙	?	Δ
⊙	⊙	?	Δ	⊢
?	?	Δ	⊢	⊙
Δ	Δ	⊢	⊙	?

a) What are the elements of the set in this mathematical system?

b) What is the binary operation?

c) Is the system closed? Explain.

d) Is there an identity element for the system under the given operation?

e) Does every element in the system have an inverse? If so, give each element and its corresponding inverse.

f) Give an example to illustrate the associative property.

g) Is the system commutative? Give an example.

h) Is this mathematical system a commutative group? Explain.

10.3

In Exercises 21–30, find the modulo class to which the number belongs for the indicated modulo system.

21. 21, mod 3   **22.** 31, mod 8

23. 31, mod 6   **24.** 59, mod 8

25. 82, mod 13   **26.** 54, mod 4

27. 52, mod 12   **28.** 54, mod 14

29. 97, mod 11   **30.** 42, mod 11

In Exercises 31–40, find all replacements (less than the modulus) for the question mark that make the statement true.

31. $5 + 8 \equiv ? \pmod 9$ **32.** $? - 3 \equiv 0 \pmod 5$

33. $4 \cdot ? \equiv 3 \pmod 6$ **34.** $6 - ? \equiv 5 \pmod 7$

35. $? \cdot 4 \equiv 0 \pmod 8$ **36.** $10 \cdot 7 \equiv ? \pmod{12}$

37. $3 - 5 \equiv ? \pmod 7$ **38.** $? \cdot 7 \equiv 3 \pmod{10}$

39. $5 \cdot ? \equiv 3 \pmod 8$ **40.** $7 \cdot ? \equiv 2 \pmod 9$

41. Construct a modulo 6 addition table. Then determine whether the modulo 6 system forms a commutative group under the operation of addition.

42. Construct a modulo 4 multiplication table. Then determine whether the modulo 4 system forms a commutative group under the operation of multiplication.

43. *Work Pattern* Toni Ranier's work pattern at the fast-food restaurant is as follows: She works 3 evenings, has 2 evenings off, then works 2 evenings, and then has 3 evenings off; then the pattern repeats. If today is the first day of the work pattern,

a) will Toni be working 18 days from today?
b) will Toni have the evening off for a party that is being held in 38 days?

CHAPTER 10 TEST

1. What is a mathematical system?

2. List the requirements needed for a mathematical system to be a commutative group.

3. Is the set of the whole numbers a commutative group under the operation of addition? Explain your answer completely.

4. Develop a clock 5 arithmetic addition table.

5. Is clock 5 arithmetic under the operation of addition a commutative group? Assume that the associative property holds. Explain your answer completely.

Determine the following in clock 5 arithmetic.

6. $4 + 3 + 2$

7. $2 - 5$

8. Consider the mathematical system

□	*W*	*S*	*T*	*R*
W	*T*	*R*	*W*	*S*
S	*R*	*W*	*S*	*T*
T	*W*	*S*	*T*	*R*
R	*S*	*T*	*R*	*W*

a) What is the binary operation?
b) Is this system closed? Explain.
c) Is there an identity element for this system under the given operation? Explain.
d) What is the inverse of the element *R*?
e) What is $(T \,\square\, R) \,\square\, W$?

In Exercises 9 and 10, determine whether the mathematical system is a commutative group. Explain your answer completely.

9.

*	*a*	*b*	*c*
a	*a*	*b*	*c*
b	*b*	*b*	*a*
c	*c*	*a*	*d*

10.

?	1	2	3
1	3	1	2
2	1	2	3
3	2	3	1

11. Determine whether the mathematical system is a commutative group. Assume that the associative property holds. Explain your answer.

○	@	$	&	%
@	%	@	$	&
$	@	$	&	%
&	$	&	%	@
%	&	%	@	$

In Exercises 12 and 13, determine the modulo class to which the number belongs for the indicated modulo system.

12. 64, mod 9   **13.** 58, mod 11

In Exercises 14–18, find all replacements for the question mark, less than the modulus, that make the statement true.

14. $7 + 7 \equiv ? \pmod 8$ **15.** $? - 3 \equiv 4 \pmod 5$

16. $3 - ? \equiv 7 \pmod 9$ **17.** $4 \cdot 2 \equiv ? \pmod 6$

18. $3 \cdot ? \equiv 2 \pmod 6$

19. To what number is 103 congruent to in modulo 7?

20. **a)** Construct a modulo 5 multiplication table.
    b) Is this mathematical system a commutative group? Explain your answer completely.

GROUP PROJECTS

1. *Rotating a Square* The square $ABCD$ below has a pin through it at point P so that the square can be rotated in a clockwise direction. The mathematical system consists of the set $\{A, B, C, D\}$ and the operation ♣. The elements of the set represent different rotations of the square clockwise, as follows.

A = rotate about the point P clockwise 90°

B = rotate about the point P clockwise 180°

C = rotate about the point P clockwise 270°

D = rotate about the point P clockwise 360°

The operation ♣ means *followed by*. For example, A ♣ B means a clockwise rotation of 90° followed by a clockwise rotation of 180° or a clockwise rotation of 270°. Since C represents a clockwise rotation of 270°, we write A ♣ $B = C$. This and two other results are shown in the following table.

♣	A	B	C	D
A		C		
B			A	
C	D			
D				

Complete the table and determine if the mathematical system is a commutative group. Explain.

2. *Product of Zero* In arithmetic and algebra the statement, "If $a \cdot b = 0$, then $a = 0$ or $b = 0$" is true. That is, for the product of two numbers to be 0, at least one of the factors must be 0. Can the product of two nonzero numbers equal 0 in a specific modulo system? If so, in what type of modulo systems can this result occur?

   a) Construct multiplication tables for modulo systems 3–9.
   b) Which, if any, of the multiplication tables in part (a) have products equal to 0 when neither factor is 0?
   c) Which, if any, of the multiplication tables in part (a) have products equal to 0 only when at least one factor is 0?
   d) Using the results in parts (b) and (c), can you write a conjecture as to which modulo systems have a product of 0 when neither factor is 0?

3. *Conjecture about Multiplication Inverses* Are there certain modulo systems where all numbers have multiplicative inverses?

   a) If you have not worked Group Projects Exercise 2, construct multiplication tables for modulo systems 3–9.
   b) Which of the multiplication tables in part (a) contain multiplicative inverses for all nonzero numbers?
   c) Which, if any, of the multiplication tables in part (a) do not contain multiplicative inverses for all nonzero numbers?
   d) Using the results in parts (b) and (c), can you write a conjecture as to which modulo systems contain multiplicative inverses for all nonzero numbers?

To some extent, money is a central aspect of everyone's life. Being knowledgeable about consumer mathematics can help you reach your financial goals.

CONSUMER MATHEMATICS

Managing your money takes much thought and planning. Your daily needs, such as food and transportation, as well as your monthly and yearly needs, such as car payments, rent or mortgage, and utility bills, must all be paid. At the same time, you should consider your long-term goals such as saving enough for large purchases—a new car or a new house—as well as for unexpected emergencies and for retirement. The decisions you make on a daily basis affect your ability to reach your long-term goals. This chapter will provide information on several areas of consumer mathematics, including loans, interest rates, and mortgages. A solid understanding of these and other consumer mathematics topics can help you achieve your financial goals.

11.1 PERCENT

The study of mathematics is crucial to understanding how to make better financial decisions. A basic topic necessary for understanding the material in this chapter is percent. This section will give you a better understanding of the meaning of percent and its use in real-life situations.

The word *percent* comes from the Latin *per centum,* meaning "per hundred." A *percent* is simply a ratio of some number to 100. Thus, $\frac{15}{100} = 15\%$, and $\frac{x}{100} = x\%$.

Percents are useful in making comparisons. Consider Ross, who took two psychology tests. On the first test Ross answered 18 of the 20 questions correctly, and on the second test he answered 23 of 25 questions correctly. On which test did he have the higher score? One way to compare the results is to write ratios of the number of correct answers to the number of questions on the test, and then convert the ratios to percents. We can find the grades in percent for each test by (a) writing a ratio of the number of correct answers to the total number of questions, (b) rewriting these ratios with a denominator of 100, and (c) expressing the ratios as percents.

Test 1   (a)   (b)   (c)

$$\frac{\text{Number of correct answers}}{\text{Number of questions on the test}} = \frac{18}{20} = \frac{18 \times 5}{20 \times 5} = \frac{90}{100} = 90\%$$

Test 2   (a)   (b)   (c)

$$\frac{\text{Number of correct answers}}{\text{Number of questions on the test}} = \frac{23}{25} = \frac{23 \times 4}{25 \times 4} = \frac{92}{100} = 92\%$$

By changing the results of both tests to percents, we have a common standard for comparison. The results show that Ross scored 90% on the first test and 92% on the second test. Thus, he had a higher score on the second test.

Another procedure to change a fraction to a percent follows.

Procedure to Change a Fraction to a Percent

1. Divide the numerator by the denominator.
2. Multiply the quotient by 100 (which has the effect of moving the decimal point two places to the right).
3. Add a percent sign.

Note that steps 2 and 3 together are the equivalent of multiplying by 100%. Since 100% = 100/100 = 1, we are not changing the *value* of the number, we are simply changing the number to a percent.

EXAMPLE 1   *Converting a Fraction to a Percent*

Change $\frac{17}{20}$ to a percent.

SOLUTION: Follow the steps in the procedure box.

1. $17 \div 20 = 0.85$ 2. $0.85 \times 100 = 85$ 3. 85%

Thus, $\frac{17}{20} = 85\%$

Procedure to Change a Decimal Number to a Percent

1. Multiply the decimal number by 100.
2. Add a percent sign.

The procedure for changing a decimal number to a percent is equivalent to moving the decimal point two places to the right and adding a percent sign.

EXAMPLE 2   *Converting a Decimal Number to a Percent*

Change 0.235 to percent.

SOLUTION: $0.235 = (0.235 \times 100)\% = 23.5\%$ ▲

To change a number given as a percent to a decimal number, follow this procedure.

Procedure to Change a Percent to a Decimal Number

1. Divide the number by 100.
2. Remove the percent sign.

The procedure for changing a percent to a decimal number is equivalent to moving the decimal point two places to the left and removing the percent sign. Another way to remember this is: percent means per hundred (or to *divide by 100*).

EXAMPLE 3   *Converting a Percent to a Decimal Number*

a) Change 35% to a decimal number.

b) Change $\frac{1}{2}\%$ to a decimal number.

SOLUTION:

a) $35\% = \dfrac{35}{100} = 0.35$. Thus, $35\% = 0.35$.

b) $\dfrac{1}{2}\% = 0.5\% = \dfrac{0.5}{100} = 0.005$. Thus, $\dfrac{1}{2}\% = 0.005$.   ▲

EXAMPLE 4   *How Old Is Old?*

A Yahoo! Question of the Week asked, "At what age do you consider someone old?" Out of the 3496 people who responded, 1017 said age 80 is old. What percent of respondents feel that age 80 is old?

SOLUTION: To find the percent that feel age 80 is old, divide the number of those who responded that age 80 is old by the total number of respondents. Then move the decimal point two places to the right and add a percent sign:

$$\text{Percent who feel age 80 is old} = \frac{1017}{3496} \approx 0.2909 = 29.09\%$$

Thus, about 29.1% (to the nearest tenth of a percent) feel that age 80 is old.   ▲

All answers in this section will be given to the nearest tenth of a percent. When rounding answers to the nearest tenth of a percent, we carry the division to four places after the decimal point (ten-thousandths) and then round to the nearest thousandths position.

EXAMPLE 5   *SARS Cases*

According to the World Health Organization, on May 1, 2003, there were 5865 reported worldwide cases of severe acute respiratory syndrome (SARS). Of these cases, 5238 were in China, 201 were in Singapore, 147 were in Canada, and 279 were in other countries.* Determine the percent of SARS cases in each of the following countries: China, Singapore, Canada, and other countries.

SOLUTION: To find each percent, divide the number of cases in each country by the total number of cases.

$$\text{Percent of cases in China} = \frac{5238}{5865} \approx 0.8931 \approx 89.3\%$$

$$\text{Percent of cases in Singapore} = \frac{201}{5865} \approx 0.0343 \approx 3.4\%$$

$$\text{Percent of cases in Canada} = \frac{147}{5865} \approx 0.0251 \approx 2.5\%$$

$$\text{Percent of cases in other countries} = \frac{279}{5865} \approx 0.0476 \approx 4.8\%$$

The sum of the percents, 89.3% + 3.4% + 2.5% + 4.8%, equals 100%.   ▲

The percent increase or decrease, or percent change, over a period of time is found by the following formula:

$$\textbf{Percent change} = \frac{\left(\begin{array}{c}\text{amount in}\\\text{latest period}\end{array}\right) - \left(\begin{array}{c}\text{amount in}\\\text{previous period}\end{array}\right)}{\text{amount in previous period}} \times 100$$

If the amount in the latest period is greater than the amount in the previous period, the answer will be positive and will indicate a percent increase. If the amount in the latest period is smaller than the amount in the previous period, the answer will be negative and will indicate a percent decrease.

EXAMPLE 6   *Most Improved Baseball Record*

In 2002, the Major League baseball team with the most improved record was the Anaheim Angels. In 2001, the Angels won 75 games. In 2002, the Angels won 99 games. Find the percent increase in games won from 2001 to 2002.

---

*On May 1, 2003, there were 54 reported cases of SARS in the United States.

SOLUTION: The previous period is 2001 and the latest period is 2002.

$$\text{Percent change} = \frac{\left(\begin{array}{c}\text{amount in}\\\text{latest period}\end{array}\right) - \left(\begin{array}{c}\text{amount in}\\\text{previous period}\end{array}\right)}{\text{amount in previous period}} \times 100$$

$$= \frac{99 - 75}{75} \times 100$$

$$= \frac{24}{75} \times 100$$

$$= 0.32 \times 100$$

$$= 32$$

Therefore, there was a 32% increase in the number of games won by the Angels from 2001 to 2002.   ▲

EXAMPLE 7   *Labor Union Membership*

In 1991, there were approximately 16,568,000 labor union members in the United States. By 2001, this number had dropped to 16,275,000 (see the figure in the margin). Find the percent change in labor union membership from 1991 to 2001.

SOLUTION: The previous period is 1991 and the latest period is 2001.

$$\text{Percent change} = \frac{16,275,000 - 16,568,000}{16,568,000} \times 100$$

$$= \frac{-293,000}{16,568,000} \times 100$$

$$\approx -0.0177 \times 100$$

$$\approx -1.8$$

Thus, union membership decreased by about 1.8% over this period.   ▲

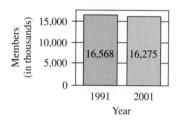

Labor Union Membership

Source: U.S. Bureau of Labor Statistics

A similar formula is used to calculate percent markup or markdown on cost. A positive answer indicates a markup and a negative answer indicates a markdown.

> **Percent markup on cost** $= \dfrac{\text{selling price} - \text{dealer's cost}}{\text{dealer's cost}} \times 100$

EXAMPLE 8   *Determining Percent Markup*

Holdren Hardware stores pay $48.76 for glass fireplace screens. They regularly sell them for $79.88. At a sale they sell them for $69.99. Find

a) the percent markup on the regular price.

b) the percent markup on the sale price.

c) the percent decrease of the sale price from the regular price.

To Insure Promptness

Tꜣhe practice of tipping began in an English coffeehouse in the eighteenth century. Legend has it that a hurried businessman dropped a few pence on the table as a friendly incentive to the waiter. In fact, the coffeehouses eventually installed small collection boxes marked **T**o **I**nsure **P**romptness. The tip, as it became known, was paid before, not after, the meal. Today, there are many books and Internet web sites devoted to the guidelines of tipping. For example, according to the Original Tipping Page (*www.tipping.org*), it is proper to tip waiters and waitresses 15–20% of the total restaurant bill. Hair stylists should be tipped 15% of the total bill and pizza delivery persons should receive $1–$3, depending on the distance driven. Skycaps at the airport should be tipped at least $1 per bag and newspaper delivery persons should receive $15–$25 at holiday time.

SOLUTION:

a) We determine the percent markup on the regular price as follows.

$$\text{Percent markup} = \frac{\text{selling price} - \text{dealer's cost}}{\text{dealer's cost}} \times 100$$

$$= \frac{\$79.88 - \$48.76}{\$48.76} \times 100$$

$$\approx 0.6382 \times 100$$

$$\approx 63.8$$

Thus, the percent markup on the regular price was about 63.8%.

b) We determine the percent markup on the sale price as follows.

$$\text{Percent markup} = \frac{\$69.99 - \$48.76}{\$48.76} \times 100$$

$$\approx 0.4354 \times 100$$

$$\approx 43.5$$

Thus, the percent markup on the sale price was about 43.5%.

c) Based on the regular price, we determine the percent decrease of the sale price.

$$\text{Percent decrease} = \frac{\$69.99 - \$79.88}{\$79.88} \times 100$$

$$\approx -0.1238 \times 100$$

$$\approx -12.4$$

The sale price is about 12.4% lower than the regular price.   ▲

In daily life we may need to know how to solve any one of the following three types of problems involving percent:

1. What is a 15% tip on a restaurant bill of $24.66? The problem can be stated as

   15% of $24.66 is what number?

2. If Nancy Johnson made a sale of $500 and received a commission of $25, what percent of the sale is the commission? The problem can be stated as

   What percent of $500 is $25?

3. If the price of a jacket was reduced by 25% or $12.50, what was the original price of the jacket? The problem can be stated as

   25% of what number is 12.50?

To answer these questions we will write each problem as an equation. The word *is* means "is equal to," or =. In each problem we will represent the unknown quantity with the letter x. Therefore, the preceding problems can be represented as

1. 15% of $24.66 = x 2. x% of $500 = $25   3. 25% of x = $12.50

The word *of* in such problems indicates multiplication. To solve each problem, change the percent to a decimal number and express the problem as an equation; then solve the equation for the variable x. The solutions follow.

598   CHAPTER 11 CONSUMER MATHEMATICS

1. 15% of $24.66 = x

    $$0.15(24.66) = x \qquad \text{15\% is written as 0.15 in decimal form.}$$
    $$3.699 = x$$

    Since 15% of $24.66 is $3.699, the tip would be $3.70.

2. x% of $500 = $25

    $$(0.01x)500 = 25 \qquad \text{x\% is written as 0.01x in decimal form.}$$
    $$5x = 25$$
    $$\frac{5x}{5} = \frac{25}{5}$$
    $$x = 5$$

    Since 5% of $500 is $25, the commission is 5% of the sale.

3. 25% of x = $12.50

    $$0.25(x) = 12.50 \qquad \text{25\% is written as 0.25 in decimal form.}$$
    $$\frac{0.25x}{0.25} = \frac{12.50}{0.25}$$
    $$x = 50$$

    Since 25% of $50 is $12.50, the original price of the jacket was $50.00.

EXAMPLE 9   *Down Payment on a House*

Melissa Bell wishes to buy a house for $87,000. To obtain a mortgage, she needs to pay 20% of the selling price as a down payment. Determine the amount of Melissa's down payment.

SOLUTION: We want to find the amount of the down payment. Let x = the down payment. Then

$$x = 20\% \text{ of the selling price}$$
$$= 20\% \text{ of } \$87,000$$
$$= 0.20(87,000)$$
$$= 17,400.$$

Melissa will have a down payment of $17,400.   ▲

EXAMPLE 10   *Chess Tournaments*

In 2002, about 50,000 out of the 88,000 U.S. Chess Federation (USCF) members competed in USCF tournaments. What percent of USCF members competed in USCF tournaments?

SOLUTION: We need to determine what percent of 88,000 is 50,000. Let x = percent of USCF members who competed in USCF tournaments. Then

$$x\% \text{ of } 88,000 = 50,000$$
$$0.01x(88,000) = 50,000$$
$$880x = 50,000$$
$$x = \frac{50,000}{880}$$
$$x \approx 56.8$$

Therefore, about 56.8% of USCF members competed in USCF tournaments in 2002.

Mexico City, Mexico

---EXAMPLE 11   *Population of Mexico*

About 35,640,000, or 36%, of Mexico's population is younger than 15 years old. What is the population of Mexico?

SOLUTION: This problem can be stated as, 36% of what number is 35,640,000? Let x = the population of Mexico. Then

$$36\% \text{ of } x = 35,640,000$$
$$0.36x = 35,640,000$$
$$x = \frac{35,640,000}{0.36}$$
$$x = 99,000,000$$

Therefore, the population of Mexico is about 99,000,000 people.

SECTION 11.1   EXERCISES

Concept/Writing Exercises

1. What is a percent?
2. Explain how to change a percent to a decimal number.
3. Explain how to change a fraction to a percent.
4. Explain how to change a decimal number to a percent.
5. Explain how to determine percent change.
6. Explain how to determine percent markup on cost.

Practice the Skills

In Exercises 7–14, change the number to a percent. Express your answer to the nearest tenth of a percent.

7. $\frac{1}{2}$ 8. $\frac{1}{4}$ 9. $\frac{2}{5}$

10. $\frac{7}{8}$ 11. 0.007654   12. 0.5688

13. 3.78   14. 13.678

In Exercises 15–24, change the percent to a decimal number.

15. 4%   16. 6.9%   17. 1.34%   18. 0.0005%

19. $\frac{1}{4}\%$ 20. $\frac{3}{8}\%$ 21. $\frac{1}{5}\%$ 22. 135.9%

23. 1%   24. 0.50%

Problem Solving

For Exercises 25–46, round answers to the nearest tenth of a percent.

25. *Potassium* The U.S. Department of Agriculture's recommended daily allowance (USRDA) of potassium for adults is 3500 mg. One serving of Cheerios provides 95 mg of potassium. What percent of the USRDA of potassium does one serving of Cheerios provide?

26. *Disney Tickets* As of April 18, 2003, tickets for one day at Disney World are $50 for adults and $40 for children. In addition, if the tickets are purchased at Disney World, visitors must pay a 6% sales tax and a 6% tourist tax. However, if the tickets are purchased at any AAA office in Florida, visitors only pay the 6% sales tax. How much can Clarence and Joy Greenhalgh and their two children Martin and Thompson save by purchasing their tickets at a Florida AAA office?

27. *Reduced Fat Milk* One serving of whole milk contains 8 g of fat. Reduced-fat milk contains 41.25% less fat per serving than whole milk. How many grams of fat does one serving of reduced-fat milk contain?

28. *River Pollution* In a study of U.S. rivers, 693,905 miles of river were studied. According to the U.S. Environmental Protection Agency, it was found that 36% of the total miles of rivers studied had impaired water quality. How many miles of rivers had impaired quality?

Kentucky Lottery In Exercises 29–32, use the circle graph to answer the questions. In 2001, the Kentucky Lottery had total sales of $591 million. The areas where this money was used along with the corresponding percents are represented in the circle graph below.

2001 Kentucky Lottery Expenditures

Source: Kentucky Lottery Internet Website

29. Determine the amount used on operating expenses.

30. Determine the amount used on retailer commissions.

31. Determine the amount used on state revenue.

32. Determine the amount used on winnings.

Inventory Shrinkage In Exercises 33–36, use the circle graph to answer the questions. In 2002, U.S. companies lost $32.3 billion due to "inventory shrinkage." Each sector of the circle graph shows the percent of this total due to each of four sources.

Inventory Shrinkage

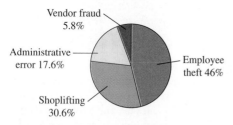

Source: Center for Retailing Education,
University of Florida

33. Determine the amount lost to administrative error.

34. Determine the amount lost to vendor fraud.

35. Determine the amount lost to shoplifting.

36. Determine the amount lost to employee theft.

Top Five Advertisers In Exercises 37–40, use the circle graph to answer the questions. The top five advertisers spent $8105 million in 2001.

**Top Five Advertisers in 2001
(in millions of dollars)**

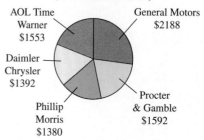

Source: Competitive Media Reporting

37. What percent of the $8105 million did AOL Time Warner spend?

38. What percent of the $8105 million did DaimlerChrysler spend?

39. What percent of the $8105 million did Procter & Gamble spend?

40. What percent of the $8105 million did General Motors spend?

41. *Decreasing Population* In 1990, the population of Pittsfield, Massachusetts, was 48,622. In 2000, the population had decreased to 45,793. Determine the percent decrease in Pittsfield's population from 1990 to 2000.

42. *Increasing Population* The population of the United States rose from approximately 248.7 million in 1990 to approximately 288.4 million in 2002.
   a) Determine the percent increase in population from 1990 to 2002.
   b) What will the population be in the year 2014 if it increases at the same percent as it did from 1990 to 2002?

43. *California Milk Production* The graph shows milk production in California for the years 1960, 1970, 1980, 1990, and 2000.

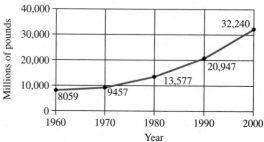

Source: U.S. Department of Agriculture

a) Determine the percent increase in California milk production from 1960 to 1970.
b) Determine the percent increase in California milk production from 1970 to 1980.
c) Determine the percent increase in California milk production from 1980 to 1990.
d) Determine the percent increase in California milk production from 1990 to 2000.

44. *IRS Audits* The graph shows the number of individual audits conducted by the Internal Revenue Service (IRS) during the years 1996, 1997, 1998, 1999, and 2000.

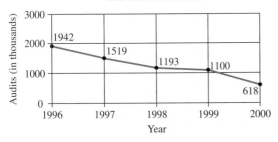

IRS Individual Audits

Source: Internal Revenue Service

a) Determine the percent decrease in the number of individual audits from 1996 to 1997.
b) Determine the percent decrease in the number of individual audits from 1997 to 1998.
c) Determine the percent decrease in the number of individual audits from 1998 to 1999.
d) Determine the percent decrease in the number of individual audits from 1999 to 2000.

45. *Dow Jones 2002* The following graph shows the closing Dow Jones Industrial Average (DJIA) for the months January through October 2002.

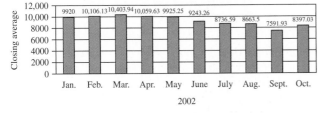

Dow Jones Industrial Average

Source: *New York Times*

a) Determine the percent increase in the DJIA from January 2002 through March 2002.
b) Determine the percent decrease in the DJIA from March 2002 through September 2002.
c) Determine the percent decrease in the DJIA from January 2002 through September 2002.
d) Determine the percent increase in the DJIA from September 2002 through October 2002.

46. *Presidential Salary* The following graph shows the annual salary for the president of the United States for selected years from 1789 to 2001.

Annual U.S. Presidential Salary

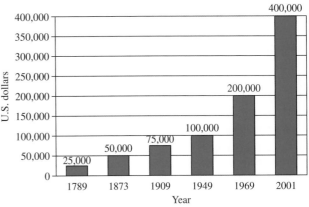

Source: *Congressional Quarterly*

a) Determine the percent increase in annual salary from 1789 to 1873.
b) Determine the percent increase in annual salary from 1909 to 1949.
c) Determine the percent increase in annual salary from 1969 to 2001.
d) Determine the percent increase in annual salary from 1789 to 2001.

In Exercises 47–52, determine the answer to the question.

47. What is 15% of $45.00?
48. What is 6.5% of $150.00?
49. What percent of 96 is 24?
50. What percent of 75 is 15?
51. Five percent of what number is 15?
52. Ten percent of what number is 75?

53. *Tax and Tip* According to the Original Tipping Page (*www.tipping.org*), it is proper to tip waiters and waitresses 15–20% of the total restaurant bill, *including the tax*. Mary and Keith's dinner costs $43.50 before tax, and the tax rate is 6%.
a) What is the tax on Mary and Keith's dinner?
b) What is the total bill, including tax, before the tip?
c) If Mary and Keith decide to tip 15% of the total bill, how much is the tip?
d) What is the total cost of the dinner including tax and tip?

54. *Fishing* The Gordon and Stallard Charter Fishing Boat Company has recently increased the number of crewmembers by 25%, or 10 crewmembers. What was the original number of crewmembers?

55. *Percentage of A's* In a mathematics class, eighteen students received an A on the third test, which is 150% of the students who received an A on the second test. How many students received an A on the second test?

56. *Employee Increase* The Fastlock Company hired 57 new employees, which increased its staff by 30%. What was the original number of employees?

57. *Salary Increase* Qami Brown's present salary is $36,500. He is getting an increase of 7% in his salary next year. What will his new salary be?

58. *Salad Dressing Preference* In a survey of 300 people, 17% prefer ranch dressing on their salad. How many people in the surveyed group prefer ranch dressing?

59. *Vacuum Cleaner Sales* A Kirby vacuum cleaner dealership sold 430 units in 2003 and 407 units in 2004. Find the percent increase or decrease in the number of units sold.

60. *Vacuum Cleaner Markup* If the Kirby dealership in Exercise 59 pays $320 for each unit and sells it for $699, what is the percent markup?

61. *Poverty in the United States* In the United States in 1993, there were 39.3 million people classified as living in poverty. In 2000, there were 31.1 million people classified as living in poverty. Find the percent decrease in the number of people living in poverty from 1993 to 2000.

62. *More Grandchildren* The Ngs had eight grandchildren in 2002. In 2003 they had 12 grandchildren. Find the percent increase in the number of grandchildren from 2002 to 2003.

63. *Television Sale* The regular price of a Phillips color TV is $539.62. During a sale, Hill TV is selling the TV for $439. Find the percent decrease in the price of this TV.

64. *Restaurant Markup* The cost of a fish dinner to the owner of the Golden Wharf restaurant is $7.95. The fish dinner is sold for $11.95. Find the percent markup.

65. *Truck Sale Profit* Bonnie James sold a truck and made a profit of $675. Her profit was 18% of the sale price. What was the sale price?

66. *Furniture Sale* Kane's Furniture Store advertised a table at a 15% discount. The original price was $115, and the sale price was $100. Was the sale price consistent with the ad? Explain.

67. *Reselling a Car* Quincy Carter purchased a used car for $1000. He decided to sell the car for 10% above his purchase price. Quincy could not sell the car so he reduced his asking price by 10%. If he sells the car at the reduced price, will he have a profit or a loss or will he break even? Explain how you arrived at your answer.

Challenge Problems/Group Activities

68. *Comparing Markdowns*
   a) A coat is marked down 10%, and the customer is given a second discount of 15%. Is that the same as a single discount of 25%? Explain.
   b) The regular price of a chair is $189.99. Determine the sale price of the chair if the regular price is reduced by 10% and this price is then reduced another 15%.
   c) Determine the sale price of the chair if the regular price of $189.99 is reduced by 25%.
   d) Examine the answers obtained in parts (b) and (c). Does your answer to part (a) appear to be correct? Explain.

69. *Selling Ties* The Tie Shoppe paid $5901.79 for a shipment of 500 ties and wants to make a profit of 40% of the cost on the whole shipment. The store is having two special sales. At the first sale it plans to sell 100 ties for $9.00 each, and at the second sale it plans to sell 150 ties for $12.50 each. What should be the selling price of the other 250 ties for the Tie Shoppe to make a 40% profit on the whole shipment?

Recreational Mathematics

70. In parts a) through d) determine which is the greater amount, and by how much.
   a) $100 increased by 25% or $200 decreased by 25%.
   b) $100 increased by 50% or $200 decreased by 50%.
   c) $100 increased by 100% or $200 decreased by 100%.

Internet/Research Activity

71. Find two circle graphs in newspapers, magazines, or on the Internet whose data are not given in percents. Redraw the graphs and label them with percents.

11.2 PERSONAL LOANS AND SIMPLE INTEREST

Often consumers want to buy clothing, appliances, or furniture but do not have the cash to do so. They then have to determine whether the cost of borrowing the money is worth the convenience or pleasure of having the item today versus waiting several months or years and paying cash. If you are faced with this choice, you may decide that you must have the item today and may choose to borrow the money from a bank or other lending institution. The money a bank is willing to lend you is called the amount of *credit* extended or the *principal of the loan*.

DID YOU KNOW

Seasonal Loan

The most common type of loan is the short-term (seasonal) loan. Originally, the loans were agricultural loans provided to farmers to plant their crops and see them through the period between planting and harvesting. In fact, "seed" loans were first recorded in ancient Babylonia.

The amount of credit and the interest rate that you may obtain depend on the assurance that you can give the lender that you will be able to repay the loan. Your credit is determined by your business reputation for honesty, by your earning power, and by what you can pledge as security to cover the loan. *Security* (or *collateral*) is anything of value pledged by the borrower that the lender may sell or keep if the borrower does not repay the loan. Acceptable security may be a business, a mortgage on a property, the title to an automobile, savings accounts, or stocks or bonds. The more marketable the security, the easier it is to obtain the loan, and in some cases marketability may help in getting a lower interest rate.

Bankers sometimes grant loans without security, but they require the signature of one or more other persons, called *cosigners*, who guarantee the loan will be repaid. For either of the two types of loans, the secured loan or the cosigner loan, the borrower (and cosigner, if there is one) must sign an agreement called a *personal note*. This document states the terms and conditions of the loan.

The most common way for individuals to borrow money is through an installment loan or using a credit card. (Installment loans and credit cards are discussed in Section 11.4.)

The concept of simple interest is essential to the understanding of installment buying. *Interest* is the money the borrower pays for the use of the lender's money. One type of interest is called simple interest. *Simple interest* is based on the entire amount of the loan for the total period of the loan. The formula used to find simple interest follows.

Simple Interest Formula

Interest = principal $\times$ rate $\times$ time

$$i = prt$$

In the simple interest formula the *principal*, p, is the amount of money lent, the *rate*, r, is the rate of interest expressed as a percent, and the *time*, t, is the number of days, months, or years for which the money will be lent. Time is expressed in the same period as the rate. For example, if the rate is 2% per month, the time must be expressed in months. Typically, rate means the annual rate unless otherwise stated. Principal and interest are expressed in dollars in the United States.

Ordinary Interest

The most common type of simple interest is called *ordinary interest*. For computing ordinary interest, each month has 30 days and a year has 12 months or 360 days. On the due date of a *simple interest note* the borrower must repay the principal plus the interest. (*Note:* Simple interest will mean ordinary interest unless stated otherwise.)

⌈EXAMPLE 1   *Calculating Interest and Payback Amount*

Chi Tran needs to borrow $1600 to have corrective eye surgery. From her credit union, she obtains a 9-month loan with an annual simple interest rate of 6.5%.

a) Calculate the simple interest on the loan.

b) Determine the amount (principal + interest) that Chi will pay the credit union at the end of the 9 months.

DID YOU KNOW

Pawn Loans

S ince ancient times, pawnbroking has been a source of credit for people who cannot obtain loans from other financial institutions. A typical pawn transaction involves the customer presenting an item of value to a pawnbroker. The pawnbroker makes a loan to the customer based on a percentage of the value of the item. The pawnbroker keeps the item as collateral until the customer repays the loan plus the interest. If the customer defaults on the loan, the pawnbroker keeps the item and usually offers it for sale in his or her pawnshop. Due to the 15 to 20% default rate, as well as the need to pay for retail space, pawn loans usually have a significantly higher rate of interest than other financial institutions (see Example 3).

SOLUTION:

a) To find the interest on the loan, we use the formula $i = prt$. We know that $p = \$1600$, $r = 6.5\%$ (or converted to a decimal, 0.065), and t in years $= \frac{9}{12} = 0.75$. We substitute the appropriate values in the formula

$$i = p \times r \times t$$
$$= \$1600 \times 0.065 \times 0.75$$
$$= \$78$$

The simple interest on $1600 at 6.5% for 9 months is $78.

b) The amount to be repaid is equal to the principal plus interest, or

$$A = p + i$$
$$= \$1600 + \$78$$
$$= \$1678$$

To pay off her loan, Chi will pay the credit union $1678 at the end of 9 months. ▲

EXAMPLE 2   Determining the Annual Rate of Interest

Patricia Allaire lent her friend Dan Marcum $300 to help him pay his income taxes. Six months later Dan repaid the original $300 plus $15.00 interest. What annual rate of interest did Patricia receive?

SOLUTION: We need to solve for the interest rate, r. Since the time is 6 months, the time in years is $\frac{6}{12}$ or 0.5. Using the formula $i = prt$, we get

$$\$15 = \$300 \times r \times 0.50$$
$$15 = 150r$$
$$\frac{15}{150} = r$$
$$0.1 = r$$

The annual rate of interest paid is 10%. ▲

EXAMPLE 3   A Pawn Loan

To obtain money for new eyeglasses, Gilbert French decides to pawn his trumpet. Gilbert borrows $240 and after 30 days he gets his trumpet back by paying the pawnbroker $288. What annual rate of interest did Gilbert pay?

SOLUTION: Gilbert paid $288 $-$ $240 $=$ $48 in interest, and the length of the loan is for one month or $\frac{1}{12}$ of a year.
Using the formula $i = prt$, we get

$$\$48 = \$240 \times r \times \frac{1}{12}$$
$$48 = 20r$$
$$\frac{48}{20} = r$$
$$2.4 = r$$

The annual rate of interest as a decimal number is 2.4. To change this number to a percent, multiply the number by 100 and add a percent sign. Thus, the annual rate of interest paid is 240%. ▲

In Examples 1, 2, and 3, we illustrated a simple interest loan, for which the interest and principal are paid on the due date of the note. There is another type of loan, the *discount note*, for which the interest is paid at the time the borrower receives the loan. The interest charged in advance is called the *bank discount*. A Federal Reserve Treasury bill is a bank discount note issued by the U.S. government. Example 4 illustrates a discount note.

EXAMPLE 4   *True Interest Rate of a Discount Note*

Siegrid Cook borrowed $500 on a 10% discount note for a period of 3 months. Find

a) the interest she must pay to the bank on the date she receives the loan.

b) the net amount of money she receives from the bank.

c) the actual rate of interest for the loan.

SOLUTION:

a) To find the interest, use the simple interest formula.

$$i = prt$$
$$= \$500 \times 0.10 \times \frac{3}{12}$$
$$= \$12.50$$

b) Since Siegrid must pay $12.50 interest when she first receives the loan, the net amount she receives is $500 − $12.50 or $487.50.

c) We calculate the actual rate of interest charged using the simple interest formula. In the formula for the principal, we use the amount Siegrid received from the bank. For the interest we use the interest calculated in part a).

$$i = prt$$
$$\$12.50 = \$487.50 \times r \times \frac{3}{12}$$
$$12.50 = 121.875 \times r$$
$$\frac{12.50}{121.875} = r$$
$$0.1026 \approx r$$

Thus, the actual rate of interest is about 10.3% rather than the quoted 10%.   ▲

EXAMPLE 5   *Partial Payments*

Ken Hurley wishes to purchase a new racing bicycle but does not have the $2000 purchase price. Luckily, the bike shop has two payment options. With option 1, Ken can pay $1000 as a down payment and then pay $1150 in 6 months. With option 2, Ken can pay $500 as a down payment and then pay $1700 in 6 months. Which payment option has a higher annual simple interest rate?

SOLUTION: Option 1: To determine the principal of the loan, subtract the down payment from the purchase price of the bicycle. Therefore, $p = \$2000 − \$1000 = \$1000$.

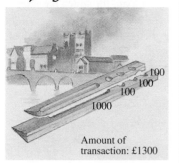
To determine the interest charged, subtract the purchase price of the bicycle from the total amount paid. Therefore, $i = (\$1000 + \$1150) - \$2000 = \$150$. Then

$$i = p \times r \times t$$
$$150 = 1000 \times r \times \frac{1}{2}$$
$$150 = 500r$$
$$\frac{150}{500} = r$$
$$0.3 = r$$

Option 1 has a 30% annual simple interest rate.

Option 2: The principal is $p = \$2000 - \$500 = \$1500$, and interest is $i = (\$500 + \$1700) - \$2000 = \$200$. Then

$$i = p \times r \times t$$
$$200 = 1500 \times r \times \frac{1}{2}$$
$$200 = 750r$$
$$\frac{200}{750} = r$$
$$0.2667 \approx r$$

Option 2 has about 26.7% annual simple interest rate. Therefore, option 1 charges a higher annual simple interest rate than option 2.   ▲

The United States Rule

A loan has a date of maturity, at which time the principal and interest are due. It is possible to make payments on a loan before the date of maturity. A Supreme Court decision specified the method by which these payments are credited. The procedure is called the *United States rule*.

The United States rule states that if a partial payment is made on the loan, interest is computed on the principal from the first day of the loan until the date of the partial payment. The partial payment is used to pay the interest first; then the rest of the payment is used to reduce the principal. The next time a partial payment is made, interest is calculated on the unpaid principal from the date of the previous date of payment. Again, the payment goes first to pay the interest, with the rest of the payment used to reduce the principal. An individual can make as many partial payments as he or she wishes; the procedure is repeated for each payment. The balance due on the date of maturity is found by computing interest due since the last partial payment and adding this interest to the unpaid principal.

The *Banker's rule* is used to calculate simple interest when applying the United States rule. The Banker's rule considers a year to have 360 days, and any fractional part of a year is the exact number of days of the loan.

To determine the exact number of days in a period, we can use Table 11.1. Example 6 illustrates how to use the table.

TABLE 11.1

						Days in Each Month						
	31	28	31	30	31	30	31	31	30	31	30	31
Day of Month	Jan.	Feb.	Mar.	Apr.	May	June	July	Aug.	Sept.	Oct.	Nov.	Dec.
Day 1	1	32	60	91	121	152	182	213	244	274	305	335
Day 2	2	33	61	92	122	153	183	214	245	275	306	336
Day 3	3	34	62	93	123	154	184	215	246	276	307	337
Day 4	4	35	63	94	124	155	185	216	247	277	308	338
Day 5	5	36	64	95	125	156	186	217	248	278	309	339
Day 6	6	37	65	96	126	157	187	218	249	279	310	340
Day 7	7	38	66	97	127	158	188	219	250	280	311	341
Day 8	8	39	67	98	128	159	189	220	251	281	312	342
Day 9	9	40	68	99	129	160	190	221	252	282	313	343
Day 10	10	41	69	100	130	161	191	222	253	283	314	344
Day 11	11	42	70	101	131	162	192	223	254	284	315	345
Day 12	12	43	71	102	132	163	193	224	255	285	316	346
Day 13	13	44	72	103	133	164	(194)	225	256	286	317	347
Day 14	14	45	73	104	134	165	195	226	257	287	318	348
Day 15	15	46	(74)	105	135	166	196	227	258	288	319	349
Day 16	16	47	75	106	136	167	197	228	259	289	320	350
Day 17	17	48	76	107	137	168	198	229	260	290	321	351
Day 18	18	49	77	108	138	169	199	230	261	291	322	352
Day 19	19	50	78	109	139	170	200	231	262	292	323	353
Day 20	20	51	79	110	140	171	201	232	263	293	324	354
Day 21	21	52	80	111	141	172	202	233	264	294	325	355
Day 22	22	53	81	112	142	173	203	234	265	295	326	356
Day 23	23	54	82	113	143	174	204	235	266	296	327	357
Day 24	24	55	83	114	144	175	205	236	267	297	328	358
Day 25	25	56	84	115	145	176	206	237	268	298	329	359
Day 26	26	57	85	116	146	177	207	238	269	299	330	360
Day 27	27	58	86	117	147	178	208	239	270	300	331	361
Day 28	28	59	87	118	148	179	209	240	271	301	332	362
Day 29	29		88	119	149	180	210	241	272	302	333	363
Day 30	30		89	120	150	181	211	242	273	303	334	364
Day 31	31		90		151		212	243		304		365

Add 1 day for leap year if February 29 falls between the two dates under consideration.

EXAMPLE 6   *Determining the Due Date of a Note*

Use Table 11.1 to find (a) the due date of a loan made on March 15 for 120 days and (b) the number of days from April 18 to July 31.

SOLUTION:

a) To determine the due date of the loan, do the following. In Table 11.1 find Day 15 in the left column (with heading Day of Month), and then move three columns to the right (heading at the top of the column is March) to find the number 74 (circled in red). Thus, March 15 is the 74th day of the year. Add 120 to 74, since the loan will be due 120 days after March 15:

$$74 + 120 = 194$$

Thus, the due date of the note is the 194th day of the year. Find 194 (circled in blue) in Table 11.1 in the column headed July. The number in the same row as 194 in the left column is Day 13. Thus, the due date of the note is July 13.

b) To determine the number of days from April 18 to July 31, use Table 11.1 to find that April 18 is the 108th day of the year and that July 31 is the 212th day of the year. Then find the difference: $212 - 108 = 104$. Thus, the number of days from April 18 to July 31 is 104 days. ▲

EXAMPLE 7   *Using the Banker's Rule*

Determine the simple interest that will be paid on a $300 loan at an interest rate of 5% for the period March 3 to May 3 using the Banker's rule.

SOLUTION: The exact number of days from March 3 to May 3 is 61. The period of time in years is 61/360. Substituting in the simple interest formula gives

$$i = prt$$
$$= \$300 \times 0.05 \times \frac{61}{360}$$
$$\approx \$2.54$$

The interest is $2.54. ▲

DID YOU KNOW

Investing in Stocks

When the owners of a company wish to raise money for expanding their company, they often decide to sell part of the company to investors. When an investor purchases a portion of a company, the investor is said to own *stock* in the company. The unit of measure of the stock is called a *share*. By selling shares of stock, a company is selling ownership of the company. By buying shares of stock, an investor is becoming a part owner, or *shareholder*, of the company. The shares of many companies' stock are often bought and sold, or *traded*, by investors through a *stock exchange*. There are many stock exchanges located throughout the world, but the largest is the New York Stock Exchange. Shares of stock may also be bought and sold through the National Association of Securities Dealers Automated Quotation system (commonly referred to as the NASDAQ).

Large companies may have many millions or even billions of shares of stock available for trading to the general public. For example, in 2002, there were over 2 billion shares of the Coca-Cola Company owned by over 300,000 investors. On April 11, 2003, each of these shares was worth $41.43.

Companies will often distribute their profits to their shareholders in the form of *dividends*. After the company declares the dividend per share, the amount the investor receives depends on the number of shares owned by the investor. Shareholders may also make money when they sell their shares if they sell them at a higher price than the price at which they bought the shares. Such an increase is referred to as a *capital gain*. Because companies do not always distribute dividends and the price of stocks may go down as well as go up, investing in stocks involves some risk of losing all or part of your investment. Investing in stocks over long periods of time, however, is usually a good investment. Since 1926, shareholders of large established companies have seen an average annual increase in their investment of 11.3%. This return exceeds the average annual increase in bonds, savings accounts, or certificates of deposit.

The next example illustrates how a partial payment is credited under the United States rule. Making partial payments reduces the amount of interest paid and the cost of the loan.

EXAMPLE 8   *Using the United States Rule*

Cathy Panik is a mathematics teacher and she plans to attend a national conference. To pay for her airfare, on November 1, 2002, Cathy takes out a 120-day loan for

$400 at an interest rate of 12.5%. Cathy uses some birthday gift money to make a partial payment of $150 on January 5, 2003. She makes a second partial payment of $100 on February 2, 2003.

a) Determine the due date of the loan.

b) Determine the interest and the amount credited to the principal on January 5.

c) Determine the interest and the amount credited to the principal on February 2.

d) Determine the amount that Cathy must pay on the due date.

SOLUTION:

a) Using Table 11.1, we see that November 1 is the 305th day of the year. Next, we note that the sum of 305 and 120 is 425. Since this due date will extend into the next year, we subtract 365 from 425 to get 60. From Table 11.1, we see that the 60th day of the year is March 1. Therefore, the loan due date is March 1, 2003. Had 2003 been a leap year, the due date would have been February 29, 2003.

b) Using Table 11.1, January 5 is the 5th day of the year and November 1 is the 305th day of the year. The number of days from November 1 to January 5 can be computed as follows: $(365 - 305) + 5 = 65$. Then using $i = prt$, and the Banker's rule, we get:

$$i = \$400 \times 0.125 \times \frac{65}{360}$$
$$\approx \$9.03$$

The interest of $9.03 that is due January 5, 2003, is deducted from the payment of $150. The remaining payment of $150 − $9.03 or $140.97 is then credited to the principal. Therefore, the adjusted principal is now $400 − $140.97, or $259.03.

Note that, if this had been the only partial payment made, then the balance due on March 1, 2003, would be calculated by determining the interest on the balance, $259.03, for the remainder of the loan, 55 days, and adding this interest to the principal of $259.03. If this payment was the only partial payment made, then the balance due on March 1 would be

$$\text{Balance due} = \text{principal} + \text{interest}$$
$$\approx 259.03 + \left(259.03 \times 0.125 \times \frac{55}{360} \right)$$
$$\approx 259.03 + 4.95$$
$$\approx 263.98$$

c) Since there was a second partial payment made, we use the Banker's rule to calculate the interest on the unpaid principal for the period from January 5 to February 2. According to Table 11.1, the number of days from January 5 to February 2 is $33 - 5$, or 28 days.

$$i = \$259.03 \times 0.125 \times \frac{28}{360}$$
$$\approx \$2.52$$

The interest of $2.52 that is due February 2, 2003, is deducted from the payment of $100. The remaining payment of $100 − $2.52, or $97.48, is then credited to the principal. Therefore, the new adjusted principal is now $259.03 − $97.48, or $161.55.

d) The due date of the loan is March 1. Using Table 11.1, we see that there are

$60 - 33$ or 27 days from February 2 to March 1. The interest is computed on the remaining balance of $161.51 by using the simple interest formula.

$$i = \$161.55 \times 0.125 \times \frac{27}{360}$$

$$\approx \$1.51$$

Therefore, the balance due on the maturity date of the loan is the sum of the principal and the interest, $161.55 + $1.51, or $163.06. *Note:* The sum of the days in the three calculations, $65 + 28 + 27$, equals the total number of days in the loan, 120. ▲

SECTION 11.2 EXERCISES

Concept/Writing Exercises

1. What is interest?
2. What is credit?
3. What is security (or collateral)?
4. What is a cosigner?
5. Explain what each letter in the simple interest formula, $i = prt$, represents.
6. What is a personal note?
7. Explain the United States rule.
8. Explain the difference between ordinary interest and interest under the Banker's rule.

In Exercises 9–18, determine the simple interest. (The rate is an annual rate unless otherwise noted. Assume 360 days in a year.)

Practice the Skills

9. $p = \$300, r = 4\%, t = 5$ years
10. $p = \$450, r = 5.5\%, t = 2$ years
11. $p = \$900, r = 3.75\%, t = 30$ days
12. $p = \$365.45, r = 11\frac{1}{2}\%, t = 8$ months
13. $p = \$587, r = 0.045\%$ per day, $t = 2$ months
14. $p = \$6742.75, r = 6.05\%, t = 90$ days
15. $p = \$2,756.78, r = 10.15\%, t = 103$ days
16. $p = \$550.31, r = 8.9\%, t = 67$ days
17. $p = \$1372.11, r = 1\frac{3}{8}\%$ per month, $t = 6$ months
18. $p = \$41,864, r = 0.0375\%$ per day, $t = 60$ days

In Exercises 19–24, use the simple interest formula to determine the missing value.

19. $p = \$1500, r = ?, t = 3$ years, $i = \$450$
20. $p = ?, r = 3\%, t = 90$ days, $i = \$600$
21. $p = ?, r = 8\%, t = 3$ months, $i = \$12.00$
22. $p = \$800.00, r = 6\%, t = ?, i = \$64.00$
23. $p = \$957.62, r = 6.5\%, t = ?, i = \$124.49$
24. $p = \$1650.00, r = ?, t = 6.5$ years, $i = \$343.20$

Problem Solving

25. *School Loan* To encourage employees to take courses at the local community college, DCR Industries offers loans of $1000 at an annual simple interest rate of 3.0%. If Darren Sharper gets one such loan, determine how much Darren needs to repay his employer after 6 months.

26. *Credit Union Loan* Steve and Laurie Carah borrowed $4500 from their credit union to remodel their kitchen. The simple interest rate was 4.75% and the length of the loan was 3 years.

a) How much did the Carahs pay for the use of the money?
b) Determine the amount the Carahs paid to the credit union on the date of maturity of the loan.

27. *Bank Personal Note* Kelly Droessler borrowed $3500 from the bank for 6 months. Her friend Ms. Harris was cosigner of Kelly's personal note. The bank collected $7\frac{1}{2}\%$ simple interest on the date of maturity.
a) How much did Kelly pay for the use of the money?
b) Find the amount she repaid to the bank on the due date of the note.

28. *Bank Discount Note* Kwame Adebele borrowed $2500 for 5 months from his bank, using U.S. government bonds as security. The bank discounted the loan at 8%.
a) How much interest did Kwame pay the bank for the use of its money?

b) How much did he receive from the bank?

c) What was the actual rate of interest he paid?

29. *Bank Discount Note* Julie Jansen borrowed $3650 from her bank for 8 months. The bank discounted the loan at 7.5%.

a) How much interest did Julie pay the bank for the use of its money?

b) How much did she receive from the bank?

c) What was the actual rate of interest she paid?

30. *Credit Union Loan* Enrico Montoyo wants to borrow $350 for 6 months from his credit union, using his savings account as security. The credit union's policy is that the maximum amount a person can borrow is 80% of the amount in the person's savings account. The interest rate is 2% higher than the interest rate being paid on the savings account. The current rate on the savings account is $3\frac{1}{4}$%.

a) How much money must Enrico have in his account in order to borrow $350?

b) What is the rate of interest the credit union will charge for the loan?

c) Find the amount Enrico must repay in 6 months.

31. *Investing Tuition Payments* Sand Ridge School is requiring parents to pay half of the yearly tuition at the time of registration and half on the date classes begin. Registration is held 5 months prior to the beginning of school, and administrators expect 470 students to register. If annual tuition is $4500 and if the money paid at the time of registration is placed in an account paying 5.4% simple interest, how much interest will Sand Ridge School earn by the time school begins?

32. *A Pawn Loan* Jeffrey Kowalski wants to take his mother out for dinner on her birthday, but he doesn't get paid until the following week. To borrow money, Jeffrey pawns his watch. Based on the value of the watch, the pawnbroker loans Jeffrey $75. Fourteen days later Jeffrey gets his watch back by paying the pawnbroker $80.25. What annual simple interest rate did the pawnbroker charge Jeffrey?

In Exercises 33–38, determine the exact time from the first date to the second date. Use Table 11.1. Assume the year is not a leap year unless otherwise indicated.

33. January 17 to July 4

34. February 12 to June 19 (the loan is due in a leap year)

35. March 17 to December 8

36. June 14 to January 24

37. August 24 to May 15

38. December 21 to April 28

In Exercises 39–42, determine the due date of the loan, using the exact time, if the loan is made on the given date for the given number of days.

39. April 15 for 60 days

40. May 18 for 180 days

41. November 25 for 120 days (the loan is due in a leap year)

42. July 5 for 210 days

In Exercises 43–52, a partial payment is made on the date(s) indicated. Use the United States rule to determine the balance due on the note at the date of maturity. (The Effective Date is the date the note was written.) Assume the year is not a leap year.

	Prin-cipal	Rate	Effec-tive date	Partial payment(s)		Matu-rity date
				Amount	Date(s)	
43.	$2000	5%	Mar. 1	$400	Apr. 1	May 1
44.	$4500	3%	Jan. 15	$2000	Mar. 1	Apr. 15
45.	$7000	5.75%	Aug. 1	$3500	Nov. 15	Dec. 15
46.	$7500	12%	April 15	$1000	Aug. 1	Oct. 1
47.	$9000	6%	July 15	$4000	Dec. 27	Feb. 1
48.	$1000	12.5%	Jan. 1	$300	Jan. 15	Feb. 15
49.	$1800	15%	Aug. 1	$500	Sept. 1	Nov. 1
				$500	Oct. 1	
50.	$5000	14%	Oct. 15	$800	Nov. 15	Jan. 1
				$800	Dec. 15	
51.	$11,600	6%	Mar. 1	$2000	Aug. 1	Dec. 1
				$4000	Nov. 15	
52.	$21,000	$4\frac{3}{8}$%	July 12	$8000	Oct. 10	Jan. 30
				$6000	Dec. 8	

53. *Company Loan* On March 1 the Zwick Balloon Company signed a $6500 note with simple interest of $10\frac{1}{2}$% for 180 days. The company made payments of $1750 on May 1 and $2350 on July 1. How much will the company owe on the date of maturity?

54. *Restaurant Loan* The Sweet Tooth Restaurant borrowed $3000 on a note dated May 15 with simple interest of 11%. The maturity date of the loan is September 1. The restaurant made partial payments of $875 on June 15 and $940 on August 1. Find the amount due on the maturity date of the loan.

55. *U.S. Treasury Bills* The U.S. government borrows money by selling Treasury bills. Treasury bills are discounted notes issued by the U.S. government. On May 5, 2004, Kris Greenhalgh purchased a 182-day, $1000 U.S. Treasury bill at a 4.34% discount. On the date of maturity Kris will receive $1000.
  a) What is the date of maturity of the Treasury bill?
  b) How much did Kris actually pay for the Treasury bill?
  c) How much interest did the U.S. goverment pay Kris on the date of maturity?
  d) What is the actual rate of interest of the Treasury bill? (Round the answer to the nearest hundredth of a percent.)

56. *U.S. Treasury Bills* On August 31, 2003, Trinity Lopez purchased a 364-day, $6000 U.S. Treasury bill at a 4.4% discount. (See Exercise 55.)
  a) What is the date of maturity of the Treasury bill (2004 is a leap year)?
  b) How much did Trinity actually pay for the Treasury bill?
  c) How much interest did the U.S. government pay Trinity on the date of maturity?
  d) What is the actual rate of interest of the Treasury bill?

57. *Tax Preparation Loan* Many tax preparation organizations will prepay customers' tax refunds if they pay a one time finance charge. In essence, the customer is borrowing the money (the refund minus the finance charge) from the tax preparer, prepaying the interest (as in a discount note) and then repaying the loan with the tax refund. This procedure allows customers access to their tax refund money without having to wait. Joy Stallard had a tax refund of $743.21 due. She was able to get her tax refund immediately by paying a finance charge of $39.95. What annual simple interest rate is Joy paying for this loan assuming
  a) the tax refund check would be available in 5 days?
  b) the tax refund check would be available in 10 days?
  c) the tax refund check would be available in 20 days?

58. *Prime Interest Rate* Nick St. Louis borrowed $600 for 3 months. The banker said that Nick must repay the loan at the rate of $200 per month plus interest. The bank was charging a rate of 2% above the prime interest rate. The *prime interest rate* is the rate charged to preferred customers of the bank. During the first month the prime interest rate was 4.75%, during the second month it was 5%, and during the third month it was 5.25%.
  a) Find the amount Nick paid the bank at the end of the

first month, at the end of the second month, and at the end of the third month.
  b) What was the total amount of interest Nick paid the bank?

Challenge Problem/Group Activity

59. *U.S. Treasury Bills* Mark Beiley purchased a 52-week U.S. Treasury bill (see Exercises 55 and 56) for $93,337. The par value (the value of the bill upon maturity) was $100,000.
  a) What was the discount rate?
  b) What was the actual interest rate Mark received?
  c) Since U.S. Treasury bills are sold through auctions at Federal Reserve Banks, Mark did not know the purchase price of his Treasury bill until after he was notified by mail. If Mark had sent the Federal Reserve Bank a check for $100,000 to purchase the Treasury bill, how much would the Federal Reserve Bank have to rebate him upon notice of his purchase?
  d) On the day he received the rebate that was discussed in part (c) he invested it in a 1-year certificate of deposit yielding 5% interest. What is the total amount of interest he will receive from both investments?

Recreational Mathematics

60. *Columbus Investment* On August 3, 1492 Christopher Columbus set sail on a voyage that would eventually lead him to the Americas. If on this day Columbus had invested $1 in a 5% simple interest account, determine the amount of interest the account would have earned by the following dates. Use a scientific calculator and disregard leap years in your calculations.
  a) December 11, 1620 (Pilgrims land on Plymouth Rock)
  b) July 4, 1776 (Declaration of Independence)
  c) December 7, 1941 (U.S. enters World War II)
  d) Today's date

Internet/Research Activities

61. *Banking Practices* Three types of simple interest may be calculated with the simple interest formula. They are ordinary, Banker's rule, and exact time.
  a) Visit a local lending institution to determine how exact time is used in the simple interest formula.
  b) Compare the results for each method on a loan for $500 at 8% for the period January 2, 2004, to April 2, 2004.

62. *Loan Sources* Consider the following places where a loan may be obtained: banks, savings and loans, credit unions, and pawn shops. Write a report that includes the following information:
  a) Describe the ownership of each.
  b) Historically, what need is each fulfilling?
  c) What are the advantages and disadvantages of obtaining a loan from each of those listed?

11.3 COMPOUND INTEREST

Albert Einstein was once asked to name the greatest discovery of man. His reply was, "Compound interest."

In this section we discuss some ways to put your money to work for your benefit.

An *investment* is the use of money or capital for income or profit. We can divide investments into two classes: fixed investments and variable investments. In a *fixed investment*, the amount invested as principal is guaranteed and the interest is computed at a fixed rate. *Guaranteed* means that the exact amount invested will be paid back together with any accumulated interest. Examples of a fixed investment are savings accounts and certificates of deposit. Another fixed investment is a government savings bond. In a *variable investment*, neither the principal nor the interest is guaranteed. Examples of variable investments are stocks, mutual funds, and commercial bonds.

Simple interest, introduced earlier in the chapter, is calculated once for the period of a loan using the formula $i = prt$. The interest paid on savings accounts at most banks is compound interest. A bank computes the interest periodically (for example, daily or quarterly) and adds this interest to the original principal. The interest for the following period is computed by using the new principal (original principal plus interest). In effect, the bank is computing interest on interest, which is called compound interest.

> Interest that is computed on the principal and any accumulated interest is called **compound interest.**

DID YOU KNOW

A Penny Saved...

"Money makes money and the money that money makes makes more money." So said Benjamin Franklin, who in his will left 1000 pounds sterling (£) to the city of Boston, where he was born. The money was to be lent to young apprentices who would pay $\frac{1}{10}$ of the principal each year plus 5% interest compounded yearly. The money earned was to be used to benefit the inhabitants of Boston. By 1894, the fund's value had increased to 90,000 £. Part of this legacy became the Franklin Institute of Boston, a 2-year technical college founded in 1908.

EXAMPLE 1   *Computing Compound Interest*

Marjorie Thrall recently won the $1000 first prize in a raffle contest. Marjorie deposits the $1000 in a 1-year certificate of deposit paying 2.0% compounded quarterly. Find the amount, A, to which the $1000 will grow in 1 year.

SOLUTION: Compute the interest for the first quarter using the simple interest formula. Add this interest to the principal to find the amount at the end of the first quarter. In our calculation, time is $\frac{1}{4}$ of a year, or $t = 0.25$.

$$i = prt$$
$$= \$1000 \times 0.02 \times 0.25 = \$5.00$$
$$A = \$1000 + \$5 = \$1005$$

Now repeat the process for the second quarter, this time using a principal of $1005.

$$i = \$1005 \times 0.02 \times 0.25 \approx \$5.03$$
$$A = \$1005 + \$5.03 = \$1010.03$$

For the third quarter, use a principal of $1010.03.

$$i = \$1010.03 \times 0.02 \times 0.25 \approx \$5.05$$
$$A = \$1010.03 + \$5.05 = \$1015.08$$

For the fourth quarter, use a principal of $1015.08.

$$i = \$1015.08 \times 0.02 \times 0.25 \approx \$5.08$$
$$A = \$1015.08 + \$5.08 = \$1020.16$$

Hence, the $1000 grows to a final value of $1020.16 over the 1-year period. ▲

This example shows the effect of earning interest on interest, or compounding interest. In 1 year, the amount of $1000 has grown to $1020.16, compared with $1020 that would have been obtained with a simple interest rate of 2%. Thus, in 1 year alone the gain was $0.16 more with compound interest than with simple interest.

A simpler and less time-consuming way to calculate compound interest is to use the compound interest formula and a calculator.

> **Compound Interest Formula**
>
> $$A = p\left(1 + \frac{r}{n}\right)^{nt}$$

In this formula, A is the amount, p is the principal, r is the annual rate of interest, t is the time in years, and n is the number of compounding periods per year.

EXAMPLE 2   *Using the Compound Interest Formula*

When Alexander was born, he received several gifts of cash from his relatives and his parents' friends. His father invested this money in a money market account that had a rate of 3% compounded monthly. If the amount invested was $3200, determine the amount in the account after 5 years.

SOLUTION: We will use the formula for compound interest, $A = p\left(1 + \frac{r}{n}\right)^{nt}$.

Since the interest is compounded monthly, there are 12 periods per year. Thus, $n = 12$. Since the money is invested for 5 years, $t = 5$.

$$A = 3200\left(1 + \frac{0.03}{12}\right)^{(12)(5)}$$
$$= 3200(1 + 0.0025)^{60}$$
$$= 3200(1.0025)^{60}$$
$$\approx 3200(1.1616168)$$
$$\approx 3717.17$$

Thus, the amount in the account after 5 years would be $3717.17. ▲

In Example 2, to find the value of $(1.0025)^{60}$ using a scientific calculator, you can use the $\boxed{y^x}$ key. The keystrokes are

$$1.0025 \ \boxed{y^x} \ \boxed{60} \ \boxed{=} \ 1.161617$$

Note: Some scientific calculators have an $\boxed{x^y}$ or a $\boxed{\wedge}$ key in place of a $\boxed{y^x}$ key. In either case, the procedure works the same: Enter the base then the key ($\boxed{y^x}$, $\boxed{x^y}$ or $\boxed{\wedge}$), the exponent, and then the $\boxed{=}$ key.

EXAMPLE 3   *Calculating Compound Interest*

Calculate the interest on $650 at 8% compounded semiannually for 3 years, using the compound interest formula.

SOLUTION: Since interest is compounded semiannually, there are two periods per year. Thus, $n = 2$, $r = 0.08$, and $t = 3$. Substituting into the formula, we find the amount, A.

$$A = p\left(1 + \frac{r}{n}\right)^{nt}$$

$$= 650\left(1 + \frac{0.08}{2}\right)^{(2)(3)}$$

$$= 650(1.04)^6$$

$$\approx 650(1.2653190)$$

$$\approx \$822.46$$

Since the total amount is \$822.46 and the original principal is \$650, the interest must be \$822.46 − \$650, or \$172.46.   ▲

In Example 3, the interest rate is stated as an annual rate of 8%, but the number of compounding periods per year is two. In applying the compound interest formula, the rate for one period is $r \div n$, which was 8% ÷ 2, or 4% per period.

Now we will calculate the amount, and interest, on \$1 invested at 8% compounded semiannually for 1 year. The result is

$$A = 1\left(1 + \frac{0.08}{2}\right)^{(2)(1)} = 1.0816$$

Interest = amount − principal

$$i = 1.0816 - 1$$

$$= 0.0816$$

The interest for 1 year is 0.0816. This amount written as a percent, 8.16%, is called the *effective annual yield. Most financial institutions refer to the effective annual yield as the annual percentage yield (APY).* If \$1 was invested at a simple interest rate of 8.16% and \$1 was invested at 8% interest compounded semiannually (equivalent to an effective yield of 8.16%), the interest from both investments would be the same.

> The **effective annual yield** or **annual percentage yield (APY)** is the simple interest rate that gives the same amount of interest as a compound rate over the same period of time.

Many banks compound interest daily. When computing the effective annual yield, they use 360 for the number of periods in a year. To find the effective annual yield for any interest rate, calculate the amount using the compound interest formula where p is \$1. Then subtract \$1 from that amount. The difference, written as a percent, is the effective annual yield, as illustrated in Example 4.

The sign in the margin shows interest rates and the corresponding annual percentage yields (APY) that were available for certificates of deposit (CDs) from Suncoast Schools Credit Union on November 2, 2002. To determine the effective

Suncoast Schools Credit Union

CD Rates

Type	Rate	APY*
12 mo	3.25%	3.30%
24 mo	3.83%	3.90%
36 mo	4.21%	4.30%
48 mo	4.59%	4.70%

* Annual Percentage Yield

annual yield (or the APY) for the 48-month CD, calculate the amount of interest earned on $1 for 1 year.

$$A = \left(1 + \frac{0.0459}{360}\right)^{360} \approx 1.0469666 \approx 1.0470$$

From this result we subtract 1 to get $1.0470 - 1 = 0.0470$, or 4.70%. This result confirms that the effective annual yield for a rate of 4.59% is 4.70%. Confirm that the other effective yields shown on the sign are correct now.

EXAMPLE 4 *Determining Annual Percentage Yield*

Determine the annual percentage yield or the effective annual yield for $1 invested for 1 year at

a) 8% compounded daily.

b) 6% compounded quarterly.

SOLUTION:

a) With daily compounding $n = 360$.

$$A = p\left(1 + \frac{r}{n}\right)^{nt}$$

$$= 1\left(1 + \frac{0.08}{360}\right)^{(360)(1)}$$

$$\approx 1.0832774 \approx 1.0833$$

$$i = A - 1$$

$$\approx 1.0833 - 1$$

$$\approx 0.0833$$

Thus, when the interest is 8% compounded daily, the annual percentage yield or the effective annual yield is about 8.33%.

b) With quarterly compounding, $n = 4$.

$$A = p\left(1 + \frac{r}{n}\right)^{nt}$$

$$= 1\left(1 + \frac{0.06}{4}\right)^{(4)(1)}$$

$$\approx 1.06136355 \approx 1.0614$$

$$i = A - 1$$

$$\approx 1.0614 - 1$$

$$\approx 0.0614$$

Thus, when the interest is 6% compounded quarterly, the annual percentage yield or the effective annual yield is about 6.14%. ▲

There are numerous types of savings accounts. Many savings institutions compound interest daily. Some pay interest from the day of deposit to the day of withdrawal, and others pay interest from the first of the month on all deposits made before the tenth of the month. In each of these accounts in which interest is compounded daily, interest is

DID YOU KNOW

Investing in Bonds

A *bond* is a type of loan. When government agencies or corporations need money they often borrow money from investors by selling, or *issuing*, bonds. When an investor purchases a bond, the investor is actually lending money to the bond's issuer. The issuer agrees to pay the investor a certain interest rate over a stated period of time, usually from 1 to 30 years. The date on which the issuer repays the loan is called the *date of maturity*. Although bonds are generally considered safer investments than stocks, they do have some risks. On rare occasions, issuers may fail to make interest payments or may fail to return the investment entirely. A more common risk is that the value of a bond may decrease if interest rates increase. Such a decrease may cause investors to lose some of their investment if they decide to sell their bond before the date of maturity.

Most bonds fit into one of three distinct categories: Treasury, corporate, or municipal bonds. The U.S. government issues *Treasury bonds*. Because the U.S. government backs them, Treasury bonds are considered extremely safe investments. Corporations issue *corporate bonds*. The amount of risk to the investor of corporate bonds varies widely, depending on the issuer. State and local governments or other public agencies issue *municipal bonds*. Like corporate bonds, municipal bonds vary greatly in risk to the investor. Investors in municipal bonds may gain an additional benefit because the interest earned may be free of state and local taxes. In general, bonds offer a very stable investment that usually provide a higher return on investment than savings accounts or certificates of deposit without many of the risks associated with investing in stocks.

entered into the depositor's account only once each quarter. Some savings institutions will not pay any interest on a day-to-day account if the balance falls below a set amount.

Present Value

You may wonder about what amount of money you must deposit in an account today to have a certain amount of money in the future. For example, how much must you deposit in an account today at a given rate of interest so it will accumulate to $25,000 to pay your child's college costs in 4 years? The principal, p, which would have to be invested now is called the *present value*. Following is a formula for determining the present value.

Present Value Formula

$$p = \frac{A}{\left(1 + \dfrac{r}{n}\right)^{nt}}$$

In the formula, A represents the amount to be accumulated in n years. Note that the present value formula is a variation of the compound interest formula.

EXAMPLE 5   *Savings for College*

Nicholas Christos is currently in the eighth grade and intends to attend a state college when he finishes high school. Nicholas's parents currently have some money invested in mutual funds, but would like to invest this money in a more secure investment now to pay for college in 4 years. If they will need $25,000, how much do Nicholas's parents have to invest now in a 48-month CD that has a rate of 4.59% compounded monthly?

SOLUTION: To answer this question we will use the present value formula.

$$p = \frac{A}{\left(1 + \dfrac{r}{n}\right)^{nt}}$$

$$= \frac{25,000}{\left(1 + \dfrac{0.0459}{12}\right)^{(12)(4)}}$$

$$= \frac{25,000}{(1.003825)^{48}}$$

$$\approx \frac{25,000}{1.2011}$$

$$\approx 20,814.25$$

Nicholas Christos's parents need to invest approximately $20,814.25 now to have $25,000 in 4 years.   ▲

In Example 5, when we evaluated $(1.003825)^{48}$ we rounded the answer to four decimal places to obtain 1.2011. Using the value 1.2011 we obtained an answer of $20,814.25. Had we not rounded the answer to $(1.003825)^{48}$ and instead used the value given by a calculator for $(1.003825)^{48}$, we would have obtained an answer of $20,814.00, rounded to the nearest cent.

SECTION 11.3   EXERCISES

Concept/Writing Exercises

1. What is an investment?

2. What is a fixed investment?

3. What is a variable investment?

4. What is compound interest?

5. **a)** What is effective annual yield?
   b) What is another name for effective annual yield?

6. What is meant by present value in the present value formula?

Practice the Skills

In Exercises 7–16, use the compound interest formula

$$A = p\left(1 + \frac{r}{n}\right)^{nt}$$

to compute

   a) the total amount.
   b) the interest earned on each investment.

7. $2000 for 3 years at 2.00% compounded annually

8. $2000 for 3 years at 2.00% compounded semiannually

9. $3500 for 4 years at 3.00% compounded semiannually

10. $3500 for 4 years at 3.00% compounded annually

11. $1500 for 3 years at 4.75% compounded quarterly

12. $1500 for 4 years at 4.75% compounded quarterly

13. $2500 for 2 years at 6.25% compounded monthly

14. $3000 for 2 years at 6.25% compounded monthly

15. $4000 for 4 years at 4.59% compounded daily (use $n = 360$)

16. $4000 for 8 years at 4.59% compounded daily (use $n = 360$)

Problem Solving

17. *Textbook Advance* Lynae Sakshaug, a textbook author, deposited her $7500 advance in a money market account

that pays 2.66% interest compounded semiannually. How much money will Lynae have in this account after 4 years?

18. *Automobile Sale* Bill Palow sells his vintage 1974 Plymouth Road Runner for $9500. He uses this money to invest in a 36-month CD that pays 4.12% interest compounded quarterly. How much money will Bill receive when he cashes in the CD at the end of the 36 months?

19. *Class Trip* To help pay for a class trip at the end of their senior year, the sophomore class at Cortez High School invests $1500 from fund-raisers in a 30-month CD paying 3.9% interest compounded monthly. Determine the amount the class will receive when it cashes in the CD after 30 months.

20. *Investing Prize Winnings* Marcella Laddon wins third prize in the Clearinghouse Sweepstakes and receives a check for $250,000. After spending $10,000 on a vacation, she decides to invest the rest in a money market account that pays 1.5% interest compounded monthly. How much money will be in the account after 10 years?

21. *Investing Gifts and Scholarships* Cliff Morris just graduated from high school and has received $800 in gifts of cash from friends and relatives. Additionally, Cliff received three scholarships in the amounts of $150, $300, and $1000. If Cliff takes all his gift and scholarship money and invests it in a 24-month CD paying 2% interest compounded daily, how much will he have when he cashes in the CD at the end of the 24 months?

22. *Investing a Signing Bonus* Joe Gallegos just started a new job and has received a $5000 signing bonus. Joe decides to invest this money now so that he can buy a new car in 5 years. If Joe invests in a CD paying 3.35% interest compounded quarterly, how much money will he receive from his CD in 5 years?

23. *Savings Account Investment* When Richard Zucker was born, his father deposited $2000 in his name in a savings account. The account was paying 5% interest compounded semiannually.
   a) If the rate did not change, what was the value of the account after 15 years?
   b) If the money had been invested at 5% compounded quarterly, what would the value of the account have been after 15 years?

24. *Savings and Loan Investment* When Lois Martin was born, her father deposited $2000 in a savings account in her name at a savings and loan association. At the time, the savings and loan was paying 6% interest compounded semiannually on savings accounts. After 10 years, the savings and loan association changed to an interest rate of 6% compounded quarterly. How much had the $2000 amounted to after 18 years when the money was withdrawn for Lois to use to help pay her college expenses?

25. *Personal Loan* Brent Pickett borrowed $3000 from his brother Dave. He agreed to repay the money at the end of 2 years, giving Dave the same amount of interest that he would have received if the money had been invested at 1.75% compounded quarterly. How much money did Brent repay his brother?

26. *Forgoing Interest* Rikki Blair borrowed $6000 from her daughter, Lynette. She repaid the $6000 at the end of 2 years. If Lynette had left the money in a bank account that paid an interest rate of $5\frac{1}{4}\%$ compounded monthly, how much interest would she have accumulated?

27. *Saving for a Down Payment* Jean Woody invested $6000 at 8% compounded quarterly. Three years later she withdrew the full amount and used it for the down payment on a house. How much money did she put down on the house?

28. *Investing a Salary* After Karen Estes began her job as a waitress, she invested in a money market account paying 5.6% interest compounded daily. What was the effective annual yield of this account?

29. *Doubling the Rate* Determine the total amount and the interest paid on $1000 with interest compounded semiannually for 2 years at
   a) 2%.   **b)** 4%.   **c)** 8%.
   d) Is there a predictable outcome in either the amount or the interest when the rate is doubled? Explain.

30. *Doubling the Principal* Compute the total amount and the interest paid at 12% compounded monthly for 2 years for the following principals.
   a) $100   **b)** $200   **c)** $400
   d) Is there a predictable outcome in the interest when the principal is doubled? Explain.

31. *Doubling the Time* Compute the total amount and the interest paid on $1000 at 6% compounded semiannually for
   a) 2 years.   **b)** 4 years.   **c)** 8 years.
   d) Is there a predictable outcome in the amount when the time is doubled? Explain.

32. *Doubling the Compounding Period* Compute the total amount and the interest paid after 1 year on $1000 at 4% interest compounded
   a) annually.   **b)** semiannually.   **c)** quarterly.
   d) Is there a predictable outcome in the amount when the compounding period is doubled? Explain.

33. *Determining Effective Annual Yield* Determine the effective annual yield for $1 invested for 1 year at 3.5% compounded semiannually.

34. *Determining Effective Annual Yield* Determine the effective annual yield for $1 invested for 1 year at 4.75% compounded monthly.

35. *Verifying APY* Suppose at your local bank you saw a sign that said, "2.4% rate compounded monthly—2.6% Annual Percentage Yield (APY)." Is there anything wrong with the sign? Explain.

36. *Verifying APY* Suppose you saw an advertisement in the newspaper for a financial planner who was recommending a certificate of deposit that paid 4.5% interest compounded quarterly. In the fine print at the bottom of the advertisement it stated that the APY on the CD was 4.58%. Was this advertisement accurate? Explain.

37. *Comparing Investments* Dave Dudley won a photography contest and received a $1000 cash prize. Will he earn more interest in 1 year if he invests his winnings in a simple interest account that pays 5% or in an account that pays 4.75% interest compounded monthly?

38. *Comparing Loan Sources* Tom Angelo needs to borrow $1500 to expand his farm implement maintenance business. He learns that the local bank will lend him the money for 2 years at a rate of 10% compounded quarterly. After hearing this, Tom's grandfather offers to lend him the money for 2 years with a simple interest rate of 7%. How much money will Tom save by borrowing the money from his grandfather?

39. *A New Water Tower* The village of Kieler completes an exploratory study and finds that the current village water tower will need replacement in 10 years at a cost of $290,000. To finance this amount, the village board will at this time assess its 958 homeowners with a one-time surcharge and then invest this amount in a 10-year CD paying 8.25% interest compounded semiannually.

   a) How much will the village of Kieler need to invest at this time in this CD to raise the $290,000 in 10 years?
   b) What amount should each homeowner pay as a surcharge?

40. *Water Tower Surcharge* (See Exercise 39.) After seeing its neighboring village raise the money to invest in a new water tower, the city board of East Dubuque decides to adopt a similar plan. However, since East Dubuque is a much larger community, they will need to raise $783,000 to build three new water towers in 15 years. At this time the city board plans to assess its 2682 homeowners with a one-time surcharge and then invest the money received in a money market account paying 9% interest compounded monthly.
   a) How much money will the city board need to raise at this time to meet the city's water tower needs at the end of 15 years?
   b) Before applying the surcharge, the city board decides to use a $50,000 benefactor gift toward the water tower investment. Taking this gift into account, how much should the surcharge be on each homeowner?

41. *Saving for a Tractor* Jim Roznowski wants to invest some money now to buy a new tractor in the future. If he wants to have $30,000 available in 5 years, how much does he need to invest now in a CD paying 5.15% interest compounded monthly?

42. *Investing for Retirement* The Pearsons are planning to retire in 20 years and believe that they will need $200,000 in addition to income from their retirement plans. How much must they invest today at 7.5% compounded quarterly to accomplish their goal?

43. *Investment for a Newborn* How much money should parents invest at the birth of their child to provide their child with $50,000 at age 18? Assume that the money earns interest at 8% compounded quarterly.

44. *Future Value* How much money must Harry Kim invest today to have $20,000 in 15 years? Assume that the money earns interest at 7% compounded quarterly.

Challenge Problems/Group Activities

45. *A Loaf of Bread* If the cost of a loaf of bread was $1.35 in 2004 and the annual average inflation rate is $2\frac{1}{2}\%$, what will be the cost of a loaf of bread in 2009?

46. *Finding the Interest Rate* For a total accumulated amount of $3586.58, a principal of $2000, and a time period of 5 years, use the compound interest formula to find r if interest is compounded monthly.

47. *Rule of 72* A simple formula can help you estimate the number of years required to double your money. It's called the *rule of 72*. You simply divide 72 by the interest rate (without the percent sign). For example, with an interest rate of 4%, your money would double in approximately $72 \div 4$ or 18 years. In (a)–(d), determine the approximate number of years it will take for $1000 to double at the given interest rate.
a) 3%   **b)** 6%   **c)** 8%   **d)** 12%
e) If $120 doubles in approximately 22 years, estimate the rate of interest.

48. *Finding the Interest Rate* Richard Maruszewski borrowed $2000 from Linda Tonolli. The terms of the loan are as follows: The period of the loan is 3 years, and the rate of interest is 8% compounded semiannually. What rate of simple interest would be equivalent to the rate Linda charged Richard?

49. *Investing with an Annuity* The question may be asked, If I deposit a fixed sum of money monthly, quarterly, semiannually, or annually at a fixed rate of interest, how much money will I have accumulated in x years? This scenario is called an *annuity*. The formula for determining the value of the annuity is

$$ S = \frac{R\left[\left(1 + \dfrac{r}{n}\right)^{nt} - 1\right]}{\dfrac{r}{n}} $$

where S is the value of the annuity in t years, R is the amount invested each period, r is the annual rate of interest, n is the number of payments per year, and t is the num-

ber of years. After Denisse Brown's birth, her parents invested $500 semiannually (every 6 months) at an annual rate of 5.5% compounded semiannually. What is the value of the annuity after 17 years?

50. *A Retirement Annuity* To supplement her retirement income, Chris Dunn is investing $50 each quarter at 8% compounded quarterly. How many dollars will she accumulate in 30 years? (See Exercise 49.)

51. *Investing in Annuities* Rodney is saving money to send his sons to college by investing in annuities. (See Exercise 49.) For his oldest son, Jacob, Rodney is investing $150 per month in an annuity that pays 5.6% interest compounded monthly. For his second oldest son, Justin, he is investing $900 twice a year in an annuity that pays 5.8% interest compounded semiannually.
a) If Rodney started Jacob's annuity when he was born, how much would the annuity be worth when Jacob turns 18 years old?
b) If Rodney started Justin's annuity when he was born, how much would the annuity be worth when Justin turns 18 years old?

Recreational Mathematics

52. *Interest Comparison* You are given a choice of taking the simple interest on $100,000 invested for 4 years at a rate of 5% or the interest on $100,000 invested for 4 years at an interest rate of 5% compounded daily. Which would you select? Explain your answer and give the difference in the two investments.

Internet/Research Activities

53. Imagine you have $4000 to invest and that you need this money to grow to $5000 by investing in a CD. Contact a local bank, a savings and loan, and a credit union to obtain CD information: the interest rate, the length of the term, and the number of times per year the CD is compounded. Find out how long it would take you to reach your goal with the institution selected. Write a report summarizing your findings.

54. Write a paper on the history of simple interest and compound interest. Answer the questions: When was simple interest first charged on loans? When was compound interest first given on investments?

11.4 INSTALLMENT BUYING

In Section 11.2, we discussed personal notes and discounted notes. When borrowing money by either of these methods, the borrower normally repays the loan as a single payment at the end of the specified time period. There may be circumstances under which it is more convenient for the borrower to repay the loan on a weekly or monthly basis or to use some other convenient time period. One method of doing so is to borrow money on an *installment plan*.

There are two types of installment loans: open-end and fixed payment. An *open-end installment loan* is a loan on which you can make variable payments each month. Credit cards, such as MasterCard, Visa, and Discover, are actually open-end installment loans, used to purchase items such as clothing, textbooks, and meals. A *fixed installment loan* is one on which you pay a fixed amount of money for a set number of payments. Examples of items purchased with fixed-payment installment loans are college tuition loans and loans for cars, boats, appliances, and furniture. These loans are generally repaid in 24, 36, 48, or 60 equal monthly payments.

Lenders give any individual wishing to borrow money or purchase goods or services on the installment plan a credit rating to determine if the borrower is likely to repay the loan. The lending institution determines whether the applicant is a good "credit risk" by examining the individual's income, assets, liabilities, and history of repaying debts.

The advantage of installment buying is that the buyer has the use of an article while paying for it. If the article is essential, installment buying may serve a real need. A disadvantage is that some people buy more on the installment plan than they can afford. Another disadvantage is the interest the borrower pays for the loan. The method of determining the interest charged on an installment plan may vary with different lenders.

To provide the borrower with a way to compare interest charged, Congress passed the Truth in Lending Act in 1969. The law requires that the lending institution tell the borrower two things: the annual percentage rate and the finance charge. The *annual percentage rate (APR)* is the true rate of interest charged for the loan. The APR is calculated by using a complex formula, so we use a table to determine the APR. The technique of using a table to find the APR is illustrated in Example 1. The total *finance charge* is the total amount of money the borrower must pay for its use. The finance charge includes the interest plus any additional fees charged. The additional fees may include service charges, credit investigation fees, mandatory insurance premiums, and so on.

The finance charge a consumer pays when purchasing goods or services on an installment plan is the difference between the total installment price and the cash price. The *total installment price* is the sum of all the monthly payments and the down payment, if any.

Fixed Installment Loan

In Example 1, we learn how to determine the finance charge and the monthly payment on a fixed installment loan.

┌ **EXAMPLE 1**   *High-Definition Plasma Television*

Johnny Lott wishes to buy a high-definition plasma display television for $4500. The electronics store has an advertised finance option of no down payment and 7% APR for 24 months.

a) Determine the finance charge.

b) Determine the monthly payment.

SOLUTION:

a) Table 11.2 on page 623 gives the finance charge per $100 of the amount financed. The table shows that the finance charge per $100 of the amount financed for 24 months at 7% is $7.45 (circled in red). Since Johnny is financing $4500, the number of hundreds of dollars financed is $\frac{4500}{100} = 45$. To determine the total finace charge we multiply the finance charge per $100 by the number of hundreds of dollars financed.

$$\text{Total finance charge} = \$7.45 \times 45 = \$335.25$$

Therefore, Johnny will pay a total finance charge of $335.25.

b) To determine the monthly payments, we first calculate the total installment price by adding the finance charge to the purchase price:

$$\text{Total installment price} = \$4500 + \$335.25 = \$4835.25$$

Next, to determine the monthly payment we divide the total installment price by the number of payments:

$$\text{Monthly payment} = \frac{\$4835.25}{24} \approx \$201.47$$

Johnny will have 24 monthly payments of $201.47.

TABLE 11.2   Annual Percentage Rate Table for Monthly Payment Plans

Number of Payments	Annual Percentage Rate												
	3.0%	3.5%	4.0%	4.5%	5.0%	5.5%	6.0%	6.5%	7.0%	7.5%	8.0%	8.5%	9.0%
	(Finance charge per $100 of amount financed)												
6	0.88	1.02	1.17	1.32	1.46	1.61	1.76	1.90	2.05	2.20	2.35	2.49	2.64
12	1.63	1.91	2.18	2.45	2.73	3.00	3.28	3.56	3.83	4.11	4.39	4.66	4.94
18	2.39	2.79	3.20	3.60	4.00	4.41	4.82	5.22	5.63	6.04	6.45	6.86	7.28
24	3.15	3.69	4.22	4.75	5.29	5.83	6.37	6.91	(7.45)	8.00	8.54	9.09	9.64
30	3.92	4.58	5.25	5.92	6.59	7.26	7.94	8.61	9.30	9.98	10.66	11.35	12.04
36	4.69	5.49	6.29	7.09	7.90	(8.71)	9.52	10.34	11.16	11.98	12.81	13.64	14.48
48	6.24	7.31	8.38	9.46	10.54	11.63	12.73	13.83	14.94	(16.06)	17.18	18.31	19.45
60	7.81	9.15	10.50	11.86	13.23	14.61	16.00	17.40	18.81	20.23	21.66	23.10	24.55

Our next example shows how to determine the annual percentage rate on a loan that has a schedule for repaying a fixed amount each period.

┌ **EXAMPLE 2**   *Determining the APR*

Al and Albina Cannavach are purchasing a piano for $5000, including taxes. They decide to make a $1000 down payment and finance the balance, $4000, through their credit union. The loan officer informs them that their payment will be $121 per month for 36 months.

a) Determine the finance charge.   b) Determine the APR.

SOLUTION:

a) The total installment price is the down payment plus the total monthly installment payments.

$$\text{Total installment price} = \$1000 + (36 \times \$121)$$
$$= \$1000 + \$4356 = \$5356$$

The finance charge is the total installment price minus the cash price.

$$\text{Finance charge} = \$5356 - \$5000 = \$356$$

b) To determine the annual percentage rate, use Table 11.2. First divide the finance charge by the amount financed and multiply the quotient by 100. The result is the finance charge per $100 of the amount financed.

$$\frac{\text{Finance charge}}{\text{Amount financed}} \times 100 = \frac{356}{4000} \times 100 = 0.089 \times 100 = 8.9$$

Thus, the Cannavaciolos pay $8.90 for each $100 being financed. To use Table 11.2 look for 36 in the left column under the heading Number of Payments. Then move across to the right until you find the value closest to $8.90. The value closest to $8.90 is $8.71 (circled in blue). At the top of this column is the value 5.5%. Therefore, the annual percentage rate is approximately 5.5%.   ▲

Much more complete APR tables similar to Table 11.2 are available at your local lending institution or on the Internet.

EXAMPLE 3   *Financing a Restored Car*

Tino Garcia borrowed $9800 to purchase a classic 1965 Ford Mustang. He does not recall the APR of the loan but remembers that there are 48 payments of $237. If he did not make a down payment on the car, determine the APR.

SOLUTION: First determine the finance charge by subtracting the cash price from the total amount paid.

$$\begin{aligned}
\text{Finance charge} &= (237 \times 48) - 9800 \\
&= 11{,}376 - 9800 \\
&= \$1576
\end{aligned}$$

Next divide the finance charge by the amount of the loan and multiply this quotient by 100.

$$\frac{1576}{9800} \times 100 \approx 16.08$$

Next find 48 payments in the left column of Table 11.2. Move to the right until you find the value that is closest to 16.08. The value closest to 16.08 is 16.06 (circled in green). At the top of the column is the APR of 7.5%.   ▲

In Example 3, if Tino made all 48 payments his finance charge would be $1576. If he decides to repay the loan after making 30 payments, must he pay the total finance charge? The answer is no. Two methods are used to determine the finance charge when you repay an installment loan early: the *actuarial method* and the *rule of 78s*. The actuarial method uses the APR tables, whereas the less frequently used method, the rule of 78s, does not. On top of page 625 we give the formulas used to calculate the unearned interest using both the actuarial method and the rule of 78s. The *unearned interest* is the interest saved by paying off the loan early.

DID YOU KNOW

Actuarial Method versus Rule of 78s

When making automobile or other installment loans, consumers should be aware of the "fine print" described in the loan agreement. If a consumer repays a loan early, the lender is required by law to rebate a portion of the original finance charge or interest. Two methods exist for determining this rebate. The actuarial method is the primary method used by financial institutions today. This method provides the consumer with an accurate interest rebate for repaying the loan early. The second method, the rule of 78s, however, is still used by some lenders. The rule of 78s charges the consumer more interest during the first few months of the loan. The result is a lower interest rebate for the consumer. The rule of 78s originated as an easy way for lenders to compute interest rebates. It has been phased out gradually as calculators and computers become more available. Today the rule of 78s is most likely to be applied by used automobile dealers who specialize in offering loans to borrowers with a poor credit history.

In 1992, the U.S. Congress outlawed the use of the rule of 78s for loans longer than 61 months. In 2001, federal legislation was introduced to outlaw it altogether. At present, 17 states outlaw the use of the rule of 78s for all loans.

Actuarial method	**Rule of 78s**
$$u = \dfrac{n \cdot P \cdot V}{100 + V}$$	$$u = \dfrac{f \cdot k(k + 1)}{n(n + 1)}$$
u = unearned interest	u = unearned interest
n = number of remaining monthly payments (excluding current payment)	f = original finance charge
	k = number of remaining monthly payments (excluding current payment)
P = monthly payment	n = original number of payments
V = the value from the APR table that corresponds to the annual percentage rate for the number of remaining payments (excluding current payment)	

Example 4 illustrates the actuarial method used for calculating the unearned interest, and Example 5 illustrates the rule of 78s used for calculating the unearned interest.

EXAMPLE 4   Using the Actuarial Method

In Example 3, we determined the APR of Tino's loan to be 7.5%. Instead of making his 30th payment of his 48-payment loan, Tino wishes to pay his remaining balance and terminate the loan.

a) Use the actuarial method to determine how much interest Tino will save (the unearned interest, u) by repaying the loan early.

b) What is the total amount due to pay off the loan early on the day he makes his final payment?

SOLUTION:

a) Recall from Example 3 that Tino's monthly payments are $237.00. After 30 payments have been made, 18 payments remain. Thus, $n = 18$ and $P = \$237$. To determine V, use the APR table (Table 11.2). In the Number of Payments column find the number of remaining payments, 18, and then look to the right until you reach the column headed by 7.5%, the APR. This row and column intersect at 6.04. Thus, $V = 6.04$. Now use the actuarial method formula to determine the unearned interest, u.

$$u = \frac{n \cdot P \cdot V}{100 + V}$$

$$= \frac{(18)(237)(6.04)}{100 + 6.04}$$

$$\approx 242.99$$

Tino will save $242.99 in interest by the actuarial method.

b) Because the remaining payments total 18($237) = $4266, Tino's remaining balance is

$4266.00	Total of remaining payments (which includes interest)
− 242.99	Interest saved (unearned interest)
$4023.01	Balance due

A payment of $4023.01 plus the 30th monthly payment of $237 will terminate Tino's installment loan. The total amount due is $4023.01 + $237 = $4260.01. ▲

EXAMPLE 5   Using the Rule of 78s

In Example 3, we determine the APR of Tino's loan to be 7.5%. Instead of making his 30th payment of his 48 payment loan, Tino decides to pay his remaining balance and terminate the loan.

a) Use the rule of 78s to determine how much interest Tino will save by repaying the loan early.

b) What is the total amount due to pay off the loan early on the day he makes his final payment?

SOLUTION:

a) After the 30 payments have been made, 18 payments remain. Thus $k = 18$ and $n = 48$. From Example 3 we know the original finance charge, f, is $1576.

$$u = \frac{f \cdot k(k + 1)}{n(n + 1)}$$

$$= \frac{1576 \cdot 18(18 + 1)}{48(48 + 1)}$$

$$= \$229.16$$

Tino saves $229.16 in interest by the rule of 78s.

b) Tino's balance is computed in a manner similar to the method in Example 4.

$$
\begin{array}{ll}
\$4266.00 & \text{Total of remaining payments} \\
- \ 229.16 & \text{Interest saved} \\
\hline
\$4036.84 & \text{Balance due}
\end{array}
$$

A payment of $4036.84 plus the 30th monthly payment of $237 will terminate Tino's installment loan. The total amount due is $4036.84 + $237 = $4273.84. ▲

Open-End Installment Loan

A credit card is a popular way of making purchases or borrowing money. Use of a credit card is an example of an open-end installment loan. A typical charge account with a bank or store may have the terms in Table 11.3 on page 627.

Typically, credit card monthly statements contain the following information: balance at the beginning of the period, balance at the end of the period (or new balance), the transactions for the period, statement closing date (or billing date), payment due date, and the minimum payment due. For *purchases* there is no finance or interest charge if there is no previous balance due and you pay the entire new balance by the payment due date. However, if you borrow money (*cash advances*) through this account, a finance charge is applied from the date you borrowed the money until the date you repay the money. When you make purchases or borrow money, the minimum monthly payment is sometimes determined by dividing the balance due by 36 and rounding the answer up to the nearest whole dollar, thus ensuring repayment in 36 months. However, if the balance due for any month is less than $360, the minimum monthly payment is typically $10. These general guidelines may vary by bank and store.

TABLE 11.3   Credit Card Terms

Type of Charge	Daily Periodic Rate*	Annual Percentage Rate*
Purchases	0.03490%	12.74%
Cash advances	0.05477%	19.99%

These rates vary with different charge accounts and localities.

EXAMPLE 6   *Holiday Shopping Charges*

While doing her holiday shopping in November, Jan Reckard charged the following items to her Discover card: a set of tools for her husband ($250), an original print from a local artist for her daughter ($155), a set of classical music compact discs for her best friend ($100), and a gift certificate to a bookstore for her boss ($15). Her balance on December 1 is $250 + $155 + $100 + $15, or $520. The bank requires repayment within 36 months and charges an interest rate of 0.03490% per day.

a) Determine the minimum payment due on December 1.

b) On December 1, Jan makes a payment of $100. Determine the balance due on January 1, assuming that there are no additional charges or cash advances.

SOLUTION:

a) To determine the minimum payment, we divide the balance due on December 1 by 36. $520 ÷ 36 = $14.44. Rounding up to the nearest dollar, we determine that the minimum payment due on December 1 is $15.

b) With no additional purchases or cash advances and paying $100 on December 1, the balance on January 1 is $520 − $100 or $420. In addition, she must pay interest on the outstanding balance of $420 for the month of December. December has 31 days. The interest is

$$i = prt$$
$$= \$420(0.0003490)(31)$$
$$= \$4.54$$

Therefore, the balance due on January 1 is $420 + $4.54, or $424.54.   ▲

In Example 6, there were no additional transactions in the account for the period. When additional charges are made during the period, the finance charges on open-end installment loans or credit cards are generally calculated in one of two ways: the *unpaid balance method* or the *average daily balance method*. Example 7 illustrates the unpaid balance method and Example 8 illustrates the average daily balance method.

With the *unpaid balance method*, the borrower is charged interest or a finance charge on the unpaid balance from the previous charge period.

EXAMPLE 7   *Finance Charges Using the Unpaid Balance Method*

Ed Laughbaum charged all the supplies for his Halloween party to his Visa card. On November 5, the billing date, Ed had a balance due of $275. From November 5 through December 4, he did some shopping and charged items totaling $320, and he also made a payment of $145.

a) Find the finance charge due on December 5, using the unpaid balance method. Assume that the interest rate charged is 1.3% per month.

b) Find the new account balance on December 5.

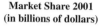
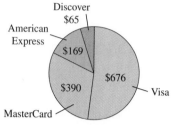
SOLUTION:

a) The finance charge is based on the $275 balance due on November 5. To find the finance charge due on December 5 we used the simple interest formula with a time of 1 month.

$$i = \$275 \times 0.013 \times 1 \approx \$3.58$$

The finance charge on December 5 is $3.58.

b) The balance due on December 5 is found by adding the costs of the new purchases and the calculated interest to the balance due on November 5, and then subtracting the payment made from this sum.

$$\$275 + \$320 + \$3.58 - \$145 = \$453.58$$

The balance due on December 5 is $453.58. The finance charge on January 5 is based on $453.58.   ▲

Many lending institutions use the *average daily balance method* of calculating the finance charge because they believe that it is fairer to the customer.

With the average daily balance method, a balance is determined each day of the billing period for which there is a transaction in the account. The average daily balance method is illustrated in Example 8.

EXAMPLE 8   *Finance Charges Using the Average Daily Balance Method*

The balance on Min Zeng's credit card account on July 1, the billing date, was $375.80. The following transactions occurred during the month of July.

July 5	Payment	$150.00
July 10	Charge: Toy store	74.35
July 18	Charge: Garage	123.50
July 28	Charge: Restaurant	42.50

a) Find the average daily balance for the billing period.
b) Find the finance charge to be paid on August 1. Assume that the interest rate is 1.3% per month.
c) Find the balance due on August 1.

SOLUTION:

a) To determine the average daily balance, we do the following. (i) Find the balance due for each transaction date.

July 1	$375.80				
July 5	$375.80	−	$150	=	$225.80
July 10	$225.80	+	$74.35	=	$300.15
July 18	$300.15	+	$123.50	=	$423.65
July 28	$423.65	+	$42.50	=	$466.15

(ii) Find the number of days that the balance did not change between each transaction. Count the first day in the period but not the last day. Note that from July 28 through August 1, the beginning of the next billing cycle, is 4 days.
(iii) Multiply the balance due by the number of days the balance did not change.
(iv) Find the sum of the products.

Date	(i) Balance due	(ii) Number of days balance did not change	(iii) (Balance)(Days)
July 1	$375.80	4	($375.80)(4) = $1503.20
July 5	$225.80	5	($225.80)(5) = $1129.00
July 10	$300.15	8	($300.15)(8) = $2401.20
July 18	$423.65	10	($423.65)(10) = $4236.50
July 28	$466.15	4	($466.15)(4) = $1864.60
		31	(iv) Sum = $11,134.50

(v) Divide this sum by the number of days in the billing cycle (in the month). The number of days may be found by adding the days in column (ii).

$$\frac{\$11,134.50}{31} = \$359.18$$

Thus, the average daily balance is $359.18.

b) The finance charge for the month is found using the simple interest formula with the average daily balance as the principal.

$$i = \$359.18 \times 0.013 \times 1 = \$4.67$$

c) Since the finance charge for the month is $4.67, the balance owed on August 1 is $466.15 + $4.67 or $470.82. ▲

The calculations in Example 8 are tedious. These calculations, however, are made almost instantaneously with computers.

Example 9 illustrates how a credit card may be used to borrow money.

EXAMPLE 9   *Using a Credit Card for a Cash Advance*

To obtain money to buy a stereo system at a garage sale Bobby Bueker obtained a cash advance of $1500 from his credit card. He borrowed the money on July 10 and repaid it on July 31. If Bobby is charged an interest rate of 0.05477% per day, how much did Bobby pay the credit card company on July 31?

SOLUTION: The amount Bobby pays is the original principal plus any accrued interest. Interest on cash advances is generally calculated for the exact number of days of the loan, starting with the day the money is obtained. The time of the loan in this case is 21 days. Using the simple interest formula we get the following:

$$
\begin{aligned}
i &= prt \\
&= \$1500 \times 0.0005477 \times 21 \\
&= \$17.25
\end{aligned}
$$

Therefore, Bobby must repay the credit card company $1500 + $17.25, or $1517.25. ▲

Anyone purchasing a car or other costly items should consider a number of different sources for a loan. Example 10 on page 630 illustrates one method of making a comparison.

DID YOU KNOW

No More PINs

An emeging technology may make *personal identification numbers* (PINs) at automatic teller machines (ATMs) a thing of the past. Iris-based identification systems use a series of cameras to identify people by the characteristics of the irises in their eyes. No two irises are identical, not even an individual's left and right irises. A representation of one of your irises would be obtained and stored electronically when you open an account. Each time you used your ATM card, instead of entering your PIN, the system would scan your eye and compare this to the representation on file. Similar systems have been successfully used at highly classified military installations throughout the United States. The system has been successfully tested at ATMs in London and may soon be tested in the United States. The technology also has huge potential to reduce credit card, debit card, and telephone calling card fraud.

EXAMPLE 10   *Comparing Loan Sources*

Franz Helfenstein purchased carpeting costing $2400 with his credit card. When the bill comes due on February 1, Franz realizes he can pay $350 per month until the debt is paid off. His credit card charges 1.5% interest per month.

a) Assuming that Franz makes no other purchases with this credit card, how many payments are necessary to retire this debt?

b) What is the total interest Franz will pay?

c) How much money could Franz have saved by obtaining a fixed installment loan of $2400 with an annual percentage rate of 6% interest with 6 equal monthly payments?

SOLUTION:

a) Franz would make his first monthly payment of $350 on February 1, resulting in a new balance of $2400 − $350 = $2050. His next bill reflects the $2050 balance plus the monthly interest. He continues to make payments until the debt is retired. For each date indicated the amount on the far right represents the amount due on that date.

February 1 $2400 − $350 = $2050

March 1 $2050 + 0.015($2050) = $2080.75; $2080.75 − $350 = $1730.75

April 1 $1730.75 + 0.015($1730.75) = $1756.71; $1756.71 − $350 = $1406.71

May 1 $1406.71 + 0.015($1406.71) = $1427.81; $1427.81 − $350 = $1077.81

June 1 $1077.81 + 0.015($1077.81) = $1093.98; $1093.98 − $350 = $743.98

July 1 $743.98 + 0.015($743.98) = $755.14; $755.14 − $350 = $405.14

August 1 $405.14 + 0.015($405.14) = $411.22; $411.22 − $350 = $61.22

September 1 $61.22 + 0.015($61.22) = $62.14

After eight payments—seven for $350 and one for $62.14—Franz has paid off his credit card bill for his carpeting.

b) To calculate the total interest paid, we add up all his payments and then subtract the cost of the carpeting:

$$\text{Total of all payments} = 7(\$350) + \$62.14$$
$$= \$2512.14$$
$$\text{Total interest} = \$2512.14 - \$2400$$
$$= \$112.14$$

c) To determine the interest that Franz pays, we will use Table 11.2 on page 623. From Table 11.2, we see that a fixed installment loan with an APR of 6% for 6 months corresponds to a finance charge of $1.76 per $100 of the amount financed. So the interest, or finance charge, is

$$\text{Finance charge} = 1.76\left(\frac{2400}{100}\right)$$
$$= 1.76(24)$$
$$= \$42.24$$

Therefore, Franz would save $112.14 − $42.24 = $69.90 in interest by using an installment loan instead of a credit card. ▲

SECTION 11.4 EXERCISES

Concept/Writing Exercises

1. Explain the difference between an open-end installment loan and a fixed installment loan.

2. Explain how an installment plan differs from a personal note.

3. What is an annual percentage rate (APR)?

4. What is a finance charge?

5. What is a total installment price?

6. Name the two methods used to determine the unearned interest when a loan is repaid early.

7. Name the two methods used to determine the finance charge on an open-end installment loan.

8. What is a cash advance?

Practice the Skills/Problem Solving

9. *Financing a New Boat* Pablo Silonto purchased a new boat for $43,000. He paid 15% as a down payment and financed the balance of the purchase with a 60-month fixed installment loan with an APR of 5.5%.
   a) Determine Pablo's total finance charge.
   b) Determine Pablo's monthly payment.

10. *New Appliances* Becky Kubiac wishes to purchase new appliances for her home. The total cost for the appliances is $2900. To finance the purchase, Becky must pay 20% down, with the balance being financed with a 24-month installment loan with an APR of 8.5%.
    a) Determine Becky's total finance charge.
    b) Determine Becky's monthly payment.

11. *Financing Student Loans* Joni Gile has a total of $4000 in student loans that will be paid with a 60-month installment loan with an APR of 7.5%.
    a) Determine Joni's total finance charge.
    b) Determine Joni's monthly payment.

12. *Financing Eye Surgery* Peg Pankowski plans to have laser eye surgery. The total cost of $2500 will be paid with a 48-month installment loan with an APR of 4.5%.
    a) Determine Peg's total finance charge.
    b) Determine Peg's monthly payment.

13. *Financing a New Business* Cheryl Sisson is a hair designer and wishes to convert her garage into a hair salon to use for her own business. The entire project would have a cash price of $3200. She decides to finance the project by paying 20% down, with the balance paid in 60 monthly payments of $53.14.
    a) What finance charge will Cheryl pay?
    b) What is the APR to the nearest half percent?

14. *Financing a Computer* Ilga Ross purchased a new laptop computer on a monthly purchase plan. The computer sold for $1495. Ilga paid 5% down and $64 a month for 24 months.
    a) What finance charge did Ilga pay?
    b) What is the APR to the nearest half percent?

15. *Financing a Used Car* Jack Keating wishes to purchase a used car that has a cash price of $12,000. The installment terms include a down payment of $3,000 and 48 monthly payments of $224.
    a) What finance charge will Jack pay?
    b) What is the APR to the nearest half percent?

16. *Financing Furniture* Mr. and Mrs. Chan want to buy furniture that has a cash price of $3450. On the installment plan they must pay 25% of the cash price as a down payment and make six monthly payments of $437.
    a) What finance charge will the Chans pay?
    b) What is the APR to the nearest half percent?

17. *Early Repayment Using the Actuarial Method* Ray Flagg took out a 60-month fixed installment loan of $12,000 to open a new pet store. He paid no money down and began making monthly payments of $232. Ray's business does better than expected and instead of making his 24th payment, Ray wishes to repay his loan in full.
    a) Determine the APR of the installment loan.
    b) How much interest will Ray save (use the actuarial method)?
    c) What is the total amount due to pay off the loan?

18. *Early Repayment Using the Actuarial Method* Coba Ling has a 48-month installment loan, with a fixed monthly payment of $167.67. The amount borrowed was $7500. Instead of making her 18th payment, Coba is paying the remaining balance on the loan.
    a) Determine the APR of the installment loan.

b) How much interest will Coba save (use the actuarial method)?

c) What is the total amount due to pay off the loan?

19. *Early Repayment Using the Actuarial Method* Nina Abu buys a new sport utility vehicle for $32,000. She trades in her old truck and receives $10,000, which she uses as a down payment. She finances the balance at 8% APR over 36 months. Before making her 24th payment, she decides to pay off the loan.

a) Use Table 11.2 to determine the total interest Nina would pay if all 36 payments were made.

b) What were Nina's monthly payments?

c) How much interest will Nina save (use the actuarial method)?

d) What is the total amount due to pay off the loan?

20. *Early Repayment Using the Actuarial Method* The cash price for furniture for Kathy Mowers's apartment was $6520. She made a down payment of $3962 and financed the balance on a 24-month fixed payment installment loan. The monthly payments are $110.52. Instead of making her 12th payment, Kathy decides to pay off the loan.

a) Determine the APR on the installment loan.

b) How much interest will Kathy save (use the actuarial method)?

c) What is the total amount due to pay off the loan?

21. *Early Repayment Using the Rule of 78s* Robert Malena wishes to purchase new equipment worth $7345, including taxes, for his landscaping business. Robert is able to secure a no-money-down, 48-month, 8.5% APR fixed installment loan from his local bank. Before making his 12th payment, Robert decides to pay off the loan with some of his yearly profits.

a) What was Robert's original finance charge?

b) What was Robert's original monthly payment?

c) How much interest will Robert save (use the rule of 78s)?

d) What is the total amount due to pay off the loan?

22. *Early Repayment Using the Rule of 78s* To pay for remodeling their kitchen the Leesebergs obtained a no-money down, 36-month, 8.5% fixed installment loan for the amount of $3600. Before making their 12th payment, the Leesebergs decide to pay off the loan.

a) What was the Leesebergs' original finance charge?

b) What was the Leesebergs' original monthly payment?

c) How much interest will the Leesebergs save (use the rule of 78s)?

d) What is the total amount due to pay off the loan?

23. *Early Repayment Using the Rule of 78s* Tony Gambino is buying a $3000 sound system by making a down payment of $500 and 18 monthly payments of $151.39. Instead of making his 12th payment, Tony decides to pay off the loan.

a) How much interest will Tony save (use the rule of 78s)?

b) What is the total amount due to pay off the loan?

24. *Early Repayment Using the Rule of 78s* Roger Golden purchased woodworking tools for $2375. He made a down payment of $850 and financed the balance with a 12-month fixed payment installment loan. Instead of making his sixth monthly payment of 134.71, he decides to pay off the loan.

a) How much interest will Roger save (use the rule of 78s)?

b) What is the total amount due to pay off the loan?

25. *Travel Expenses* To pay for his trip to Portland, Oregon for a teaching conference in November, David Dean charged the following expenses to his credit card: airfare ($365), hotel ($180), conference fee ($195), and meals ($84). David had a previous balance of zero, he bought no other items with this credit card, and on December 1 he made a payment of $200. The bank that issued the card requires repayment within 48 months and charges an interest rate of 1.1% per month.

a) What is the minimum payment due on December 1?

b) What is the balance due on January 1?

Portland, Oregon

26. *College Expenses* Brian Hickey uses his credit card in August to purchase the following college supplies: books ($425), yearlong bus pass ($175), food service meal ticket ($450), and season tickets to the basketball games ($125). On September 1, he used $650 of his financial aid check to reduce the balance. The issuing bank charges 1.2% interest per month and requires full payment within 36 months. Brian had a previous balance of zero and he makes no other purchases with this card.

a) What is the minimum payment due September 1?

b) What is the balance due on October 1?

27. *Business Expenses* In February, Denny Droessler used his credit card to pay for the following business expenses: truck repair ($423), lunch for himself and three of his

clients ($36), laundering of business uniforms ($145), and maintenance of equipment ($491). On March 1, he received payment from a client in the amount of $548 which he used as payment on his credit card. The issuing credit union charges 1.1% interest per month and requires full payment within 36 months. Denny had a previous balance of zero and he makes no other purchases with this card.
a) What is the minimum payment due March 1?
b) What is the balance due on April 1?

28. *Vacation Expenses* In June, while on vacation, the Greenbergs charged the following expenses to their credit card: airfare ($512), car rental ($172), meals ($190), and hotel ($350). On July 1, the Greenbergs paid $500 to reduce the balance. The issuing savings and loan charges 1.3% interest per month and requires full payment within 48 months. The Greenbergs make no other purchases with this card.
a) What is the minimum payment due on July 1?
b) What is the balance due on August 1?

29. *Unpaid Balance Method* On the April 5 billing date, Michaelle Chappell had a balance due of $1097.86 on her credit card. From April 5 through May 4, Michaelle charged an additional $425.79 and makes a payment of $800.
a) Find the finance charge on May 5, using the unpaid balance method. Assume that the interest rate is 1.8% per month.
b) Find the new balance on May 5.

30. *Unpaid Balance Method* On September 5, the billing date, Verna Brown had a balance due of $567.20 on her credit card. The transactions during the following month were

September 8	Payment	$275.00
September 21	Charge: Airline ticket	330.00
September 27	Charge: Hotel bill	190.80
October 2	Charge: Clothing	84.75

a) Find the finance charge on October 5, using the unpaid balance method. Assume that the interest rate is 1.1% per month.
b) Find the new balance on October 5.

31. *Unpaid Balance Method* On February 3, the billing date, Carol Ann Bluesky had a balance due of $124.78 on her credit card. Her bank charges an interest rate of 1.25% per month. She made the following transactions during the month:

February 8	Charge: Art supplies	$25.64
February 12	Payment	100.00
February 14	Charge: Flowers delivered	67.23
February 25	Charge: Music CD	13.90

a) Find the finance charge on March 3, using the unpaid balance method.
b) Find the new balance on March 3.

32. *Unpaid Balance Method* On April 15, the billing date, Gabrielle Michaelis had a balance due of $57.88 on her

credit card. She is redecorating her apartment and has the following transactions.

April 16	Charge: Paint	$64.75
April 20	Payment	45.00
May 3	Charge: Curtains	72.85
May 10	Charge: Chair	135.50

a) Find the finance charge on May 15, using the unpaid balance method. Assume that the interest rate is 1.35% per month.
b) Find the new balance on May 15.

33. *Average Daily Balance Method* The balance on the Razazada's credit card on May 12, their billing date, was $378.50. For the period ending June 12, they had the following transactions.

May 13	Charge: Toys	$129.79
May 15	Payment	50.00
June 1	Charge: Clothing	135.85
June 8	Charge: Housewares	37.63

a) Find the average daily balance for the billing period.
b) Find the finance charge to be paid on June 12. Assume an interest rate of 1.3% per month.
c) Find the balance due on June 12.

34. *Average Daily Balance Method* The Levy's credit card statement shows a balance due of $1578.25 on March 23, the billing date. For the period ending April 23, they had the following transactions.

March 26	Charge: Party supplies	$79.98
March 30	Charge: Restaurant meal	52.76
April 3	Payment	250.00
April 15	Charge: Clothing	190.52
April 22	Charge: Car repairs	190.85

a) Find the average daily balance for the billing period.
b) Find the finance charge to be paid on April 23. Assume an interest rate of 1.3% per month.
c) Find the balance due on April 23.

35. *Average Daily Balance Method* Refer to Exercise 31. Instead of the unpaid balance method, suppose that Carol Ann's bank uses the average daily balance method.
a) Find Carol Ann's average daily balance for the billing period from February 3 to March 3.
b) Find the finance charge to be paid on March 3.
c) Find the balance due on March 3.
d) Compare these answers with those in Exercise 31.

36. *Average Daily Balance Method* Refer to Exercise 30. Instead of the unpaid balance method, suppose Verna's bank uses the average daily balance method.
a) Find Verna's average daily balance for the billing period from September 5 to October 5.
b) Find the finance charge to be paid on October 5.
c) Find the balance due on October 5.
d) Compare these answers with those in Exercise 30.

37. *A Cash Advance* Travis Thompson uses his credit card to obtain a cash advance of $600 to pay for his textbooks in medical school. The interest rate charged for the loan is 0.05477% per day. Travis repays the money plus the interest after 27 days.
a) Determine the interest charged for the cash advance.
b) When he repaid the loan, how much did he pay the credit card company?

38. *A Cash Advance* John Richards borrowed $875 against his charge account on September 12 and repaid the loan on October 14 (32 days later). Assume that the interest rate is 0.04273% per day.
a) How much interest did John pay on the loan?
b) What amount did he pay the bank when he repaid the loan?

39. *Comparing Loan Sources* Grisha Stewart needs to borrow $1000 for an automobile repair. She finds that State National Bank charges 5% simple interest on the amount borrowed for the duration of the loan and requires the loan to be repaid in 6 equal monthly payments. Consumer's Credit Union offers loans of $1000 to be repaid in 12 monthly payments of $86.30.
a) How much interest is charged by the State National Bank?
b) How much interest is charged by the Consumer's Credit Union?
c) What is the APR, to the nearest half percent, on the State National Bank loan?
d) What is the APR, to the nearest half percent, on the Consumer Credit Union loan?

40. *Comparing Loan Options* Sara Lin wants to purchase a new television set. The purchase price is $890. If she purchases the set today and pays cash, she must take money out of her savings account. Another option is to charge the TV on her credit card, take the set home today, and pay next month. Next month she will have cash and can pay her credit card balance without paying any interest. The simple interest rate on her savings account is $5\frac{1}{4}\%$. How much is she saving by using the credit card instead of taking the money out of her savings account?

Challenge Problems/Group Activity

41. *Comparing Loans* Suppose the Chans in Exercise 16 use a credit card rather than an installment plan. Assume that

they make the same down payment, have no finance charge the first month, make no additional purchases on their credit card, and pay $432 per month plus the finance charge starting with the second month. If the interest rate is 1.3% per month
a) How many months will it take them to repay the loan?
b) How much interest will they pay on the loan?
c) Which method of borrowing will cost the Chans the least amount of interest, the installment loan in Exercise 16 or the credit card?

42. *Determining Purchase Price* Ken Tucker bought a new car, but now he cannot remember the original purchase price. His payments are $379.50 per month for 36 months. He remembers that the salesperson said the simple interest rate for the period of the loan was 6%. He also recalls he was allowed $2500 on his old car. Find the original purchase price.

43. *Repayment Comparisons* Joscelyn Jarrett obtained a new sport utility vehicle that had a cash price of $35,000 by paying 15% down and financing the balance with a 60-month fixed installment loan. The APR on the loan was 8.5%. Before making the 24th payment, Joscelyn decides to pay off the loan.
a) Determine the original finance charge on the 60-month loan.
b) Determine Joscelyn's monthly payment.
c) If the actuarial method is used, determine the amount of interest Joscelyn will save by paying the loan off early.
d) If the rule of 78s is used, determine the amount of interest Joscelyn will save by paying the loan off early.

44. *Repayment Comparisons* Christine Biko obtained a new speedboat that had a cash price of $23,000 by paying 10% down and financing the balance with a 48-month fixed installment loan. The APR on the loan was 6.0%. Before making the 12th payment, Christine decides to pay off the loan.
a) Determine the original finance charge on the 48-month loan.
b) Determine Christine's monthly payment.
c) If the actuarial method is used, determine the amount of interest Christine will save by paying the loan off early.
d) If the rule of 78s is used, determine the amount of interest Christine will save by paying the loan off early.

Recreational Mathematics

45. *Borrowing Money Interest Free* Martina Saul wants to buy a camera in time for a June 30 family gathering. She knows that she will not have the money to pay for the camera until August 5. The billing date on her credit card is the 25th of the month and she has a 20-day grace period from the billing date to pay the bill with no finance charge. Explain how she can buy the camera before June 30, pay for it after August 5, and pay no interest.

Internet/Research Activities

46. Write a brief report giving the advantages and disadvantages of leasing a car. Determine all the individual costs involved with leasing a car. Indicate why you would prefer to lease or purchase a car at the present time.

47. Assume that you are married and have a child. You don't own a washer and dryer and have no money to buy the appliances. Would it be cheaper to borrow money on an installment loan and buy the appliances or to continue to go to the local coin-operated laundry for 5 years until you have saved enough to pay cash for a washer and dryer?

    With the aid of parents or friends, establish how many loads of laundry you would be doing each week. Then determine the cost of doing that number of loads at a coin-operated laundry. (Don't forget the cost of transportation to the laundry.) Shop around for a washer and dryer, and determine the total cost on an installment plan. Don't forget to include the cost of gas, electricity, and water. This information can be obtained from a local gas and electric company. With this information, you should be able to make a decision about whether to buy now or wait for 5 years.

48. Do research on the features offered by MasterCard, Visa, Discover, and American Express. Include discussions of regular, gold, and platinum cards if they exist. For example, features might include life insurance when traveling by a common carrier, miles toward air travel, discounts on automobiles, cash back at the end of the year, insurance on rental cars, and the like. Determine which card or cards have the most appropriate features for you and explain why you arrived at that conclusion.

11.5 BUYING A HOUSE WITH A MORTGAGE

Buying a house is the largest purchase of a lifetime for most people. The purchaser will normally be committed to 10, 15, 20, 25, or 30 years of mortgage payments. Before selecting the "dream house," the buyer should consider the following questions: "Can I afford it?" and "Does it suit my needs?"

The question "Can I afford the house?" must be answered carefully and accurately. If a family buys a house beyond its means, it will have a difficult time living within its income. When deciding whether to purchase a particular house, the purchaser must also consider crucial questions such as "Do I have enough cash for the down payment and closing costs?" and "Can I afford the monthly payments with my current income?" These items, down payment, closing costs, and mortgage payments over time, constitute the buyer's total cost of buying a house.

Buyers usually seek a *mortgage* from a bank or other lending institution. Before approving a mortgage, which is a long-term loan, the bank will require the buyer to have a specified minimum amount for the down payment. The *down payment* is the amount of cash the buyer must pay to the seller before the lending institution will grant the buyer a mortgage. If the buyer has the down payment and meets the other criteria for the mortgage, the lending institution prepares a written agreement called the mortgage, stating the terms of the loan. The loan specifies the repayment schedule, the duration of the loan, whether the loan can be assumed by another party, and the penalty if payments are late. The party borrowing the money accepts the terms of this agreement and gives the lending institution the title or deed to the property as security.

Homeowner's Mortgage
A long-term loan in which the property is pledged as security for payment of the difference between the down payment and the sale price.

The two most popular types of mortgage loans available today are the *adjustable-rate loan* (or *variable-rate loan*) and the *conventional loan*. The major difference between the two is that the interest rate for a conventional loan is fixed for the duration of the loan, whereas the interest rate for the variable-rate loan may change every period, as specified in the loan. We will first discuss the requirements that are the same for both types of loans.

The size of the down payment required depends on who is lending the money, how old the property is, and whether or not it is easy to borrow money at that particular time. The down payment required by the lending institution can vary from 5% to 50% of the purchase price. A larger down payment is required when money is "tight," that is, when it is difficult to borrow money. Furthermore, most lending institutions tend to require larger down payments on older homes and smaller down payments on newer homes.

Most lending institutions may require the buyer to pay one or more *points* for their loan at the time of the *closing* (the final step in the sale process). *One point* amounts to 1% of the mortgage money (the amount being borrowed). By charging points, the bank reduces the rate of interest on the mortgage, thus reducing the size of the monthly payments and enabling more people to purchase houses. However, because they charge points, the rate of interest that banks state is not the APR (annual percentage rate) for the loan. The APR would be determined by adding the amount paid for points to the total interest paid and then using an APR table.

Conventional Loans

Example 1 illustrates purchasing a house with a conventional mortgage loan.

EXAMPLE 1   *Calculating Down Payment and Points*

Chris and Daryl Cahill want to purchase a house selling for $125,000. Their bank requires a 15% down payment and a payment of 1 point at the time of closing.
a) Determine the Cahill's down payment.
b) With a 15% down payment, determine the Cahill's mortgage.
c) What is the cost of the point paid by the Cahills on their mortgage.

SOLUTION:
a) The down payment is 15% of $125,000, or

$$0.15 \times \$125,000 = \$18,750$$

b) The mortgage on the Cahill's new home is the selling price minus the down payment.

$$\$125,000 - \$18,750 = \$106,250$$

c) One point equals 1% of the mortgage amount.

$$0.01 \times \$106,250 = \$1062.50$$

At the closing, the Cahills will pay the down payment of $18,750 to the seller and the 1 point, or $1062.50, to their bank.   ▲

Banks use a formula to determine the maximum monthly payment that they believe is within the purchaser's ability to pay. A mortgage loan officer first determines the buyer's *adjusted monthly income* by subtracting from the gross monthly income

(total income before any deductions) any fixed monthly payments with more than 10 months remaining (such as for a student loan, a car, furniture, or a television). The loan officer then multiplies the adjusted monthly income by 28%. (This percent, and the maximum number of payments remaining on other fixed loans, may vary in different locations.) In general, this product is the maximum monthly house payment the lending institution believes the purchaser can afford to pay. This payment must cover principal, interest, property taxes, and insurance. Taxes and insurance are not necessarily paid to the bank; they may be paid directly to the tax collector and the insurance company. Example 2 shows how a bank uses the formula to determine whether a prospective buyer qualifies for a mortgage.

EXAMPLE 2 *Qualifying for a Mortgage*

Suppose that the Cahill's (see Example 1) gross monthly income is $4200 and that they have 15 remaining payments of $185 per month on their car loan and 14 remaining payments of $35 per month on a loan used to purchase a new washer and dryer. The taxes on the house they want to purchase are $135 per month and the insurance is $38 per month.

a) What maximum monthly payment does the bank's loan officer think the Cahills can afford?

b) The Cahills want a 30-year $106,250 mortgage. If the interest rate is 6.5%, determine whether the Cahills qualify for the mortgage.

SOLUTION:

a) To find the maximum monthly payment the bank's loan officer believes the Cahills can afford first determine their adjusted monthly income.

$$\begin{array}{ll} \$4200 & \text{Gross income} \\ -\,220 & \text{Monthly payments (car and appliance loans)} \\ \hline \$3980 & \text{Adjusted monthly income} \end{array}$$

Next find 28% of the adjusted monthly income.

$$0.28 \times \$3980 = \$1114.40$$

The loan officer determines that the Cahills can afford a maximum monthly payment—including principal, interest, taxes, and insurance—of $1114.40.

b) To determine whether the Cahills qualify for a 30-year conventional mortgage with their current income calculate the total monthly payment the Cahills would have to pay, including principal, interest, property taxes, and insurance. Then compare the calculated total monthly payment with the maximum payment the bank's loan officer thinks the Cahills can afford, which was calculated in part (a).

Lending institutions and lawyers use computer programs or calculators to determine monthly mortgage payments, per thousand dollars, for a specific number of years at a specific rate. This information can also obtained from one of many mortgage calculator webpages on the Internet. Table 11.4 on page 638 gives monthly mortgage payments, including principal and interest, per $1000 of mortgage. With an interest rate of 6.5%, a 30-year loan would have a monthly mortgage payment of $6.32 (circled in blue) per thousand dollars of mortgage.

To determine the Cahill's monthly mortgage payment of principal and interest first divide the mortgage by $1000. This will give the number of thousands of dollars of the mortgage.

$$\frac{106{,}250}{1000} = 106.25$$

Then find the monthly mortgage payment by multiplying the number of thousands of dollars of mortgage, 106.25, by the value found in Table 11.4, $6.32.

$$\$106.25 \times \$6.32 = \$671.50$$

The monthly payment for principal and interest is $671.50. To the $671.50, add the monthly cost of real estate taxes, $135, and insurance of $38, for a total cost of $844.50. Since $844.50 is less than $1114.40, the maximum monthly payment the loan officer determined the Cahills can afford, the Cahills will most likely be granted the loan. ▲

TABLE 11.4   Monthly Payment per $1000 of Mortgage, Including Principal and Interest

| | | Number of Years | | | |
Rate %	10	15	20	25	30
4	$10.12	$7.40	$6.06	$5.28	$4.77
4.5	10.36	7.65	6.33	5.56	5.07
5	10.61	7.91	6.60	5.85	5.37
5.5	10.85	8.17	6.88	6.14	5.68
6	11.10	8.44	7.16	6.44	6.00
6.5	11.35	8.71	7.46	6.75	6.32
7	11.61	8.99	7.75	7.07	6.65
7.5	11.87	9.27	8.06	7.39	6.99
8	12.13	9.56	8.36	7.72	7.34
8.5	12.40	9.85	8.68	8.05	7.69
9	12.67	10.14	9.00	8.40	8.05
9.5	12.94	10.44	9.33	8.74	8.41
10	13.22	10.75	9.66	9.09	8.70
10.5	13.49	11.05	9.98	9.44	9.15
11	13.78	11.37	10.32	9.80	9.52
11.5	14.06	11.68	10.66	10.16	9.90
12	14.35	12.00	11.01	10.53	10.29

What is the effect on the monthly payments when only the period of time has been changed? The total monthly payments for the Cahills in Example 2 would have been $1378.94 for 10 years, $1098.44 for 15 years, $965.63 for 20 years, $890.19 for 25 years, and $844.50 for 30 years. (You should verify these numbers yourself.) Increasing the length of time decreases the monthly payment but increases the total amount of interest paid because the borrower is paying for a longer period of time. The longer the term of a mortgage, the more expensive the total cost of the house.

EXAMPLE 3   *The Total Cost of a House*

The Cahills of Examples 1 and 2 obtained a house selling for $125,000. They made a 15% down payment and obtained a 30-year conventional mortgage for $106,250 at 6.5%. They also paid 1 point at closing. Their monthly mortgage payment of principal and interest is $671.50.

a) Determine the total amount including principal, interest, the down payment, and the points that the Cahills will pay the bank for their house over 30 years.

b) How much of the cost will be interest?

c) How much of the first payment on the mortgage is applied to the principal?

SOLUTION:

a) To find the total amount the Cahills will pay for their house perform the following computation:

	$671.50	Mortgage payment for 1 month
×	12	Number of months in a year
	$8058.00	Mortgage payments for 1 year
×	30	Number of years in the mortgage
	$241,740.00	Total mortgage payments
+	18,750.00	Down payment
+	1,062.50	1 point
	$261,552.50	Total cost of the house

Note: The result might not be the exact cost of the house, since the final payment on the mortgage might be slightly more or less than the regular monthly payment.

b) To determine the amount of interest paid over 30 years subtract the purchase price of the house and the cost of the points from the total cost.

$261,552.50	Total cost
−125,000.00	Purchase price
$136,552.50	Total interest including one point
− 1,062.50	1 point
$135,490.00	Total interest on mortgage payments

c) To find the amount of the first payment that is applied to the principal subtract the amount of interest on the first payment from the monthly mortgage payment. Use the simple interest formula to find the interest on the first payment.

$$i = prt$$

$$= \$106,250 \times 0.065 \times \frac{1}{12}$$

$$\approx \$575.52$$

Now subtract the interest for the first month from the monthly mortgage payment. The difference will be the amount paid on the principal for the first month.

$671.50	Monthly mortgage payment
−575.52	Interest paid for the first month
$95.98	Principal paid for the first month

Thus, the first payment of $671.50 consists of $575.52 in interest and $95.98 in principal. The $95.98 is applied to reduce the loan. Thus, the balance due after the first payment is $106,250 − $95.98, or $106,154.02.   ▲

By repeatedly using the simple interest formula month-to-month on the unpaid balance, you could calculate the principal and the interest for all the payments—a tedious task. However, a list containing the payment number, payment on the interest, payment on the principal, and balance of the loan, can be prepared using a computer. Such a list is called a loan *amortization schedule*. One way to obtain an amortization schedule is by using a computer spreadsheet program. Another way is to access an amortization "calculator" program on the Internet. A part of the amortization schedule for the Cahill's loan in Example 3 is given in Table 11.5. This schedule was generated from an Internet site called *Monthly Mortgage Payment Calculator* (*www.hsh.com*). Note that the monthly payment in Table 11.5 ($671.57) is slightly more than the monthly payment we calculated using Table 11.4 ($671.50). This difference is due to a rounding error that occurs when estimating the monthly principal and interest payment from Table 11.4.

TABLE 11.5 Amortization Schedule

Annual % Rate: 6.5 Loan: $106,250 Periods: 360		Monthly Payment: $671.57 Term: Years 30, Months 0	
Payment Number	Interest	Principal	Balance of Loan
1	$575.52	$96.05	$106,153.95
2	$575.00	$96.57	$106,057.38
3	$574.48	$97.09	$105,960.28
4	$573.95	$97.62	$105,862.66
11	$570.19	$101.38	$105,164.35
12	$569.64	$101.93	$105,062.42
119	$489.88	$181.69	$90,257.31
120	$488.89	$182.68	$90,074.63
239	$324.14	$347.43	$59,493.68
240	$322.26	$349.31	$59,144.36
359	$7.22	$664.36	$667.95
360	$3.62	$667.95	$0.00

Adjustable-Rate Mortgages

Now let's consider *adjustable-rate mortgages*, ARMs (also called *variable-rate mortgages*). The rules for ARMs vary from state to state and from bank to bank, so the material presented on ARMs may not apply in your state or at your local lending institution. Generally, with adjustable-rate mortgages, the monthly mortgage payment remains the same for a 1-, 2-, or 5-year period even though the interest rate of the mortgage may change every 3 months, 6 months, or some other predetermined period. The interest rate for an adjustable-rate mortgage may be based on an index that is determined by the Federal Home Loan Bank Association or it may be based on the interest rate of a 3-month, 6-month, or 1-year Treasury bill. The interest rate of a 3-month Treasury bill may change every 3 months, the interest rate on a 6-month Treasury bill may change every 6 months, and so on. When the base is a Treasury bill, the actual interest rate charged for the mortgage is often determined by adding 3% to $3\frac{1}{2}$%, called the *add on rate* or *margin*, to the rate of the Treasury bill. Thus, if the rate of the Treasury bill is 6% and the add on rate is 3%, the interest rate charged is 9%.

EXAMPLE 4   *An Adjustable-Rate Mortgage*

Tony and Keisha Torrence purchased a house for $115,000 with a down payment of $23,100. They obtained a 30-year adjustable-rate mortgage with the following terms. The interest rate is based on a 6-month Treasury bill. The interest rate charged is 3% above the interest rate of the 6-month Treasury bill (3% is the add on rate). The interest rate is adjusted every 6 months on the date of adjustment. The interest rate will not change more than 1% (up or down) when the interest rate is adjusted. The maximum interest rate for the duration of the loan is 12%. There is no lower limit on the interest rate. The initial mortgage interest rate is 5.5%, and the monthly payments (including principal and interest) are adjusted every 5 years.

a) Determine the initial monthly payment.

b) Determine the adjusted interest rate in 6 months if the interest rate on the Treasury bill at that time is 2%.

SOLUTION:

a) To determine the initial monthly payment of interest and principal divide the amount of the loan, $115,000 − $23,100 = $91,900, by $1000. The result is 91.9. Now multiply the number of thousands of dollars of mortgage, 91.9, by the value found in Table 11.4 with $r = 5.5\%$ for 30 years. The value found in the table is $5.68.

$$\$5.68 \times 91.9 \approx \$521.99$$

Thus, the initial monthly payment for principal and interest is $521.99. This amount will not change for the first 5 years of the mortgage.

b) The adjusted interest rate in 6 months will be the Treasury bill rate plus the add on rate.

$$2\% + 3\% = 5\%$$

In Example 4(b), note that the rate after 6 months, 5%, is lower than the initial rate of 5.5%. Since the monthly payment remains the same, the additional money paid the bank is applied to reduce the principal. The monthly interest and principal payment of $521.99 would pay off the loan in 30 years if the interest remained constant at 5.5%. What happens if the interest rate drops and stays lower than the initial 5.5% for the length of the loan? In this case, at the end of each 5-year period the bank reduces the monthly payment so that the loan will be paid off in 30 years. What happens if the interest rate increases above the initial 5.5% rate? In this case, part of, or if necessary, all of the mortgage payment that would normally go toward repaying the principal would be used to meet the interest obligation. At the end of the 5-year period, the bank will increase the monthly payment so that the loan can be repaid by the end of the 30-year period. Or the bank may increase the time period of the loan beyond 30 years so that the monthly payment is affordable.

To prevent rapid increases in interest rates, some banks have a rate cap. A *rate cap* limits the maximum amount the interest rate may change. A *periodic rate cap* limits the amount the interest rate may increase in any one period. For example, your mortgage could provide that, even if the index increases by 2% in 1 year, your rate can only go up 1% per year. An *aggregate rate cap* limits the interest rate increase and decrease over the entire life of the loan. If the initial interest rate is 6% and the aggregate rate cap is 2%, the interest rate could go no higher than 8% and no lower than 4% over the life of the mortgage. A *payment cap* limits the amount the monthly payment may change but does not limit changes in interest rates. If interest rates increase rapidly on a loan with a payment cap, the monthly payment may not be large enough to pay the monthly principal and interest on the loan. If that happens, the borrower could end up paying interest on interest.

Other Types of Mortgages

Conventional mortgages and adjustable-rate mortgages are not the only methods of financing the purchase of a house. Next, we briefly describe four other methods, and we briefly discuss home equity loans.

FHA Mortgage

A house can be purchased with a smaller down payment than with a conventional mortgage if the individual qualifies for a Federal Housing Administration (FHA) loan. The loan application is made through a local bank. The bank's loan officer determines the maximum monthly payment a loan applicant can afford by taking 29% of the adjusted monthly income. The bank provides the money, but the FHA insures the loan. The down payment for an FHA loan is as low as 2.5% of the purchase price, rather than the standard 5–50%. Another advantage is FHA loans can be assumed at the original rate of interest on the loan. For example, if you purchase a home today that already has a 6% FHA mortgage, you, the new buyer, can assume that 6% mortgage regardless of the current interest rates. However, to be able to assume a mortgage, the purchaser must be able to make a down payment equal to the difference between the purchase price of the house and the balance due on the original mortgage. The government sets the maximum interest rate the lender may charge.

One drawback to FHA loans is that the borrower must pay an FHA insurance premium as part of the monthly mortgage payment. The insurance premium is calculated at a rate of one-half percent (0.5%) of the unpaid balance of the loan on the anniversary date of the loan. Thus, even though the insurance premium decreases each year, it adds to the monthly payments.

VA Mortgage

A veteran certified by the Department of Veterans Affairs (VA) who wants to purchase a house applies for a mortgage with a bank or lending institution. The individual must meet the requirements set by the bank or lending institution for a mortgage. The VA guarantees repayment of a certain percentage of the loan obtained by the individual should the individual default on the loan. For example, if the loan is less than $45,000, the VA guarantees 50% of the loan. For loans from $45,000 to $144,000, the VA guarantees the lesser of 40% of the loan or $36,000. Since the bank has this guarantee from the VA, qualified veterans often do not have to make a down payment. A veteran who can make the monthly mortgage payments may therefore obtain a certain mortgage without a down payment.

The government sets the maximum interest rate that the lender may charge. A VA loan is always assumable. With a VA loan, the seller may be asked to pay points, but there is no monthly insurance premium.

Graduated Payment Mortgage (GPM)

A GPM mortgage is designed so that for the first 5 to 10 years the size of the mortgage payment is smaller than the payments for the remaining time of the mortgage. After the first 5- to 10-year period, the mortgage payments are increased. The mortgage payments then remain constant for the duration of the mortgage. Depending on the size of the mortgage, the lender might find that the monthly payments made for the first few years may actually be less than the interest owed on the loan for those few years. The interest not paid during the first few years of the mortgage is then added to the original loan. This type of loan is strictly for those who are confident their annual incomes will increase as rapidly as the mortgage payments do.

Balloon-Payment Mortgage (BPM)

The BPM type of loan could be for the person who needs time to find a permanent loan. It may work this way: The individual pays the interest for 3 to 8 years, the period of the loan. At the end of the 3- to 8-year period, the buyer must repay the entire principal unless the lender agrees to a loan extension. Balloon-payment loans generally offer lower rates than conventional mortgages. This type of loan may be advantageous if the buyer plans to sell the house before the maturity date of the balloon-payment mortgage.

Home Equity Loans

As you make monthly payments and pay off the principal you owe on your home, you are said to be gaining *equity* in your home. **Equity** is the difference between the appraised value of your home and your loan balance. This equity can be used as collateral in obtaining a loan. Such a loan is referred to as a **home equity loan** or a **second mortgage.** One advantage of home equity loans over other types of loans (such as installment loans) is that the interest charged on a home equity loan is often tax deductible on federal income taxes. Home equity loans are commonly used for home improvements, for bill consolidation, or to pay for college education expenses.

For further information about the types of mortgages or loans discussed in this section, consult a loan officer at a local bank, a savings and loan, or a credit union. Additional information on buying a house may be obtained from the U.S. Government Printing Office in Pueblo, CO 81009. This information is also available on the Internet at *http://www.access.gpo.gov*.

DID YOU KNOW

Investing in Mutual Funds

A *mutual fund* is an investment tool that enables investors to indirectly own a wide variety of stocks, bonds, or other investments. When investors purchase shares in a mutual fund, they are actually placing their money in a pool along with many other investors. An investment company that invests in many different stocks, bonds, or other investments manages this pool of money. The investments within a mutual fund are called the mutual fund's *portfolio*. The investors of a mutual fund share the gains and losses from the investments within the portfolio. There are some distinct advantages to investing in mutual funds rather than investing in individual stocks and bonds. First, investors in mutual funds have their money managed by full-time professionals who research and evaluate hundreds of stocks and bonds every day. Such management may help investors avoid poor investments. Second, because large sums of money are managed within a mutual fund, costs related to investing, known as *commissions,* are generally lower than they are for purchasing individual stocks and bonds. Third, when investors purchase shares in a mutual fund, they are indirectly purchasing shares in a multitude of stocks or bonds. This diversification can greatly help to reduce some of the risks of investing. Finally, investors can easily buy and sell shares in a mutual fund through the mail, over the telephone, or on the Internet, often without having to pay commissions.

One disadvantage of mutual fund investing is the potential to miss out on a large return on investment. For example, if on October 1, 2002, an investor had invested $1000 in stock shares of Dobson Communications, by January 1, 2003, this investment would have been worth $6620.70. Meanwhile, despite this remarkable gain, several mutual funds that included Dobson Communications in their portfolios actually lost money over the same period because of poor performance by other stocks in their portfolios. In general, though, investing in mutual funds is considered an excellent way to begin investing and to maintain diverse ownership in a variety of investments.

SECTION 11.5   EXERCISES

Concept/Writing Exercises

1. What is a mortgage?

2. What is a down payment?

3. What is the difference between a variable-rate mortgage and a conventional mortgage?

4. **a)** What are points in a mortgage agreement?
   b) Explain how to determine the cost of x points.

5. Explain how to determine a buyer's adjusted monthly income.

6. What is an add on rate, or margin?

7. What is an amortization schedule?

8. Who insures an FHA loan? Who provides the money for an FHA loan?

9. What is equity?

10. What is a home equity loan?

Problem Solving

11. *Buying a House* Sally Jacobs wishes to buy a house selling for $250,000. Her credit union requires her to make a 15% down payment. The current mortgage rate is 4.5%.
    a) Determine the amount of the required down payment.
    b) Determine the monthly mortgage payment for a 15-year loan with a 15% down payment.

12. *Down Payment and Mortgage Payment* Thomas Osler is buying a townhouse selling for $175,000. His bank is requiring a minimum down payment of 20%. The current mortgage rate is 5.5%.
    a) Determine the amount of the required down payment.
    b) Determine the monthly mortgage payment for a 30-year loan with the minimum down payment.

13. *Monthly Payment on a Condominium* Mary Beth and Ken Henkel are buying a new condominium for $210,000. Their bank is requiring a minimum down payment of 10%. The current mortgage rate is 5%.
    a) Determine the amount of the required down payment.
    b) Determine the monthly mortgage payment for a 20-year loan with the minimum down payment.

14. *Buying a First Home* Sandra Coleman's family is purchasing their first home, which is selling for $95,000. The credit union is requiring a minimum down payment of 5%. The current mortgage rate is 7%.
    a) Determine the amount of the required down payment.

b) Determine the monthly mortgage payment for a 30-year loan with the minimum down payment.

15. *Paying Points* Martha Cutler is buying a house selling for $195,000. The bank is requiring a minimum down payment of 20%. To obtain a 20-year mortgage at 6% interest she must pay 2 points at the time of closing.
    a) What is the required down payment?
    b) With the 20% down payment, what is the amount of the mortgage?
    c) What is the cost of the 2 points?

16. *Down Payment and Points* The Nicols are buying a house selling for $245,000. They pay a down payment of $45,000 from the sale of their current house. To obtain a 15-year mortgage at 4.5% interest the Nicols must pay 1.5 points at the time of closing.
    a) What is the amount of the mortgage?
    b) What is the cost of the 1.5 points?

17. *Qualifying for a Mortgage* Pietr and Helga Guenther's gross monthly income is $3200. They have 25 remaining car payments of $335. The Guenthers are applying for a 15-year, $150,000 mortgage at 5% interest to buy a new house. The taxes and insurance on the house are $225 per month.
    a) Determine the Guenther's adjusted monthly income.
    b) Determine the maximum monthly payment a lender feels the Guenthers can afford.
    c) Determine the monthly mortgage payment plus taxes and insurance.
    d) Do the Guenthers qualify for this mortgage?

18. *Qualifying for a Mortgage* Ting-Fang and Su-hua Zheng's gross monthly income is $4100. They have 18 remaining boat payments of $505. The Zhengs are applying for a 20-year, $275,000 mortgage at 9% interest to buy a new house. The taxes and insurance on the house are $425 per month.
    a) Determine the Zheng's adjusted monthly income.
    b) Determine the maximum monthly payment a lender feels the Zhengs can afford.

c) Determine the monthly mortgage payment plus taxes and insurance.

d) Do the Zhengs qualify for this mortgage?

19. *A 30-Year Conventional Mortgage* Ingrid Holzner obtains a 30-year, $63,750 conventional mortgage at 8.5% on a house selling for $75,000. Her monthly payment, including principal and interest, is $490.24.

a) Determine the total amount Ingrid will pay for her house.

b) How much of the cost will be interest?

c) How much of the first payment on the mortgage is applied to the principal?

20. *A 25-Year Conventional Mortgage* Mr. and Mrs. Alan Bell obtain a 25-year, $110,000 conventional mortgage at 10.5% on a house selling for $160,000. Their monthly mortgage payment, including principal and interest, is $1038.40.

a) Determine the total amount the Bells will pay for their house.

b) How much of the cost will be interest?

c) How much of the first payment on the mortgage is applied to the principal?

21. *Evaluating a Loan Request* The Rosens found a house selling for $113,500. The taxes on the house are $1200 per year, and insurance is $320 per year. They are requesting a conventional loan from the local bank. The bank is currently requiring a 28% down payment and 3 points, and the interest rate is 10%. The Rosen's monthly income is $4750. They have more than 10 monthly payments remaining on a car, a boat, and furniture. The total monthly payments for these items is $420.

a) Determine the required down payment.

b) Determine the cost of the 3 points.

c) Determine their adjusted monthly income.

d) Determine the maximum monthly payment the bank's loan officer believes they can afford.

e) Determine the monthly payments of principal and interest for a 20-year loan.

f) Determine their total monthly payment, including insurance and taxes.

g) Determine whether the Rosens qualify for the 20-year loan.

h) Determine how much of the first payment on the loan is applied to the principal.

22. *Evaluating a Loan Request* Kathy Fields wants to buy a condominium selling for $95,000. The taxes on the property are $1500 per year, and insurance is $336 per year. Kathy's gross monthly income is $4000. She has 15 monthly payments of $135 remaining on her van. The bank is requiring 20% down and is charging 9.5% interest.

a) Determine the required down payment.

b) Determine the maximum monthly payment the bank's loan officer believes Kathy can afford.

c) Determine the monthly payment of principal and interest for a 25-year loan.

d) Determine her total monthly payment, including insurance and taxes.

e) Does Kathy qualify for the loan?

f) Determine how much of the first payment on the mortgage is applied to the principal.

g) Determine the total amount she pays for the condominium with a 25-year conventional loan. (Do not include taxes or insurance.)

h) Determine the total interest paid for the 25-year loan.

23. *Comparing Loans* The Riveras are negotiating with two banks for a mortgage to buy a house selling for $105,000. The terms at bank A are a 10% down payment, an interest rate of 10%, a 30-year conventional mortgage, and 3 points to be paid at the time of closing. The terms at bank B are a 20% down payment, an interest rate of 11.5%, a 25-year conventional mortgage, and no points. Which loan should the Riveras select in order for the total cost of the house to be less?

24. *Comparing Loans* Paul Westerberg is negotiating with two credit unions for a mortgage to buy a condominium selling for $525,000. The terms at Grant County Teacher's Credit Union are a 20% down payment, an interest rate of 7.5%, a 15-year mortgage, and 1 point to be paid at the time of closing. The terms at Sinnipee Consumer's Credit Union are a 15% down payment, an interest rate of 8.5%, a 20-year mortgage, and no points. Which loan should Paul select for the total cost of the down payment, points, and total mortgage payments of the house to be less?

Challenge Problems/Group Activities

25. *An Adjustable-Rate Mortgage* The Simpsons purchased a house for $105,000 with a down payment of $5000. They obtained a 30-year adjustable-rate mortgage. The terms of the mortgage are as follows: The interest rate is based on a 3-month Treasury bill, the interest rate charged is 3.25% above the rate of the Treasury bill on the date of adjustment, the interest rate is adjusted every 3 months, the interest rate will not change more than 1% (up or down) when the interest rate is adjusted, the maximum interest rate that can be charged for the duration of the loan is 16%, there is no lower limit on the interest rate, the initial mortgage interest rate is 9%, and the monthly payment of interest and principal is adjusted semiannually.

a) Determine the initial monthly payment for interest and principal.

b) Determine an amortization schedule for months 1–3.

c) Determine the interest rate for months 4–6 if the interest rate on the Treasury bill at the time is 6.13%.

d) Determine an amortization schedule for months 4–6.

e) Determine the interest rate for months 7–9 if the interest rate on the Treasury bill at the time is 6.21%.

26. *An Adjustable-Rate Mortgage* The Bretz family purchased a house for $95,000 with a down payment of $13,000. They obtained a 30-year adjustable-rate mortgage. The terms of the mortgage are as follows: The interest rate is based on a 3-month Treasury bill, the interest rate charged is 3.25% above the rate of the Treasury bill on the date of adjustment, the interest rate is adjusted every 3 months, the interest rate will not change more than 1% (up or down) when the interest rate is adjusted, the maximum interest rate that can be charged for the duration of the loan is 16%, there is no lower limit on the interest rate, the initial mortgage interest rate is 8.5%, and the monthly payment of interest and principal is adjusted annually.

a) Determine the initial monthly payment for interest and principal.

b) Determine the interest rate in 3 months if the interest rate on the Treasury bill at the time is 5.65%.

c) Determine the interest rate in 6 months if the interest rate on the Treasury bill at the time is 4.85%.

27. *How Much House Can They Afford?* A bank's loan officer determines that the Pappys can afford to make a $950 monthly mortgage payment. If the bank will give them a 25-year conventional mortgage at 9% and requires a 25% down payment, what is

a) the maximum mortgage the bank will grant the Pappys?

b) the highest-priced house they can afford?

28. *Comparing Mortgages* The Hassads are applying for a $90,000 mortgage. They can choose between a conventional mortgage and a variable-rate mortgage. The interest rate on a 30-year conventional mortgage is 9.5%. The terms of the variable-rate mortgage are 6.5% interest rate the first year, an annual cap of 1%, and an aggregate cap of 6%. The interest rates and the mortgage payments are adjusted annually. Assume that the interest rates for the variable-rate mortgage increase by the maximum amount each year. Then the monthly mortgage payments for the variable-rate mortgage for years 1–6 are $568.86, $628.05, $688.29, $749.35, $811.02, and $873.11, respectively.

a) Knowing that they will be in the house for only 6 years, which mortgage, the conventional mortgage or the variable-rate mortgage, will be the least expensive for that period?

b) How much will they save by choosing the less expensive mortgage?

Internet/Research Activities

29. *Finding Your Dream Home* Examine a local newspaper to find your "dream home" and note the asking price. Next contact a loan officer from your local bank, savings and loan, or credit union. Assuming you can make a 20% down payment, determine the interest rates for a 15-year and a 30-year mortgage. Use an amortization calculator (see page 640) with the data you obtained to print amortizations schedules. Compare the monthly payments with the 15-year mortgage to those of the 30-year mortgage. Compare the total interest costs of the 15-year mortgage with those of the 30-year mortgage. Write a report summarizing your findings.

30. *Closing Costs* An important part of buying a house is the closing. The exact procedures for the closing differ with individual cases and in different parts of the country. In any closing, however, both the buyer and the seller have certain expenses. To determine what is involved in the closing of a property in your community, contact a lawyer, a real estate agent, or a banker. Explain that you are a student and that your objective is to understand the procedure for closing a real estate purchase and the costs to both buyer and seller. Select a specific piece of property that is for sale. Use the asking price to determine the total closing costs to both buyer and seller. The following is a partial list of the most common costs. Consider them in your research.

a) Fee for title search and title insurance

b) Credit report on buyer

c) Fees to the lender for services in granting the loan

d) Fee for property survey

e) Fee for recording of the deed

f) Appraisal fee

g) Lawyer's fee

h) Escrow accounts (taxes, insurance)

i) Mortgage assumption fee

CHAPTER 11 SUMMARY

IMPORTANT FACTS

Ordinary interest

When computing ordinary interest, each month is considered to have 30 days and a year is considered to have 360 days.

United States rule

If a partial payment is made on a loan, interest is computed on the principal from the first day of the loan until the date of the partial payment. The partial payment is used to pay the interest first; then the rest of the payment is used to reduce the principal.

Banker's rule

When computing interest with the Banker's rule, a year is considered to have 360 days and any fractional part of a year is the exact number of days.

Simple interest formula

Interest $=$ principal $\times$ rate $\times$ time or $i = prt$

$$\text{Percent change} = \frac{\text{amount in latest period} - \text{amount in previous period}}{\text{amount in previous period}} \times 100$$

$$\text{Percent markup on cost} = \frac{\text{selling price} - \text{dealer's cost}}{\text{dealer's cost}} \times 100$$

Compound interest formula

$$A = p\left(1 + \frac{r}{n}\right)^{nt}$$

Present value formula

$$p = \frac{A}{\left(1 + \frac{r}{n}\right)^{nt}}$$

Actuarial method

$$u = \frac{u \cdot P \cdot V}{100 + V}$$

Rule of 78s

$$u = \frac{f \cdot k(k + 1)}{n(n + 1)}$$

CHAPTER 11   REVIEW EXERCISES

11.1

Change the number to a percent. Express your answer to the nearest tenth of a percent.

1. $\dfrac{3}{5}$ 2. $\dfrac{2}{3}$ 3. $\dfrac{5}{8}$

4. 0.041   5. 0.0098   6. 3.141

Change the percent to a decimal number.

7. 3%   8. 12.1%   9. 123%

10. $\dfrac{1}{4}\%$ 11. $\dfrac{5}{6}\%$ 12. 0.00045%

13. *Lambeau Field* Before undergoing renovations, the seating capacity at Lambeau Field (in Green Bay, Wisconsin) was 60,790. After the renovations were complete the seating capacity was 71,500. Determine the percent increase (to the nearest tenth of a percent) in the seating capacity of Lambeau Field.

Lambeau Field

14. *Salary Increase* Charlotte Newsom had a salary of $46,200 in 2003 and a salary of $51,300 in 2004. Determine the percent increase in Charlotte's salary from 2003 to 2004.

In Exercises 15–17, solve for the unknown quantity.

15. What percent of 80 is 25?

16. Forty-four is 16% of what number?

17. What is 17% of 540?

18. *Tipping* At Empress Garden Restaurant, Vishnu and Krishna's bill comes to $42.79, including tax. If they wish to leave a 15% tip on the total bill, how much should they tip the waiter?

19. *Increased Membership* If the number of people in your chess club increased by 20%, or 8 people, what was the original number of people in the club?

20. *Increased Membership* The Sarasota Wheelers skateboard club had 75 members and increased the number of members to 95. What is the percent increase in the number of members?

11.2

In Exercises 21–24, find the missing quantity by using the simple interest formula.

21. $p = \$2500, r = 4\%, t = 60$ days, $i = ?$

22. $p = \$1575, r = ?, t = 100$ days, $i = \$41.56$

23. $p = ?, r = 8\frac{1}{2}\%, t = 3$ years, $i = \$114.75$

24. $p = \$5500, r = 11\frac{1}{2}\%, t = ?, i = \$316.25$

25. *Roof Replacement Loan* Chris Sharek borrowed $5300 from his father to replace the roof on his house. The loan was for 36 months and had a simple interest rate of 5.75%. Determine the amount Chris paid his father on the date of maturity of the loan.

26. *A Bank Loan* Lori Holdren borrowed $3000 from her bank for 240 days at a simple interest rate of 8.1%.
  a) How much interest did she pay for the use of the money?
  b) How much did she pay the bank on the date of maturity?

27. *A Bank Loan* Nikos Pappas borrowed $6000 for 24 months from the bank, using stock as security. The bank discounted the loan at $11\frac{1}{2}\%$.
  a) How much interest did Nikos pay the bank for the use of the money?
  b) How much did he receive from the bank?
  c) What was the actual rate of interest?

28. *Savings as Security* Golda Frankl borrowed $800 for 6 months from her bank, using her savings account as security. A bank rule limits the amount that can be borrowed in this manner to 85% of the amount in the borrower's savings account. The rate of interest is 2% higher than the interest rate being paid on the savings account. The current rate on the savings account is $5\frac{1}{2}\%$.
  a) What rate of interest will the bank charge for the loan?
  b) Find the amount that Golda must repay in 6 months.
  c) How much money must she have in her account in order to borrow $800?

11.3

29. *Comparing Compounding Periods* Determine the amount and the interest when $1000 is invested for 5 years at 10%
  a) compounded annually.
  b) compounded semi-annually.
  c) compounded quarterly.
  d) compounded monthly.
  e) compounded daily (use $n = 360$).

30. *Total Amount* Choi deposited $2500 in a savings account that pays 4.75% interest compounded quarterly. What will be the total amount of money in the account 15 years from the day of deposit?

31. *Effective Annual Yield* Determine the effective annual yield of an investment if the interest is compounded daily at an annual rate of 5.6%.

32. *Present Value* How many dollars must you invest today to have $40,000 in 20 years? Assume that the money earns 5.5% interest compounded quarterly.

11.4

33. *Actuarial Method* Bill Jordan has a 48-month installment loan, with a fixed monthly payment of $176.14. The

amount borrowed was $7500. Instead of making his 24th payment, Bill is paying the remaining balance on the loan.
a) Determine the APR of the installment loan.
b) How much interest will Bill save, computed by the actuarial method?
c) What is the total amount due on that day?

34. *Rule of 78s* Carter Fenton is buying a book collection that costs $4000. He is making a down payment of $500 and 24 monthly payments of $163.33. Instead of making his 12th payment, Carter decides to pay the total remaining balance and terminate the loan.

a) How much interest will Carter save, computed by the rule of 78s?
b) What is the total amount due on that day?

35. *Installment Loan* Dara Holliday's cost for a new wardrobe was $3420. She made a down payment of $860 and financed the balance on a 24-month fixed payment installment loan. The monthly payments are $111.73. Instead of making her 12th payment, Dara decides to pay the total remaining balance and terminate the loan.
a) Determine the APR of the installment loan.
b) How much interest will Dara save, computed by the actuarial method?
c) What is the total amount due on that day?

36. *Finance Charge Comparison* On June 1, the billing date, Krishna Muhundan had a balance due of $485.75 on his credit card. The transactions during the month of June were

June 4	Payment	$375.00
June 8	Charge: Car repair	370.00
June 21	Charge: Airline ticket	175.80
June 28	Charge: Clothing	184.75

a) Find the finance charge on July 1 by using the unpaid balance method. Assume that the interest rate is 1.3% per month.
b) Find the new account balance on July 1 using the finance charge found in part (a).
c) Find the average daily balance for the period.
d) Find the finance charge on July 1 by using the average daily balance method. Assume that the interest rate is 1.3% per month.

e) Find the new account balance on July 1 using the finance charge found in part (d).

37. *Finance Charge Comparison* On August 5, the billing date, Pat Schaefer had a balance due of $185.72 on her credit card. The transactions during the month of August were

August 8	Charge: Shoes	$85.75
August 10	Payment	75.00
August 15	Charge: Dry cleaning	72.85
August 21	Charge: Textbooks	275.00

a) Find the finance charge on September 5 by using the unpaid balance method. Assume that the interest rate is 1.4% per month.
b) Find the new account balance on September 5 using the finance charge found in part (a).
c) Find the average daily balance for the period.
d) Find the finance charge on September 5 by using the average daily balance method. Assume that the interest rate is 1.4% per month.
e) Find the new account balance on September 5 using the finance charge found in part (d).

38. *Financing a Corvette* David Snodgress bought a new Chevrolet Corvette for $52,000. He made a 20% down payment and financed the balance with the dealer on a 48-month payment plan. The monthly payments were $930.02.
a) Determine the down payment.
b) Determine the amount to be financed.
c) Determine the total finance charge.
d) Determine the APR.

39. *Financing a Ski Outfit* Lucille Groenke can buy a cross-country skiing outfit for $275. The store is offering the following terms: $50 down and 12 monthly payments of $19.62.
a) Find the interest paid.
b) Find the APR.

11.5

40. *Building a House* The Freemans have decided to build a new house. The contractor quoted them a price of $135,700. The taxes on the house will be $3450 per year, and insurance will be $350 per year. They have applied for a conventional loan from a local bank. The bank is requiring a 25% down payment, and the interest rate on the loan is 9.5%. The Freemans' annual income is $64,000. They have more than 10 monthly payments remaining on each of the following: $218 on a car, $120 on new furniture, and $190 on a camper. Determine

a) the required down payment.
b) their adjusted monthly income.
c) the maximum monthly payment the bank's loan officer believes they can afford.
d) the monthly payment of principal and interest for a 30-year loan.
e) their total monthly payment, including insurance and taxes.
f) Do the Freemans qualify for the mortgage?

41. *Thirty-Year Mortgage* James Whitehead purchased a home selling for $89,900 with a 15% down payment. The period of the mortgage is 30 years, and the interest rate is 11.5%. Determine the

a) amount of the down payment.
b) monthly mortgage payment.
c) amount of the first payment applied to the principal.
d) total cost of the house.
e) total interest paid.

42. *Adjustable-Rate Mortgage* The Nguyens purchased a house for $105,000 with a down payment of $26,250. They obtained a 30-year adjustable-rate mortgage. The terms of the mortgage are as follows: The interest rate is based on the 6-month Treasury bill, the interest rate charged is 3.00% above the rate of the Treasury bill on the

date of adjustment, the interest rate is adjusted every 6 months, the interest rate will not change more than 1% (up or down) when the interest rate is adjusted, the maximum interest rate that can be charged for the duration of the loan is 16%, there is no lower limit on the interest rate, the initial mortgage interest rate is 7.5%, and the monthly payment of interest and principal is adjusted annually. Determine the

a) initial monthly payment for principal and interest.
b) interest rate in 6 months if the interest rate on the Treasury bill at the time is 5.00%.
c) interest rate in 6 months if the interest rate on the Treasury bill at the time is 4.75%.

CHAPTER 11 TEST

In Exercises 1 and 2, find the missing quantity by using the simple interest formula.

1. $i = ?, p = \$2000, r = 4\%$ per year, $t = 6$ months
2. $i = \$288, p = \$1200, r = 8\%$ per year, $t = ?$

In Exercises 3 and 4, Greg Wright borrowed $5000 from a bank for 18 months. The rate of simple interest charged is 8.5%.

3. How much interest did he pay for the use of the money?

4. What is the amount he repaid to the bank on the due date of the loan?

In Exercises 5 and 6, Yolanda Fernandez received a $5400 loan with interest at 12.5% for 90 days on August 1. Yolanda made a payment of $3000 on September 15.

5. How much did she owe the bank on the date of maturity?

6. What total amount of interest did she pay on the loan?

In Exercises 7 and 8, compute the amount and the compound interest.

	Principal	Time	Rate	Compounded
7.	$7500	2 years	3%	Quarterly
8.	$2500	3 years	6.5%	Monthly

A New Printer In Exercises 9–11, a new laser color printer sells for $2350. To finance the laser printer through a bank the bank will require a down payment of 15% and monthly payments of $90.79 for 24 months.

9. How much money will the purchaser borrow from the bank?

10. What finance charge will the individual pay the bank?

11. What is the APR?

12. *Rule of 78s* Sandi Abramowicz purchased a used fishing boat for $6750. She made a down payment of $1550 and financed the balance with a 12-month fixed-payment installment loan. Instead of making the sixth monthly payment of $465.85, she decides to pay off the loan.
    a) How much interest will Sandi save (use the rule of 78s)?
    b) What is the total amount due to pay off the loan?

13. *Actuarial Method* Gino Sedillo borrowed $7500. To repay the loan he was scheduled to make 36 monthly installment payments of $223.10. Instead of making his 24th payment, Gino decides to pay off the loan.
    a) Determine the APR of the installment loan.
    b) How much interest will Gino save (use the actuarial method)?
    c) What is the total amount due to pay off the loan?

14. *Unpaid Balance Method* Michael Murphy's credit card statement shows a balance due of $878.25 on March 23, the billing date. For the period ending on April 23, he had the following transactions.

March 26	Charge: Groceries	$ 95.89
March 30	Charge: Restaurant bill	68.76
April 3	Payment	450.00
April 15	Charge: Clothing	90.52
April 22	Charge: Eyeglasses	450.85

a) Find the finance charge on March 23 by using the unpaid balance method. Assume that the interest rate is 1.4% per month.

b) Find the new account balance on April 23 using the finance charge found in part (a).

c) Find the average daily balance for the period.

d) Find the finance charge on March 23 by using the average daily balance method. Assume that the interest rate is 1.4% per month.

e) Find the new account balance on April 23 using the finance charge found in part (d).

Building a House In Exercises 15–21, the Leungs decided to build a new house. The contractor quoted them a price of $144,500, including the lot. The taxes on the house would be $3200 per year, and insurance would cost $450 per year. They have applied for a conventional loan from a bank. The bank is requiring a 15% down payment, and the interest rate is $10\frac{1}{2}$%. The Leung's annual income is $86,500. They have more than 10 monthly payments remaining on each of the following: $220 for a car, $175 for new furniture, and $210 on a college education loan.

15. What is the required down payment?

16. Determine their adjusted monthly income.

17. What is the maximum monthly payment the bank's loan officer believes the Leungs can afford?

18. Determine the monthly payments of principal and interest for a 30-year loan.

19. Determine their total monthly payments, including insurance and taxes.

20. Does the bank's loan officer believe that the Leungs meet the requirements for the mortgage?

21. a) Find the total cost of the house (excluding insurance and taxes) after 30 years.
    b) How much of the total cost is interest?

GROUP PROJECTS

Mortgage Loan

1. The Young family is purchasing a $130,000 house with a VA mortgage. The bank is offering them a 25-year mortgage with an interest rate of 9.5%. They have $20,000 invested that could be used for a down payment. Since they do not need a down payment, Mr. Young wants to keep the money invested. Mrs. Young believes that they should make a down payment of $20,000.
   a) Determine the total cost of the house with no down payment.
   b) Determine the total cost of the house if they make a down payment of $20,000.
   c) Mr. Young believes that the $20,000 investment will have an annual rate of return of 10% compounded quarterly. Assuming that Mr. Young is right, calculate the value of the investment in 25 years. (See Section 11.3.)
   d) If the Youngs use the $20,000 as a down payment, their monthly payments will decrease. Determine the difference of the monthly payments in parts (a) and (b).
   e) Assume that the difference in monthly payments, part (d), is invested each month at a rate of 6% compounded monthly for 25 years. Determine the value of the investment in 25 years. (See Exercise 49 in Section 11.3.)
   f) Use the information from parts (a)–(e) to analyze the problem. Would you recommend that the Youngs make the down payment of $20,000 and invest the difference in their monthly payments as in part (e) or that they do not make the down payment and keep the $20,000 invested as in part (c)? Explain.

Credit Card Terms

2. With each credit card comes a credit agreement (or security agreement) the cardholder must sign. Select two members of your group who have a major credit card (MasterCard, Visa, Discover, or American Express). If possible, one of the credit cards should be a gold or platinum card. Obtain a copy of the credit agreement signed by each cardholder and answer questions (a)–(p).
   a) What are the cardholder's responsibilities?
   b) What is the cardholder's maximum line of credit?
   c) What restrictions apply to the use of the credit card?
   d) How many days after the billing date does the cardholder have to make a payment without being charged interest?
   e) What is the minimum monthly payment required, and how is it determined?
   f) What is the interest rate charged on purchases?
   g) How does the bank determine when to start charging interest on purchases?
   h) Is there an annual fee for the credit card? If so, what is it?
   i) What late charge applies if payments are not made on time?
   j) What information is given on the monthly statement?
   k) How is the finance charge computed?
   l) What other fees, if any, may the bank charge you?
   m) If the card is lost, what is the responsibility of the cardholder?
   n) If the card is lost, what is the liability of the cardholder?
   o) What are the advantages of a gold or platinum card over a regular card?
   p) In your opinion, which of the two cards is more desirable? Explain.

Retirement Plans

3. Working men and women often have the benefit of contributing to various retirement plans. Such plans include traditional and Roth IRAs, 403(b) plans, 401(k) plans, IRA–SEP plans, and Keogh plans. Research each of these plans and answer questions (a)–(d).
   a) What type of employees are eligible to use each type of plan?
   b) What is the maximum annual contribution that can be made to each plan?
   c) What type of investments can be made through each of these plans?
   d) What are the tax advantages of each type of plan?

GROUP PROJECTS

Watching TV

1. Do you think that men or women, aged 17–20, watch more hours of TV weekly, or do you think that they watch the same number of hours?

   a) Write a procedure to use to determine the answer to that question. In your procedure, use a sample of 30 men and 30 women. State how you will obtain an unbiased sample.

   b) Collect 30 pieces of data from men aged 17–20 and 30 pieces of data from women aged 17–20. Round answers to the nearest 0.5 hr. Follow the procedure developed in part (a) to obtain your unbiased sample.

   c) Compute the mean for your two groups of data to the nearest tenth.

   d) Using the means obtained in part (c), answer the question asked at the beginning of the problem.

   e) Is it possible that your conclusion in part (d) is wrong? Explain.

   f) Compute the standard deviation for each group to the nearest tenth. How do the standard deviations compare?

   g) Do you believe that the distribution of data from either or both groups resembles a normal distribution? Explain.

   h) Add the two groups of data to get one group of 60 pieces of data. If these 60 pieces of data are added and divided by 60, will you obtain the same mean as when you add the two means from part (c) and divide the sum by 2? Explain.

   i) Compute the mean of the 60 pieces of data by using both methods mentioned in part (h). Are they the same? If so, why? If not, why not?

   j) Do you believe that this group of 60 pieces of data represents a normal distribution? Explain.

Binomial Probability Experiment

2. a) Have your group select a category of bivariate data that it thinks has a strong negative correlation. Indicate the variable that you will designate as the independent variable and the variable that you will designate as the dependent variable. Explain why your group believes that the bivariate data have a strong negative correlation.

   b) Collect at least 10 pieces of bivariate data that can be used to determine the correlation coefficient. Explain how your group chose these data.

   c) Plot a scatter diagram.

   d) Calculate the correlation coefficient.

   e) Is there a negative correlation at $\alpha = 0.05$? Explain your answer.

   f) Calculate the equation of the line of best fit.

   g) Explain how the equation in part (f) may be used.

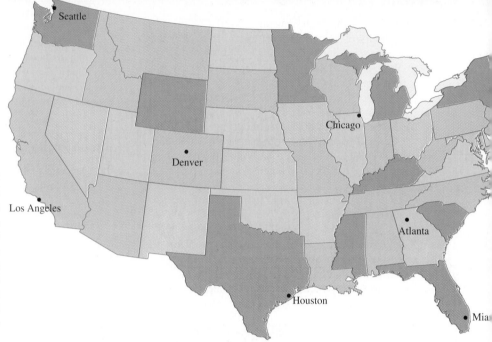

If a family living in one of the cities shown on the map wished to visit each of the other cities shown during a single vacation, they would have numerous routes from which to choose. There are 5040 different routes available to visit each city and return home. In this chapter, we will explain how a family could determine the shortest or the least expensive route.

GRAPH THEORY

A s part of our everyday lives, we often face problems that require us to carry out several tasks to reach a desired solution. When similar problems arise in a business setting, the decisions made may greatly affect the efficiency of the company, which in turn may affect the profit or loss of the company. The use of special diagrams called *graphs* is a valuable tool for representing and analyzing such problems. In this chapter, we will introduce an important field of mathematics known as *graph theory*. We will use graph theory to represent and solve many real-world problems. For instance, we will explain how to find the least expensive way for someone to visit the cities shown on the map above when the cost of traveling between each city is known.

14.1 GRAPHS, PATHS, AND CIRCUITS

The study of graph theory can be traced back to the eighteenth century when people of the East Prussian town of Königsberg sought the solution to a popular problem. Königsberg was situated on both banks and two islands of the Prigel River. From Fig. 14.1, we see that the sections of town were connected with a series of seven bridges. The townspeople wondered if one could walk through town and cross all seven bridges without crossing any of the bridges twice. This question was presented to the Swiss mathematician Leonhard Euler (pronounced "oiler," 1707–1783). To study this problem, Euler reduced the problem to one that could be represented with a series of dots and lines. This problem came to be known as the Königsberg bridge problem.

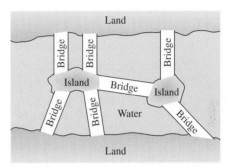

Figure 14.1

We will revisit the Königsberg bridge problem several times in this section and in Section 14.2. Our main focus in this section is to introduce definitions of graph theory and to explain how these definitions can be helpful in representing problems from the physical world. In the next section, we introduce some basic graph theory used to solve these problems.

A *graph* is a finite set of points called *vertices* (singular form is *vertex*) connected by line segments (not necessarily straight) called *edges*. An edge that connects a vertex to itself is called a *loop*. Vertices, edges, and a loop are displayed in the graph in Fig. 14.2. We generally refer to vertices with capitalized letters. The edge between two vertices will be referred to using the two vertices. For example, in Fig. 14.2, the edge that connects vertex A to vertex B is referred to as edge AB or as edge BA. The loop in Fig. 14.2 is referred to as edge BB or loop BB. Not every place where two edges cross is a vertex. A point must be present to represent a vertex. For instance, in Fig. 14.2, even though edges AD and BC cross, since no point is indicated, the place where these lines cross is not a vertex.

With these basic definitions, we can begin using graphs to represent physical settings.

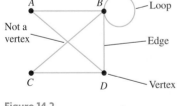

Figure 14.2

┌EXAMPLE 1   *Representing the Königsberg Bridge Problem*

Using the definitions of vertex and edge, represent the Königsberg bridge problem with a graph.

SOLUTION: Notice that each bridge in Fig. 14.1 connects two pieces of land in a manner similar to an edge connecting two vertices. To begin representing the Königsberg bridge problem as a graph we will label each piece of land with a capital letter, as shown in Fig. 14.3 on page 828.

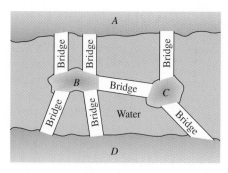

Figure 14.3

Next, we draw edges to represent the bridges. Notice that there are two bridges connecting land *A* to land *B* in Fig. 14.3. Therefore, we need two edges to connect vertex *A* to vertex *B* in our graph. Notice that there is one bridge connecting land *A* to land *C* in Fig. 14.3. Therefore, we need one edge to connect vertex *A* to vertex *C* in our graph. We continue to let edges represent bridges, and the resulting graph is given in Fig. 14.4.

Although the picture and the graph do not look very similar, the graph represents the key aspects of the problem: the land is represented with vertices and the bridges are represented with edges.   ▲

Graphs are powerful tools in problem solving because they allow us to focus on the key aspects of problems without getting distracted with unnecessary details. Our next three examples show other ways that graphs can be used to represent settings from the physical world.

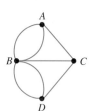

Figure 14.4

EXAMPLE 2   *Weather Map*

The map shown in Fig. 14.5 shows the states that make up the Northwest region of the weather map from Weather Underground, Inc. Construct a graph to show the states that share a common border.

Figure 14.5

Figure 14.6

SOLUTION: In our graph, each vertex will represent one of the five states in the Northwest region. We begin our graph by placing the five vertices in the same relative positions as the five states on the map and then labeling each vertex with the two-letter state abbreviation (see Fig. 14.6). The exact placement of the vertices is not critical.

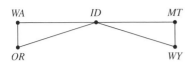

Figure 14.7

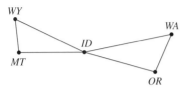

Figure 14.8

Next, examine the map in Fig. 14.5. If two states share a common border, connect the respective vertices with an edge. For example, Washington shares a common border with Oregon and Idaho, so there will be an edge that connects vertex *WA* to vertex *OR* and an edge that connects vertex *WA* to vertex *ID*, as shown in Fig. 14.7. Similarly, there will be edges that connect vertex *OR* to vertex *ID*, vertex *ID* to vertex *MT*, vertex *ID* to vertex *WY*, and vertex *MT* to vertex *WY*.

The graph shown in Fig. 14.7 is only one possible arrangement of vertices and edges that can be used to show which states share a common border. Many other graphs that display the same relationship are equally valid. Figure 14.8 shows one such graph. Although the vertices in the graph in Fig. 14.8 do not resemble the respective locations of the states they represent, the relationship between vertices is the same as in Fig. 14.7.

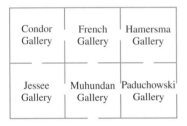

Figure 14.9

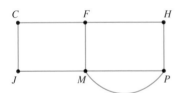

Figure 14.10

EXAMPLE 3   *Representing a Floor Plan*

Figure 14.9 shows the floor plan of the Mears Museum of Nashua, New Hampshire. Each of the six galleries within the museum contains at least one doorway. Use a graph to represent this floor plan.

SOLUTION: To create a graph we start by letting vertices represent the six galleries. We will label these vertices with the first letter of the gallery name. Next, connect the vertices with edges. To determine placement of the edges visualize how a person could walk from one gallery to another. For instance, a person can walk from the Condor Gallery directly into the French Gallery. Therefore, we will have an edge connecting vertex *C* and vertex *F*. The resulting graph is shown in Fig. 14.10.

Notice that vertex *M* and vertex *P* are connected with two edges in the graph. This is because a person could walk directly through the door between the two galleries, or the person could walk around the outside of the museum to get from one gallery to the other.

EXAMPLE 4   *Representing a Neighborhood*

Figure 14.11 shows a sketch of the Country Oaks subdivision of homes. Use a graph to represent the streets of this neighborhood.

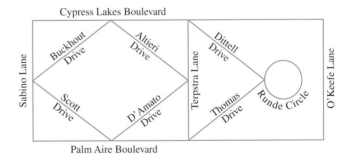

Figure 14.11

SOLUTION: In this problem, the vertices will represent the street intersections and the edges will represent the street blocks. We will use letters to name the vertices. The resulting graph is shown in Fig. 14.12 on page 830.

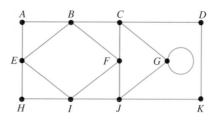

Figure 14.12

Now that we have some experience using graphs to represent real-life settings, we will introduce some additional vocabulary used in graph theory. We will begin with a method of classifying vertices. The *degree* of a vertex is the number of edges that connect to that vertex. For instance, in Fig. 14.13, vertex A has two edges connected to it. Therefore, the degree of vertex A is two. We also see from Fig. 14.13 that vertex B has three edges connected to it, as does vertex C. Therefore, vertices B and C each have degree three. Vertex D has a loop connected to it. A question arises: Should loop DD count as one edge or two edges when determining the degree of vertex D? We will agree to count each end of a loop when determining the degree of a vertex. Thus, vertex D from Fig. 14.13 will have degree four. A vertex with an even number of edges connected to it is an *even vertex*, and a vertex with an odd number of edges connected to it is an *odd vertex*. In Fig. 14.13, vertices A and D are even and vertices B and C are odd.

We next introduce some definitions of graph theory that can be used to describe "movement."

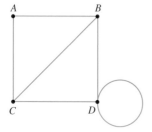

Figure 14.13

A **path** is a sequence of adjacent vertices and the edges connecting them.

By adjacent vertices, we mean two vertices that are connected by a common edge. For example, in Fig. 14.13, vertices A and B are adjacent vertices since there is a common edge between vertex A and vertex B. Vertices A and D are not adjacent vertices since there is not a common edge between vertex A and vertex D. An example of a path is given in Fig. 14.14. It is important to recognize the difference between a graph and a path. The *graph* is the set of black vertices and the blue edges connecting them. The *path,* shown in red, can be thought of as movement from vertex C to vertex D to vertex A to vertex B. For convenience, and to help in explanations, paths will be referred to with the sequence of vertices separated by commas. For example, the path in Fig. 14.14 will be referred to as path C, D, A, B.

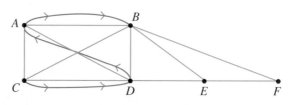

Figure 14.14

Notice that a path does not need to include every edge and every vertex of a graph. Also notice that a path could include the same vertices and the same edges several times. For example, in Fig. 14.15, we see a graph with four vertices. The path *A*, *B*, *C*, *D*, *A*, *B*, *C*, *D*, *A*, *B*, *C*, *D*, *A*, *B*, *C* starts at vertex *A*, "circles" the graph three times, and then goes through vertex *B* to vertex *C*.

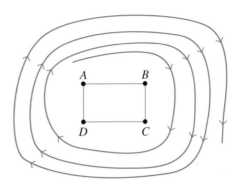

Figure 14.15

A **circuit** is a path that begins and ends at the same vertex.

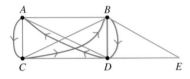

Figure 14.16

Examine Fig. 14.16. The path given by *A*, *C*, *B*, *D*, *A* forms a circuit. The path given by *B*, *D*, *E*, *B* forms another circuit.

Note that every circuit is, by definition, a path; however, not every path is a circuit. A circuit needs to start and stop at the same vertex. In Section 14.2 and 14.3, we will discuss paths and circuits in more depth.

Our next definitions classify graphs themselves. A graph is *connected* if, for any two vertices in the graph, there is a path that connects them. All the graphs we have studied thus far have been connected because a path existed between each pair of vertices in each graph. If a graph is not connected, it is *disconnected*. Figure 14.17 shows three examples of disconnected graphs. Notice in Fig. 14.17(c) that although edge *AD* and edge *BC* cross, these edges are not connected because there is no vertex indicated where they cross.

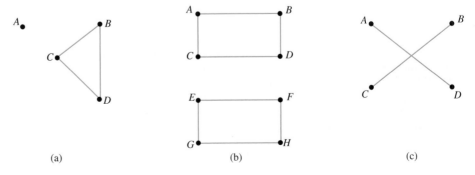

(a)   (b)   (c)

Figure 14.17

DID YOU KNOW

Graph Theory Representations

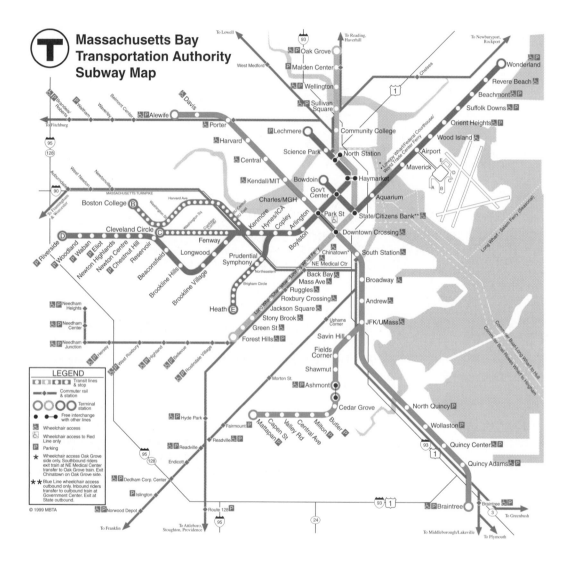

Simple graphs consisting of points called vertices and lines called edges can represent numerous applications used in many professions. Chemists use graphs to sketch atoms in a molecule. Engineers use graphs in schematic drawings of electrical networks. Genealogists use graphs to represent family trees. Transportation officials use graphs to represent airline, railway, and ground transportation routes. Industrial scientists use graphs to represent human and machine interaction times in factories. All these applications can be represented and studied with the branch of mathematics called graph theory, the origins of which can be traced back to Leonhard Euler (1707–1783). The subway map above for the city and surrounding area of Boston, MA is a graph of vertices and edges.

A **bridge** is an edge that if removed from a connected graph would create a discon-nected graph.

Figure 14.18 shows graphs with bridges indicated. Compare these graphs with those in Fig. 14.17. The graphs in Fig. 14.18 are the same graphs as those in Fig. 14.17 with a bridge added. Notice in Fig. 14.18(c), in addition to edge *AB* which we added, that edges *AD* and *BC* are also bridges. If edge *AD* were removed, vertex *D* would be isolated from the rest of the graph. If edge *BC* were removed, vertex *C* would be isolated from the rest of the graph. Note that our graph theory definition of *bridge* is different from bridges as they are used in the Königsberg bridge problem. In the Königsberg bridge problem, none of the edges that represents real bridges is a bridge in the graph theory sense.

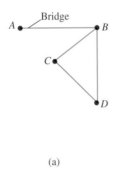

(a)

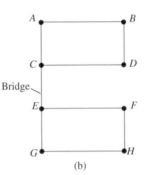

(b)

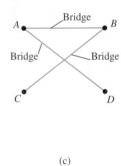

(c)

Figure 14.18

SECTION 14.1 EXERCISES

Concept/Writing Exercises

1. Using one sentence, define *graph, vertex,* and *edge*.

2. Draw an example of a graph that contains four vertices and six edges.

3. Draw an example of a graph that contains a loop.

4. Explain how to determine the degree of a vertex.

5. Explain how to determine if a vertex is odd or even.

6. Draw an example of a graph that contains a bridge. Iden-tify the bridge and explain why this edge is a bridge.

7. **a)** What is a path?
   b) What is a circuit?
   c) Give an example of a path that is not a circuit and an example of a path that is a circuit.

8. Draw an example of a graph that is connected and an ex-ample of a graph that is disconnected. Explain why your second graph is disconnected.

Practice the Skills

In Exercises 9–14, create a graph with the given properties. There are many possible answers for each problem.

9. Three even vertices

10. Four odd vertices

11. Two even and two odd vertices

12. Seven vertices with no bridges

13. Seven vertices with one bridge

14. Seven vertices with two bridges

In Exercises 15–20, use the graph below to answer the following questions.

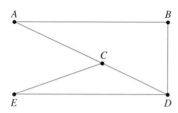

15. Is *A, B, C, D, E* a path? Explain.

16. **Which** edge(s) shown on the graph are not included in the following path: *A, B, D, E, C*?

17. On the graph, is it possible to determine a path that begins with vertex *A*, contains all the vertices exactly once, and ends with vertex *B*? If so, determine one such path.

18. On the graph, is it possible to determine a circuit that includes only three distinct vertices? If so, determine one such circuit.

19. On the graph, can you determine a path that includes all the edges without using any edge twice? If so, determine one such path.

20. On the graph, can you determine a circuit that includes all the vertices without using any vertex (other than the beginning and ending vertex) twice? If so, determine one such circuit.

Problem Solving

Modified Königsberg Bridge Problems **In Exercises 21–22,** *suppose that the people of Königsberg decide to add several bridges to their city. Two such possibilities are shown. Create graphs that would represent the Königsberg bridge problem with these new bridges.*

21.

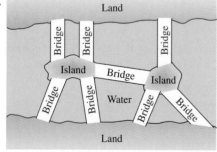

22.

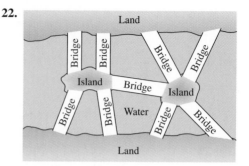

Representing Other Regions **In Exercises 23 and 24,** *maps of states that make up other regions of the weather map from Weather Underground (see Example 2) are shown. Represent each map as a graph where each vertex represents a state and each edge represents a common border between the states.*

23. The Southwest region

24. The South-Central region

25. *Central America* The map below shows the countries of Belize (*B*), Costa Rica (*C*), El Salvador (*E*), Guatemala (*G*), Honduras (*H*), Nicaragua (*N*), and Panama (*P*). Represent the map as a graph where each vertex represents a country and each edge represents a common border between the countries. Use the letters indicated in parentheses to label the vertices.

26. *Northern Africa* The map below shows the countries of Algeria (*A*), Egypt (*E*), Libya (*L*), Morocco (*M*), Sudan (*S*), Tunisia (*T*), and Western Sahara (*W*). Represent the map as a graph where each vertex represents a country and each edge represents a common border between the countries. Use the letters indicated in parentheses to label the vertices.

27. *Floor Plan* The drawing above and to the right shows the first-floor plan of the Aloha model home offered by Burbach Builders of Waipahu, Hawaii. Use a graph to represent this model.

28. *Floor Plan* The drawing below shows the floor plan of the Sun Valley model home offered by Wubben Builders of Pocatello, Idaho. Use a graph to represent this model.

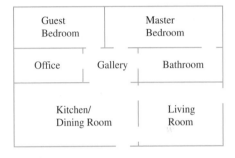

29. *Floor Plan* The drawing below shows the floor plan of the first floor of the Oleander model home offered by Nisely Builders of Albuquerque, New Mexico. Use a graph to represent this model.

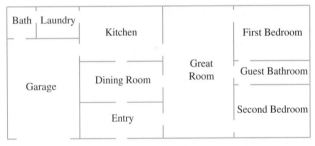

30. *Floor Plan* The drawing below shows the floor plan of the Bougainvillea model home offered by Alstrom Builders of Waco, Texas. Use a graph to represent this model.

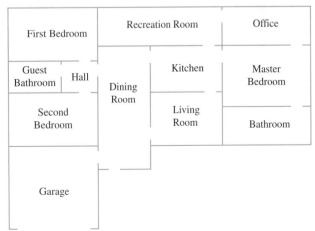

31. *Representing a Neighborhood* The map of the Tree Tops subdivision in Prince George County, Virginia, is shown below. Use a graph to represent this subdivision. Use letters to label the vertices.

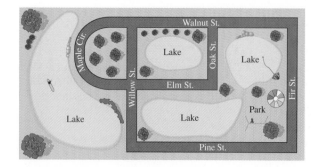

32. *Representing a Neighborhood* The map of the Crescent Lakes subdivision in Essex County, Maryland, is shown below. Use a graph to represent this subdivision. Use letters to label the vertices.

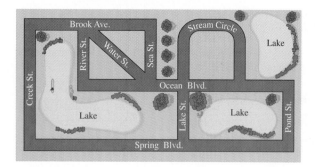

In Exercises 33–36, determine whether the graph shown is connected or disconnected.

33.

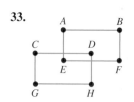

34.

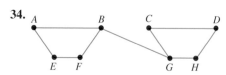

35.

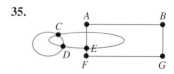

36.

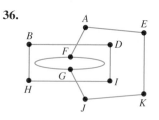

In Exercises 37–40, a connected graph is shown. Identify any bridges in each graph.

37.

38.

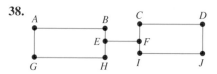

39.

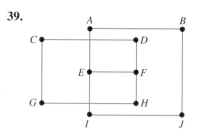

40.

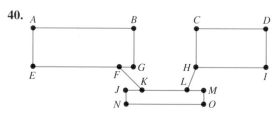

Challenge Problems/Group Activities

41. Draw a graph that conveys the following friendships among five children in a kindergarten class. Alex is friends with Drew, Hayden, Joshua, and Tony. Drew is friends with Alex and Tony. Hayden is friends with Alex and Joshua. Joshua is friends with Alex, Hayden, and Tony. Tony is friends with Alex, Drew, and Joshua.

42. Poll your entire class to determine which students knew each other prior to taking this course. Draw a graph that shows this relationship.

43. Attempt to draw a graph that has an odd number of odd vertices. What conclusion can you draw from this exercise?

44. Draw four different graphs and then record the following information for each graph:
    a) Determine the degree of each vertex.
    b) Determine the sum of the degrees from all vertices from this same graph.
    c) Determine the number of edges on this same graph.
    d) What conclusion relating the sum of the degrees of vertices to the number of edges can you draw from this exercise? Explain why this conclusion is true.

Recreational Mathematics

45. Use a graph to represent
    a) The floor plan of your home.
    b) The streets in your neighborhood within $\frac{1}{2}$ mile from your home in all directions.

Internet/Research Activity

46. Choose a continent other than North America or Australia and create a graph showing the common boundaries between countries. Be sure to use a current map.

14.2   EULER PATHS AND EULER CIRCUITS

Section 14.1 provided us with some of the basic definitions of graph theory. Although we were able to represent physical settings with graphs, we have not yet discussed solving problems related to these settings. In this section, we will provide more details of graph theory, which allows us to reach solutions to the Königsberg bridge problem and other real-world problems. Before we do so, we need to give two more definitions.

> An **Euler path** is a path that passes through each edge of a graph exactly one time.

Recall that a circuit is a path that begins and ends at the same vertex.

> An **Euler circuit** is a circuit that passes through each edge of a graph exactly one time.

The difference between an Euler path and an Euler circuit is that an Euler circuit must start and end at the same vertex. An alternate definition for an Euler circuit is that it is an Euler path that begins and ends at the same vertex. To become familiar with Euler paths and Euler circuits, examine the graphs in Fig. 14.19(a) and (b). As we discuss each graph, trace each path or circuit with a pencil or with your finger, or draw the path or circuit on a separate sheet of paper.

In Fig. 14.19(a), the path $D, E, B, C, A, B, D, C, E$ is an Euler path since each edge was traced only one time. However, since the path begins at vertex D and ends at a different vertex, E, the path is not a circuit and therefore is not an Euler circuit. In Fig. 14.19(b), the path $D, E, B, C, A, B, D, C, E, F, D$ is an Euler path since each edge was traced only one time. Furthermore, since the path begins and ends with the same vertex, D, it is also an Euler circuit. Note that every Euler circuit is an Euler path, but not every Euler path is an Euler circuit.

Our next task is to determine whether a given graph has an Euler path, an Euler circuit, neither, or both. In the next example, we will use trial and error to find Euler paths and Euler circuits. Our discussion will help us introduce *Euler's theorem,* which will be used to solve the Königsberg bridge problem and other problems involving graph theory.

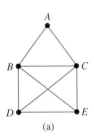

An Euler path
$D, E, B, C, A, B, D, C, E$

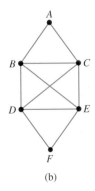

An Euler circuit
$D, E, B, C, A, B, D, C, E, F, D$

Figure 14.19

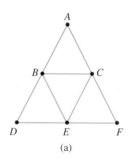

(a)

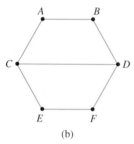

(b)

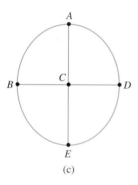

(c)

Figure 14.20

EXAMPLE 1   *Finding Euler Paths and Circuits*

For the graphs shown in Fig. 14.20, determine if an Euler path, an Euler circuit, neither, or both exist.

SOLUTION:

a) The graph in Fig. 14.20(a) has many Euler circuits, each of which is also an Euler path. One Euler circuit is *A, B, D, E, B, C, E, F, C, A*. Trace this circuit now. Notice that you traced each edge exactly one time and that you started and finished with vertex *A*. Notice that this graph has no odd vertices (and therefore has all even vertices). This graph has both Euler paths and Euler circuits.

b) Using trial and error, we can see that the graph in Fig. 14.20(b) has an Euler path but it does not have an Euler circuit. One Euler path is *C, A, B, D, C, E, F, D*. Another Euler path is *D, B, A, C, D, F, E, C*. There are actually several Euler paths for this graph but each one must begin at either vertex *C* or vertex *D* and end at the other vertex (you should try to find a few more to confirm this observation). Notice that there are exactly two odd vertices, vertex *C* and vertex *D*.

c) Our attempts to trace the graph in Fig. 14.20(c) lead to either tracing at least one edge twice or to omitting at least one of the edges. We must therefore conclude that this graph has neither an Euler path nor an Euler circuit. Notice that this graph has more than two odd vertices.   ▲

We are now ready to introduce Euler's theorem, which is used to determine if a graph contains Euler paths and Euler circuits. As you will see, the number of *odd* vertices of a graph determines whether the graph has Euler paths and Euler circuits.

Euler's Theorem

For a connected graph, the following statements are true:

1. A graph with *no odd vertices* (all even vertices) has at least one Euler path, which is also an Euler circuit. An Euler circuit can be started at any vertex and it will end at the same vertex.

2. A graph with *exactly two odd vertices* has at least one Euler path but no Euler circuits. Each Euler path must begin at one of the two odd vertices and it will end at the other odd vertex.

3. A graph with *more than two odd vertices* has neither an Euler path nor an Euler circuit.

The proof of this theorem is beyond the scope of this book. In Example 2, we will reexamine the graphs used in Example 1. However, this time we will use Euler's theorem to determine if the graph has Euler paths and Euler circuits.

EXAMPLE 2   *Using Euler's Theorem*

Use Euler's theorem to determine whether an Euler path or an Euler circuit exists in Fig. 14.20a), b), and c). Compare these results with those obtained in Example 1.

SOLUTION:

a) The graph in Fig. 14.20(a) has no odd vertices (all the vertices are even). According to item 1 in Euler's theorem, at least one Euler circuit exists. An Euler circuit can be determined starting at any vertex. The Euler circuit will end at the vertex from which it started. Recall that each Euler circuit is also an Euler path.

b) We see that the graph in Fig. 14.20(b) has four even vertices (A, B, E, and F) and two odd vertices (C and D). Based on item 2 in Euler's theorem, we conclude that since there are exactly two odd vertices, at least one Euler path exists but no Euler circuit exists. Each Euler path must begin at one of the odd vertices and end at the other odd vertex.

c) The graph in Fig. 14.20(c) has four odd vertices (A, B, D, and E) and one even vertex (C). According to item 3 in Euler's theorem, since this graph has more than two odd vertices, the graph has neither an Euler path nor an Euler circuit.

DID YOU KNOW

Topology

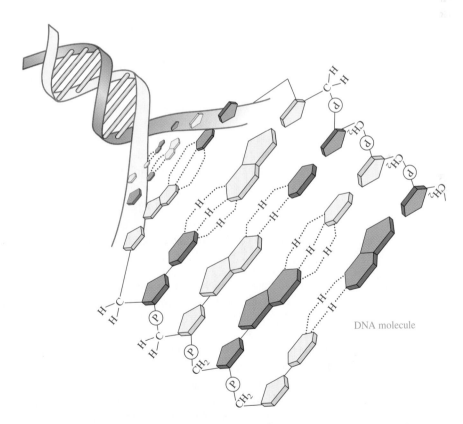

DNA molecule

Graph theory is part of a larger branch of mathematics known as *topology*. Although topology involves concepts from other older branches of mathematics such as geometry, algebra, and analysis, the name *topology* wasn't used until 1930 in a paper by Solomon Lefschetz. Topology is frequently referred to as rubber-sheet geometry. This descriptive name refers to topology's focus on geometric properties that remain consistent even when an object is bent, twisted, or stretched. One of the more interesting areas within topology is knot theory. Once a very obscure area of mathematics, knot theory is increasingly important due to its applications to science. Among other things, knot theory is used to study DNA molecules, to find new drugs, and to study how infectious diseases spread.

The results found in Example 2 using Euler's theorem are the same as the results we found in Example 1 using trial and error. Although both methods led to the same result, Euler's theorem is superior to trial and error because it gives us a tool to examine more complicated graphs.

Next, we will use Euler's theorem to solve questions regarding the Königsberg bridge problem as well as problems relating to the graphs we developed in Section 14.1.

EXAMPLE 3   *Solving the Königsberg Bridge Problem*

In Section 14.1, Example 1 on page 827, we discussed the Königsberg bridge problem and drew a graph to represent the situation. The graph is repeated in Fig. 14.21. Could a walk be taken through Königsberg during which each bridge is crossed exactly one time?

SOLUTION: The vertices of the graph given in Fig. 14.21 represent the land areas and the edges of the graph represent the bridges in the Königsberg bridge problem. The original problem posed by the townspeople of Königsberg, in graph theory terms, was whether or not an Euler path exists for the graph in Fig. 14.21. From the figure, we see that the graph has four odd vertices (A, B, C, and D). Thus, according to item 3 of Euler's theorem, no Euler path exists. Therefore, no walk could be taken through Königsberg in which each bridge was crossed exactly one time. ▲

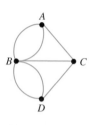

Figure 14.21

EXAMPLE 4   *Visiting Weather Stations*

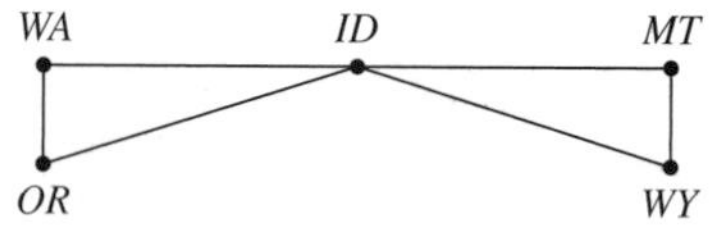

In Section 14.1, Example 2 on page 828, we discussed the states that make up the Northwest region of the weather map from Weather Underground. We drew a graph that showed the states that share a common border. The graph is repeated in Fig. 14.22. To monitor the weather stations within the Northwest region, Alan Stermberg, a researcher for Weather Underground, wishes to visit each state within that region. To plan the most efficient trip, Alan wishes to travel between these states and cross each common state border exactly one time.

a) Is it possible for Alan to travel among these five states and cross each common state border exactly one time?

b) If it is possible, can he start and end in the same state?

SOLUTION:

a) Since Alan must use each edge (or common border) exactly one time, he is seeking an Euler path for the graph in Fig. 14.22. Notice that this graph has no odd vertices. According to item 1 of Euler's theorem, at least one Euler path exists. Therefore, yes, it is possible for Alan to travel among these states and cross each common state border exactly one time.

b) Because Alan must start and end at the same vertex and use each edge exactly one time, Alan is seeking an Euler circuit for the graph in Fig. 14.22. According to item 1 of Euler's theorem, since there are no odd vertices in this graph, an Euler circuit can be started at any vertex and will end at the same vertex. Therefore, yes, Alan may start and end his trip in the same state. One such Euler circuit would be *WA, ID, MT, WY, ID, OR, WA*. There are many other Euler circuits on this graph. You should try to find at least two now. ▲

Figure 14.22

Euler's theorem can be used to determine whether a graph has an Euler path or an Euler circuit. If an Euler path or Euler circuit exists, how can we determine it? We can always attempt to determine Euler paths and Euler circuits using trial and error. This strategy might work well—and indeed it might be rather entertaining—for simpler graphs. However, we would like to attempt this task with a more systematic approach. Our final topic in this section, Fleury's algorithm, will give us such an approach. An *algorithm* is a procedure for accomplishing some task.

Fleury's Algorithm

To determine an Euler path or an Euler circuit:

1. Use Euler's theorem to determine whether an Euler path or an Euler circuit exists. If one exists, proceed with steps 2–5.

2. If the graph has no odd vertices (therefore has an Euler circuit, which is also an Euler path), choose any vertex as the starting point. If the graph has exactly two odd vertices (therefore has only an Euler path), choose one of the two odd vertices as the starting point.

3. Begin to trace edges as you move through the graph. Number the edges as you trace them. Since you can't trace any edges twice in Euler paths and Euler circuits, once an edge is traced consider it "invisible."

4. When faced with a choice of edges to trace, if possible, choose an edge that is not a bridge (i.e., don't create a disconnected graph with your choice of edges).

5. Continue until each edge of the entire graph has been traced once.

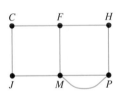

Figure 14.23

EXAMPLE 5   *A Museum Problem*

In Section 14.1, Example 3, we introduced the Mears Art Museum and drew the graph that represents its floor plan. The graph is repeated in Fig. 14.23. The museum has hired an artistic wood carver to build and paint decorative doorways. The wood carver wishes to find a way to move through the museum using each doorway exactly once.

a) Is it possible for the wood carver to move through the museum by going through each doorway (or using each edge) of the museum exactly one time? (In other words, does an Euler path exist?)

b) If yes, determine an Euler path that would take the wood carver through each doorway exactly once.

SOLUTION:

a) To determine if there is an Euler path we will use Euler's theorem. The graph in Fig. 14.23 contains exactly two odd vertices, *F* and *P*. By item 2 of Euler's theorem, the graph has an Euler path (but not an Euler circuit). By Euler's theorem, the Euler path would have to begin at one of the two odd vertices, either *F* or *P*, and end at the other odd vertex. So the wood carver could move through the museum by using each doorway exactly one time by starting with vertex *F* or vertex *P*.

b) In part (a), we determined that an Euler path exists. Now we use Fleury's algorithm to find one such path. We can start at either one of the odd vertices, *F* or *P*. Let us choose to start at vertex *P* (see Fig. 14.24). As a matter of convention, once we trace an edge, we will redraw it as a dashed line. The dashes indicate that the edge has already been traced and so it cannot be traced again. At vertex *P*, there are three choices of edges, *PH*, *PM* (the straight edge), or *PM* (the curved edge). None of these edges is a bridge. Thus, if we were to remove any

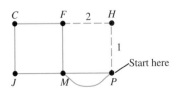

Figure 14.24

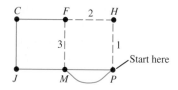

Figure 14.25

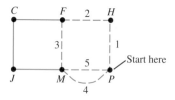

Figure 14.26

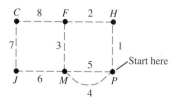

Figure 14.27

of these edges, we would not create a disconnected graph. Since none of these edges is a bridge, we can choose to trace any one of these edges. Let us choose to trace edge *PH* first and number it 1, as our first edge. This will put us at vertex *H*. At vertex *H*, we have no choice but to next choose edge *HF*. Let us choose this edge and label it 2. We now are at vertex *F* and must choose between edge *FC* and edge *FM*. Since neither edge is a bridge, we can choose either edge. Let us choose edge *FM* and label it 3. Figure 14.25 shows our choices so far.

Now closely examine our position at vertex *M*. There are three choices of edges: *MJ*, *MP* (the straight edge), or *MP* (the curved edge). Examine edge *MJ*. Notice that this edge is a bridge. If we were to remove it from the untraced portion of the graph, it would create a disconnected graph, separating vertices *J, C,* and *F* from vertices *M* and *P*. Therefore, we must choose an edge other than edge *MJ*. Let us choose the curved edge *MP* and label this 4. That will put us at vertex *P* with the straight-edge *PM* as our only choice. We will choose this edge, labeled 5, which will bring us back to vertex *M*. Our moves up to this point are shown in Fig. 14.26.

We now are at vertex *M*. We only have one choice, so we will choose edge *MJ*, followed by edge *JC*, followed by edge *CF*. The completed Euler path is given in Fig. 14.27.

Notice that we started at one odd vertex, *P*, and ended at the other odd vertex, *F*. So if the wood carver starts in the room represented by the letter *P* and proceeds to galleries represented by letters *H, F, M, P, M, J, C,* and *F*, each doorway would be passed through only once. There are other paths that would also work. You will be asked to find another path in Exercise 49.   ▲

EXAMPLE 6   *Crime Stoppers Problem*

In Section 14.1, Example 4, we introduced the Country Oaks subdivision of homes and drew a graph to represent it. The graph is repeated in Fig. 14.28. The Country Oaks Neighborhood Association is planning to organize a crime stopper group in which residents take turns walking through the neighborhood with cell phones to report any suspicious activity to the police.

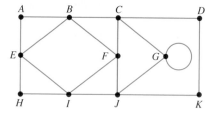

Figure 14.28

a) Can the residents of Country Oaks start at one intersection (or vertex) and walk each street block (or edge) in the neighborhood exactly once and return to the intersection where they started?

b) If yes, determine a circuit that could be followed to accomplish their walk.

SOLUTION:

a) Since the residents wish to start at one intersection (or vertex) and return to the same intersection (or vertex), we need to determine if this graph has an Euler circuit. From Fig. 14.28 we see that there are no odd vertices. Therefore, by item 1 of Euler's theorem, we determine that there is at least one Euler circuit.

b) In part (a), we determined that an Euler circuit exists. Now we use Fleury's algorithm to determine one such circuit. Euler's theorem states we can start at any vertex to determine an Euler circuit. Let us choose to begin at vertex A. We face a choice of tracing edge AB or edge AE. Since neither edge AB nor edge AE is a bridge, we can choose either edge. Let us choose edge AB. Our first choice is indicated in Fig. 14.29.

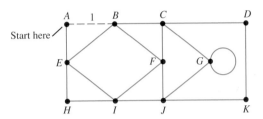

Figure 14.29

We will continue to trace from vertex to vertex around the outside of the graph, as indicated in Fig. 14.30. Notice that none of the edges chosen is a bridge.

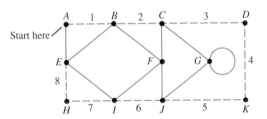

Figure 14.30

We are now at vertex E. Our choices are edge EA, edge EB, or edge EI. Edge EA is a bridge because removing edge EA would leave vertex A disconnected from the rest of the untraced graph. Therefore, we need to choose either edge EB or edge EI. Let us choose edge EB. Now we are at vertex B and must choose edge BF. Our choices so far are shown in Fig. 14.31.

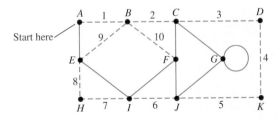

Figure 14.31

We are now at vertex F with choices of edge FC, edge FJ, or edge FI. Notice that edge FI is a bridge (it connects vertices A, E, and I to the rest of the untraced graph). We can therefore choose either edge FC or edge FJ. Let us choose edge FC, which will put us at vertex C (see Fig. 14.32 on page 844). At vertex C, our only choice is edge CG.

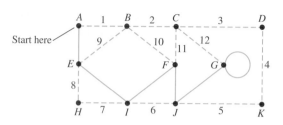

Figure 14.32

We are now at vertex G and have to choose between edge GJ and the edge GG (which is a loop): see Fig. 14.32. Since GJ is a bridge, we choose the edge GG. We then are back at vertex G. Here and throughout the rest of our circuit we only have one choice at each of the remaining vertices. We trace each of these remaining edges to get the result given in Fig. 14.33.

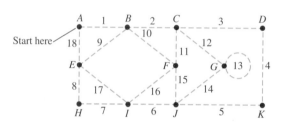

Figure 14.33

The circuit given in Fig. 14.33 gives one possible Euler circuit that would provide the residents of Country Oaks with one way to cover each street block exactly one time. Fleury's algorithm could be used to find many alternative circuits. You will be asked to find several such alternative circuits in exercises 50 through 53.

In our first two sections on graph theory, we have introduced key concepts and theory that allowed us to represent physical settings as graphs and to solve some problems relating to these settings. We have solved problems dealing with the bridges of Königsberg, the states of the Northwest region of a weather map, the doorways of an art museum, and the street blocks involved in a neighborhood crime stopper program. Although these problems are very different, they are all related because in each case a graph is used to represent a physical setting.

There are many other examples of how Euler paths and Euler circuits can be applied to real-life problems. They include problems that deal with the most efficient route for a snowplow or a street sweeper. Another example of a path problem is found in the classic arcade games Pac-Man and Ms. Pac-Man (Fig. 14.34). In both these games, the ideal path (disregarding the ghosts) would be an Euler path.

Figure 14.34
The game Ms. Pac-Man

SECTION 14.2 EXERCISES

Concept/Writing Exercises

1. **a)** What is an Euler path?
   b) Draw a graph that contains an Euler path and give an example of a path that is an Euler path.
   c) Using the same graph as in part b), give an example of a path that is not an Euler path.

2. **a)** What is an Euler circuit?
   b) Draw a graph that contains an Euler circuit and give an example of a circuit that is an Euler circuit.
   c) Using the same graph as in part b), give an example of a circuit that is not an Euler circuit.

3. Does a graph have an Euler path if the graph has
   a) no odd vertices?
   b) exactly two odd vertices?
   c) more than two odd vertices?

4. Does a graph have an Euler circuit if the graph has
   a) no odd vertices?
   b) exactly two odd vertices?
   c) more than two odd vertices?

5. Explain in your own words how to tell if a graph has an Euler circuit.

6. **a)** Explain in your own words how to determine an Euler path provided one exists for a given graph.
   b) Explain in your own words how to determine an Euler circuit provided one exists for a given graph.

Practice the Skills

For Exercises 7–10, use the following graph.

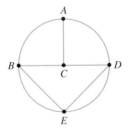

7. Determine an Euler path that begins with vertex *A*.
8. Determine an Euler path that begins with vertex *C*.
9. Is it possible to determine an Euler path that begins with vertex *B*? Explain.
10. Is it possible to determine an Euler circuit for this graph? Explain.

For Exercises 11–14, use the following graph.

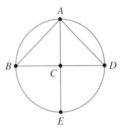

11. Determine an Euler path that begins with vertex *A*.
12. Determine an Euler path that begins with vertex *E*.
13. Is it possible to determine an Euler circuit for this graph? Explain.
14. Is it possible to determine an Euler path that begins with vertex *C*? Explain.

For Exercises 15–20, use the following graph.

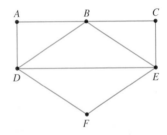

15. Determine an Euler circuit that begins and ends with vertex *A*.
16. Determine an Euler circuit that begins and ends with vertex *B*.
17. Determine an Euler circuit that begins and ends with vertex *C*.
18. Determine an Euler circuit that begins and ends with vertex *D*.
19. Determine an Euler circuit that begins and ends with vertex *E*.
20. Determine an Euler circuit that begins and ends with vertex *F*.

21. Imagine a very large graph that has 400 even vertices and no odd vertices.
    a) Does an Euler path exist for this graph? Explain.
    b) Does an Euler circuit exist for this graph? Explain.

22. Imagine a very large graph that has two odd vertices and 398 even vertices.
    a) Does an Euler path exist for this graph? Explain.
    b) Does an Euler circuit exist for this graph? Explain.

23. Imagine a very large graph that has 400 odd vertices and no even vertices.
    a) Does an Euler path exist for this graph? Explain.
    b) Does an Euler circuit exist for this graph? Explain.

24. Imagine a very large graph that has 200 odd vertices and 200 even vertices.
  a) Does an Euler path exist for this graph? Explain.
  b) Does an Euler circuit exist for this graph? Explain.

Problem Solving

Revisiting the Königsberg Bridge Problem In Exercises 25 and 26, suppose that the people of Königsberg decide to add several bridges to their city. Two such possibilities are shown.
  a) *Would the townspeople be able to walk across all the bridges without crossing the same bridge twice?*
  b) *If so, where should they begin and where would they end?*

25.

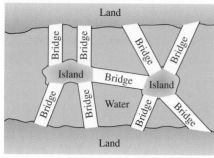

26.

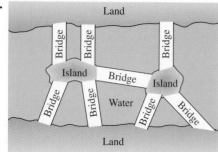

Areas of the World In Exercises 27–32, for each map shown,
  a) *Represent the map as a graph. Use the letter indicated in parentheses to label vertices of the graph.*
  b) *Determine (state yes or no) whether the graph in part (a) has an Euler path. If yes, give one such Euler path.*
  c) *Determine (state yes or no) whether the graph in part (a) has an Euler circuit. If yes, give one such Euler circuit.*

27. *Northern Africa* Algeria (A), Chad (C), Libya (L), Niger (N), and Tunisia (T)

28. *Southeast Asia* Burma (B), Cambodia (C), Laos (L), Thailand (T), and Vietnam (V)

29. *Southwest Asia* Afghanistan (A), Iran (N), Iraq (Q), Jordan (J), Pakistan (P), and Turkey (T)

30. *Central Europe* Austria (A), Czech Republic (C), Germany (G), Italy (I), Poland (P), and Switzerland (S)

31. *Western Canada* Alberta (A), British Columbia (B), Manitoba (M), Northwest Territories (T), Nunavut (N), Saskatchewan (S), and Yukon (Y)

32. *South America* Argentina (A), Bolivia (B), Brazil (Z), Chile (C), Paraguay (P), and Uruguay (U)

Art Museum Doorways Dr. Michael J. Mears, chairman of the board of the Mears Art Museum (see Example 5 on page 841), has decided to open additional museums. Mears has decided to hire the same wood carver to work on the doorways of his new museums. In Exercises 33–36, the floor plans of the new museums are shown.

a) For each floor plan, determine whether the wood carver can establish a path through the museum so that each doorway is passed through exactly once.

b) If this is possible, determine such a path.

33. Rutland Museum

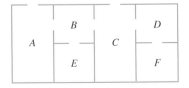

34. North Adams Museum

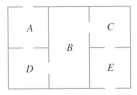

35. Torrington Museum

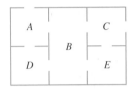

36. Sanford Museum

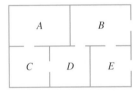

Crime Stopper Routes The Country Oaks crime stopper organization (see Example 6 on page 842) was so successful that the residents shared their strategies with friends living in the subdivisions of Crescent Lakes and Tree Tops. In Exercises 37 and 38, the respective maps of these communities are given.

a) Determine whether the residents in each subdivision will be able to establish a path through their communities so that each street block is walked exactly one time.

b) If yes, where would the residents need to start their walk?

37. Tree Tops

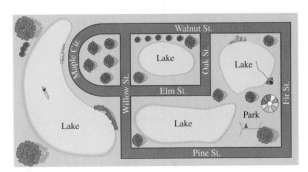

38. Crescent Lakes

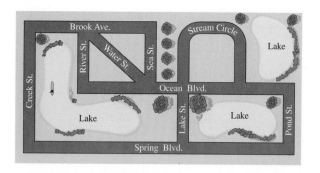

In Exercises 39–42, use Fleury's algorithm to determine an Euler path.

39.

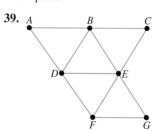

40.

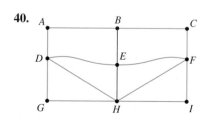

41.

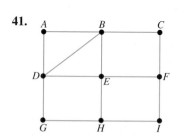

42.

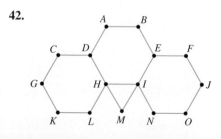

In Exercises 43–48, use Fleury's algorithm to find an Euler circuit.

43.

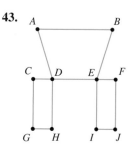

44.

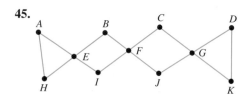

45.

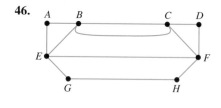

46.

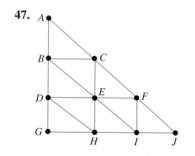

47.

48.

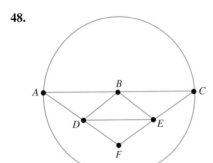

49. Determine an Euler path through the Mears Art Museum (see Example 5) that begins with the French Gallery (i.e., begin with vertex *F*).

50. Determine an Euler circuit for the Country Oaks crime stopper group (see Example 6) that begins with vertex *B* followed by vertex *A*.

51. Determine an Euler circuit for the Country Oaks crime stopper group (see Example 6) that begins with vertex *B* followed by vertex *E*.

52. Determine an Euler circuit for the Country Oaks crime stopper group that begins with vertex *J* followed by vertex *G*.

53. Determine an Euler circuit for the Country Oaks crime stopper group that begins with vertex *J* followed by vertex *F*.

Challenge Problems/Group Activities

54. Look at the map of the contiguous United States on page 826. Imagine a graph with 48 vertices in which each vertex represents one of the contiguous states. Each edge would represent a common border between states.
   a) Would this graph have an Euler path?
   b) Explain why or why not.

55. Attempt to draw a graph with an Euler circuit that has a bridge. What conclusion can you develop from this exercise?

Recreational Mathematics

56. a) Draw a graph with one vertex that has both an Euler path and an Euler circuit.
   b) Draw a graph with two vertices that has an Euler path but no Euler circuit.
   c) Draw a graph with two vertices that has both an Euler path and an Euler circuit.

Internet/Research Activity

57. Write a paper on the history and development of the branch of mathematics known as graph theory.

14.3 HAMILTON PATHS AND HAMILTON CIRCUITS

Introduction

In this section, we continue our study of graph theory by studying Hamilton paths and Hamilton circuits. These paths and circuits are named for the Irish mathematician and astronomer William Rowan Hamilton (1805–1865); see the Profile in Mathematics on page 850. Before formally defining Hamilton paths and Hamilton circuits, we will introduce an example that will be examined at several points throughout this section.

┌ **EXAMPLE 1**   *A Transportation Problem*

Julienne Ward has just been promoted to Southeast District Sales Director for the Addison Wesley Longman Publishing Company. She lives in Orlando, Florida, and oversees regional sales offices in Orlando; Atlanta, Georgia; Memphis, Tennessee; and New Orleans, Louisiana. She frequently needs to fly to each regional office for sales meetings. She would like to determine the least expensive route to visit each city one time and then return to Orlando. To help analyze this problem Julienne used the Internet to find the least expensive one-way fares offered between each of the four cities (see Table 14.1).

TABLE 14.1

	Orlando	Atlanta	Memphis	New Orleans
Orlando (*O*)	*	$67	$95	$69
Atlanta (*A*)	$67	*	$57	$68
Memphis (*M*)	$95	$57	*	$99
New Orleans (*N*)	$69	$68	$99	*

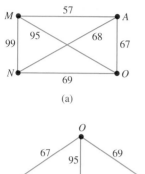

(a)

(b)

Figure 14.35

Use this table to create a graph. Let the vertices represent the cities, then connect each pair of cities with an edge. List the airfare between each two cities on the respective edges.

SOLUTION: First we note that the cost of a one-way flight between two given cities in the table is the same regardless from which city Julienne starts. For example, the one-way fare from New Orleans to Atlanta is $68 and the one-way fare from Atlanta to New Orleans is also $68. This information will allow us to list the flight cost along an edge with a single number. Next we draw a graph with four vertices that represent the four cities and six edges that represent the flights between each city. We also include the price of one-way flights along the appropriate edge. Two such graphs are shown in Fig. 14.35. There are many other graphs that could also display this information. ▲

Problems like the one in Example 1 are called *traveling salesman problems*. There are usually variations to the situation, but these problems generally involve seeking the least expensive or shortest way to travel among several locations. To help analyze traveling salesman problems, the costs or distances are indicated along each edge of a graph. Such a graph, as in Fig. 14.35(a) or (b), is called a *weighted graph*. We will use weighted graphs to solve traveling salesman problems, but first we need to introduce Hamilton paths and Hamilton circuits.

Hamilton Paths, Hamilton Circuits, and Complete Graphs

Now we introduce another important definition of graph theory.

A **Hamilton path** is a path that contains each *vertex* of a graph exactly once.

PROFILE IN MATHEMATICS

WILLIAM ROWAN HAMILTON

Born in Dublin, Ireland, Sir William Rowan Hamilton (1805–1865) made many contributions to the fields of physics, astronomy, and optics in addition to being one of the most influential mathematicians of the nineteenth century. His work involved many areas of mathematics including abstract algebra, calculus, geometry, graph theory, logic, and number theory. Perhaps his most important work involved the use of *quaternions* in abstract algebra. Quaternions are elements in a noncommutative group (see Chapter 10 for a discussion of group theory) that Hamilton labeled with the letters i, j, and k. For years, Hamilton puzzled over how to multiply the quaternions. Finally, one day while walking with his wife, he realized the solution. In his excitement, Hamilton carved the solution in the stone of Brougham Bridge as he and his wife passed by on their walk: $i^2 = j^2 = k^2 = ijk = -1$. To this day there is a plaque on this bridge commemorating Hamilton's discovery.

Hamilton's interests also included philosophy, religion, foreign languages, and poetry. While on vacation, he met the poet William Wordsworth and the two became lifelong friends. Hamilton also invented a game called the *Icosian Game* (see Exercise 35) that includes many aspects of graph theory you will study in this section. For more information on Hamilton, see the Profiles in Mathematics on page 406.

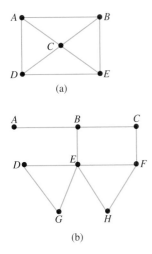

(a)

(b)

Figure 14.36

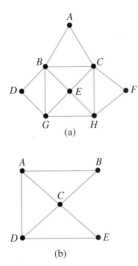

(a)

(b)

Figure 14.37

The graph in Fig. 14.36(a) has Hamilton path A, B, C, E, D. The graph in Fig. 14.36(a) also has Hamilton path C, B, A, D, E. The graph in Fig. 14.36(b) has a Hamilton path A, B, C, F, H, E, G, D. The graph in Fig. 14.36(b) also has Hamilton path G, D, E, H, F, C, B, A. Both of the graphs in Fig. 14.36 have other Hamilton paths. Can you find some of them?

Notice that, unlike Euler paths, not every edge needs to be traced in a Hamilton path. To help distinguish between Euler paths and Hamilton paths remember that *Euler paths are concerned with visiting all the edges, whereas Hamilton paths are concerned with visiting all the vertices.*

Now we introduce Hamilton circuits.

A **Hamilton circuit** is a path that begins and ends at the same vertex and passes through all other vertices of a graph exactly one time.

An alternate definition for a Hamilton circuit is that a Hamilton circuit is a Hamilton path that starts and ends at the same vertex. For example, the graph in Fig. 14.37(a) has Hamilton circuit $A, B, D, G, E, H, F, C, A$. The graph in Fig. 14.37(a) also has Hamilton circuit $E, G, D, B, A, C, F, H, E$. The graph in Fig. 14.37(b) has Hamilton circuit A, B, C, E, D, A. The graph in 14.37(b) also has Hamilton circuit B, A, D, E, C, B. Note that in an *Euler* circuit, the path followed must include every edge and must begin and end at the same vertex. In a *Hamilton* circuit, the path followed must include every vertex and must begin and end at the same vertex, but unlike the Euler circuit, a Hamilton circuit does not have to include every edge.

In Section 14.2, we were fortunate that Euler's theorem could tell us under what conditions an Euler path or an Euler circuit would exist. We are not as fortunate with Hamilton paths and Hamilton circuits; no such general theorem exists. We now shift our focus to graphs that are guaranteed to have Hamilton circuits.

A *complete graph* is a graph that has an edge between each pair of its vertices. Figure 14.38 shows complete graphs with three, four, and five vertices, respectively.

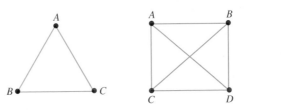

Figure 14.38

Complete graphs are important because *every complete graph has a Hamilton circuit* (but not necessarily an Euler circuit), and traveling salesman problems can be represented by complete graphs. Since each pair of vertices on a complete graph is connected, we can create a Hamilton circuit by simply starting at any vertex and moving from vertex to vertex until we have passed through each vertex exactly one time. Then to complete the circuit we simply move back to the vertex from which we started. Notice in Fig. 14.38 that although all the graphs have Hamilton circuits, only the first and third graphs have Euler circuits.

EXAMPLE 2   *Finding Hamilton Circuits*

Determine a Hamilton circuit for the complete graph shown in Fig. 14.39.

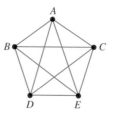

Figure 14.39

SOLUTION: We can determine many Hamilton circuits in this complete graph. For example, one is *A, B, C, D, E, A*. Another is *B, A, D, C, E, B*. Another is *E, B, C, D, A, E*. To build a Hamilton circuit from this complete graph we can list all five vertices in any order and then return to the first vertex. ▲

A question that naturally arises from Example 2 is, "How many different Hamilton circuits are there in a complete graph?" Before we can give a formula that answers this question, we need to discuss *factorials*, which were presented in Section 12.8. We will review that material here. The symbol, 5!, is read "five factorial" and means to multiply 5 by each natural number less than 5. So $5! = 5 \cdot 4 \cdot 3 \cdot 2 \cdot 1 = 120$. Also $3! = 3 \cdot 2 \cdot 1 = 6$ and $7! = 7 \cdot 6 \cdot 5 \cdot 4 \cdot 3 \cdot 2 \cdot 1 = 5040$. Note that 0! is defined to be 1.

Number of Unique Hamilton Circuits in a Complete Graph

The number of unique Hamilton circuits in a complete graph with *n* vertices is $(n - 1)!$

$$\text{where } (n - 1)! = (n - 1)(n - 2)(n - 3)\ldots(3)(2)(1)$$

EXAMPLE 3   *Number of Hamilton Circuits*

How many unique Hamilton circuits are there in a complete graph with the following number of vertices?

a) Three   b) Seven   c) Ten   d) Twelve

SOLUTION:

a) According to our formula, a complete graph with three vertices has $(3 - 1)! = 2! = 2(1) = 2$ unique Hamilton circuits.

b) A complete graph with seven vertices has $(7 - 1)! = 6! = 6 \cdot 5 \cdot 4 \cdot 3 \cdot 2 \cdot 1 = 720$ unique Hamilton circuits.

c) A complete graph with ten vertices has $(10 - 1)! = 9! = 9 \cdot 8 \cdot 7 \cdot 6 \cdot 5 \cdot 4 \cdot 3 \cdot 2 \cdot 1 = 362,880$ unique Hamilton circuits.

d) A complete graph with twelve vertices has $(12 - 1)! = 11! = 11 \cdot 10 \cdot 9 \cdot 8 \cdot 7 \cdot 6 \cdot 5 \cdot 4 \cdot 3 \cdot 2 \cdot 1 = 39,916,800$ unique Hamilton circuits. ▲

As we see from Example 3, as the number of vertices in a complete graph increases the number of Hamilton circuits increases rapidly.

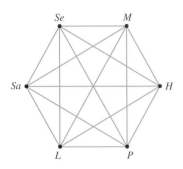

Figure 14.40

A WNBA game

---EXAMPLE 4   *Visiting Teams in the WNBA*

Women's National Basketball Association (WNBA) President Val Ackerman is currently in Los Angeles (L) viewing a Los Angeles Sparks game. Following this game she wishes to visit the home court of five other Western Conference Teams: Houston (H), Minnesota (M), Phoenix (P), Sacramento (Sa), and Seattle (Se). How many different ways can she visit each team one time and return to Los Angeles?

SOLUTION: We can represent this problem with the complete graph in Fig. 14.40. In the graph, the six vertices represent the six locations and the edges represent the one-way flights between these locations.

To determine the number of possible routes we need to determine the number of Hamilton circuits within this graph. We know that there are $(6 - 1)! = 5! = 5 \cdot 4 \cdot 3 \cdot 2 \cdot 1 = 120$ different Hamilton circuits within this graph. So the WNBA president has 120 different ways to start in Los Angeles, visit each of these five teams, and return to Los Angeles.   ▲

Now that we have been introduced to Hamilton circuits, we will apply this knowledge to solving traveling salesman problems.

Traveling Salesman Problems

In Examples 1 and 4, we saw how complete graphs can represent cities and the process of traveling between these cities. Our goal in a traveling salesman problem is to find the least expensive or shortest way to visit each city once and return home. In terms of graph theory, our goal is to find the Hamilton circuit with the lowest associated cost or distance. The Hamilton circuit with the lowest associated cost (or shortest distance, etc.) is called the *optimal solution*. We will discuss two methods, the *Brute Force method* and the *Nearest Neighbor method,* for determining the optimal solution. In both methods, we will use the term *complete, weighted graph*. A *complete, weighted graph* is a complete graph with the weights (or numbers) listed on the edges, as illustrated in Fig. 14.41 on page 854. We now introduce the Brute Force method.

> **The Brute Force Method of Solving Traveling Salesman Problems**
> To determine the optimal solution:
> 1. Represent the problem with a complete, weighted graph.
> 2. List all possible Hamilton circuits for this graph.
> 3. Determine the cost (or distance) associated with each of these Hamilton circuits.
> 4. The Hamilton circuit with the lowest cost (or shortest distance) is the optimal solution.

---EXAMPLE 5   *Using the Brute Force Method*

In Example 1 on page 849, we introduced Julienne Ward, the Southeast District Sales Director for Addison Wesley Longman. We now want to use the Brute Force method to determine the optimal solution for Julienne to visit her regional sales offices. She will start in Orlando (O); visit offices in Atlanta (A), Memphis (M), and New Orleans (N); and then return to Orlando.

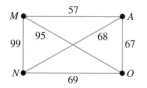

Figure 14.41

SOLUTION: We illustrated a complete, weighted graph for the example in Fig. 14.35a) on page 850. The graph is repeated in Fig. 14.41. The numbers shown represent the one-way fares, in dollars, between the two cities.

We know that since there are 4 cities that must be visited, there are $(4 - 1)! = 3! = 6$ possible unique Hamilton circuits we need to examine for cost. These Hamilton circuits are listed in the first column of Table 14.2.

TABLE 14.2

Hamilton Circuit	First Leg/Cost	Second Leg/Cost	Third Leg/Cost	Fourth Leg/Cost	Total Cost
O, A, M, N, O	O to A $67	A to M $57	M to N $99	N to O $69	$292
O, A, N, M, O	O to A $67	A to N $68	N to M $99	M to O $95	$329
O, M, A, N, O	O to M $95	M to A $57	A to N $68	N to O $69	($289)
O, M, N, A, O	O to M $95	M to N $99	N to A $68	A to O $67	$329
O, N, A, M, O	O to N $69	N to A $68	A to M $57	M to O $95	($289)
O, N, M, A, O	O to N $69	N to M $99	M to A $57	A to O $67	$292

The Hamilton circuits are listed in the column on the left. In the next four columns, we place the cost associated with each leg of the given circuit. In the last column, we place the total cost of travel using the given circuit. From this last column, we see that two circuits have the lowest cost of $289 (circled). Julienne has two choices for an optimal solution. She can either fly from Orlando to Memphis to Atlanta to New Orleans then back to Orlando, or she can fly from Orlando to New Orleans to Atlanta to Memphis then back to Orlando. These two Hamilton circuits are shown on the maps in Fig. 14.42. Notice that the second circuit involves visiting the cities in the exact reverse order of the first circuit. Although these are different circuits, the cost is the same regardless of the direction flown. Either circuit provides Julienne with the least expensive way to visit each of her regional sales offices.

Figure 14.42

Although we used the Brute Force method in Example 5, it becomes impractical as the number of vertices increases. In fact, on more complex problems, the Brute Force method is impractical on even the world's fastest supercomputers. For example, suppose that a presidential candidate wished to visit each of the 31 largest cities in the United States. The candidate would have 30! or about 3×10^{32} choices to accomplish this trip. To understand the magnitude of this number, consider that it would take the world's fastest supercomputer about 6,300,000,000,000 (6.3 *trillion*) YEARS to perform the Brute Force method to find the optimal solution. Computer scientists and mathematicians have developed much more efficient algorithms for seeking the optimal solution to traveling salesman problems.

Now we introduce a method for finding an *approximate solution* to a traveling salesman problem. Approximate solutions can be used in cases where finding the optimal solution is not reasonable. One method for finding an approximate solution is the *Nearest Neighbor method*. In this method, the salesperson begins at a given location. If the salesperson wishes to minimize the distance traveled, the salesperson first visits the city (or location) closest to his or her starting location. Then the salesperson visits the next city (or location) closest to his or her present location. This process continues until all the cities (or locations) are visited. Thus, the salesperson moves to the *nearest neighbor*. Sometimes the salesperson wishes to minimize the cost of travel, such as airfare. In this case, from the starting location the salesperson first visits the city (or location) where the cost of travel is a minimum. Then from the present location the salesperson visits the city (or location) where the cost of travel is a minimum. This process continues until all the cities (or locations) are visited. Approximate solutions will always be Hamilton circuits.

Nearest Neighbor Method of Determining an Approximate Solution to a Traveling Salesman Problem

To approximate the optimal solution:

1. Represent the problem with a complete, weighted graph.

2. Identify the starting vertex.

3. Of all the edges attached to the starting vertex, choose the edge that has the smallest weight. This edge is generally either the shortest distance or the lowest cost. Travel along this edge to the second vertex.

4. At the second vertex, choose the edge that has the smallest weight that does not lead to a vertex already visited. Travel along this edge to the third vertex.

5. Continue this process, each time moving along the edge with the smallest weight until all vertices are visited.

6. Travel back to the original vertex.

EXAMPLE 6   *Using the Nearest Neighbor Method*

In Example 4 on page 853, we discussed Val Ackerman's plan to visit six WNBA Western Conference teams, starting from Los Angeles. Use the Nearest Neighbor method to determine an approximate solution for Val's visits. The one-way flight prices between cities are given in Table 14.3 on page 856.

TABLE 14.3

	Houston	Los Angeles	Minnesota	Phoenix	Sacramento	Seattle
Houston (H)	*	$156	$114	$154	$150	$170
Los Angeles (L)	$156	*	$124	$64	$105	$198
Minnesota (M)	$114	$124	*	$144	$125	$134
Phoenix (P)	$154	$64	$144	*	$94	$149
Sacramento (Sa)	$150	$105	$125	$94	*	$131
Seattle (Se)	$170	$198	$134	$149	$131	*

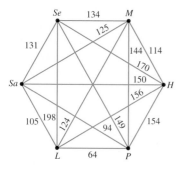

Figure 14.43

SOLUTION: We begin by modifying the graph from Example 4 by putting the prices into place, making it a weighted graph (see Fig. 14.43).

Val starts in Los Angeles and chooses the least expensive flight, which is to Phoenix ($64). In Phoenix, she chooses the least expensive flight to a location she has not already visited, Sacramento ($94). Next, in Sacramento, she chooses the least expensive flight to a location she has not already visited, Minnesota ($125). In Minnesota, she chooses the least expensive flight to a location she has not already visited, Houston ($114). Once in Houston Val has no choice but to fly to the only location not yet visited, Seattle ($170). Since she began in Los Angeles, is now in Seattle, and has visited all six teams, she now returns to Los Angeles ($198) to complete her trip. The Nearest Neighbor method would produce a Hamilton circuit of *L, P, Sa, M, H, Se, L*. The total cost is $64 + $94 + $125 + $114 + $170 + $198 = $765. ▲

For the sake of comparison, let's look at four other randomly chosen Hamilton circuits from Example 6 and the costs associated with them (see Table 14.4).

TABLE 14.4

Randomly Chosen Hamilton Circuit	Cost Calculation	Total Cost
L, Se, H, P, M, Sa, L	$198 + $170 + $154 + $144 + $125 + $105	$896
L, Sa, H, M, Se, P, L	$105 + $150 + $114 + $134 + $149 + $64	$716
L, H, Sa, Se, M, P, L	$156 + $150 + $131 + $134 + $144 + $64	$779
L, H, Se, P, Sa, M, L	$156 + $170 + $149 + $94 + $125 + $124	$818

From Table 14.4 we see that the Hamilton circuit *L, Sa, H, M, Se, P, L* results in a total cost of $716, which is less than the $765 we obtained in Example 6. Thus, we see that the Nearest Neighbor method does not always produce the optimal solution. Without using the Brute Force method we cannot determine if the Hamilton circuit *L, Sa, H, M, Se, P, L* is the optimal solution. It is important to remember that the Nearest Neighbor method produces an *approximation* for the optimal solution. Also note that the Nearest Neighbor method did produce a Hamilton circuit that was less expensive than three of the four randomly chosen Hamilton circuits.

SECTION 14.3   EXERCISES

Concept/Writing Exercises

1. **a)** What is a Hamilton circuit?
   b) What is the difference between a Hamilton circuit and an Euler circuit?

2. **a)** What is a Hamilton path?
   b) What is the difference between a Hamilton path and an Euler path?

3. **a)** What is a weighted graph?
   b) What is a complete graph?
   c) What is a complete, weighted graph?

4. **a)** Describe how to compute the factorial of a given number.
   b) Determine 7!
   c) Determine 8!
   d) Determine 10!

5. **a)** Describe how to determine the number of unique Hamilton circuits that exist in a complete graph with n vertices.
   b) How many unique Hamilton circuits exist in a complete graph with four vertices?
   c) How many unique Hamilton circuits exist in a complete graph with nine vertices?

6. What is meant by the optimal solution to a traveling salesman problem?

7. Describe in your own words the Brute Force method for determining the optimal solution to a traveling salesman problem.

8. Describe in your own words the Nearest Neighbor method for approximating the optimal solution to a traveling salesman problem.

Practice the Skills

In Exercises 9–14, determine two different Hamilton paths in each of the following graphs.

9.
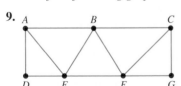

10.
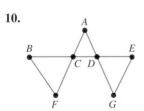

11.
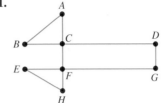

12.
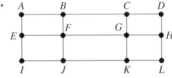

13.
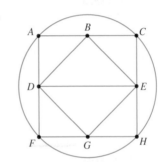

14.
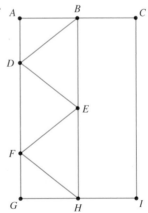

In Exercises 15–18, determine two different Hamilton circuits in each of the following graphs.

15.

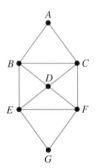

16.

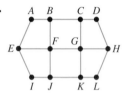

17.

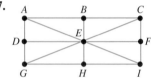

18.

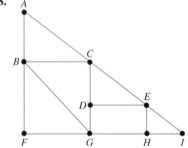

19. Draw a complete graph with four vertices.

20. Draw a complete graph with five vertices.

Problem Solving

21. *Visiting Relatives* Rita Hinderman lives in Sumter, South Carolina, and wishes to visit relatives in the following South Carolina cities: Anderson, Charleston, Columbia, Florence, Greenville, Rock Hill, and Spartanburg. In how many ways can she visit each of these cities and return to her home in Sumter?

22. *Inspecting Weigh Stations* Sally Ivan lives in Nashville, Tennessee, and works for the Department of Transportation. She wishes to inspect weigh stations in the following Tennessee cities: Caruthersville, Clarksville, Cleveland, Dyersburg, Jackson, Johnson City, Kingsport, Knoxville, Memphis, Murfreesboro, Oak Ridge, and Pulaski. In how many ways can she visit each of these cities and return to her home in Nashville?

A Weigh Station

23. *A Milk Truck Route* Dale Klitzke is a milk truck driver for Swiss Valley Farms Cooperative in eastern Iowa. Dale has to start at the processing plant and pick up milk on 10 different farms. In how many ways can Dale visit each farm and return to the processing plant?

24. *Federal Reserve Banks* Federal Reserve Chairman Alan Greenspan is in New York and wishes to visit the Federal Reserve Banks in Atlanta, Boston, Chicago, Cleveland, Dallas, Kansas City, Minneapolis, New York, Philadelphia, Richmond, San Francisco, and St. Louis. In how many different ways can he visit each bank once and return to New York?

Alan Greenspan

25. *Job Interviews* Christina Dwyer is searching for a new job. She lives in Shreveport, Louisiana, and has interviews in Barrow, Alaska; Tucson, Arizona; and Rochester, New York. The costs of the one-way flights between these four cities are as follows: Shreveport to Barrow costs $855, Shreveport to Tucson costs $803, Shreveport to Rochester costs $113, Barrow to Tucson costs $393, Barrow to Rochester costs $337, and Tucson to Rochester costs $841.

a) Represent this traveling salesman problem with a complete, weighted graph showing the prices of the flights on the appropriate edges.

b) Use the Brute Force method to determine the least expensive route for Christina to travel to each city and return home to Shreveport.

c) What is the minimum cost she can pay?

26. *A Vacationing Family* John and Robyn Pearse promised their three sons that they will each get to pick one spot within 500 miles from their home in Chicago to visit on their vacation. Scott chooses to visit St. Louis so that he can go up in the Gateway Arch. Jacob chooses to visit Green Bay so that he can visit the National Railroad Museum. Jevon chooses to visit Ottawa, Illinois, so that he can visit his grandparents. The approximate distances between these cities are as follows: Chicago to St. Louis is 300 miles, Chicago to Green Bay is 205 miles, Chicago to Ottawa is 80 miles, St. Louis to Green Bay is 500 miles, St. Louis to Ottawa is 245 miles, and Green Bay to Ottawa is 280 miles.

The Gateway Arch in St. Louis, MO

a) Represent this traveling salesman problem with a complete, weighted graph showing the distances on the appropriate edges.

b) Use the Brute Force method to determine the shortest route for the Pearses to complete their vacation.

c) What is the minimum distance the Pearses can travel?

27. *Running Errands* Paul Crocket has several errands to run around town. He is at home and needs to go to the hardware store, get his hair cut, and drop off his suit for dry cleaning. Paul estimates the distances among these locations as follows: home to the hardware store is 1.5 miles, home to the barbershop is 4 miles, home to the dry cleaners is 2 miles, hardware store to the barbershop is 2.5 miles, hardware store to the dry cleaners is 3.5 miles, and barbershop to the dry cleaners is 3 miles.

a) Represent this traveling salesman problem with a complete, weighted graph showing the distances on the appropriate edges.

b) Use the Brute Force method to determine the shortest route for Paul to run his errands and return home.

c) What is the minimum distance Paul can travel?

28. *Running Errands on Campus* Mary Mahan needs to run errands on the campus of Clarke College. She is in her office and needs to go to the duplicating center, student center, and library. She estimates the walking distances as follows: from her office to the duplicating center is 150 feet, from her office to the student center is 100 feet, from her office to the library is 400 feet, from the duplicating center to the student center is 125 feet, from the duplicating center to the library is 450 feet, and from the student center to the library is 250 feet.

Clarke College in Dubuque, IA

a) Represent this traveling salesman problem with a complete, weighted graph showing the distances on the appropriate edges.

b) Use the Brute Force method to determine the shortest route for Mary to accomplish her errands and then return back to her office.

c) What is the minimum distance Mary can walk?

29. *Cranberry Plants* Altay Ozgener lives in Boston, Massachusetts, and works for Ocean Spray Cranberries, Inc. Altay wishes to visit cranberry farms in the following locations: Madison, Wisconsin; Princeton, New Jersey; Salem, Oregon; and Walla Walla, Washington. The one-way flight prices are given in the following table.

	Boston	Madison	Princeton	Salem	Walla Walla
Boston	*	$131	$256	$298	$576
Madison	$131	*	$154	$356	$970
Princeton	$256	$154	*	$353	$1164
Salem	$298	$356	$353	*	$179
Walla Walla	$576	$970	$1164	$179	*

a) Represent this traveling salesman problem with a complete, weighted graph showing the prices of flights on the appropriate edges.

b) Use the Nearest Neighbor method to approximate the optimal route for Altay to travel to each city and return to Boston. Give the cost of the route determined.

c) Randomly select another route for Altay to travel from Boston to the other cities and return to Boston and then compute the cost of this route. Compare this cost with the cost found in part (b).

30. *Postmaster General Search* As part of her role as chair of a search committee for the new postmaster general, Marcia Echenique must leave her home in Albany, New York, and visit post offices in the following cities: Billings, Montana,

Cedar Rapids, Iowa, Denver, Colorado, and El Paso, Texas. The one-way flight prices are given in the table.

	Albany	Billings	Cedar Rapids	Denver	El Paso
Albany	*	$365	$252	$351	$1008
Billings	$365	*	$246	$159	$257
Cedar Rapids	$252	$246	*	$174	$278
Denver	$351	$159	$174	*	$124
El Paso	$1008	$257	$278	$124	*

a) Represent this traveling salesman problem with a complete, weighted graph showing the prices of flights on the appropriate edges.

b) Use the Nearest Neighbor method to approximate the optimal route for Marcia to travel to each city and return to Albany. Give the cost of the route determined.

c) Randomly select another route for Marcia to travel from Albany to the other cities and return to Albany and then compute the cost of this route. Compare this cost with the cost determined in part (b).

31. *Presenting Awards* Donna DeSimone lives in Cleveland and works for the Tupperware Corporation. Donna's job requires her to award prizes to the top five sales representatives in the country. In 2003, the top five sales representatives were in Cleveland, Ohio; Detroit, Michigan; Grand Forks, North Dakota; Morgantown, West Virginia; and Tupelo, Mississippi. The costs of one-way flights between these cities are given in the table below.

	Cleveland	Detroit	Grand Forks	Morgan-town	Tupelo
Cleveland	*	$39	$418	$119	$105
Detroit	$39	*	$319	$109	$128
Grand Forks	$418	$319	*	$271	$520
Morgantown	$119	$109	$271	*	$701
Tupelo	$105	$128	$520	$701	*

a) Represent this traveling salesman problem with a complete, weighted graph showing the prices of the flights on the appropriate edges.

b) Use the Nearest Neighbor method to approximate the optimal route for Donna to travel to each city and return to Cleveland. Give the cost of the route determined.

c) Randomly select another route for Donna to travel from Cleveland to the other cities and return to Cleveland and then compute the cost of this route. Compare this cost with the cost determined in part (b).

32. *Locations for a New Factory* Darren Magot works for US Paper Products in New York City. His company is investigating locations for a new factory that will produce a line of disposable clothing. The cities Darren needs to visit are Atlanta, Dallas, Philadelphia, and Washington, D.C. The one-way flight prices between these cities are given in the table above and to the right.

	Atlanta	Dallas	New York	Philadel-phia	Washing-ton, D.C.
Atlanta	*	$182	$197	$159	$180
Dallas	$182	*	$115	$115	$110
New York	$197	$115	*	$55	$156
Philadelphia	$159	$115	$55	*	$205
Washington, D.C.	$180	$110	$156	$205	*

a) Represent this traveling salesman problem with a complete, weighted graph showing the prices of the flights on the appropriate edges.

b) Use the Nearest Neighbor method to approximate the optimal route for Darren to travel to each city and return to New York City. Give the cost of the route determined.

c) Randomly select another route for Darren to travel from New York City to the other cities and return to New York City and then compute the cost of this route. Compare this cost with the cost determined in part (b).

Challenge Problems/Group Activities

33. *Visiting Five Cities* Come up with a list of five cities you would like to visit. Use the Internet to search for airline prices between these five cities (make sure to include the city with the airport nearest your home from which you would start and end your trip).

a) Draw a complete, weighted graph that represents these cities and the costs associated with flying between each pair of cities.

b) Use the Brute Force method to determine the optimal solution to visiting each city and returning home.

c) Use the Nearest Neighbor method to approximate the optimal solution.

d) How much money does the optimal solution, obtained in part (b), save you over the approximation obtained in part (c)?

34. *Number of Circuits* The following tasks are intended to help you understand the formula for finding the number of unique Hamilton circuits in a complete graph.

a) Draw a complete graph with three vertices labeled A, B, and C. Assume that you are starting at vertex A and wish to move to another vertex. How many choices do you have for moving to the second vertex? Once you choose the second vertex, how many choices do you have for moving to a third vertex? Multiply the number of choices you had from vertex A by the number of choices you had from the second vertex. Compare the number you obtained with the number of Hamilton circuits found by using $(n - 1)!$.

b) Draw a complete graph with four vertices labeled A, B, C, and D. Assume that you are starting at vertex A and wish to move to a second vertex. How many choices do you have for moving to this second vertex? Once you choose the second vertex, how many choices do you have for moving to the third vertex? Once you choose the third vertex, how many choices do you have for the fourth vertex? Multiply the number of choices you had from each vertex together. Compare the number you obtained with the number of Hamilton circuits found by using $(n - 1)!$

c) Repeat this process for complete graphs with five and six vertices.

d) In your own words, explain why $(n - 1)!$ gives the number of Hamilton circuits in a complete graph with n vertices.

Recreational Mathematics

35. *The Icosian Game* In 1857, William Rowan Hamilton invented the game called the Icosian Game. The game consisted of a round board with 20 holes and 20 numbered pegs. On the surface of the board was a pattern similar to the graphs we have studied in this chapter (see photo below and artwork at the right).

In essence, the object of the game was to use the pegs to form a Hamilton circuit on the graph. The graph below is taken from the Icosian Game. Determine a Hamilton circuit on this graph.

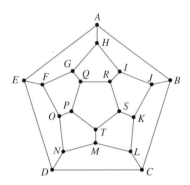

Internet/Research Activity

36. Write a paper on traveling salesman problems. Include a brief history of the problems. Also include advances made toward reducing the computational time of determining the optimal solution as well as advances made toward determining better approximate solutions.

14.4 TREES

In this chapter, we have introduced graphs as a means to represent problems from everyday life (Section 14.1). We used graph theory to solve a variety of problems by finding Euler paths and Euler circuits (Section 14.2). We also used graph theory to find the optimal and approximate solutions to traveling salesman problems using Hamilton circuits (Section 14.3). We now turn our attention to another type of graph, called a *tree*, which is also frequently used to represent problems from everyday life. Before we define a *tree*, let's look at Example 1, in which we create a family tree.

EXAMPLE 1 *A Family Tree*

Pat has two daughters: Sue and Kris. Sue has four children: John, Thomas, Lee, and Rhiannon. Kris has three children: Alex, Nicholas, and Max. Use a graph to represent this family.

SOLUTION: We will construct this graph with three layers, one for each generation. The vertices represent the people and the edges represent the parent–child relationship. Start with Pat, then branch to the two daughters, Sue and Kris. Finally, make branches to the children.

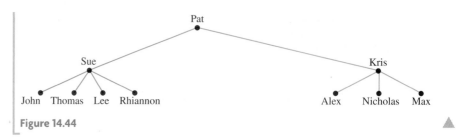

Figure 14.44

The graph shown in Fig. 14.44 is an example of a tree.

A **tree** is a connected graph in which each edge is a bridge.

Recall from Section 14.1 that a bridge is an edge that if removed from a connected graph would create a disconnected graph. Thus, if you remove *any edge* in a tree, it creates a disconnected graph. Since each edge would create a disconnected graph if removed, a tree cannot have any Euler circuits or Hamilton circuits. Can you explain why? Fig. 14.45(a) gives four examples of graphs that are trees, and Fig. 14.45(b) gives four examples of graphs that are not trees.

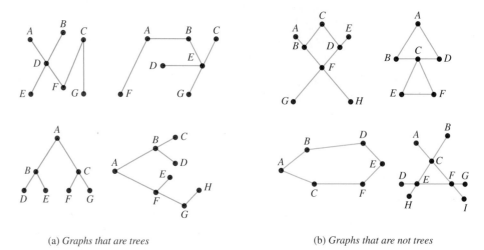

(a) *Graphs that are trees*   (b) *Graphs that are not trees*

Figure 14.45

Some applications, like the family tree in Example 1, can be represented with a graph that is a tree. In other applications, the problem may initially be represented with a graph that is not a tree. In this section, to solve certain problems, we will need to remove edges from a graph that is not a tree to form a tree known as a *spanning tree*. We now define spanning tree.

A **spanning tree** is a tree that is created from another graph by removing edges while still maintaining a path to each vertex.

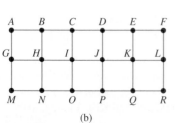

Figure 14.46

EXAMPLE 2   *Determining Spanning Trees*

Determine two different spanning trees for each graph shown in Fig. 14.46.

SOLUTION: Each of the spanning trees we create will need to have a path connecting all vertices, but cannot have any circuits. To create a spanning tree from a graph we remove

In our current "information age," data networks support so many daily conveniences that we probably don't even realize a network is involved. Each time we place a telephone call, fly in an airplane, send an e-mail, or use the Internet, we are using some form of modern data network. Each of these networks can be represented as a graph with many vertices and edges. It might surprise you that data networks predate the twentieth century. The most well known example of a primitive data network is the electromagnetic telegraph used in the nineteenth century in the United States and around the world prior to the invention of the telephone. An even older example of a data network is the optical telegraph (with nearly 1000 stations) used in the eighteenth century all across Europe. Perhaps the oldest, yet maybe the slowest, form of data network is one still in use today: the writing and sending of letters!

edges one at a time while leaving all the vertices in place. When we remove an edge, we must make sure the edge is not a bridge. Removing a bridge would create a disconnected graph. We need to reduce our original graph to one that is still connected. Keeping these guidelines in mind, we continue removing edges until the remaining graph is a tree. Two spanning trees formed from each graph in Fig. 14.46(a) and (b) are given in Fig. 14.47(a) and (b), respectively. Other spanning trees are possible in each case.

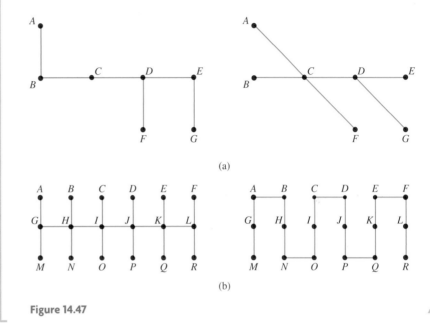

Figure 14.47

Notice in all four spanning trees in Example 2 that each edge is a bridge and that no circuits are present. Our next example provides an application of spanning trees.

EXAMPLE 3   *A Spanning Tree Problem*

Schoolcraft College is considering adding awnings above its sidewalks to help shelter students from the snow and rain while they walk between some of the buildings on campus. A diagram of the buildings and the connecting sidewalks where the awnings are to be added is given in Fig. 14.48.

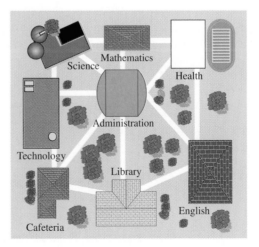

Figure 14.48

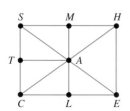

Figure 14.49

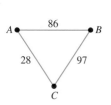

Figure 14.51

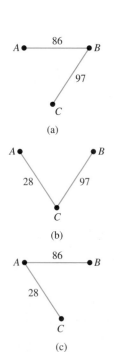

Figure 14.52

Originally, the president of the college wished to have awnings placed over all the sidewalks shown in Fig. 14.48, but that was found to be too costly. Instead, the president has proposed to place just enough awnings over a select number of sidewalks so that, by moving from building to building, students would still be able to reach any location shown without being exposed to the elements.

a) Represent all the buildings and sidewalks shown with a graph.

b) Create three different spanning trees from this graph that would satisfy the president's proposal.

SOLUTION:

a) Using letters to represent the building names, vertices to represent the buildings, and edges to represent the sidewalks between buildings, we generate the graph in Fig. 14.49.

b) To create a spanning tree we remove nonbridge edges until a tree is created. Three possible spanning trees are given in Fig. 14.50; however, many others are possible.

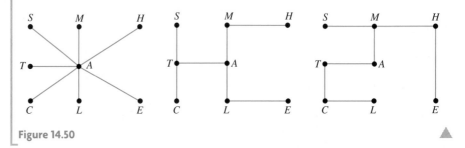

Figure 14.50

Example 3 shows us how spanning trees can be used to represent a real-life problem. However, the administrators at Schoolcraft College still have a problem: Which sidewalks should be chosen to cover with awnings (or which spanning tree should be selected)? Problems like the one faced by Schoolcraft College usually have additional considerations that need to be included in the decision-making process. The most common consideration is the cost of the project. To help analyze these problems weighted graphs—graphs with costs or distances associated with each edge—and minimum-cost spanning trees are used.

> A **minimum-cost spanning tree** is the least expensive spanning tree of all spanning trees under consideration.

Example 4 will explain how we determine a minimum-cost spanning tree for a graph with three edges.

EXAMPLE 4   *Finding a Minimum-Cost Spanning Tree*

Examine the weighted graph in Fig. 14.51. This graph shows the costs, in dollars, associated with each edge.

Determine the minimum-cost spanning tree for this graph.

SOLUTION: There are three spanning trees associated with this graph; they are shown in Fig. 14.52.

The spanning tree in Fig. 14.52(a) has a cost of $86 + $97 = $183. The spanning tree in Fig. 14.52(b) has a cost of $28 + $97 = $125. The spanning tree in Fig. 14.52(c) has a cost of $86 + $28 = $114. Therefore, the minimum-cost spanning tree is shown in Fig. 14.52(c). It has a cost of $114. ▲

The process used in Example 4 is similar to the Brute Force method used to find the optimal solution to traveling salesman problems in Section 14.3. Although this process is easy to carry out for a small graph, such a process would be impossible for graphs with a large number of vertices. Fortunately, we have an algorithm, called Kruskal's algorithm, to determine the minimum-cost spanning tree.

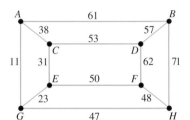

Figure 14.53

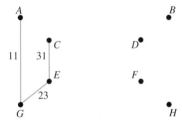

Figure 14.54

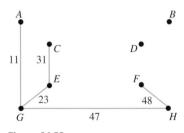

Figure 14.55

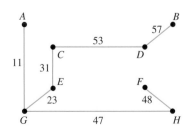

Figure 14.56

Kruskal's Algorithm

To construct the minimum-cost spanning tree from a weighted graph:

1. Select the lowest-cost edge on the graph.
2. Select the next lowest-cost edge that does not form a circuit with the first edge.
3. Select the next lowest-cost edge that does not form a circuit with previously selected edges.
4. Continue selecting the lowest-cost edges that do not form circuits with the previously selected edges.
5. When a spanning tree is complete, you have the minimum-cost spanning tree.

EXAMPLE 5   *Using Kruskal's Algorithm*

Use Kruskal's algorithm to determine the minimum-cost spanning tree for the weighted graph shown in Fig. 14.53. The numbers along the edges in Fig. 14.53 represent dollars.

SOLUTION: We begin by selecting the lowest-cost edge of the graph, edge *AG*, which is $11 (see Fig. 14.54). Next we select the next lowest-cost edge that does not form a circuit, edge *GE*, which is $23. Once again, looking for the lowest-cost edge that does not form a circuit, we select edge *CE* which is $31. The result of our first three selections is shown in Fig. 14.54.

Looking at the original weighted graph in Fig. 14.53, we see that the next lowest-cost edge is edge *AC*, which is $38. However, selecting edge *AC* would create a circuit among vertices *A, C, E,* and *G*. So we must not select edge *AC*. Instead, we select edge *GH*, which is $47, since this is the next lowest-cost edge and its selection does not lead to a circuit; see Fig. 14.55. Next, we select edge *FH*, which is $48.

The next lowest-cost edge not yet selected is edge *EF*, which is $50. However, this edge would create a circuit among vertices *E, F, H,* and *G*. Instead, we select edge *CD*, which is $53, followed by selecting edge *BD*, which is $57. The result of our selections thus far is shown in Fig. 14.56.

Notice that the graph in Fig. 14.56 is a spanning tree. According to Kruskal's algorithm, the tree in Fig. 14.56 is the minimum-cost spanning tree for the original weighted graph. ▲

Note that in Example 5 all the edges selected were connected to edges we had already selected. However, that will not always be the case. In Example 6, when we select the edges, some will be disconnected at the time we select them.

We now will apply our knowledge of minimum-cost spanning trees. Note that in examples and exercises, the graphs need not be drawn to scale.

EXAMPLE 6   *An Application Using Kruskal's Algorithm*

Recall from Example 3 that Schoolcraft College is considering the construction of awnings over a select number of sidewalks on campus. The distances, in feet, between buildings are shown in the weighted graph in Fig. 14.57.

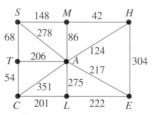

Figure 14.57

a) Determine the shortest series of sidewalks to cover so that students would be able to move between any buildings shown without being exposed to the elements.

b) The cost of the awnings is $23 per foot of sidewalk regardless of where they are placed on campus. What will it cost to cover the sidewalks found in part (a)?

SOLUTION:

a) Schoolcraft College is seeking a minimum-cost spanning tree for the weighted graph shown in Fig. 14.57. To determine the minimum-cost spanning tree we use Kruskal's algorithm. First, we select the edge *MH* since it has the shortest distance and therefore has the lowest cost. We next select the edge *TC* since it has the second shortest distance and it doesn't form a circuit with our previously selected edge (see Fig. 14.58). Our third and fourth choices will be edge *ST* and edge *MA*, respectively, since these edges have the next shortest distances and they do not form a circuit with previously selected edges. The result of our first four selections is shown in Fig. 14.58.

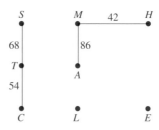

Figure 14.58

The next lowest-cost edge is edge *AH*. However, selection of edge *AH* would form a circuit with vertices *A*, *H*, and *M*. Instead, we choose the next lowest cost edge—edge *SM*—since it does not form a circuit with the previously selected edges (see Fig. 14.59 on page 867). Our next lowest cost edge will be edge *CL*. Note that edge *CL* does not form a circuit with the previously selected edges. The result of all our selections so far is shown in Fig. 14.59.

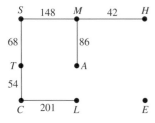

Figure 14.59

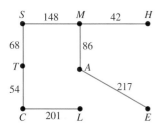

Figure 14.60

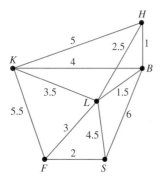

Figure 14.61

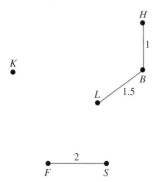

Figure 14.62

We note that the next lowest-cost edge is edge *TA*, but selecting this edge would create a circuit with vertices *S, M, A,* and *T*. So we select edge *AE*. The result of our selections so far is shown in Fig. 14.60.

From Fig. 14.60, we can see that we have formed a spanning tree. According to Kruskal's algorithm, this is the minimum-cost spanning tree. Therefore, Fig. 14.60 shows which sidewalks should be covered with the awnings. Covering these sidewalks will provide protection to students at the lowest cost to Schoolcraft College.

b) From Fig. 14.60, we see that there are $148 + 42 + 68 + 86 + 54 + 217 + 201 = 816$ feet of sidewalks that need to be covered. At $23 per foot, the cost to cover these sidewalks is $23 \times 816 = \$18,768$. ▲

EXAMPLE 7

Schools in Budville, Fairplay, Happy Corners, Kieler, Louisburg, and Sinsinawa, Wisconsin, all wish to establish a fiber-optic computer network to share information and to obtain Internet access. The most efficient method of establishing such a network would be to install fiber-optic cable along roadsides. The weighted graph in Fig. 14.61 shows the distance in miles between schools along existing roads.

a) Determine the shortest distance to link these six schools.

b) The cost to install fiber-optic cable is $1257 per mile. What will it cost to install the fiber-optic cable along the roadsides determined in part (a)?

SOLUTION:

a) We are seeking a minimum-cost spanning tree. We will carry out Kruskal's algorithm to find it. The first three edges selected will be edge *HB* (1 mile), edge *BL* (1.5 miles), and edge *FS* (2 miles). Note that these are the three lowest-cost edges, and their selection does not lead to a circuit. The result of our first three selections is shown in Fig. 14.62.

The next lowest-cost edge is edge *HL* (2.5 miles), but selecting this edge would lead to a circuit between vertices *H, B,* and *L*. Instead, we select the next lowest-cost edge, edge *LF* (3 miles). This edge is followed by the next lowest-cost edge, edge *KL* (3.5 miles). The result of all our selections so far is shown in Fig. 14.63. We now have a spanning tree.

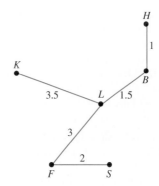

Figure 14.63

According to Kruskal's algorithm, Fig. 14.63 shows the minimum-cost spanning tree. Therefore, Fig. 14.63 gives the paths along which fiber-optic cable should be placed to connect the schools for the minimum cost.

b) From Fig. 14.63, we can see that there are $1 + 1.5 + 3.5 + 3 + 2 = 11$ miles of fiber-optic cable needed for this network. At $1257 per mile, the cost to install this fiber-optic network would be $1257 \times 11 = \$13,827$.   ▲

SECTION 14.4   EXERCISES

Concept/Writing Exercises

1. What is a tree?

2. How does a tree differ from a graph that is not a tree?

3. Consider two distinct vertices connected by one edge. Is this graph a tree? Explain.

4. How is a spanning tree obtained from a graph that is not a tree?

5. What is a minimum-cost spanning tree?

6. Describe in your own words how to find a minimum-cost spanning tree from a weighted graph.

Practice the Skills

7. *A Family Tree* Use a tree to show the parent–child relationships in the following family. Joe has two children: Allan and Rosemary. Allan has three children: Christopher, Donetta, and AJ. Rosemary has three children: Peter, Paula, and Martin.

8. *A Family Tree* Use a tree to show the parent–child relationships in the following family. Rita has two children: Arturo and Maria. Arturo has four children: Josephine, David, Mario, and Rickardo. Maria has one child: Tito.

9. *Employment Structure* Use a tree to show the employee relationships at Sierra Nevada College. President Rosen has three vice presidents working for him: Martin, Pearse, and Kent. Martin has three department heads working for her: Burnette, Fields, and Buckles. Pearse has two department heads working for him: Jones and DiTaranto. Kent has two department heads working for her: Freeman and Kowalski.

10. *Corporate Structure* Use a tree to show the following employee relationships at DTX Industries. Kroger is president and has three vice presidents: Dorfman, Blutarsky, and Hoover. Dorfman has three managers: Stratton, Day, and Stork. Blutarsky has three managers: Schoenstein, De Pasto, and Liebowitz. Hoover has two managers: Jennings and Wormer.

In Exercises 11–18, determine two different spanning trees for the given graph.

11.

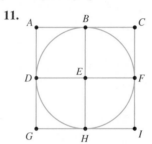

12.

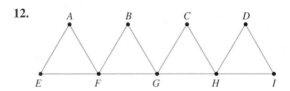

13.

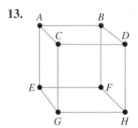

14.

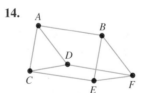

15.

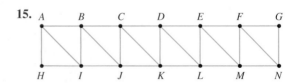

16.

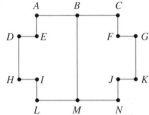

17.

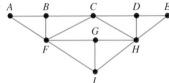

18.

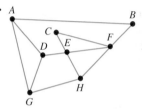

In Exercises 19–26, determine the minimum-cost spanning trees for the given graph.

19.

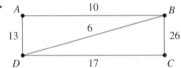

20.

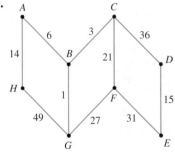

21.

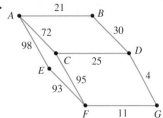

22.

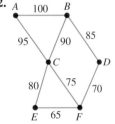

23.

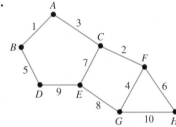

24.

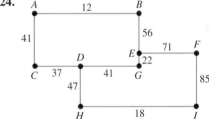

25.

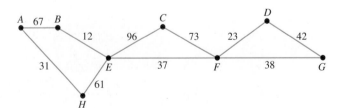

26.

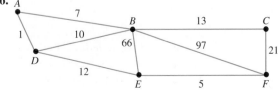

Problem Solving

27. *An Irrigation System* Larry and Mona Riemersma are considering installing an irrigation system to water their five flower gardens. The distances in feet between the gardens are shown in the figure below.

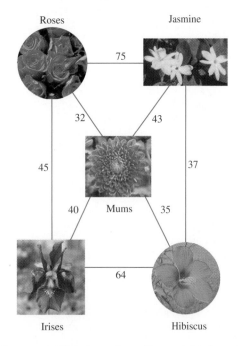

Roses   Jasmine

75

32   43

45   37

40   Mums   35

64

Irises   Hibiscus

a) Represent this information with a weighted graph.
b) Use Kruskal's algorithm to determine the minimum-cost spanning tree.
c) If the cost of installing irrigation pipe is $15 per foot, determine the minimum cost of installing the irrigation system from part (b).

28. *Art Sculpture* Joe Loccisano is creating a modern art sculpture that needs to have electricity available at five different sites. The figure below shows the items included in the sculpture. The distances shown are in inches.

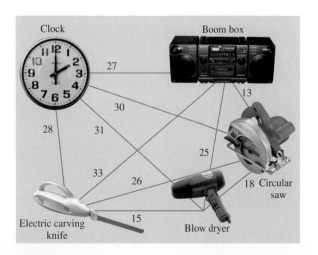

Clock   Boom box

27

30   13

28   31

25

33

26   18 Circular
                saw

15

Electric carving   Blow dryer
knife

a) Represent this sculpture with a weighted graph.
b) Use Kruskal's algorithm to determine the minimum-cost spanning tree that would provide electricity to each site on the sculpture.
c) If the cost of installing wiring on the sculpture is $0.75 per inch, determine the minimum cost for wiring this sculpture.

29. *Linking Universities* The five Universities of Wisconsin located in the southern part of the state would like to establish a direct telephone network. The universities in this circuit include Parkside, Platteville, Madison, Milwaukee, and Whitewater. The map shown below gives the distances in miles between these universities.

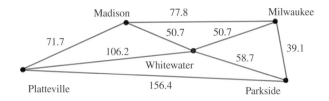

Madison   77.8   Milwaukee

50.7   50.7

71.7   39.1

106.2   58.7

Whitewater

Platteville   156.4   Parkside

a) Use Kruskal's algorithm to determine the minimum-cost spanning tree that would link each university to create the telephone network with the shortest distance.
b) If it costs $895 per mile to put the telephone lines in place, how much will it cost to produce the network determined in part (a)?

30. *Commuter Train System* Several communities of eastern Pennsylvania wish to establish a commuter rail train system between the cities shown in the map below (distances are in miles).

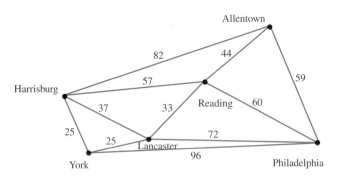

Allentown

82   44

57   59

Harrisburg

37   33   Reading   60

25

25   72

Lancaster

York   96   Philadelphia

a) Use Kruskal's algorithm to determine the minimum-cost spanning tree that would link the cities using the shortest distance.
b) If it costs $6800 per mile of railroad track, how much does the commuter rail system found in part (a) cost?

31. *Horse Trails* The Darlington County, South Carolina, tourism office wishes to build a horse trail that connects the towns of Darlington, Hartsville, Lamar, and Society Hill. The distances, in miles, between these cities are given in the table on the next page.

	Darlington	Hartsville	Lamar	Society Hill
Darlington	*	12	14	15
Hartsville	12	*	13	16
Lamar	14	13	*	26
Society Hill	15	16	26	*

a) Represent this information with a complete, weighted graph (see Section 14.3 for the definition of a complete, weighted graph).
b) Use Kruskal's algorithm to determine the minimum-cost spanning tree that would link each city to create the least expensive horse trail.
c) If the cost of building such a trail is $3500 per mile, what is the cost of building the trail determined in part (b)?

32. *Electrical Power Lines* The Eastern Ohio Electric Cooperative wishes to connect cities within its district with new, higher-quality electrical power lines. The cities include Akron, Canton, Cleveland, Columbus, and Youngstown. The distances in miles between the cities involved are given in the table below.

	Akron	Canton	Cleveland	Columbus	Youngstown
Akron	*	23	45	127	48
Canton	23	*	68	125	53
Cleveland	45	68	*	146	75
Columbus	127	125	146	*	178
Youngstown	48	53	75	178	*

a) Represent this information with a complete, weighted graph.
b) Use Kruskal's algorithm to determine the minimum-cost spanning tree that would link each city to create the least expensive power line network.
c) If the cost to establish electrical power lines is $2300 per mile, determine the cost of creating the electrical power lines determined in part (b).

33. *Bicycle Path* The State Recreation League of Arkansas would like to build a bicycle path that connects the cities of Blytheville, El Dorado, Fort Smith, Little Rock, and Pine Bluff. The distances in miles between these cities are given in the following table.

	Blytheville	El Dorado	Fort Smith	Little Rock	Pine Bluff
Blytheville	*	286	325	184	195
El Dorado	286	*	237	116	91
Fort Smith	325	237	*	160	197
Little Rock	184	116	160	*	43
Pine Bluff	195	91	197	43	*

a) Represent this information with a complete, weighted graph.
b) Use Kruskal's algorithm to determine the minimum-cost spanning tree that would link each city to create the least expensive bicycle path.

c) If the cost of building such a path is $2500 per mile, what is the cost of building the path determined in part (b)?

34. *Light-Rail Transit System* The state of Illinois is applying for a grant to connect several metropolitan areas of the state with a light-rail transport system. The cities involved are Champaign, Chicago, Peoria, Rockford, and Springfield. The distances in miles between these cities are given in the following table.

	Champaign	Chicago	Peoria	Rockford	Springfield
Champaign	*	135	89	181	86
Chicago	135	*	170	85	202
Peoria	89	170	*	129	74
Rockford	181	85	129	*	193
Springfield	86	202	74	193	*

a) Represent this information with a complete, weighted graph.
b) Use Kruskal's algorithm to determine the minimum-cost spanning tree that would link each city using the shortest distance.
c) What would be the total distance of the light rail transportation system determined in part (b)?

Challenge Problems/Group Activities

35. *Computer Network* Create a minimum-cost spanning tree that would serve as the least expensive way to create a computer network among the five largest cities in your state. Consult maps, atlases, almanacs, or the Internet for distances. Assume that the cost per mile is the same regardless of the path taken.

36. *College Structure* Create a tree that shows the administrative structure at your college or university. Start with the highest-ranking officer (that is, president, chancellor, provost, headmaster) and work down to the department chair level.

37. *Sidewalk Covers* Create a minimum-cost spanning tree that would serve as the least expensive way to provide sheltered sidewalks between major buildings on your college campus (see Example 6 on page 866). Assume that the cost per foot is the same regardless of the path taken.

Recreational Mathematics

38. Unscramble the following letters to form the names of four influential mathematicians in the area of graph theory.
a) LUREE
b) LYFRUE
c) LOMTHINA
d) LARKSKU

Internet/Research Activity

39. Write a research paper on the life and work of Joseph Kruskal, discoverer of Kruskal's algorithm.

CHAPTER 14 SUMMARY

IMPORTANT FACTS

Paths and Circuits

A **path** is a sequence of adjacent vertices and the edges connecting them.

A **circuit** is a path that begins and ends at the same vertex.

An **Euler path** is a path that passes through each *edge* of a graph exactly one time.

An **Euler circuit** is a circuit that passes through each *edge* of a graph exactly one time.

A **Hamilton path** is a path that contains each *vertex* of a graph exactly once.

A **Hamilton circuit** is a path that begins and ends at the same vertex and passes through all *vertices* exactly one time.

Euler's theorem

For a connected graph, the following statements are true:

1. A graph with *no odd vertices* (all even vertices) has at least one Euler path, which is also an Euler circuit. An Euler circuit can be started at any vertex and it will end at the same vertex.

2. A graph with *exactly two odd vertices* has at least one Euler path but no Euler circuits. Each Euler path must begin at one of the two odd vertices and end at the other odd vertex.

3. A graph with *more than two odd vertices* has no Euler paths or Euler circuits.

Fleury's algorithm

To determine an Euler path or an Euler circuit:

1. Use Euler's theorem to determine whether an Euler path or an Euler circuit exists. If one exists, proceed with steps 2–5.

2. If the graph has no odd vertices (therefore has an Euler circuit which is also an Euler path), choose any vertex as the starting point. If the graph has exactly two odd vertices (therefore has only an Euler path), choose one of the two odd vertices as the starting point.

3. Begin to trace edges as you move through the graph. Number the edges as you trace them. Since you can't trace any edges twice in Euler paths and Euler circuits, once an edge is traced consider it "invisible."

4. When faced with a choice of edges to trace, if possible, choose an edge that is not a bridge (i.e., don't create a disconnected graph with your choice of edges).

5. Continue until each edge of the entire graph has been traced once.

Number of unique Hamilton circuits in a complete graph

The number of unique Hamilton circuits in a complete graph with n vertices is $(n - 1)!$ where

$$(n - 1)! = (n - 1)(n - 2)(n - 3) \cdots (3)(2)(1)$$

The Brute Force method of solving traveling salesman problems

To determine the optimal solution:

1. Represent the problem with a complete, weighted graph.

2. List all possible Hamilton circuits in this graph.

3. Determine the cost associated with each of these Hamilton circuits.

4. The Hamilton circuit with the lowest cost is the optimal solution.

The Nearest Neighbor method for finding an approximate solution to a traveling salesman problem

To approximate the optimal solution:

1. Represent the problem with a complete, weighted graph.

2. Identify the starting vertex.

3. Of all the edges attached to the starting vertex, choose the edge that has the smallest weight. This edge is the shortest distance or the lowest cost. Travel along this edge to the second vertex.

4. At the second vertex, choose the edge that has the smallest weight that does not lead to a vertex already visited. Travel along this edge to the third vertex.

5. Continue this process, each time moving along the edge with the smallest weight until all vertices are visited.

6. Travel back to the original vertex.

Kruskal's algorithm

To construct the minimum-cost spanning tree from a weighted graph:

1. Select the lowest-cost edge on the graph.

2. Select the next lowest-cost edge that does not form a circuit with the first edge.

3. Select the next lowest-cost edge that does not form a circuit with previously selected edges.

4. Continue selecting the lowest-cost edges that do not form circuits with the previously selected edges.

5. When a spanning tree is complete, you have the minimum-cost spanning tree.

CHAPTER 14   REVIEW EXERCISES

14.1

In Exercises 1 and 2, create a graph with the given properties.

1. Create a graph with three even vertices and a loop.

2. Create a graph with eight vertices and a bridge.

In Exercises 3 and 4, use the following graph.

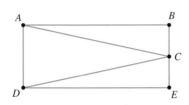

3. Determine a path that contains each edge exactly one time.

4. Is it possible to have a path that begins at vertex *A*, includes all edges exactly once, and ends at vertex *B*? Explain.

5. Represent the map as a graph where each vertex represents a state and each edge represents a common border between the states.

6. The drawing below shows the first-floor plan of the Fillmore Model home offered by the Saratoga Springs Development Group. Construct a graph to represent this model.

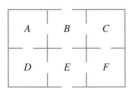

In Exercises 7 and 8, determine whether the graph shown is connected or disconnected.

7.

8.

9. Identify all bridges in the graph below.

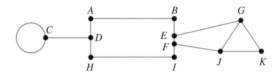

14.2

Use the following graph for Exercises 10 and 11.

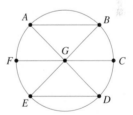

10. Determine an Euler path that begins with vertex *C*.

11. Determine an Euler path that begins with vertex *F*.

Use the following graph for Exercises 12 and 13.

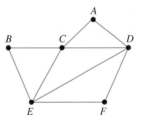

12. Determine an Euler circuit that begins with vertex *B*.

13. Determine an Euler circuit that begins with vertex *E*.

14. Consider the following map.

a) Represent the map as a graph.
b) Determine (state yes or no) whether the graph has an Euler path. If yes, give one such Euler path.
c) Determine (state yes or no) whether the graph has an Euler circuit. If yes, give one such Euler circuit.

15. a) Is it possible for a person to walk through each doorway in the house whose floor plan is shown below without using any of the doorways twice? Explain.
b) If so, where can the person start and where will the person finish? Explain.

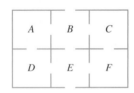

16. a) Can a police officer walk each street shown in the figure below without walking any street more than once? Explain.
b) If yes, where would the police officer have to start the walk?

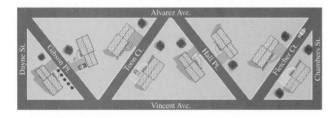

17. Use Fleury's algorithm to determine an Euler path in the following graph.

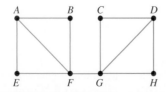

18. Use Fleury's algorithm to determine an Euler circuit in the following graph.

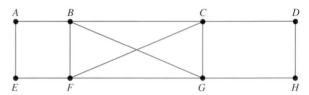

14.3

19. Determine two different Hamilton paths in the following graph.

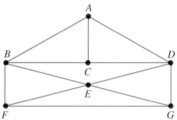

20. Determine two different Hamilton circuits in the following graph.

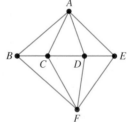

21. Draw a complete graph with five vertices.

22. *Baseball* The American League Eastern Division has the following teams: Baltimore Orioles, Boston Red Sox, New York Yankees, Tampa Bay Devil Rays, and Toronto Blue Jays. How many different possible ways could a Boston Red Sox fan visit each team in the American League Eastern Division one time and return home to Boston?

23. *Job Interviews* Lance Lopez is searching for a new job. He lives in Portland, Oregon, and has interviews in Des Moines, Iowa; Charleston, West Virginia; and Montgomery, Alabama. The costs of the one-way flights between these four cities are as follows: Portland to Des Moines is $428, Portland to Charleston is $787, Portland to Montgomery is $902, Des Moines to Charleston is $449, Des Moines to Montgomery is $458, and Charleston to Montgomery is $415.
a) Represent this traveling salesman problem with a complete, weighted graph showing the prices of the flights on the appropriate edges.
b) Use the Brute Force method to determine the least expensive route for Lance Lopez to travel to each city and return home to Portland.
c) What is the total cost of air fare for Lance's trip in part b)?

24. *Visiting Sales Offices* Jennifer Adams is the sales manager for AT&T for the state of Missouri. There are major sales offices in Columbia, Kansas City, St. Joseph, St. Louis, and Springfield. The distances in miles between these cities are given in the following table:

	Columbia	Kansas City	St. Joseph	St. Louis	Spring-field
Columbia	*	130	177	127	168
Kansas City	130	*	54	256	192
St. Joseph	177	54	*	304	224
St. Louis	127	256	304	*	210
Springfield	168	192	224	210	*

a) Represent this traveling salesman problem with a complete, weighted graph showing the prices of the flights on the appropriate edges.

b) Use the Nearest Neighbor method to approximate the optimal route for Jennifer to begin in St. Joseph, visit each city once, and return to St. Joseph.

c) Suppose that Jennifer starts in Springfield. Use the Nearest Neighbor method to approximate the optimal route for Jennifer to visit each city once and return to Springfield.

14.4

25. *Employee Relationships* Use a tree to show the employees' relationships in the Hulka Consulting Corporation. Hulka is president. Winger and Ziskey are vice presidents who work for Hulka. Markowicz, Oxburger, and Soyer are district managers who work for Winger. Elmo, Hector, and Jenesky are district managers who work for Ziskey.

26. Determine two different spanning trees for the following graph.

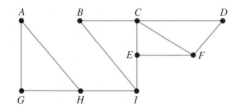

27. Determine the minimum-cost spanning tree for the following graph.

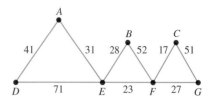

28. *An Irrigation System* Lucille Groenke wants to install an irrigation system to water all six of her flowerbeds in her back yard. The drawing shows the location of each flowerbed and the distance between them in feet.

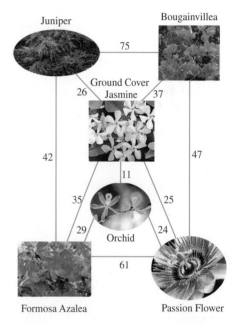

a) Represent this information with a weighted graph.

b) Use Kruskal's algorithm to determine the minimum-cost spanning tree.

c) The irrigation materials cost $2.50 per foot. Determine the cost of installing the irrigation system found in part (b).

CHAPTER 14 TEST

1. Create a graph with seven vertices, a bridge, and a loop.

2. *Part of Africa* Represent the map below as a graph where each vertex represents a country and each edge represents a common border between the countries.

3. Draw a disconnected graph.

4. In the following graph, determine an Euler path.

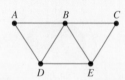

5. Is it possible for a person to walk through each doorway in the house, whose floor plan is shown below, without using any of the doorways twice? If so, indicate in which room the person may start and where he or she will end.

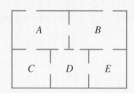

6. Use Fleury's algorithm to determine an Euler circuit in the following graph.

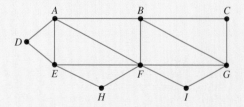

7. Determine a Hamilton circuit in the following graph.

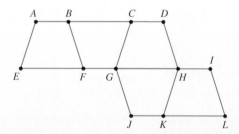

8. *Job Interviews* Tracy Harrison lives in Muskegon, Michigan, and has job interviews in the following other Michigan cities: Battle Creek, Bay City, Flint, Grand Rapids, Kalamazoo, Marquette, and Saginaw. How many different ways can Tracy visit each city and return to her home in Muskegon?

9. *Job Interviews* Kate Kozak lives in Indianapolis, Indiana, and has job interviews in Pensacola, Florida; El Paso, Texas; and Albuquerque, New Mexico. The one-way flights between these four cities are as follows: Indianapolis to Pensacola is $449, Indianapolis to El Paso is $201, Indianapolis to Albuquerque is $203, Pensacola to El Paso is $728, Pensacola to Albuquerque is $677, and El Paso to Albuquerque is $49.

a) Represent this traveling salesman problem with a complete, weighted graph showing the prices of flights on the appropriate edges.

b) Use the Brute Force method to determine the least expensive route for Kate to visit each city once and return home to Indianapolis. What is the cost when using this route?

c) Use the Nearest Neighbor method to approximate the optimal route for Kate to visit each city once and return home to Indianapolis. What is the cost when using this route?

10. Determine a spanning tree for the graph shown below.

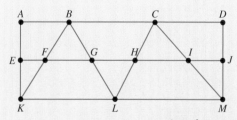

continued on next page

11. Determine the minimum-cost spanning tree for the following weighted graph.

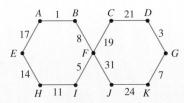

12. *Irrigation System* Daniel Kimborowicz is planning a new irrigation system for his yard. His current system has valves already in place as shown in the figure on the right. The numbers shown are in feet.
   a) Determine the minimum-cost spanning tree that reaches each valve.

b) If the new irrigation materials cost $1.25 per foot, find the cost of installing the system determined in part (a).

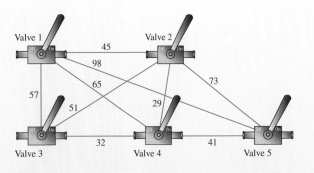

GROUP PROJECTS

1. Street Sweeper Route

Make a map of all streets or roads within 2 miles of your college campus. Now add roads as needed so that a street sweeper would be able to sweep all streets on this map, starting at the school and returning to the school without sweeping any street twice.

2. Hometown Road Trip

Select five students in your class so that no two have the same hometown. Use the Internet to find the distances between each pair of towns (MapQuest is a good source to check).

   a) Draw a complete, weighted graph that represents the five towns and the distances between them.
   b) Use the Nearest Neighbor method to determine an approximation for the optimal solution when starting at your college, visiting each hometown, and then returning to your college.
   c) Use Kruskal's algorithm to determine the minimum-cost spanning tree for the complete, weighted graph in part (a).
   d) Determine the total distance one would travel along the minimum-cost spanning tree found in part (c).

3. State Capital Tour

Identify the five state capitals closest to where you live. Use the Internet or consult an almanac to find the driving distances between these five capitals.

   a) Draw a complete, weighted graph that represents the capitals and the distances between them.
   b) Use the Nearest Neighbor method to determine an approximation for the optimal solution of starting at your state capital, visiting the other four capitals, and then returning to your state capital.
   c) Use Kruskal's algorithm to determine the minimum-cost spanning tree for the complete, weighted graph determined in part (a).
   d) Determine the total distance a person would travel along the minimum-cost spanning tree found in part (c).

4. Computer Network on Campus

Measure the distance between the five busiest buildings on your campus. Create a weighted graph showing the buildings and the distances between buildings. Determine the minimum-cost spanning tree that could be used to install a new computer/telephone network on your campus. Assume that the cost per foot is the same regardless of the path used.

In America, we have the opportunity to elect our leaders and to vote on many items of importance. People in many countries do not have this opportunity. Here we see voters casting their votes at a voting booth.

VOTING AND APPORTIONMENT

We are frequently told that it is "our civic duty to vote" in an election. We may often wonder if our vote really matters. Can one person's vote make a difference in an election? How are voting decisions made? In this chapter, we will discuss different voting methods and some of the flaws of these methods, and we will see how we use mathematics to determine the winner of an election.

Who will win the next presidential election? Which car will be chosen as "Automobile of the Year"? Which vacation spot will be called "Best Vacation Destination"? Which restaurant in your city will win "Best Service Award"? These questions may appear easy to answer, but determining the winner of an election can sometimes lead to different results depending on the voting method used.

How are the states in the United States represented in the legislature? Does each state receive equal representation regardless of its population, or does each state receive representation proportional to its population? We know the answer is both. In the Senate, each state has two representatives, and in the House of Representatives, the number of representatives is proportional to the state's population.

How do we determine how many members each state receives in the House of Representatives? How does a bus company determine how many buses to use for each route? These are examples of apportionment problems. In this chapter, we will also discuss different methods of apportionment and flaws that can occur with these methods.

ANSWERS

Chapter 1

Section 1.1, Page 5

1. a) 1, 2, 3, 4, 5, . . . **b)** Counting numbers

3. A conjecture is a belief based on specific observations that has not been proven or disproven.

5. Deductive reasoning is the process of reasoning to a specific conclusion from a general statement.

7. Inductive reasoning

9. Inductive reasoning, because a generalization was made from specific cases.

11. 1 5 10 10 5 1 **13.** $5 \times 9 = 45$

15.   **17.**   **19.** 15, 18, 21 **21.** −1, 1, −1

23. $\dfrac{1}{81}, \dfrac{1}{243}, \dfrac{1}{729}$ **25.** 36, 49, 64 **27.** 34, 55, 89 **29.** Y

31. a) 36, 49, 64 **b)** square 6, 7, 8, 9 and 10
   c) No, 72 is between 8^2 and 9^2, so it is not a square number.

33. Blue: 1, 5, 7, 10, 12 Purple: 2, 4, 6, 9, 11 Yellow: 3, 8

35. a) ≈58 million **b)** ≈45 million
   c) We are using specific cases to make a prediction.

37.

39. a) You should obtain the original number.
   b) You should obtain the original number.
   c) The result is the original number.
   d) $n, 4n, 4n + 8, \dfrac{4n + 8}{4} = n + 2, n + 2 - 2 = n$

41. a) 5 **b)** You should obtain the number 5.
   c) The result is always the number 5.
   d) $n, n + 1, \dfrac{n + (n + 1) + 9}{2} = \dfrac{2n + 10}{2} = n + 5,$
   $n + 5 - n = 5$

43. $999 \times 999 = 998,001$

45. $(3 + 2)/2 = 5/2$, which is not an even number.

47. $1 - 2 = -1$, which is not a counting number.

49. a) The sum of the measures of the interior angles should be 180°.
   b) Yes, the sum of the measures of the interior angles should be 180°.
   c) The sum of the measures of the interior angles of a triangle is 180°.

51. 129, the numbers in positions are found as follows:
   $a \quad b$
   $c \quad a + b + c$

53. Counterexample **54.** (c)

Section 1.2, Page 14

Answers in this section will vary depending on how you round your numbers. All answers are approximate.

1. 1170 **3.** 1,200,000,000 **5.** 8000 **7.** 100

9. 364,000,000 **11.** 1,200,000,000 **13.** $20

15. 8500 mi **17.** $85.70 **19.** $9000 **21.** 45 lb

23. 2000 mi **25.** $840 **27.** $6 **29.** $41 **31.** ≈ 375 mi

33. a) 32.5 million **b)** 558 counties
   c) Answers will vary.

35. a) 4 million **b)** 98 million **c)** 64 million
   d) 275 million

37. a) 83% **b)** 20% **c)** 91,771 square miles
   d) No, since we are not given the area of each state.

39. 25 **41.** ≈ 90 berries **43.** 150° **45.** 10%

47. 9 square units **49.** 150 feet

51.–59. Answers will vary. **60.** 118 ridges

61. There are 336 dimples on a regulation golf ball.

62. b) 11.6 days

63. Answers will vary. The U.S. government categorized the middle class as $32,000 − $50,000 in 2001.

Section 1.3, Page 29

1. 187.5 mi **3.** 19.36 ft **5.** $4707.53 **7.** $800

9. $12.50 **11.** $70 **13.** $57,240

15. a) ≈ 122
   b) Answers will vary. A close approximation can be obtained by multiplying the U.S. sizes by 2.54.

17. a) 9.2 min **b)** 62 min **c)** 40 min **d)** 150 min

19. a) 30,063,000 **b)** 97,000 **c)** 29,100

21. $82.08 **23. a)** $74.40 **b)** $264 **c)** $64

25. $34,600 **27.** 13,906 violations

29. a) Answers will vary. **b)** ≈ 267.65 million
   c) ≈ 1241.2 million or 1.2412 billion

31. $990, less than initial investment

33. a) 48 rolls **b)** $198 if she purchases four 10 packs and two 4 packs

35. a) Water/milk: 3 cups; salt: $\frac{3}{8}$ tsp; Cream of Wheat:
   9 tbsp (or $\frac{9}{16}$ cup)

b) Water/milk: $2\frac{7}{8}$ cups; salt: $\frac{3}{8}$ tsp; Cream of Wheat: $\frac{5}{8}$ cup (or 10 tbsp)

c) Water/milk: $2\frac{3}{4}$ cups; salt: $\frac{3}{8}$ tsp; Cream of Wheat: $\frac{9}{16}$ cup (or 9 tbsp)

d) Differences exist in water/milk because the amount for 4 servings is not twice that for 2 servings. Differences also exist in Cream of Wheat because $\frac{1}{2}$ cup is not twice 3 tbsp.

37. 144 square inches   **39.** The area is 4 times as large.

41. 1 and 9   **43.** at -1 **45.** 10 birds and 12 lizards

47. a) 30   **b)** 140

49.

```
    (4)
 (3) (2)
(5)(1)(6)
```

51.

8	6	16
18	10	2
4	14	12

53. The sum of the four corners is 4 times the number in the center.

55. Multiply the center number by 9.   **57.** 6 ways

59.

	7	
3	1	4
5	8	6
	2	

Other answers are possible, but 1 and 8 must appear in the center.

61.

1	2	3	4	5
2	3	4	5	1
3	4	5	1	2
4	5	1	2	3
5	1	2	3	4

Other answers are possible.

63. Mary is the skier.   **65.** 714 square units

66. 3 ostriches

Review Exercises, Page 35

1. 23, 28, 33   **2.** 25, 36, 49   **3.** $-48, 96, -192$

4. 25, 32, 40   **5.** 15, 9, 2   **6.** $\frac{3}{8}, \frac{3}{16}, \frac{3}{32}$

7.   **8.**   **9.** (c)

10. a) The original number and the final number are the same.

b) The original number and the final number are the same.

c) The final number is the same as the original number.

d) $n, 2n, 2n + 10, \dfrac{2n + 10}{2} = n + 5, n + 5 - 5 = n$

11. This process will always result in an answer of 3.

12. $1^2 + 2^2 = 5$

The answers to Exercises 13-25 will vary, depending upon how you round the numbers. All answers are approximate.

13. 420,000,000   **14.** 2150   **15.** 200

16. Answers will vary.   **17.** $88   **18.** $12

19. 3 mph   **20.** $14.00   **21.** 2 mi   **22.** 70%   **23.** 5%

24. 13 square units   **25.** Length $\approx$ 22 ft; height $\approx$ 8 ft

26. $7.50   **27.** $1.16

28. Berkman's is cheaper by $20.00.

29. $32,996   **30.** $16.20   **31.** $311   **32.** 7.05 mg

33. $744.80   **34.** 6 hr 45 min   **35.** July 26, 11:00 A.M.

36. a) 6.45 cm^2

b) 16.39 cm^3

c) 1 cm $\approx$ 0.39 in.

37. 201

38.

21	7	8	18
10	16	15	13
14	12	11	17
9	19	20	6

39.

23	25	15
13	21	29
27	17	19

40. 59 min 59 sec   **41.** 6

42. $25 Room
$ 3 Men
$ 2 Clerk
$30

43. 140 lb

44. Yes; 3 quarters and 4 dimes, or 1 half dollar, 1 quarter and 4 dimes, or 1 quarter and 9 dimes. Other answers are possible.

45. 216 cm^3

46. Place six coins in each pan with one coin off to the side. If it balances, the heavier coin is the one on the side. If the pan does not balance, take the six coins on the heavier side and split them into two groups of three. Select the three heavier coins and weigh two coins. If the pan balances, it is the third coin. If the pan does not balance, you can identify the heavier coin.

47. 125,250   **48.** 16 blue   **49.** 90

50. The fifth figure will be an octagon with sides of equal length. Inside the octagon will be a seven sided figure with each side of equal length. The figure will have one antenna.

51. 61

52. Some possible answers are shown. Others are possible.

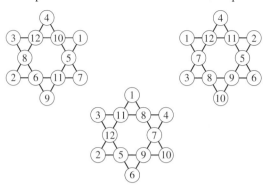

53. a) 2   **b)** 6   **c)** 24   **d)** 120
   e) $n(n - 1)(n - 2) \ldots 1$, (or $n!$), where n = the number of people in line

Chapter Test, Page 38

1. 18, 21, 24

2. $\frac{1}{81}, \frac{1}{243}, \frac{1}{729}$

3. a) The result is the original number plus 1.
   b) The result is the original number plus 1.
   c) The result will always be the original number plus 1.
   d) $n, 5n, 5n + 10, \dfrac{5n + 10}{5} = n + 2$,
      $n + 2 - 1 = n + 1$

The answers for Exercises 4–6 are approximate.

4. 6000   **5.** 33,000,000   **6.** 7 square units

7. a) ≈ 23.03
   b) He is in the at risk range.

8. 159.25 therms   **9.** 32 cans   **10.** $7\frac{1}{2}$ min

11. $\approx$ 39.5 in. by 29.6 in. (The actual dimensions are 100.5 cm by 76.5 cm)

12. $49.00

13.

40	15	20
5	25	45
30	35	10

14. Less time if she had driven at 45 mph for the entire trip

15. $2 \cdot 6 \cdot 8 \cdot 9 \cdot 13$; 11 does not divide 11,232.

16. 243 jelly beans

17. a) $11.97
   b) $11.81
   c) Save 16 cents by using the 25% off coupon.

18. 8

Chapter 2

Section 2.1, Page 46

1. A set is a collection of objects.

3. Description, roster form, and set-builder notation; the set of counting numbers less than 7, $\{1, 2, 3, 4, 5, 6\}$, and $\{x \mid x \in N \text{ and } x < 7\}$

5. An infinite set is a set that is not finite.

7. Two sets are equivalent if they contain the same number of elements.

9. The empty set is a set that contains no elements.

11. Two sets that can be placed in a one-to-one correspondence have the same cardinal number and are equivalent.

13. Not well defined   **15.** Well defined   **17.** Well defined

19. Infinite   **21.** Infinite   **23.** Infinite

25. $\{\text{Atlantic, Pacific, Arctic, Indian}\}$

27. $\{11, 12, 13, 14, \ldots, 177\}$ **29.** $B = \{2, 4, 6, 8, \ldots\}$

31. $\{\ \}$ or $\varnothing$ **33.** $E = \{6, 7, 8, 9, \ldots, 71\}$

35. $\{\text{Sony DSC-S50, Sony DSC-S70, Sony Mavica FD-90}\}$

37. $\{\text{Sony Mavica FD-73, Olympus D-360L, Sony DSC-S50, Kodak DC215, H-P Photo Smart C315}\}$

39. $\{2002, 2003, 2004, 2005, 2006, 2007, 2008\}$

41. $\{2002, 2005, 2006, 2007, 2008\}$

43. $B = \{x \mid x \in N \text{ and } 3 < x < 11\}$ or
   $B = \{x \mid x \in N \text{ and } 4 \leq x \leq 10\}$

45. $C = \{x \mid x \in N \text{ and } x \text{ is a multiple of } 3\}$

47. $E = \{x \mid x \in N \text{ and } x \text{ is odd}\}$

49. $C = \{x \mid x \text{ is February}\}$

51. Set A is the set of natural numbers less than or equal to 7.

53. Set V is the set of vowels in the English alphabet.

55. Set C is the set of companies that make calculators.

57. Set B is the set of members of the Beatles.

59. $\{\text{St. Louis}\}$ **61.** $\{\ \}$ or $\varnothing$

63. $\{1999, 2000, 2001, 2002\}$ **65.** $\{1999, 2001, 2002\}$

67. False; $\{b\}$ is a set, and not an element of the set.

69. False; h is not an element of the set.

71. False; 3 is an element of the set.

73. True   **75.** 4   **77.** 0   **79.** Both   **81.** Neither

83. Equivalent

85. a) Set A is the set of natural numbers greater than 2. Set B is the set of all numbers greater than 2.
   b) Set A contains only natural numbers. Set B contains other types of numbers, including fractions and decimal numbers.
   c) $A = \{3, 4, 5, 6, \ldots\}$

d) No; set B cannot be written in roster form since we cannot list all the elements in set B.

87. Cardinal   **89.** Ordinal   **91.** Answers will vary.

93. Answers will vary.

95.

2		7		2	
7 H 6		6 D 1		1 C 6	
8		4		3	
8		4		3	
4 F 7		7 ⬌ 5		5 E 4	
3		2		8	
3		2		8	
6 A 5		5 G 3		3 B 7	
1		6		5	

Section 2.2 Page 54

1. Set A is a subset of set B, symbolized $A \subseteq B$, if and only if all the elements of set A are also elements of set B.

3. If $A \subseteq B$, then every element of set A is an element of set B. If $A \subset B$, then every element of set A is an element of set B and set $A \neq$ set B.

5. The number of proper subsets is determined by the formula $2^n - 1$, where n is the number of elements in the set.

7. False; gold is an element of the set, not a subset.

9. True   **11.** True

13. False; the set $\{\emptyset\}$ contains the element $\emptyset$.

15. True   **17.** False; the set $\{0\}$ contains the element 0.

19. False   **21.** True

23. False; no set is a proper subset of itself.

25. $B \subseteq A, B \subset A$ **27.** $B \subseteq A, B \subset A$ **29.** $B \subseteq A, B \subset A$

31. $A = B, A \subseteq B, B \subseteq A$ **33.** $\{\ \}$

35. $\{\ \}, \{pen\}, \{pencil\}, \{pen, pencil\}$

37. a) $\{\ \}, \{a\}, \{b\}, \{c\}, \{d\}, \{a, b\}, \{a, c\}, \{a, d\}, \{b, c\}, \{b, d\}, \{c, d\}, \{a, b, c\}, \{a, b, d\}, \{a, c, d\}, \{b, c, d\}, \{a, b, c, d\}$
b) $\{a, b, c, d\}$

39. False   **41.** True   **43.** True   **45.** True   **47.** True

49. True   **51.** 2^4 or 16   **53.** 2^6 or 64   **55.** $E = F$

57. a) Yes   **b)** No   **c)** Yes   **59.** 1   **60.** Yes   **61.** Yes

62. No

Section 2.3, Page 62

1.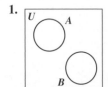

3.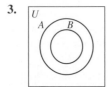

5.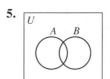

7. Combine the elements from set A and set B into one set. List any element that is contained in both sets only once.

9. Take the elements common to both set A and set B.

11. a) *Or* is generally interpreted to mean *union*.
b) *And* is generally interpreted to mean *intersection*.

13. Region II, the intersection of the two sets.

15.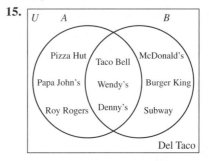

17.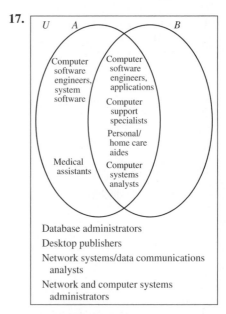

19. The set of U.S. colleges and universities that are not in the state of North Dakota

21. The set of insurance companies in the United States that do not offer life insurance

23. The set of insurance companies in the United States that offer life insurance or car insurance

25. The set of insurance companies in the United States that offer life insurance and do not offer car insurance

27. The set of U.S. corporations whose headquarters are in New York State and whose chief executive officer is a woman

29. The set of U.S. corporations whose chief executive officer is not a woman and who employ at least 100 people

31. The set of U.S. corporations whose headquarters are in New York State or whose chief executive officer is a woman or that employ at least 100 people

33. $\{b, c, t, w, a, h\}$ **35.** $\{a, h\}$

37. $\{c, w, b, t, a, h, f, g, r\}$ **39.** $\{p, m, z\}$

41. $\{L, \Delta, @, \$, *\}$

43. $\{L, \Delta, @, *, \$, R, \square, \alpha, \infty, \Sigma, Z\}$ **45.** $\{*, \$\}$

47. $\{R, \square, \alpha\}$ **49.** $\{1, 2, 3, 4, 5, 6, 8\}$

51. $\{1, 5, 7, 8\}$ **53.** $\{7\}$ **55.** $\{\ \}$ **57.** $\{7\}$

59. $\{a, e, h, i, j, k\}$ **61.** $\{a, f, i\}$

63. $\{b, c, d, e, g, h, j, k\}$ **65.** $\{a, c, d, e, f, g, h, i, j, k\}$

67. $\{a, b, c, d, e, f, g, h, i, j, k\}$, or U **69.** $\{\ \}$

71. $\{2, 4, 6, 8\}$, or B **73.** $\{7, 9\}$

75. $\{1, 3, 5, 6, 7, 8, 9\}$ **77.** $\{1, 2, 3, 4, 5, 7, 9\}$

79. $\{2, 4, 6, 8\}$, or B **81.** $\{1, 2, 3, 4, 5\}$, or C

83. A set and its complement will always be disjoint. For example, if $U = \{1, 2, 3\}$, $A = \{1, 2\}$, and $A' = \{3\}$, then $A \cap A' = \{\ \}$.

85. 49

87. a) $8 = 4 + 6 - 2$ **b)** and **c)** Answers will vary.

89. $\{1, 2, 3, 4, \dots\}$, or A **91.** $\{4, 8, 12, 16, \dots\}$, or B

93. $\{2, 4, 6, 8, \dots\}$, or C **95.** $\{2, 6, 10, 14, 18, \dots\}$

97. $\{2, 6, 10, 14, 18, \dots\}$ **99.** U **101.** A **103.** U

105. U **107.** $B \subseteq A$ **109.** A and B are disjoint sets.

111. $A \subseteq B$ **113.** $\{e, f, h\}$ **115.** $\{d, j, k\}$ **117.** $\{13\}$

119. $\{1, 2, 3, 4, 5, 6, 7, 8, 9, 10, 11, 12, 14, 15\}$

121. $\{2, 3, 4, 5, 7, 9, 10, 11, 12, 13, 14, 15\}$

123. Complement

Section 2.4, Page 71

1. 8   **3.** II, IV, VI   **5.** 8

7. a) Yes   **b)** No, one specific case cannot be used as proof.   **c)** No

9.
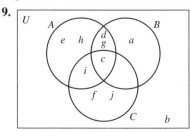

11.
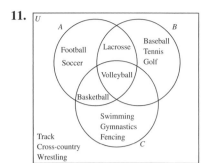

13.
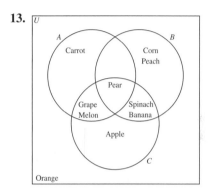

15.
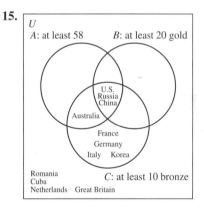

17. V   **19.** VIII   **21.** VI   **23.** IV   **25.** II   **27.** VII

29. VI   **31.** III   **33.** III   **35.** V   **37.** II   **39.** VII

41. I   **43.** VIII   **45.** VI   **47.** $\{1, 2, 3, 4, 5, 6\}$

49. $\{3, 4, 5, 7, 8, 9, 12\}$ **51.** $\{3, 4, 5\}$

53. $\{1, 2, 3, 6, 9, 10, 11, 12\}$

55. $\{1, 2, 3, 4, 5, 6, 7, 8, 9, 12\}$ **57.** $\{9, 11, 12\}$

59. $\{7, 8, 9, 10, 11, 12\}$ **61.** Yes   **63.** No   **65.** No

67. Yes   **69.** No   **71.** Yes   **73.** Yes   **75.** Yes   **77.** No

79. $(A \cup B)'$ **81.** $(A \cup B) \cap C'$

83. a) Both equal $\{6, 7\}$.   **b)** Answers will vary.
   c) Both are represented by the regions IV, V, VI.

85.

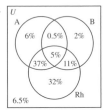

87. a)

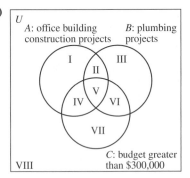

b) V; $A \cap B \cap C$
c) VI; $A' \cap B \cap C$
d) I; $A \cap B' \cap C'$

89. a)

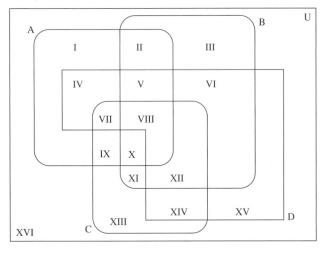

b)

Region	Set	Region	Set
I	$A \cap B' \cap C' \cap D'$	IX	$A \cap B' \cap C \cap D'$
II	$A \cap B \cap C' \cap D'$	X	$A \cap B \cap C \cap D'$
III	$A' \cap B \cap C' \cap D'$	XI	$A' \cap B \cap C \cap D'$
IV	$A \cap B' \cap C' \cap D$	XII	$A' \cap B \cap C \cap D$
V	$A \cap B \cap C' \cap D$	XIII	$A' \cap B' \cap C \cap D'$
VI	$A' \cap B \cap C' \cap D$	XIV	$A' \cap B' \cap C \cap D$
VII	$A \cap B' \cap C \cap D$	XV	$A' \cap B' \cap C' \cap D$
VIII	$A \cap B \cap C \cap D$	XVI	$A' \cap B' \cap C' \cap D'$

Section 2.5, Page 80

1.

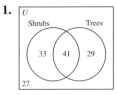

a) 33
b) 29
c) 27

3.

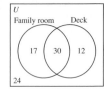

a) 17
b) 12
c) 59

5.

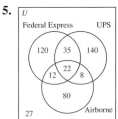

a) 27
b) 80
c) 340
d) 55
e) 337

7.

a) 22
b) 11
c) 64
d) 50
e) 23

9.

a) 17
b) 27
c) 2
d) 31
e) 2

11.

a) 10
b) 15
c) 0
d) 6

13. In a Venn diagram, regions II, IV, and V contain a total of 37 cars driven by women. This total is greater than the 35 cars driven by women, as given in the exercise.

15.

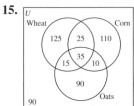

a) 410   **b)** 35   **c)** 90   **d)** 50

16. a) 10   **b)** 10   **c)** 6

Section 2.6, Page 86

1. An infinite set is a set that can be placed in a one-to-one correspondence with a proper subset of itself.

3. $\{7, 8, \ 9, \ 10, 11, \ldots, n + 6, \ldots\}$
   ↓ ↓ ↓ ↓ ↓   ↓
   $\{8, 9, 10, 11, 12, \ldots, n + 7, \ldots\}$

5. $\{3, 5, 7, \ 9, 11, \ldots, 2n + 1, \ldots\}$
   ↓ ↓ ↓ ↓ ↓   ↓
   $\{5, 7, 9, 11, 13, \ldots, 2n + 3, \ldots\}$

7. $\{4, \ 7, 10, 13, \ldots, 3n + 1, \ldots\}$
   ↓ ↓ ↓ ↓   ↓
   $\{7, 10, 13, 16, \ldots, 3n + 4, \ldots\}$

9. $\{ 6, \ 11, 16, 21, 26, \ldots, 5n + 1, \ldots\}$
   ↓ ↓ ↓ ↓ ↓   ↓
   $\{11, 16, 21, 26, 31, \ldots, 5n + 6, \ldots\}$

11. $\left\{\dfrac{1}{2}, \dfrac{1}{4}, \dfrac{1}{6}, \dfrac{1}{8}, \ldots, \dfrac{1}{2n}, \ldots\right\}$
   ↓ ↓ ↓ ↓   ↓
   $\left\{\dfrac{1}{4}, \dfrac{1}{6}, \dfrac{1}{8}, \dfrac{1}{10}, \ldots, \dfrac{1}{2n + 2}, \ldots\right\}$

13. $\{1, \ 2, \ 3, \ 4, \ \ldots, n, \ldots\}$
   ↓ ↓ ↓ ↓   ↓
   $\{6, 12, 18, 24, \ldots, 6n, \ldots\}$

15. $\{1, 2, 3, \ 4, \ldots, \ \ n, \ldots\}$
   ↓ ↓ ↓ ↓   ↓
   $\{4, 6, 8, 10, \ldots, 2n + 2, \ldots\}$

17. $\{1, 2, 3, \ 4, \ \ldots, \ \ n, \ldots\}$
   ↓ ↓ ↓ ↓   ↓
   $\{2, 5, 8, 11, \ldots, 3n - 1, \ldots\}$

19. $\{1, 2, \ 3, \ 4, \ \ldots, \ \ n, \ldots\}$
   ↓ ↓ ↓ ↓   ↓
   $\{5, 8, 11, 14, \ldots, 3n + 2, \ldots\}$

21. $\{ 1, \ 2, \ 3, \ 4, \ldots, \ \ n, \ldots\}$
   ↓ ↓ ↓ ↓   ↓
   $\left\{\dfrac{1}{3}, \dfrac{1}{4}, \dfrac{1}{5}, \dfrac{1}{6}, \ldots, \dfrac{1}{n + 2}, \ldots\right\}$

23. $\{1, 2, 3, \ 4, \ldots, n, \ldots\}$
   ↓ ↓ ↓ ↓   ↓
   $\{1, 4, 9, 16, \ldots, n^2, \ldots\}$

25. $\{1, 2, \ 3, \ \ 4, \ \ldots, n, \ldots\}$
   ↓ ↓ ↓ ↓   ↓
   $\{3, 9, 27, 81, \ldots, 3^n, \ldots\}$

27. =   28. =   29. =   30. =   31. =

Review Exercises, Page 87

1. True

2. False; the word *best* makes the statement not well defined.

3. True   4. False; no set is a proper subset of itself.

5. False; the elements 6, 12, 18, 24, … are members of both sets.

6. True

7. False; both sets do not contain exactly the same elements.

8. True   9. True   10. True   11. True   12. True

13. True   14. True   15. $A = \{7, 9, 11, 13, 15\}$

16. {California, Oregon, Idaho, Utah, Arizona}

17. $C = \{1, 2, 3, 4, \ldots, 296\}$

18. $D = \{9, 10, 11, 12, \ldots, 96\}$

19. $A = \{x \mid x \in N \text{ and } 52 < x < 100\}$

20. $B = \{x \mid x \in N \text{ and } x > 63\}$

21. $C = \{x \mid x \in N \text{ and } x < 3\}$

22. $D = \{x \mid x \in N \text{ and } 23 \leq x \leq 41\}$

23. A is the set of capital letters in the English alphabet from E through M, inclusive.

24. B is the set of U.S. coins with a value of less than a dollar.

25. C is the set of the last three lowercase letters in the English alphabet.

26. D is the set of numbers greater than or equal to 3 and less than 9.

27. $\{5, 6\}$ 28. $\{1, 2, 3, 4, 5, 6, 7, 8\}$ 29. $\{9, 10\}$

30. $\{1, 2, 4, 6, 7, 8, 10\}$ 31. 16   32. 15

33.

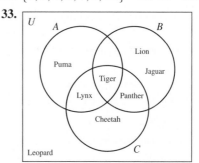

34. $\{b, e, g, k, c, d, f, a\}$ 35. $\{b, d\}$

36. $\{b, e, g, k, c, d, f, a, i\}$ 37. $\{f\}$ 38. $\{d, f, a\}$

39. $\{e, g, f, d, a, i\}$ 40. True   41. True   42. II

43. V   44. VIII   45. IV   46. IV   47. VII   48. $450

49.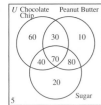

a) 315
b) 10
c) 30
d) 110

50.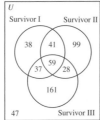

a) 38
b) 298
c) 28
d) 236
e) 106

51. $\{2, 4, 6, 8, \ldots, \quad 2n, \ldots\}$
↓ ↓ ↓ ↓   ↓
$\{4, 6, 8, 10, \ldots, 2n + 2, \ldots\}$

52. $\{3, 5, 7, 9, \ldots, 2n + 1, \ldots\}$
↓ ↓ ↓ ↓   ↓
$\{5, 7, 9, 11, \ldots, 2n + 3, \ldots\}$

53. $\{1, 2, 3, 4, \ldots, \quad n, \ldots\}$
↓ ↓ ↓ ↓   ↓
$\{5, 8, 11, 14, \ldots, 3n + 2, \ldots\}$

54. $\{1, 2, 3, 4, \ldots, \quad n, \ldots\}$
↓ ↓ ↓ ↓   ↓
$\{4, 9, 14, 19, \ldots, 5n - 1, \ldots\}$

Chapter Test, Page 90

1. True

2. False; the sets do not contain exactly the same elements.

3. True

4. False; the second set has no subset that contains the element 7.

5. False; the empty set is a proper subset of every set except itself.

6. False; the set has 2^3, or 8 subsets.   **7.** True

8. False; for any set A, $A \cup A' = U$, not $\{ \}$.   **9.** True

10. $A = \{1, 2, 3, 4, 5, 6, 7, 8\}$

11. Set A is the set of natural numbers less than 9.

12. $\{7, 9\}$ **13.** $\{3, 5, 7, 9, 13\}$

14. $\{3, 5, 7, 9\}$, or A **15.** 2

16.

17. Equal

18.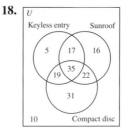

a) 52   b) 10   c) 93   d) 17   e) 38   f) 31

19. $\{7, 8, 9, 10, \ldots, n + 6, \ldots\}$
↓ ↓ ↓ ↓   ↓
$\{8, 9, 10, 11, \ldots, n + 7, \ldots\}$

20. $\{1, 2, 3, 4, \ldots, \quad n, \ldots\}$
↓ ↓ ↓ ↓   ↓
$\{1, 3, 5, 7, \ldots, 2n - 1, \ldots\}$

Chapter 3

Section 3.1, Page 103

1. a) A simple statement is a statement that conveys only one idea.
 b) Compound statements are statements consisting of two or more simple statements.

3. a) Some are   **b)** All are
 c) Some are not   **d)** None are

5. a) $\rightarrow$ **b)** $\vee$ **c)** $\wedge$ **d)** $\sim$ **e)** $\leftrightarrow$

7. When two simple statements are on the same side of the comma, they are placed together in parentheses when translated into symbolic form.

9. Compound; conjunction, $\wedge$

11. Compound; biconditional, $\leftrightarrow$

13. Compound; disjunction, $\vee$

15. Simple statement   **17.** Compound; negation, $\sim$

19. Compound; conjunction, $\wedge$

21. Compound; negation, $\sim$

23. No picnic tables are portable.

25. Some chickens do not fly.   **27.** All turtles have claws.

29. Some bicycles have three wheels.

31. All pine trees produce pinecones.

33. No pedestrians are in the crosswalk.

35. $\sim p$ **37.** $\sim q \vee \sim p$ **39.** $\sim p \rightarrow \sim q$ **41.** $\sim q \rightarrow \sim p$

43. $\sim p \wedge \sim q$ **45.** $\sim(q \rightarrow \sim p)$

47. Firemen do not work hard.

49. Firemen wear red suspenders or firemen work hard.

51. Firemen do not work hard if and only if firemen do not wear red suspenders.

53. It is false that firemen wear red suspenders or firemen work hard.

55. Firemen do not work hard and firemen do not wear red suspenders.

57. $(p \vee \sim q) \to r$ **59.** $(p \wedge q) \vee r$ **61.** $p \to (q \vee \sim r)$

63. $(r \leftrightarrow q) \wedge p$ **65.** $q \to (p \leftrightarrow r)$

67. The water is 70° or the sun is shining, and we do not go swimming.

69. The water is not 70°, and the sun is shining or we go swimming.

71. If we do not go swimming, then the sun is shining and the water is 70°.

73. If the sun is shining then we go swimming, and the water is 70°.

75. The sun is shining if and only if the water is 70°, and we go swimming.

77. Not permissible, you cannot have both soup and salad. The *or* used on menus is the exclusive *or*.

79. Not permissible, you cannot have both potatoes and pasta. The *or* used on menus is the exclusive *or*.

81. a) $(\sim p) \to q$ **b)** Conditional

83. a) $(\sim q) \wedge (\sim r)$ **b)** Conjunction

85. a) $(p \vee q) \to r$ **b)** Conditional

87. a) $r \to (p \vee q)$ **b)** Conditional

89. a) $(\sim p) \leftrightarrow (\sim q \to r)$ **b)** Biconditional

91. a) $(r \wedge \sim q) \to (q \wedge \sim p)$ **b)** Conditional

93. a) $\sim[(p \wedge q) \leftrightarrow (p \vee r)]$ **b)** Negation

95. a) $r \wedge \sim c$ **b)** Conjunction

97. a) $\sim(b \to \sim p)$ **b)** Negation

99. a) $(f \vee v) \to h$ **b)** Conditional

101. a) $c \leftrightarrow (\sim f \vee p)$ **b)** Biconditional

103. a) $(c \leftrightarrow w) \vee s$ **b)** Disjunction

105. $[(\sim q) \to (r \vee p)] \leftrightarrow [(\sim r) \wedge q]$; Biconditional

107. a) The conjunction and disjunction have the same dominance.
b) Answers will vary. **c)** Answers will vary.

Section 3.2, Page 115

1. a) 4 **b)**

p	q
T	T
T	F
F	T
F	F

3. a)

p	q	$p \vee q$
T	T	T
T	F	T
F	T	T
F	F	F

b) Only when both p and q are false

5. T T F F **7.** F T T F **9.** F F T T **11.** T F T T F F T T **13.** T F T T T F T F **15.** T F T T F F T T **17.** F F T F F F T T **19.** T T T T F F T F

21. $p \wedge q$
T
F
F
F

23. $p \wedge \sim q$
F
T
F
F

25. $\sim(p \wedge q)$
F
T
T
T

27. $p \vee (q \vee r)$
T
T
T
T
T
T
T
F

29. $p \wedge (q \vee \sim q)$
T
T
F
F

31. a) False **b)** True **33. a)** False **b)** False

35. a) True **b)** True **37. a)** False **b)** True

39. a) True **b)** True **41. a)** True **b)** True

43. True **45.** True **47.** False **49.** False

51. False **53.** True **55.** True **57.** False

59. $p \wedge \sim q$
F
T
F
F

True in case 2

61. $p \vee \sim q$
T
T
F
T

True in cases 1, 2, and 4, when p is true, or when p and q are both false.

63. $(r \lor q) \land p$

T
T
T
F
F
F
F
F

True in cases 1, 2, and 3

65. $q \lor (p \land \sim r)$

T
T
F
T
T
T
F
F

True in cases 1, 2, 4, 5, and 6. True except when p, q, r have truth values TFT, FFT, or FFF.

67. a) Mr. Duncan and Mrs. Tuttle qualify.
   b) Mrs. Rusinek does not qualify, since their combined income is less than $46,000.

69. a) Wing Park qualifies; the other four do not.
   b) Gina Vela is returning on April 2. Kara Sharo is returning on a Monday. Christos Supernaw is not staying over on a Saturday. Alex Chang is returning on a Monday.

71. T
T
T
T
F
T
F
T

73. Yes

Section 3.3, Page 125

1. a)

p	q	$p \to q$
T	T	T
T	F	F
F	T	T
F	F	T

   b) The conditional is false only when the antecedent is true and the consequent is false.

3. a) Substitute the truth values for the simple statements. Then evaluate the compound statement, using the assigned truth values.
   b) True

5. A self-contradiction is a compound statement that is never true.

7. T **9.** F **11.** F **13.** T **15.** F **17.** T **19.** F **21.** F
F   F   T   T   T   F   T   F
T   T   T   F   T   T   F   T
T   F   F   T   T   F   F   F
                              T   F   T
                              F   F   T
                              F   F   F
                              F   T   T

23. T **25.** T
T   T
T   T
T   F
T   T
F   T
F   F
F   T

27. $p \to (q \land r)$ **29.** $(p \leftrightarrow \sim q) \lor r$ **31.** $(\sim p \to q) \lor r$

T   T   T
F   F   T
F   T   T
F   T   T
T   T   T
T   T   T
T   T   T
T   F   F

33. Neither **35.** Self-contradiction **37.** Tautology

39. Not an implication **41.** Implication **43.** Implication

45. True **47.** True **49.** False **51.** True **53.** True

55. True **57.** True **59.** False **61.** True **63.** True

65. True **67.** False **69.** False **71.** True **73.** True

75. True

77. No, the statement only states what will occur if your sister gets straight A's. If your sister does not get straight A's, your parents may still get her a computer.

79. T
F
F
T
T
F
F
F

81. It is a tautology. The statement may be expressed as $(p \to q) \lor (\sim p \to q)$, where p: It is a head and q: I win. This statement is a tautology.

83.

Tiger	Boots	Sam	Sue
Blue	Yellow	Red	Green
Nine Lives	Whiskas	Friskies	Meow Mix

84. Katie was born last.

Section 3.4, Page 139

1. Statements that have exactly the same truth values

3. The two statements are equivalent.

5. a) $q \rightarrow p$ **b)** $\sim p \rightarrow \sim q$ **c)** $\sim q \rightarrow \sim p$ **7.** $\sim p \vee q$

9. Equivalent **11.** Not equivalent **13.** Equivalent

15. Equivalent **17.** Equivalent **19.** Equivalent

21. Equivalent **23.** Equivalent **25.** Not equivalent

27. Not equivalent **29.** Equivalent

31. The Mississippi River does not run through Ohio and the Ohio River does not run through Mississippi.

33. It is false that the snowmobile was an Arctic Cat or a Ski-Do.

35. It is false that the hotel has a weight room and the conference center has an auditorium.

37. If we go to Cozumel, then it is false that we will not go snorkeling and we will go to Senior Frogs.

39. You do not drink a glass of orange juice or you will get a full day supply of folic acid.

41. If Bob the Tomato didn't visit the nursing home then he did not visit the Cub Scout meeting.

43. The plumbers meet in Kansas City and the Rainmakers will not provide the entertainment.

45. It is cloudy if and only if the front is coming through.

47. If the chemistry teacher teaches mathematics then there is a shortage of mathematics teachers and if there is a shortage of mathematics teachers then the chemistry teacher teaches mathematics.

49. *Converse:* If I finish the book in one week, then the book is interesting.
Inverse: If the book is not interesting, then I will not finish the book in one week.
Contrapositive: If I do not finish the book in one week, then the book is not interesting.

51. *Converse:* If you can watch television, then you finish your homework.
Inverse: If you did not finish your homework, then you cannot watch television.
Contrapositive: If you cannot watch television, then you did not finish your homework.

53. *Converse:* If I scream, then that annoying paper clip shows up on my computer screen.
Inverse: If that annoying paper clip does not show up on my computer screen, then I will not scream.
Contrapositive: If I do not scream, then that annoying paper clip does not show up on my screen.

55. *Converse:* If we go down to the marina and take out the sailboat, then the sun is shining.
Inverse: If the sun is not shining, then we will not go down to the marina or we will not take out the sailboat.
Contrapositive: If we do not go down to the marina or we will not take out the sailboat, then the sun is not shining.

57. If a natural number is divisible by 10, then the natural number is divisible by 5. True.

59. If a natural number is not divisible by 6, then the natural number is not divisible by 3. False.

61. If two lines are not parallel, then the two lines intersect in at least one point. True.

63. If the polygon is a quadrilateral, then the sum of the interior angles of the polygon measures 360°. True.

65. b) and **c)** are equivalent. **67. a)** and **c)** are equivalent.

69. b) and **c)** are equivalent. **71. b)** and **c)** are equivalent.

73. None are equivalent. **75.** None are equivalent.

77. a) and **c)** are equivalent. **79. a)** and **b)** are equivalent.

81. True. If $p \rightarrow q$ is false, it must be of the form $T \rightarrow F$. Therefore, the converse must be of the form $F \rightarrow T$, which is true.

83. False. A conditional statement and its contrapositive always have the same truth values.

85. Answers will vary. **87.** Answers will vary.

89. a) Conditional **b)** Biconditional **c)** Inverse
d) Converse **e)** Contrapositive

Section 3.5, Page 150

1. The conclusion necessarily follows from the given set of premises.

3. Yes, if the conclusion necessarily follows from the set of premises, the argument is valid, even if the conclusion is false.

5. Yes, if the conclusion necessarily follows from the set of premises, the argument is valid, even if the premises themselves are false.

7. a) $p \vee q$
$\dfrac{\sim p}{\therefore q}$

b) Answers will vary.

9. a) $p \rightarrow q$
$\dfrac{q \rightarrow r}{\therefore p \rightarrow r}$

b) Answers will vary.

11. a) $p \rightarrow q$
$\dfrac{\sim p}{\therefore \sim q}$

b) Answers will vary.

13. Valid **15.** Valid **17.** Invalid **19.** Invalid

21. Invalid **23.** Valid **25.** Valid **27.** Invalid

29. Invalid **31.** Valid

33. a) $p \rightarrow q$

$\dfrac{\sim p}{\therefore \sim q}$

b) Invalid

35. a) $p \rightarrow q$

$\dfrac{p}{\therefore q}$

b) Valid

37. a) $p \rightarrow q$

$\dfrac{\sim q}{\therefore \sim p}$

b) Valid

39. a) $p \rightarrow q$

$\dfrac{q}{\therefore p}$

b) Invalid

41. a) $p \vee q$

$\dfrac{\sim p}{\therefore q}$

b) Valid

43. a) $p \rightarrow q$

$\dfrac{q \rightarrow r}{\therefore p \rightarrow r}$

b) Valid

45. a) $f \rightarrow w$

$\dfrac{w \wedge \sim t}{\therefore w \rightarrow \sim f}$

b) Invalid

47. a) $s \wedge g$

$\dfrac{g \rightarrow c}{\therefore s \rightarrow c}$

b) Valid

49. a) $h \rightarrow b$

$\dfrac{\sim p \rightarrow \sim b}{\therefore h \rightarrow p}$

b) Valid

51. a) $p \rightarrow q$

$\dfrac{\sim q}{\therefore \sim p}$

b) Valid

53. a) $t \vee \sim p$

$\dfrac{p}{\therefore t}$

b) Valid

55. a) $t \wedge g$

$\dfrac{\sim t \vee \sim g}{\therefore \sim t}$

b) Valid

57. a) $c \wedge \sim h$

$\dfrac{h \rightarrow c}{\therefore h}$

b) Invalid

59. a) $f \rightarrow d$

$\dfrac{d \rightarrow \sim s}{\therefore f \rightarrow s}$

b) Invalid

61. Therefore, your face will break out.

63. Therefore, a tick is an arachnid.

65. Therefore, you did not close the deal.

67. Therefore, if you do not pay off your credit card bills, then the bank makes money.

69. No. The conditional statement will always be true, and therefore it will be a tautology, and a valid argument.

Section 3.6, Page 158

1. It is an invalid argument.

3. The conclusion necessarily follows from the premises.

5. Yes, if the conclusion necessarily follows from the premises, the argument is valid.

7. Valid   **9.** Valid   **11.** Invalid   **13.** Valid

15. Invalid   **17.** Invalid   **19.** Invalid   **21.** Valid

23. Invalid   **25.** Invalid   **27.** Valid   **29.** Invalid

Review Exercises, Page 161

1. No rock bands play ballads.

2. All bananas are ripe.

3. Some chickens have lips.

4. Some panthers are not endangered.

5. Some pens do not use ink.

6. Some rabbits wear glasses.

7. The coffee is Maxwell House or the coffee is hot.

8. The coffee is not hot and the coffee is strong.

9. If the coffee is hot, then the coffee is strong and the coffee is not Maxwell House.

10. The coffee is Maxwell House if and only if the coffee is not strong.

11. The coffee is not Maxwell House, if and only if the coffee is strong and the coffee is not hot.

12. The coffee is Maxwell House or the coffee is not hot, and the coffee is not strong.

13. $r \wedge q$ **14.** $p \rightarrow r$ **15.** $(r \rightarrow q) \vee \sim p$

16. $(q \leftrightarrow p) \wedge \sim r$ **17.** $(r \wedge q) \vee \sim p$ **18.** $\sim(r \wedge q)$

19. F   **20.** T   **21.** T   **22.** T   **23.** F   **24.** F
   F   F   T   F   T   T
   T   F   T   T   F   T
   F   F   T   T   F   T
                   T   F   T   T
                   F   F   T   T
                   F   F   T   T
                   T   F   T   T

25. False   **26.** True   **27.** False   **28.** True   **29.** True

30. True   **31.** True   **32.** True   **33.** False   **34.** False

35. Not equivalent   **36.** Equivalent   **37.** Equivalent

38. Not equivalent

39. It is false that Johnny Cash is not in the Rock and Roll Hall of Fame or India Arie did not record *Acoustic Soul*.

40. If her foot did not fall asleep then she injured her ankle.

41. Altec Lansing does not produce only speakers and Harman Kardon does not produce only stereo receivers.

42. It is false that Travis Tritt won an Academy Award or Randy Jackson does commercials for Milk Bone Dog Biscuits.

43. The temperature is above 32° or we will go ice fishing at O'Leary's Lake.

44. a) If you enjoy life, then you hear a beautiful songbird today.

b) If you do not hear a beautiful songbird today, then you do not enjoy life.

c) If you do not enjoy life, then you do not hear a beautiful songbird today.

45. a) If the quilt has a uniform design, then you followed the correct pattern.

b) If you did not follow the correct pattern, then the quilt does not have a uniform design.

c) If the quilt does not have a uniform design, then you did not follow the correct pattern.

46. a) If Maureen Gerald is helping at the school, then she is not in attendance.

b) If Maureen Gerald is in attendance, then she is not helping at the school.

c) If Maureen Gerald is not helping at the school, then she is in attendance.

47. a) If we will not buy a desk at Miller's Furniture, then the desk is made by Winner's Only and the desk is in the Rose catalog.

b) If the desk is not made by Winner's Only or the desk is not in the Rose catalog, then we will buy a desk at Miller's Furniture.

c) If we will buy a desk at Miller's Furniture, then the desk is not made by Winner's Only or the desk is not in the Rose catalog.

48. a) If I let you attend the prom, then you will get straight A's on your report card.

b) If you do not get straight A's on your report card, then I will not let you attend the prom.

c) If I will not let you attend the prom, then you did not get straight A's on your report card.

49. a), b), and **c)** are equivalent.   **50.** None are equivalent.

51. a) and **c)** are equivalent.   **52.** None are equivalent.

53. Invalid   **54.** Valid   **55.** Invalid   **56.** Valid

57. Invalid   **58.** Invalid

Chapter Test, Page 163

1. $(p \wedge r) \vee \sim q$ **2.** $(r \rightarrow q) \vee \sim p$ **3.** $\sim(r \leftrightarrow \sim q)$

4. Ann is the secretary, if and only if Dick is the vice president and Elaine is the president.

5. It is false that if Ann is the secretary, then Elaine is not the president.

6. F   **7.** T
   T   T
   F   T
   F   T
   F   F
   F   T
   F   T
   F   F

8. True   **9.** True   **10.** True   **11.** True   **12.** Equivalent

13. a) and **b)** are equivalent.   **14. a)** and **b)** are equivalent.

15. $s \rightarrow f$ **16.** Invalid
   $f \rightarrow p$
   $\therefore s \rightarrow p$
   Valid

17. Some leopards are not spotted.

18. No jacks-in-the-box are electronic.

19. *Converse:* If today is Saturday, then the garbage truck comes.
Inverse: If the garbage truck does not come, then today is not Saturday.
Contrapositive: If today is not Saturday, then the garbage truck does not come.

20. Yes

Chapter 4

Section 4.1, Page 173

1. A number is a quantity, and it answers the question "How many?" A numeral is a symbol used to represent the number.

3. A system of numeration consists of a set of numerals and a scheme or rule for combining the numerals to represent numbers.

5. The Hindu–Arabic numeration system

7. In a multiplicative system, there are numerals for each number less than the base and for powers of the base. Each numeral less than the base is multiplied by a numeral for the power of the base, and these products are added to obtain the number.

9. 142   **11.** 2423   **13.** 334,214

15. 999999∩∩∩||||| **17.** ⌇⌇∩∩∩|||||

19. ∝⫯⫯⫯⫯⫯⌇⌇⌇99999999∩∩∩|||||

21. 19   **23.** 547   **25.** 1492   **27.** 2946   **29.** 12,666

31. 9464   **33.** LIX   **35.** CXXXIV   **37.** MMV

39. $\overline{\text{IV}}$DCCXCIII   **41.** $\overline{\text{IX}}$CMXCIX   **43.** $\overline{\text{XX}}$DCXLIV

45. 74   **47.** 4081   **49.** 8550   **51.** 4003

53. 五十三   **55.** 三百七十八   **57.** 四千二百六十   **59.** 七千零五十六

61. 341   **63.** 22,505   **65.** 9607   **67.** $\nu\theta$ **69.** $\psi\kappa\zeta$

71. $\pi'\beta'\psi\delta$

73. Advantage: You can write some numbers more compactly. Disadvantage: There are more numerals to memorize.

75. Advantage: You can write some numbers more compactly. Disadvantage: There are more numerals to memorize.

77. 1936, ⌇999999999∩∩|||||| , $\alpha' \top \lambda \zeta$, 一千九百三十六

79. 422, 9999∩∩II, CDXXII, 四百二十二

81. ℼ′Q′θ′ ℼ Q θ   **83.** Turn the book upside down.

84. MM   **85.** 1888, MDCCCLXXXVIII

Section 4.2, Page 180

1. A base 10 place-value system   **3.** Four tens, four hundreds

5. A symbol for zero and for each counting number less than the base are required.

7. Write each digit times its corresponding positional value.

9. a) There may be confusion because numbers could be interpreted in different ways. For example, I could be interpreted to be either 1 or 60.

b) II <III for both numbers.

11. 1, 20, 18 × 20, 18 × $(20)^2$, 18 × $(20)^3$

13. $(6 \times 10) + (3 \times 1)$

15. $(3 \times 100) + (5 \times 10) + (9 \times 1)$

17. $(8 \times 100) + (9 \times 10) + (7 \times 1)$

19. $(4 \times 1000) + (3 \times 100) + (8 \times 10) + (7 \times 1)$

21. $(1 \times 10{,}000) + (6 \times 1000) + (4 \times 100) + (0 \times 10) + (2 \times 1)$

23. $(3 \times 100{,}000) + (4 \times 10{,}000) + (6 \times 1000) + (8 \times 100) + (6 \times 10) + (1 \times 1)$

25. 42   **27.** 784   **29.** 4868   **31.** I <<<III

33. IIII <<<<<IIIII   **35.** I I <<IIIII

37. 92   **39.** 4321   **41.** 4000   **43.** ⁚≡   **45.** ⁚⁚≡

47. ·◯•••

49. Advantages: In general, they are more compact; large and small numbers can be written more easily; there are fewer symbols to memorize.

Disadvantage: If many of the symbols in the numeral represent zero, the place-value system may be less compact.

51. 33, ⁖≡

53. $\left(\triangle \times \square^2 \right) + \left(\square \times \bigcirc \right) + \left(\lozenge \times I \right)$

55. a) No largest number

b) IIII <<<<ÎIII <<<<IIIIII <<<<ÎI

57. II <<<<<ÎIIII

59. ••• •••• •••   **61.**

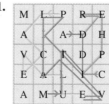

M	L	P	R	E
A	A	D	H	
V	C	T	D	P
E	A	L	I	C
A	M	U	E	V

Section 4.3, Page 187

1. Answers will vary.   **3.** 5   **5.** 22   **7.** 11   **9.** 100

11. 373   **13.** 1367   **15.** 867   **17.** 83   **19.** 6597

21. 1000_2 **23.** 10111_2 **25.** 2535_6 **27.** 1239_{12}

29. 1021_8 **31.** $17TE_{12}$ **33.** 1111110011_2 **35.** 4403_8

37. 1845   **39.** 447,415   **41.** $23D_{16}$ **43.** 1566_{16}

45. 11111010101_2 **47.** 31010_5 **49.** $11E1_{12}$

51. Incorrect; cannot have a 5 in base 5.

53. Written correctly

55. Incorrect; cannot have an 8 in base 7.   **57.** 13

59. 73   **61.** $\bigcirc\ominus_5$ **63.** $\bigcirc\bigcirc\bigcirc_5$ **65.** 7

67. 36   **69.** $\bullet\bullet_4$ **71.** $\bullet\bullet\bullet_4$

73. a) Answers will vary.   **b)** 10213_5 **c)** 1373_8

75. Answers will vary.   **77.** $b = 6$ **78.** $d = 4$

79. a) 876   **b)** $\bullet\bullet\bullet\bullet_4$

Section 4.4, Page 197

1. a) $1, b, b^2, b^3, b^4$ **b)** $1, 6, 6^2, 6^3, 6^4$

3. No, cannot have a 6 in base 5.   **5.** Answers will vary.

7. 134_5 **9.** 3201_4 **11.** $9E5_{12}$ **13.** 2200_3

15. 24001_7 **17.** 10100_2 **19.** 213_4 **21.** 400_5

23. 644_{12} **25.** 11_2 **27.** 3616_7 **29.** 1011_3 **31.** 121_5

33. 2403_7 **35.** 21020_6 **37.** 12233_9 **39.** 100011_2

41. 6031_7 **43.** 110_2 **45.** 31_5 **47.** 123_4

49. $103_4 R1_4$ **51.** $41_5 R1_5$ **53.** $45_7 R2_7$ **55.** $\ominus\bigcirc_5$

57. $\ominus\ominus\bigcirc_5$ **59.** $\bullet\bullet_4$ **61.** $\bullet\bullet\bullet_4$ **63.** $\bullet\bullet_4$

65. $\bullet\bullet\bullet_4$ **67.** 2302_5, 327   **69.** 13_5

71. a) 21252_8 **b)** 306 and 29   **c)** 8874   **d)** 8874   **e)** Yes

72. 5   **73.** $\bullet = 0, \bullet = 1, \bullet = 2, \bullet = 3$

Section 4.5, Page 201

1. Duplation and mediation, the galley method, and Napier rods

3. a) Answers will vary.   **b)** 10,498

5. 713   **7.** 1458   **9.** 8260   **11.** 8649   **13.** 2250

15. 2332   **17.** 900   **19.** 204,728   **21.** 504   **23.** 406

25. 625   **27.** 60,678   **29. a)** 46×253 **b)** 11,638
31. a) 4×382 **b)** 1528   **33.** ꟿꟿ∩∩∩∩∩∩∩∩∩ⅠⅠⅠⅠⅠ
35. Answers will vary.   **37.** 12331_5 **38. a)** 1776

Review Exercises, Page 203

1. 3103   **2.** 1211   **3.** 1311   **4.** 2114   **5.** 2314
6. 2312   **7.** *bbbbbaaaaaa*   **8.** *cbbaaaaa*
9. *ccbbbbbbbbbaaa*   **10.** *ddaaaaa*
11. *dddddcccccccccbbbbba*   **12.** *ddcccbaaaa*
13. 43   **14.** 27   **15.** 749   **16.** 4068   **17.** 5648
18. 6905   **19.** *hxb*   **20.** *byixe*   **21.** *hyfxb*
22. *czixd*   **23.** *fzd*   **24.** *bza*   **25.** 45   **26.** 308
27. 568   **28.** 46,883   **29.** 64,481   **30.** 60,529
31. qe   **32.** upb   **33.** vrc   **34.** BArg   **35.** ODvog
36. QFvrf   **37.** ⸖ꟿꟿꟿꟿ∩∩∩∩∩ⅠⅠ
38. MCDLXII   **39.** 一千四百六十二   **40.** $\alpha' \nu \xi \beta$

41. ⪡⪡ⅠⅠⅠⅠⅠ ⪡⪡ⅠⅠ   **42.** (numeral)   **43.** 222,035   **44.** 8254
45. 685   **46.** 1991   **47.** 1277   **48.** 2690   **49.** 39
50. 5   **51.** 28   **52.** 1244   **53.** 1451   **54.** 186
55. 13033_4 **56.** 122011_3 **57.** 111001111_2 **58.** 3323_5
59. 327_{12} **60.** 717_8 **61.** 140_7 **62.** 101111_2
63. 176_{12} **64.** 1023_7 **65.** 12102_5 **66.** 12423_8
67. 3411_7 **68.** 100_2 **69.** $2E3_{12}$ **70.** 3324_5 **71.** 450_8
72. 1102_3 **73.** 212_6 **74.** 1314_5 **75.** 5656_{12}
76. 21102_3 **77.** 110111_2 **78.** 13632_8 **79.** 1011_2
80. 130_4 **81.** $23_5 R1_5$ **82.** 433_6 **83.** $411_6 R1_6$
84. $664_8 R\, 2_8$ **85.** 3408   **86.** 3408   **87.** 3408

Chapter Test, Page 204

1. A number is a quantity and answers the question "How many?" A numeral is a symbol used to represent a number.
2. 3646   **3.** 1275   **4.** 8090   **5.** 969   **6.** 122,142
7. 9999   **8.** ꟿꟿꟿꟿ∩∩∩∩ⅠⅠ   **9.** $\beta' \nu o \zeta$
10. (numeral)   **11.** ⪡⪡ⅠⅠⅠⅠⅠ ⪡⪡⪡ⅠⅠⅠⅠⅠ
12. MMCCCLXXVIII
13. In an additive system, the number represented by a particular set of numerals is the sum of the values of the numerals.

14. In a multiplicative system, there are numerals for each number less than the base and for powers of the base. Each numeral less than the base is multiplied by a numeral for the power of the base, and these products are added to obtain the number.

15. In a ciphered system, the number represented by a particular set of numerals is the sum of the values of the numerals. There are numerals for each number up to and including the base and multiples of the base.

16. In a place-value system, each number is multiplied by a power of the base. The position of the numeral indicates the power of the base by which it is multiplied.

17. 41   **18.** 103   **19.** 45   **20.** 305   **21.** 100100_2
22. 333_5 **23.** 1444_{12} **24.** 11365_7 **25.** 1122_5
26. 142_6 **27.** 2003_6 **28.** 220_5 **29.** 980   **30.** 8428

Chapter 5

Section 5.1, Page 216

1. Number theory is the study of numbers and their properties.
3. a) *a* divides *b* means that *b* divided by *a* has a remainder of zero.
   b) *a* is divisible by *b* means that *a* divided by *b* has a remainder of zero.
5. A composite number is a natural number that is divisible by a number other than itself and 1.
7. a) The LCM of a set of natural numbers is the smallest natural number that is divisible by each number in the set.
   b) Answers will vary.   **c)** 80
9. Mersenne primes are prime numbers of the form $2^n - 1$, where *n* is a prime number.
11. Goldbach's conjecture states that every even number greater than or equal to 4 can be represented as the sum of two (not necessarily distinct) prime numbers.
13. The prime numbers between 1 and 100 are 2, 3, 5, 7, 11, 13, 17, 19, 23, 29, 31, 37, 41, 43, 47, 53, 59, 61, 67, 71, 73, 79, 83, 89, and 97.
15. True   **17.** False; 21 is a multiple of 7.
19. False; 56 is divisible by 8.   **21.** True
23. False; if a number is divisible by 3, then the sum of the digits of the number is divisible by 3.
25. True
27. 10,368 is divisible by 2, 3, 4, 6, 8, and 9.
29. 2,763,105 is divisible by 3 and 5.
31. 1,882,320 is divisible by 2, 3, 4, 5, 6, 8, and 10.
33. 60 (other answers are possible)
35. $45 = 3^2 \cdot 5$ **37.** $196 = 2^2 \cdot 7^2$

39. $303 = 3 \cdot 101$ **41.** $513 = 3^3 \cdot 19$

43. $1336 = 2^3 \cdot 167$ **45.** $2001 = 3 \cdot 23 \cdot 29$

47. a) 3   **b)** 30   **49. a)** 6   **b)** 432   **51. a)** 20   **b)** 1800

53. a) 4   **b)** 5088   **55. a)** 8   **b)** 384

57. 17, 19, and 29, 31

59. a) Yes   **b)** No   **c)** Yes   **d)** Yes

61. $4 = 2 + 2, 6 = 3 + 3, 8 = 3 + 5, 10 = 3 + 7,$
$12 = 5 + 7, 14 = 7 + 7, 16 = 3 + 13,$
$18 = 5 + 13, 20 = 3 + 17$

63. 70 dolls   **65.** 72 cards   **67.** 180 min   **69.** 30 days

71. a) 4, 5, 10, 20, 25   **b)** 25, 20, 10, 5, and 4, respectively

73. A number is divisible by 15 if both 3 and 5 divide the number.

75. 5   **77.** 36   **79.** 30   **81.** No   **83.** Yes

85. a) 12   **b)** 1, 2, 3, 4, 5, 6, 10, 12, 15, 20, 30, 60

87. For any three consecutive natural numbers, one of the numbers is divisible by 2 and another number is divisible by 3. Therefore, the product of the three numbers would be divisible by 6.

89. Yes

91. $8 = 2 + 3 + 3, 9 = 3 + 3 + 3, 10 = 2 + 3 + 5,$
$11 = 2 + 2 + 7, 12 = 2 + 5 + 5, 13 = 3 + 3 + 7,$
$14 = 2 + 5 + 7, 15 = 3 + 5 + 7, 16 = 2 + 7 + 7,$
$17 = 5 + 5 + 7, 18 = 2 + 5 + 11, 19 = 3 + 5 + 11,$
$20 = 2 + 7 + 11$

92. The answer most people select is Denmark, kangaroo, and orange.

Section 5.2, Page 225

1. Begin at zero. Represent the first addend with an arrow. Draw the arrow to the right if the addend is positive, to the left if negative. From the tip of the first arrow, represent the second addend with a second arrow. The sum of the two integers is at the tip of the second arrow.

3. To rewrite a subtraction problem as an addition problem, rewrite the minus sign as a plus sign and change the second number to its opposite.

5. The quotient of two numbers with like signs is positive. The quotient of two numbers with unlike signs is negative.

7. 3   **9.** 2   **11.** -5 **13.** 2   **15.** -21 **17.** -3

19. -10 **21.** -2 **23.** -6 **25.** -2 **27.** -20

29. 144   **31.** 96   **33.** -60 **35.** -720 **37.** 2   **39.** -1

41. -7 **43.** -15 **45.** -48

In Exercises 47–55, false answers can be modified in a variety of ways. We give one possible answer.

47. True

49. False; the difference of two negative integers may be a positive integer, a negative integer, or zero.

51. True   **53.** True

55. False; the sum of a positive integer and a negative integer may be a positive integer, a negative integer, or zero.

57. 6   **59.** -17 **61.** -12 **63.** -5 **65.** -6

67. $-15, -10, -5, 0, 5, 10$

69. $-6, -5, -4, -3, -2, -1$

71. 213.8°F   **73.** 210 points   **75.** 1769 ft

77. a) 9 hours   **b)** 2 hours   **79.** -1

81. $0 + 1 - 2 + 3 + 4 - 5 + 6 - 7 - 8 + 9 = 1$

Section 5.3, Page 238

1. The set of rational numbers is the set of numbers of the form p/q, where p and q are integers and $q \neq 0$.

3. a) Divide both the numerator and the denominator by their greatest common factor.
b) $\frac{5}{9}$

5. For positive mixed numbers, multiply the denominator of the fraction by the integer preceding it. Add this product to the numerator. This sum is the numerator of the improper fraction; the denominator is the same as the denominator in the mixed number. For negative mixed numbers, temporarily ignore the negative sign, perform the conversion described above, and then add the negative sign.

7. a) The reciprocal of a number is 1 divided by the number.
b) $-\frac{1}{2}$

9. a) To add or subtract two fractions with a common denominator, perform the indicated operation on the numerators. Keep the common denominator. Reduce the new fraction to lowest terms, if possible.
b) $\frac{2}{3}$ **c)** $\frac{1}{2}$

11. Answers will vary.   **13.** $\frac{2}{3}$ **15.** $\frac{2}{7}$ **17.** $\frac{21}{32}$ **19.** $\frac{7}{11}$

21. $\frac{1}{11}$ **23.** $\frac{25}{7}$ **25.** $-\frac{31}{16}$ **27.** $-\frac{79}{16}$ **29.** $\frac{17}{8}$ **31.** $\frac{15}{8}$

33. $1\frac{3}{8}$ **35.** $-12\frac{1}{6}$ **37.** $-58\frac{8}{15}$ **39.** 0.6   **41.** $0.\overline{2}$

43. 0.375   **45.** $4.\overline{3}$ **47.** $5.\overline{6}$ **49.** $\frac{25}{100} = \frac{1}{4}$ **51.** $\frac{45}{1000} = \frac{9}{200}$

53. $\frac{2}{10} = \frac{1}{5}$ **55.** $\frac{452}{1000} = \frac{113}{250}$ **57.** $\frac{1}{10,000}$ **59.** $\frac{2}{3}$ **61.** $\frac{2}{1}$

63. $\frac{15}{11}$ **65.** $\frac{46}{45}$ **67.** $\frac{574}{165}$ **69.** $\frac{3}{22}$ **71.** $\frac{2}{5}$ **73.** $\frac{49}{64}$ **75.** $\frac{36}{35}$

77. $\frac{5}{14}$ **79.** $\frac{13}{15}$ **81.** $\frac{21}{26}$ **83.** $\frac{23}{54}$ **85.** $\frac{17}{144}$ **87.** $-\frac{109}{600}$

89. $\frac{51}{40}$ **91.** $-\frac{1}{24}$ **93.** $\frac{19}{24}$ **95.** 1   **97.** $\frac{4}{11}$ **99.** $\frac{23}{42}$ **101.** $\frac{1}{12}$

103. $120\frac{3}{4}$ in.   **105. a)** $\frac{3}{8}$ cup   **b)** $\frac{3}{16}$ tsp   **c)** $\frac{3}{4}$ cup

107. $\frac{59}{60}$ **109.** 27 pages   **111.** $58\frac{7}{8}$ in.   **113.** $12\frac{7}{16}$ in.

115. $26\frac{5}{32}$ in.   **117. a)** $37\frac{5}{6}$ ft   **b)** 88 ft^2 **c)** $806\frac{2}{3}$ ft^3

In Exercises 119–125, an infinite number of answers are possible. We give one answer.

119. 0.105   **121.** -2.1755 **123.** 3.1234505

125. 4.8725   **127.** $\frac{1}{2}$ **129.** $\frac{11}{200}$ **131.** $\frac{9}{40}$ **133.** $\frac{11}{200}$

135. a) $1\frac{3}{8}$ cup water (or milk) and $\frac{3}{4}$ cup oatmeal

  b) $1\frac{1}{2}$ cup water (or milk) and $\frac{3}{4}$ cup oatmeal

137. a) $\frac{1}{8}$ **b)** $\frac{1}{16}$ **c)** 5 **d)** 6

Section 5.4, Page 247

1. A rational number can be written as a ratio of two integers. Real numbers that cannot be written as a ratio of two integers are irrational numbers.

3. A perfect square is any number that is the square of a natural number.

5. a) To add or subtract two or more square roots with the same radicand, add or subtract their coefficients and then multiply the sum or difference by the common radical.
  b) $-\sqrt{6}$

7. a) Multiply both the numerator and denominator by a radical that will result in the radicand in the denominator becoming a perfect square.
  b) $\frac{7\sqrt{3}}{3}$

9. Rational **11.** Rational **13.** Irrational **15.** Rational

17. Irrational **19.** 8 **21.** 10 **23.** -13 **25.** -15

27. -10 **29.** Rational number, integer, natural number

31. Rational number, integer, natural number

33. Rational number **35.** Rational number

37. Rational number **39.** $3\sqrt{2}$ **41.** $4\sqrt{3}$ **43.** $3\sqrt{7}$

45. $4\sqrt{5}$ **47.** $9\sqrt{2}$ **49.** $7\sqrt{6}$ **51.** $5\sqrt{3}$ **53.** $-13\sqrt{3}$

55. $4\sqrt{3}$ **57.** $23\sqrt{2}$ **59.** 4 **61.** $2\sqrt{15}$ **63.** $10\sqrt{2}$

65. $\sqrt{2}$ **67.** 3 **69.** $\frac{\sqrt{2}}{2}$ **71.** $\frac{\sqrt{21}}{7}$ **73.** $\frac{2\sqrt{15}}{3}$

75. $\frac{3\sqrt{2}}{2}$ **77.** $\frac{\sqrt{15}}{3}$

79. $\sqrt{7}$ is between 2 and 3 since 7 is between 4 and 9. $\sqrt{7}$ is between 2.5 and 3 since 7 is closer to 9 than to 4. $\sqrt{7} \approx 2.65$.

81. $\sqrt{107}$ is between 10 and 11 since 107 is between 100 and 121. $\sqrt{107}$ is between 10 and 10.5 since 107 is closer to 100 than to 121. $\sqrt{107} \approx 10.34$.

83. $\sqrt{170}$ is between 13 and 14 since 170 is between 169 and 196. $\sqrt{170}$ is between 13 and 13.5 since 170 is closer to 169 than to 196. $\sqrt{170} \approx 13.04$.

In Exercises 85–89, false answers can be modified in a variety of ways. We give one possible answer.

85. False. $\sqrt{p}$ is an irrational number for any prime number p.

87. True

89. False. The product of a rational number and an irrational number may be a rational number or an irrational number.

91. $\pi + (-\pi) = 0$ **93.** $\sqrt{2} \cdot \sqrt{3} = \sqrt{6}$

95. $\sqrt{5} \neq 2.236$ since $\sqrt{5}$ is irrational and 2.236 is rational.

97. No. π is irrational; therefore, it cannot equal $\frac{22}{7}$ or 3.14, both of which are rational.

99. $\sqrt{4 \cdot 9} = \sqrt{4} \cdot \sqrt{9}$, $\sqrt{36} = 2 \cdot 3$, $6 = 6$

101. a) 10 mph **b)** 20 mph **c)** 40 mph **d)** 80 mph

103. a) If the result on the calculator is a terminating or repeating decimal number, then the number is rational; if the result is not a terminating or repeating decimal number, then the number is irrational.
  b) Rational. $\sqrt{0.04} = 0.2$, which is a rational number.
  c) Irrational. $\sqrt{0.7} = 0.8366600265\ldots$ Since the decimal number is not a terminating or a repeating decimal number, this is an irrational number.

105. a) $(44 \div \sqrt{4}) \div \sqrt{4} = 11$ **b)** $(44 \div 4) + \sqrt{4} = 13$
  c) $4 + 4 + 4 + \sqrt{4} = 14$
  d) $\sqrt{4}(4 + 4) + \sqrt{4} = 18$

Other answers are possible.

Section 5.5, Page 254

1. The real numbers are the union of the rational numbers and the irrational numbers.

3. If whenever the operation is performed on two elements of a set the result is also an element of the set, then the set is closed under that operation.

5. $a + b = b + a$, the order in which two numbers are added is immaterial. One example is $4 + 5 = 5 + 4$.

7. $(a \cdot b) \cdot c = a \cdot (b \cdot c)$, when multiplying three numbers, you may place parentheses around any two adjacent numbers. One example is $(1 \times 2) \times 3 = 1 \times (2 \times 3)$.

9. Yes **11.** No **13.** Yes **15.** No **17.** Yes **19.** Yes

21. No **23.** No **25.** Yes **27.** No

29. Commutative property of addition. The only difference between the expressions on both sides of the equal sign is the order of $(3 + 4)$ and x being added.

31. $(-3)(-4) = (-4)(-3) = 12$

33. No. $3 \div 4 \neq 4 \div 3$.

35. $[(-2)(-3)](-4) = (-2)[(-3)(-4)] = -24$

37. No. $(16 \div 8) \div 2 \neq 16 \div (8 \div 2)$.

39. No. $(81 \div 9) \div 3 \neq 81 \div (9 \div 3)$.

41. Commutative property of addition

43. Associative property of multiplication

45. Associative property of addition

47. Commutative property of multiplication

49. Distributive property

51. Commutative property of addition

53. Distributive property

55. Commutative property of addition

57. $2c + 14$ **59.** $\frac{2}{3}x - 4$ **61.** $3x + 4$ **63.** $2x - 1$

65. $15 - 3\sqrt{5}$ **67.** $2 + \sqrt{6}$

69. a) Distributive property
   b) Associative property of addition

71. a) Distributive property
   b) Associative property of addition
   c) Commutative property of addition
   d) Associative property of addition

73. a) Distributive property
   b) Commutative property of addition
   c) Associative property of addition
   d) Commutative property of addition

75. Yes   **77.** No   **79.** Yes   **81.** Yes   **83.** Yes   **85.** Yes

87. Yes   **89.** Answers will vary.

91. No. $0 \div a = 0$ (when $a \neq 0$), but $a \div 0$ is undefined.

92. a) No   **b)** No   **c)** Answers will vary.

Section 5.6, Page 264

1. The 2 is the base and the 3 is the exponent or power.

3. a) To multiply two exponential expressions with the same base, add the exponents and use this sum as the exponent on the common base.
   b) $2^3 \cdot 2^4 = 2^{3+4} = 2^7 = 128$

5. a) Any nonzero expression raised to the power of 0 equals 1.
   b) $7^0 = 1$

7. a) Any base with an exponent raised to another exponent is equal to the base raised to the product of the exponents.
   b) $(3^2)^4 = 3^{2 \cdot 4} = 3^8 = 6561$

9. a) -1^{500} means $-(1)^{500}$ or $-1 \cdot 1^{500}$. Since 1 raised to any power equals 1, $-1^{500} = -1 \cdot 1^{500} = -1 \cdot 1 = -1$.
   b) $(-1)^{500}$ means (-1) multiplied by itself 500 times. Since 500 is even, $(-1)^{500} = 1$.
   c) -1^{501} means $-(1)^{501}$ or $-1 \cdot 1^{501}$. Since 1 raised to any power equals 1, $-1^{501} = -1 \cdot 1^{501} = -1 \cdot 1 = -1$.
   d) $(-1)^{501}$ means (-1) multiplied by itself 501 times. Since 501 is odd, $(-1)^{501} = -1$.

11. a) If the exponent is positive, move the decimal point in the number to the right the same number of places as the exponent, adding zeros where necessary. If the exponent is negative, move the decimal point in the number to the left the same number of places as the exponent, adding zeros where necessary.
   b) 0.000576

13. 25   **15.** 16   **17.** -9 **19.** $\frac{4}{9}$ **21.** 25   **23.** 72   **25.** 25

27. $\frac{1}{49}$ **29.** 1   **31.** 81   **33.** $\frac{1}{9}$ **35.** 4096   **37.** 121

39. 16   **41.** -16 **43.** $\frac{1}{64}$ **45.** 2.31×10^5

47. 1.5×10^1 **49.** 5.6×10^{-1} **51.** 1.9×10^4

53. 1.86×10^{-4} **55.** 4.23×10^{-6} **57.** 7.11×10^2

59. 1.53×10^{-1} **61.** 2300   **63.** 0.003901

65. 0.0000862   **67.** 0.312   **69.** 9,000,000   **71.** 231

73. 35,000   **75.** 10,000   **77.** 800,000   **79.** 0.0153

81. 320   **83.** 0.0021   **85.** 20   **87.** 6.0×10^{11}

89. 4.5×10^{-7} **91.** 2.0×10^3 **93.** 2.0×10^{-7}

95. 3.0×10^8

97. 8.3×10^{-4}; 3.2×10^{-1}; 4.6; 5.8×10^5

99. 8.3×10^{-5}; 0.00079; 4.1×10^3; 40,000

101. a) $\approx \$35,590.18$ **b)** $\$3.559018 \times 10^4$

103. a) $\approx 210,109,000,000,000,000,000$ sec
   b) $\approx 2.1 \times 10^{20}$ sec (about 6.7 trillion years!)

105. a) 18,000 hours   **b)** 1.8×10^4

107. a) 20,000,000,000,000,000 drops   **b)** 2×10^{16}

109. a) 18,000 times   **b)** 1.8×10^4

111. a) $\approx \$17,093.02$ per person   **b)** $\$5989.17$

113. a) $\$720,000,000$ **b)** $\$300,000,000$ **c)** $\$120,000,000$
   d) $\$60,000,000$

115. 1000   **117.** 333,333 times

119. 230,000 sec (about 2.66 days)

121. a) About 5.87×10^{12} (5.87 trillion) mi
   b) About 500 sec or 8 min 20 sec

Section 5.7, Page 273

1. A sequence is a list of numbers that are related to each other by a given rule. One example is $1, 3, 5, 7, 9, \ldots$.

3. a) An arithmetic sequence is one in which each term differs from the preceding term by a constant amount. One example is $4, 7, 10, 13, 16, \ldots$.
   b) A geometric sequence is one in which the ratio of any two successive terms is a constant amount. One example is $3, 6, 12, 24, \ldots$.

5. a) a_n is the nth term or the general term.
   b) a_1 is the first term.
   c) d is the common difference.
   d) s_n is the sum of the first n terms.

7. $3, 5, 7, 9, 11$ **9.** $-5, -2, 1, 4, 7$ **11.** $5, 3, 1, -1, -3$

13. $\frac{1}{2}, 1, \frac{3}{2}, 2, \frac{5}{2}$ **15.** 17   **17.** 13   **19.** $-\frac{91}{5}$ **21.** 9

23. $a_n = n$ **25.** $a_n = 2n$ **27.** $a_n = \frac{1}{3}n - 2$

29. $a_n = \frac{3}{2}n - \frac{9}{2}$ **31.** $s_{50} = 1275$ **33.** $s_{50} = 2500$

35. $s_8 = -52$ **37.** $s_8 = 60$ **39.** $3, 6, 12, 24, 48$

41. $2, -4, 8, -16, 32$ **43.** $-3, 3, -3, 3, -3$

45. $-16, 8, -4, 2, -1$ **47.** 3072   **49.** $\frac{3}{4}$ **51.** 8

53. $a_{10} = -39,366$

55. $a_n = 2^{n-1}$ **57.** $a_n = 3 \cdot (-1)^{n-1}$

59. $a_n = \dfrac{1}{4} \cdot (2)^{n-1}$ **61.** $a_n = 9 \cdot \left(\dfrac{1}{3}\right)^{n-1}$ **63.** 45

65. 27,305   **67.** $-620,011$ **69.** $s_{15} = -10,923$

71. 5050   **73.** 10,000   **75. a)** $28,600   **b)** $195,200

77. 12 in.   **79.** 496 pinecones   **81.** 52.4288 g

83. $45,218   **85.** $486,000   **87.** 161.4375   **89.** 267

91. 191.3568 ft

Section 5.8, Page 280

1. The first and second terms are one. Each term thereafter is the sum of the previous two terms.

3. a) The golden number is $\dfrac{\sqrt{5}+1}{2}$.

  b) When a line segment AB is divided at a point C, such that the ratio of the whole, AB, to the larger part, AC, is equal to the ratio of the larger part, AC, to the smaller part, CB, then each of the two ratios AB/AC and AC/CB is known as the golden ratio.

  c) The proportion made by using the two golden ratios, $AB/AC = AC/CB$, is known as the golden proportion.

  d) A golden rectangle is one where the ratio of the length to the width is equal to the golden number.

5. Answers will vary.   **7. a)** 1.618   **b)** 0.618   **c)** 1

9. $\frac{1}{1} = 1, \frac{2}{1} = 2, \frac{3}{2} = 1.5, \frac{5}{3} \approx 1.667, \frac{8}{5} = 1.6, \frac{13}{8} = 1.625,$ $\frac{21}{13} \approx 1.615, \frac{34}{21} \approx 1.619, \frac{55}{34} \approx 1.6176, \frac{89}{55} \approx 1.6182.$ The consecutive ratios alternate, increasing and decreasing about the golden ratio.

11. Each number in the Fibonacci sequence is either a prime number or is relatively prime with the number preceding or succeeding it in the sequence. Therefore, the GCF of any two consecutive Fibonacci numbers is 1.

13. Answers will vary.   **15.** Answers will vary.

17. Answers will vary.   **19.** Answers will vary.

21. Answers will vary.   **23.** Yes; 29, 47   **25.** No

27. Yes; 105, 170   **29.** Yes; −1, −1

31. Answers will vary.   **33.** Answers will vary.

35. a) 1, 3, 4, 7, 11, 18, 29, 47

  b) 8 + 21 = 29, 13 + 34 = 47

  c) It is the Fibonacci sequence.

37. Answers will vary.   **39.** Answers will vary.

Review Exercises, Page 283

1. 2, 3, 4, 6, 9   **2.** 2, 3, 4, 6, 9   **3.** $2^2 \cdot 3^2 \cdot 7$

4. $5 \cdot 7 \cdot 11$ **5.** $2^3 \cdot 3 \cdot 5 \cdot 7$ **6.** $2 \cdot 3^2 \cdot 7^2$ **7.** $2^2 \cdot 3 \cdot 11^2$

8. 15; 60   **9.** 9; 756   **10.** 5; 2250   **11.** 40; 6720

12. 4; 480   **13.** 36; 432   **14.** 45 days   **15.** 3   **16.** −3

17. −4   **18.** −6   **19.** −9   **20.** 3   **21.** 0   **22.** 4   **23.** 33

24. −36   **25.** −56   **26.** 5   **27.** −2   **28.** 6   **29.** 6

30. 3   **31.** 0.3   **32.** 0.6   **33.** 0.375   **34.** 3.25

35. $0.\overline{428571}$ **36.** $0.58\overline{3}$ **37.** 0.375   **38.** 0.875

39. $0.\overline{714285}$ **40.** $\frac{9}{40}$ **41.** $\frac{9}{2}$ **42.** $\frac{2}{3}$ **43.** $\frac{235}{99}$ **44.** $\frac{83}{1000}$

45. $\frac{21}{5000}$ **46.** $\frac{211}{90}$ **47.** $\frac{19}{7}$ **48.** $\frac{25}{6}$ **49.** $-\frac{13}{4}$ **50.** $-\frac{283}{8}$

51. $2\frac{1}{5}$ **52.** $1\frac{4}{5}$ **53.** $-1\frac{5}{7}$ **54.** $-27\frac{1}{5}$ **55.** $\frac{13}{10}$ **56.** $\frac{1}{8}$

57. $\frac{17}{12}$ **58.** $\frac{3}{4}$ **59.** $\frac{35}{54}$ **60.** $\frac{53}{28}$ **61.** $\frac{1}{6}$ **62.** $\frac{13}{40}$ **63.** $\frac{8}{15}$

64. $2\frac{7}{32}$ tsp   **65.** $5\sqrt{2}$ **66.** $10\sqrt{2}$ **67.** $8\sqrt{5}$ **68.** $-3\sqrt{3}$

69. $8\sqrt{2}$ **70.** $-20\sqrt{3}$ **71.** $8\sqrt{3}$ **72.** $3\sqrt{2}$ **73.** $4\sqrt{3}$

74. 3   **75.** $2\sqrt{7}$ **76.** $\dfrac{4\sqrt{3}}{3}$ **77.** $\dfrac{\sqrt{15}}{5}$ **78.** $6 + 3\sqrt{7}$

79. $4\sqrt{3} + 3\sqrt{2}$ **80.** $3\sqrt{2} + 3\sqrt{5}$

81. Commutative property of addition

82. Commutative property of multiplication

83. Associative property of addition

84. Distributive property

85. Commutative property of addition

86. Commutative property of addition

87. Associative property of multiplication

88. Commutative property of multiplication

89. Distributive property

90. Commutative property of multiplication

91. Yes   **92.** No   **93.** No   **94.** Yes   **95.** No   **96.** No

97. 9   **98.** $\frac{1}{9}$ **99.** 81   **100.** 125   **101.** 1   **102.** $\frac{1}{64}$

103. 64   **104.** 81   **105.** 2.3×10^8 **106.** 1.58×10^{-5}

107. 2.75×10^{-3} **108.** 4.95×10^6 **109.** 43,000,000

110. 0.000139   **111.** 0.000175   **112.** 100,000

113. 1.4×10^{-1} **114.** 1.0×10^5 **115.** 2.1×10^1

116. 3.0×10^0 **117.** 8,000,000,000   **118.** 0.7

119. 3200   **120.** 5   **121.** ≈388 times   **122.** ≈ $5555.56

123. Arithmetic; 14, 17   **124.** Geometric; 8, 16

125. Arithmetic; −15, −18   **126.** Geometric; $\frac{1}{32}, \frac{1}{64}$

127. Arithmetic; 16, 19   **128.** Geometric; −2, 2   **129.** 15

130. −34   **131.** 25   **132.** 48   **133.** $\frac{1}{4}$ **134.** −48

135. 1365   **136.** −25   **137.** 632   **138.** 57.5   **139.** 200

140. 80   **141.** 33   **142.** −21

143. Arithmetic; $a_n = -3n + 10$

144. Arithmetic; $a_n = 3n$ **145.** Arithmetic; $a_n = -\frac{3}{2}n + \frac{11}{2}$

146. Geometric; $a_n = 3(2)^{n-1}$

147. Geometric; $a_n = 2(-1)^{n-1}$

148. Geometric; $a_n = 5\left(\dfrac{1}{3}\right)^{n-1}$ **149.** Yes; 13, 21

150. Yes; 17, 28   **151.** No   **152.** No

Chapter Test, Page 285

1. 2, 3, 5, 6, 9, 10   **2.** $2^3 \cdot 3 \cdot 5 \cdot 7$ **3.** −7   **4.** −20

5. −175   **6.** $\frac{37}{8}$ **7.** $19\frac{5}{9}$ **8.** 0.625   **9.** $\frac{129}{20}$ **10.** $\frac{121}{240}$

11. $\frac{13}{24}$ **12.** $9\sqrt{3}$ **13.** $\frac{\sqrt{14}}{7}$

14. Yes; the product of any two integers is an integer.

15. Associative property of addition

16. Distributive property   **17.** 64   **18.** 1024   **19.** $\frac{1}{81}$

20. 8.0×10^{11} **21.** $a_n = -4n + 2$ **22.** -187 **23.** 243

24. 1023   **25.** $a_n = 3(2)^{n-1}$

26. 1, 1, 2, 3, 5, 8, 13, 21, 34, 55

Chapter 6

Section 6.1, Page 291

1. Letters of the alphabet used to represent numbers are called variables.

3. The solution to an equation is the number or numbers that replace the variable to make the equation a true statement.

5. a) The 4 is the base and the 5 is the exponent.
b) Answers will vary.

7. 12   **9.** 49   **11.** -9 **13.** 686   **15.** -3 **17.** 18

19. -27 **21.** $-\frac{10}{9}$ **23.** 7   **25.** 9   **27.** 0   **29.** No

31. No   **33.** No   **35.** Yes   **37.** Yes   **39.** $12.25

41. $426.25   **43.** 16,000,000 sec   **45.** 1.71 in.

47. The two expressions are not equal.

Section 6.2, Page 302

1. The parts that are added or subtracted in an algebraic expression are called terms. In $3x - 2y$, the $3x$ and $-2y$ are terms.

3. The numerical part of a term is called its numerical coefficient. For the term $3x$, 3 is the numerical coefficient.

5. To simplify an expression means to combine like terms by using the commutative, associative, and distributive properties.

7. If $a = b$, then $a - c = b - c$ for all real numbers a, b, and c. If $2x + 3 = 5$, then $2x + 3 - 3 = 5 - 3$.

9. If $a = b$, then $a/c = b/c$ for all real numbers a, b, and c, where $c \neq 0$. If $4x = 8$, then $\frac{4x}{4} = \frac{8}{4}$.

11. A ratio is a quotient of two quantities. An example is $\frac{7}{9}$.

13. Yes. They have the same variable and the same exponent on the variable.

15. $11x$ **17.** $2x + 12$ **19.** $3x + 11y$ **21.** $-8x + 2$

23. $-5x + 3$ **25.** $13.3x - 8.3$ **27.** $-\frac{2}{15}x - 4$

29. $13x - 7y + 3$ **31.** $8s - 17$ **33.** $1.5x - 4.2$

35. $\frac{5}{12}x + \frac{3}{7}$ **37.** $4.52x - 13.5$ **39.** 5   **41.** 1   **43.** $\frac{24}{7}$

45. $\frac{2}{3}$ **47.** 3   **49.** 3   **51.** 17   **53.** -8

55. No solution   **57.** All real numbers   **59.** $\frac{4}{3}$ **61.** -3

63. 4   **65.** $72.37   **67.** 59 times

69. 20,746,600 households

71. a) 1.6 kph   **b)** 56.25 mph   **73.** 0.3 cc

75. a) Answers will vary.   **b)** -1

77. a) An equation that has no solution.
b) You will obtain a false statement.

79. a) $2 : 5$ **b)** $m : m + n$

Section 6.3, Page 311

1. A formula is an equation that typically has a real-life application.

3. Subscripts are numbers (or letters) placed below and to the right of variables. They are used to help clarify a formula.

5. An exponential equation is of the form $y = a^x, a > 0$, $a \neq 1$.

7. 20   **9.** 56   **11.** 25   **13.** 62.8   **15.** 37.1   **17.** 2

19. 3000   **21.** 8   **23.** 25   **25.** 6   **27.** 200   **29.** 7.2

31. 14   **33.** 3240   **35.** 0.5   **37.** 14

39. $y = \dfrac{10x - 13}{4}$ or $y = \dfrac{5}{2}x - \dfrac{13}{4}$

41. $y = \dfrac{-4x + 14}{7}$ or $y = -\dfrac{4}{7}x + 2$

43. $y = \dfrac{2x + 6}{3}$ or $y = \dfrac{2}{3}x + 2$

45. $y = \dfrac{2x - z + 15}{3}$ or $y = \dfrac{2}{3}x - \dfrac{1}{3}z + 5$

47. $y = \dfrac{9x + 4z - 7}{8}$ or $y = \dfrac{9}{8}x + \dfrac{1}{2}z - \dfrac{7}{8}$

49. $R = \dfrac{E}{I}$ **51.** $a = p - b - c$ **53.** $B = \dfrac{3V}{h}$

55. $r = \dfrac{C}{2\pi}$ **57.** $b = y - mx$ **59.** $w = \dfrac{P - 2l}{2}$

61. $c = 3A - a - b$ **63.** $T = \dfrac{PV}{K}$

65. $C = \frac{5}{9}(F - 32)$ **67.** $s = \dfrac{S - \pi r^2}{\pi r}$

69. a) $12   **b)** $612   **71.** ≈ 18.4 in.^{3}

73. 486,000 bacteria   **75.** $300,976,658,300,000

77. ≈ 1051.47 in.^{3}

Section 6.4, Page 317

1. A mathematical expression is a collection of variables, numbers, parentheses, and operation symbols. An equation is two algebraic expressions joined by an equal sign.

3. $4 + 3x$ **5.** $6r + 5$ **7.** $15 - 2r$ **9.** $2m + 9$

11. $\dfrac{18 - s}{4}$ **13.** $(5y - 6) + 3$ **15.** $x - 6 = 5; 11$

17. $x - 4 = 20$; 24   **19.** $12 + 5x = 47$; 7

21. $8x + 16 = 88$; 9   **23.** $x + 11 = 3x + 1$; 5

25. $x + 10 = 2(x + 3)$; 4

27. $x + 3x = 600$; 150 tickets to nonstudents, 450 tickets to students

29. $x + 0.116x = 34.20$; ≈ 30.65 million taxpayers

31. $x - 0.10x = 15.72$; $17.47

33. $x + 3x = 12$; Samantha: 3, Josie: 9

35. $2000 + 50x = 13,350$; $227

37. a) $x + x + 3x = 45,000$; 9000 ft^2, 9000 ft^2, 27,000 ft^2
b) Yes

39. $x + 3x + 3 = 55$; United States: 13, Italy: 42

41. $3w + 2(2w) = 140$; width: 20 ft, length: 40 ft

43. $70x = 760$; ≈ 11 months

45. $\dfrac{r}{2} + 0.07r = 257$; $450.88

47. Deduct $720 from Mr. McAdams's income and $2920 from Mrs. McAdams's income.

49. $x + (x + 1) + (x + 2) = 3(x + 2) - 3$
$$3x + 3 = 3x + 6 - 3$$
$$3x + 3 = 3x + 3$$

51. $-40°$

Section 6.5, Page 326

1. Inverse variation: As one variable increases, the other decreases and vice versa.

3. Joint variation: One quantity varies directly as the product of two or more other quantities.

5. Direct   **7.** Inverse   **9.** Direct   **11.** Inverse

13. Inverse   **15.** Inverse   **17.** Direct   **19.** Direct

21. Answers will vary.   **23. a)** $y = kx$ **b)** 15

25. a) $m = \dfrac{k}{n^2}$ **b)** 0.25   **27. a)** $R = \dfrac{k}{W}$ **b)** 0.05

29. a) $F = kDE$ **b)** 210   **31. a)** $t = \dfrac{kd^2}{f}$ **b)** 200

33. a) $Z = kWY$ **b)** 100   **35. a)** $H = kL$ **b)** 3

37. a) $A = kB^2$ **b)** 720   **39. a)** $F = \dfrac{kq_1q_2}{d^2}$ **b)** 672

41. a) $R = kL$ **b)** 0.32 ohm   **43. a)** $l = \dfrac{k}{d^2}$ **b)** 80 dB

45. a) $R = \dfrac{kA}{P}$ **b)** 4800 tapes

47. a) $s = kwd^2$ **b)** 6480 pounds per square inch

49. a) $N = \dfrac{kp_1p_2}{d}$ **b)** $\approx 121,528$ calls

51. a) Inversely   **b)** Stays 0.3   **53.** $132.27

Section 6.6, Page 332

1. $a < b$ means that a is less than b, $a \leq b$ means that a is less than or equal to b, $a > b$ means that a is greater than b, $a \geq b$ means that a is greater than or equal to b.

3. When both sides of an inequality are multiplied or divided by a negative number, the direction of the inequality symbol must be reversed.

5. Yes, the inequality symbol points to the -3 in both cases.

7.

9.

11.

13.

15.

17.

19.

21. No solution

23.

25.

27.

29.

31.

33.

35.

37.

39.

41.

43.

45. a) 2000, 2001   **b)** 1997, 1998
c) 1997, 1998, 1999, 2000   **d)** 1998, 1999, 2000, 2001

47. 19 videos   **49.** Less than 360 mi   **51.** $x \leq \$15.57$

53. $0.5 < t < 1.5$

55. $94 \leq x \leq 100$, assuming 100 is the highest grade possible

57. $6.875 \leq x \leq 11$

59. The student's answer is $x \leq -12$, whereas the correct answer is $x \geq -12$. Yes, -12 is in both solution sets.

Section 6.7, Page 344

1. A graph is an illustration of all the points whose coordinates satisfy an equation.

3. To find the y-intercept, set $x = 0$ and solve the equation for y.

5. a) Answers will vary. **b)** $-\frac{1}{3}$

7. a) First **b)** Second

For Exercises 9–15, see the following figure.

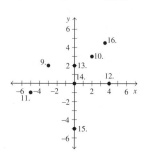

For Exercises 17–23, see the following figure.

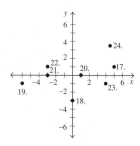

25. $(0, 2)$ **27.** $(-2, 0)$ **29.** $(-5, -3)$ **31.** $(2, -3)$
33. $(2, 2)$ **35.** $(1, 4), (-1, 10)$ **37.** $(5, 0), (0, -\frac{10}{3})$
39. $(-3, -2)$ **41.** $(0, \frac{8}{3}), (4, 0)$

43.

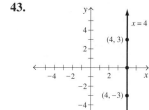

Slope: undefined

45.

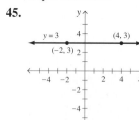

Slope is 0.

47.

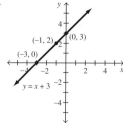

49.

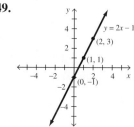

51.

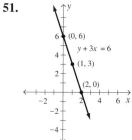

53.

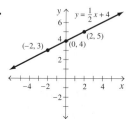

55.

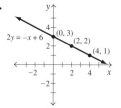

57.

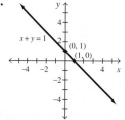

59.

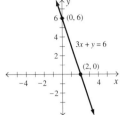

61.

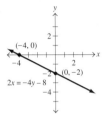

63.

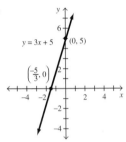

65.

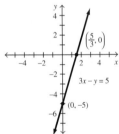

67. 2 **69.** $\frac{15}{7}$ **71.** 0 **73.** Undefined **75.** $-\frac{4}{3}$

77.

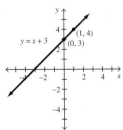

79.

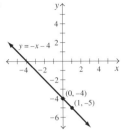

81.

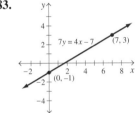

83.

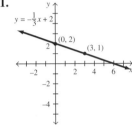

85.

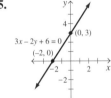

87. $y = -\frac{3}{4}x + 3$ **89.** $y = 3x + 2$

91. a) $D(-1, 2)$ **b)** $A = 10$ square units

93. $(7, 2)$ or $(-1, 2)$ **95.** 3 **97.** 3

99. a)

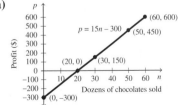

b) \$300 **c)** 20 dozens of chocolates

101. a)

b) $15.55   **c)** 36 pictures

103. a) 10.75   **b)** $y = 10.75x + 53$
c) 85.25   **d)** ≈ 2.5 hours

105. a) $-\frac{8}{15}$ **b)** $y = -\frac{8}{15}x + 40$
c) 32%   **d)** 18.75 years after 1970 or 1988

107. a) Solve the equations for y to put them in slope–intercept form. Then compare the slopes and y-intercepts. If the slopes are equal but the y-intercepts are different, then the lines are parallel.
b) The lines are parallel.

Section 6.8, Page 350

1. (1) Mentally substitute the equal sign for the inequality sign and plot points as if you were graphing the equation. (2) If the inequality is $<$ or $>$, draw a dashed line through the points. If the inequality is $\leq$ or $\geq$, draw a solid line through the points. (3) Select a test point not on the line and substitute the x- and y-coordinates into the inequality. If the substitution results in a true statement, shade in the area on the same side of the line as the test point. If the test point results in a false statement, shade in the area on the opposite side of the line as the test point.

3.

5.

7.

9.

11.

13.

15.

17.

19.
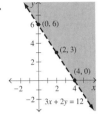

21.
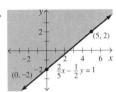

23.
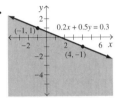

25. a) $x + y \leq 300$
b)
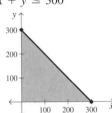

27. a) $x =$ the number of acres of land, $y =$ the number of square feet in the house
b)
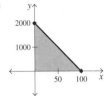

c) 2.5 acres or less
d) 1900 ft^2 or less

29. (a), (b), and (d)

Section 6.9, Page 360

1. A binomial is an expression that contains two terms in which each exponent that appears on the variable is a whole number. $2x + 3$, $x - 7$, $x^2 - 9$

3. Answers will vary.

5. $ax^2 + bx + c = 0$, $a \neq 0$ **7.** $(x + 6)(x + 3)$

9. $(x - 3)(x + 2)$ **11.** $(x + 6)(x - 4)$

13. $(x + 1)(x - 3)$ **15.** $(x - 7)(x - 3)$

17. $(x - 5)(x + 5)$ **19.** $(x + 7)(x - 4)$

21. $(x + 9)(x - 7)$ **23.** $(2x - 5)(x + 2)$

25. $(4x + 1)(x + 3)$ **27.** $(5x + 2)(x + 2)$

29. $(4x + 3)(x + 2)$ **31.** $(4x - 3)(x - 2)$

33. $(3x + 4)(x - 6)$ **35.** $1, -2$ **37.** $-\frac{4}{3}, \frac{1}{2}$

39. $-7, -3$ **41.** $3, 1$ **43.** $5, -3$ **45.** $3, 1$ **47.** $9, -9$

49. $-9, 4$ **51.** $\frac{2}{3}, -4$ **53.** $-\frac{1}{5}, -2$ **55.** $\frac{1}{3}, 1$ **57.** $\frac{1}{4}, 2$

59. $3, -5$ **61.** $6, -3$ **63.** $9, -1$ **65.** No real solution

67. $2 \pm \sqrt{2}$ **69.** $\dfrac{4 \pm \sqrt{13}}{3}$ **71.** $\dfrac{1 \pm \sqrt{17}}{8}$ **73.** $-1, -\frac{5}{2}$

75. $\frac{7}{3}, 1$ **77.** No real solution

79. Width $= 12$ m, length $= 22$ m

81. a) The zero-factor property cannot be used.
b) ≈ 8.37, ≈ 2.63

83. $x^2 - 2x - 3 = 0$

Section 6.10, Page 372

1. A function is a special type of relation where each value of the independent variable corresponds to a unique value of the dependent variable.

3. The domain of a function is the set of values that can be used for the independent variable.

5. If a vertical line touches more than one point on the graph, then for each value of x there is not a unique value for y and the graph does not represent a function.

7. Not a function   **9.** Function, domain: $\mathbb{R}$; range: $\mathbb{R}$

11. Function, domain: $\mathbb{R}$; range: $y = 2$

13. Function, domain: $\mathbb{R}$; range: $y \geq -4$

15. Not a function

17. Function, domain: $0 \leq x < 12$; range: $y = 1, 2, 3$

19. Not a function

21. Function, domain: $\mathbb{R}$; range: $y > 0$

23. Not a function

25. Yes   **27.** No   **29.** Yes   **31.** 5   **33.** 1   **35.** -6

37. 5   **39.** 4   **41.** -38 **43.** -17

45.
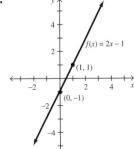

47.

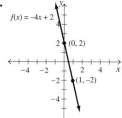

$f(x) = -4x + 2$
$(0, 2)$
$(1, -2)$

49.

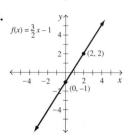

$f(x) = \frac{3}{2}x - 1$
$(2, 2)$
$(0, -1)$

51. a) Upward **b)** $x = 0$ **c)** $(0, -16)$ **d)** $(0, -16)$
e) $(4, 0), (-4, 0)$
f)

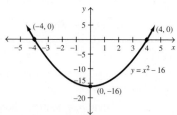

$(-4, 0)$ $(4, 0)$
$y = x^2 - 16$
$(0, -16)$

g) Domain: $\mathbb{R}$; range: $y \geq -16$

53. a) Downward **b)** $x = 0$ **c)** $(0, 4)$ **d)** $(0, 4)$
e) $(-2, 0), (2, 0)$
f)

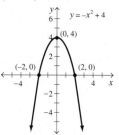

$y = -x^2 + 4$
$(0, 4)$
$(-2, 0)$ $(2, 0)$

g) Domain: $\mathbb{R}$; range: $y \leq 4$

55. a) Downward **b)** $x = 0$ **c)** $(0, -4)$ **d)** $(0, -4)$
e) No x-intercepts
f)

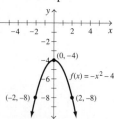

$(0, -4)$
$f(x) = -x^2 - 4$
$(-2, -8)$ $(2, -8)$

g) Domain: $\mathbb{R}$; range: $y \leq -4$

57. a) Upward **b)** $x = 0$ **c)** $(0, -3)$ **d)** $(0, -3)$
e) $(-1.22, 0), (1.22, 0)$

f)

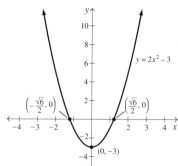

$y = 2x^2 - 3$
$\left(-\frac{\sqrt{6}}{2}, 0\right)$ $\left(\frac{\sqrt{6}}{2}, 0\right)$
$(0, -3)$

g) Domain: $\mathbb{R}$; range: $y \geq -3$

59. a) Upward **b)** $x = -1$ **c)** $(-1, 5)$ **d)** $(0, 6)$
e) No x-intercepts
f)

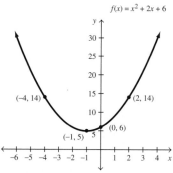

$f(x) = x^2 + 2x + 6$
$(-4, 14)$ $(2, 14)$
$(0, 6)$
$(-1, 5)$

g) Domain: $\mathbb{R}$; range: $y \geq 5$

61. a) Upward **b)** $x = -\frac{5}{2}$ **c)** $(-2.5, -0.25)$ **d)** $(0, 6)$
e) $(-3, 0), (-2, 0)$
f)

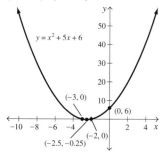

$y = x^2 + 5x + 6$
$(-3, 0)$
$(0, 6)$
$(-2, 0)$
$(-2.5, -0.25)$

g) Domain: $\mathbb{R}$; range: $y \geq -0.25$

63. a) Downward **b)** $x = 2$ **c)** $(2, -2)$ **d)** $(0, -6)$
e) No x-intercepts
f)

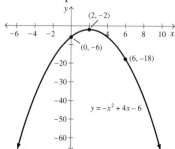

$(2, -2)$
$(0, -6)$
$(6, -18)$
$y = -x^2 + 4x - 6$

g) Domain: $\mathbb{R}$; range: $y \leq -2$

65. a) Downward   **b)** $x = \frac{7}{3}$ **c)** $\left(\frac{7}{3}, \frac{25}{3}\right)$ **d)** $(0, -8)$
  e) $\left(\frac{2}{3}, 0\right), (4, 0)$
  f)

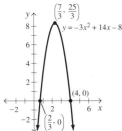

  g) Domain: $\mathbb{R}$; range: $y \le \frac{25}{3}$

67. Domain: $\mathbb{R}$; range: $y > 0$

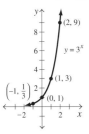

69. Domain: $\mathbb{R}$; range: $y > 0$

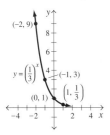

71. Domain: $\mathbb{R}$; range: $y > 1$

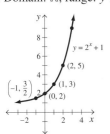

73. Domain: $\mathbb{R}$; range: $y > 1$

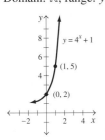

75. Domain: $\mathbb{R}$; range: $y > 0$

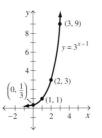

77. Domain: $\mathbb{R}$; range: $y > 0$

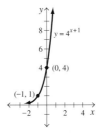

79. $2300

81. a) 52.23%   **b)** 1997   **c)** $x \approx 4.85; \approx 46.67\%$

83. a) 5200 people   **b)** $\approx 14,852$ people

85. a) Yes   **b)** ≈ 6500 scooter injuries

87. a) 23.2 cm   **b)** 55.2 cm   **c)** 69.5 cm

89. a) 170 beats per minute
  b) ≈ 162 beats per minute
  c) ≈ 145 beats per minute
  d) 136 beats per minute
  e) 120 years of age

Review Exercises, Page 376

 1. 21   **2.** -10 **3.** 17   **4.** $\frac{1}{4}$ **5.** -65 **6.** 13
 7. $4x + 1$ **8.** $13x - 8$ **9.** $7x - 3$ **10.** -10
 11. 7   **12.** 11   **13.** -31 **14.** $\frac{128}{5}$ **15.** $\frac{1}{2}$ cup
 16. 250 min, or 4 hr 10 min   **17.** 48   **18.** ≈ 173.1
 19. 101.5   **20.** 10

21. $y = \dfrac{3x - 18}{9}$ or $y = \dfrac{1}{3}x - 2$

22. $y = \dfrac{-2x + 12}{5}$ or $y = -\dfrac{2}{5}x + \dfrac{12}{5}$

23. $y = \dfrac{2x + 22}{3}$ or $y = \dfrac{2}{3}x + \dfrac{22}{3}$

24. $y = \dfrac{-3x + 5z - 4}{4}$ or $y = -\dfrac{3}{4}x + \dfrac{5}{4}z - 1$

25. $w = \dfrac{A}{l}$

26. $w = \dfrac{P - 2l}{2}$

27. $l = \dfrac{L - 2wh}{2h}$ or $l = \dfrac{L}{2h} - w$

28. $d = \dfrac{a_n - a_1}{n - 1}$

29. $8 + 2x$ **30.** $3y - 7$ **31.** $10 + 3r$ **32.** $\dfrac{8}{q} - 11$

33. $4 + 3x = 22; x = 6$ **34.** $3x + 8 = x - 6; x = -7$

35. $5(x - 4) = 45; x = 13$

36. $10x + 14 = 8(x + 12); x = 41$

37. $x + 2x = 15{,}000$; bonds: $5000, mutual funds: $10,000

38. $9.50x + 15{,}000 = 95{,}000; \approx 8421$ chairs

39. $x + 2x + 140 = 1130$; Philadelphia: 330,
San Diego: 800

40. $x + (x + 12{,}000) = 68{,}000$; $28,000 for B and $40,000
for A

41. 6   **42.** 98   **43.** 20   **44.** ≈ 426.7

45. a) 150 lb   **b)** 5 bags   **46.** 4 in.   **47.** $119.88

48. 400 ft

49.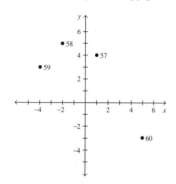

50.

51.

52.

53.

54.

55.

56.

For Exercises 57–60, see the following figure.

61. $D(-3, -1)$; area $= 20$ square units

62. $D(4, 1)$; area $= 21$ square units

63.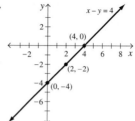

64.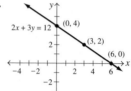

65.

66.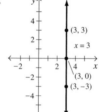

67.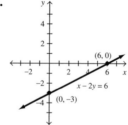

68.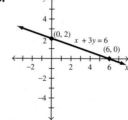

69.

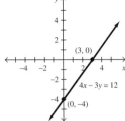

70.

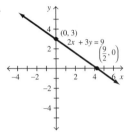

71. $\frac{2}{5}$ **72.** $-\frac{3}{2}$ **73.** $\frac{7}{3}$ **74.** Undefined

75.

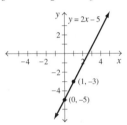

76.

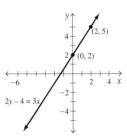

77.

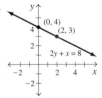

78.

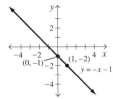

79. $y = 2x + 4$ **80.** $y = -x + 1$

81. a)

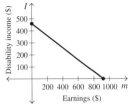

b) About $160   **c)** About $160

82. a)

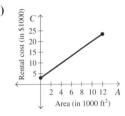

b) About $6400   **c)** About 4120 ft^2

83.

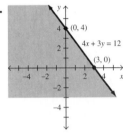

84.

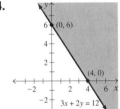

85.

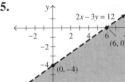

86.

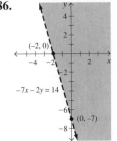

87. $(x + 3)(x + 6)$ **88.** $(x + 5)(x - 4)$
89. $(x - 6)(x - 4)$ **90.** $(x - 5)(x - 4)$

91. $(3x - 1)(2x + 3)$ **92.** $(2x - 1)(x + 7)$

93. $-1, -2$ **94.** $1, 4$ **95.** $\frac{2}{3}, 5$

96. $-2, -\frac{1}{3}$ **97.** $2 \pm \sqrt{5}$ **98.** $1, 2$

99. No real solution   **100.** $-1, \frac{3}{2}$

101. Function, domain: $x = -2, -1, 2, 3$; range: $y = -1, 0, 2$

102. Not a function   **103.** Not a function

104. Function, domain: $\mathbb{R}$; range: $\mathbb{R}$

105. 18   **106.** 13   **107.** 39   **108.** -27

109. a) Downward   **b)** $x = -2$ **c)** $(-2, 25)$ **d)** $(0, 21)$
e) $(-7, 0), (3, 0)$
f)

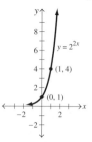

g) Domain: $\mathbb{R}$; range: $y \leq 25$

110. a) Upward   **b)** $x = 2$ **c)** $(2, 2)$ **d)** $(0, 10)$
e) No x-intercepts
f)

g) Domain: $\mathbb{R}$; range: $y \geq 2$

111. Domain: $\mathbb{R}$; range: $y > 0$

112. Domain: $\mathbb{R}$; range: $y > 0$

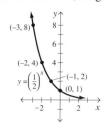

113. 22.8 mpg

114. a) 4208   **b)** 4250

115. $\approx 68.7\%$

Chapter Test, Page 380

1. 3   **2.** $\frac{19}{5}$ **3.** 18   **4.** $2x + 7 = 25$; 9

5. $x + 0.07x = 26{,}750$; $\$25{,}000$ **6.** 84

7. $y = \dfrac{-3x + 11}{5}$ or $y = -\dfrac{3}{5}x + \dfrac{11}{5}$

8. $3\frac{1}{3}$ **9.** 6.75 ft

10.

11. $\frac{7}{10}$

12.

13.

14.

15. $7, -4$ **16.** $\frac{4}{3}, -2$

17. It is a function   **18.** 11

19. a) Upward   **b)** $x = 1$ **c)** $(1, 3)$ **d)** $(0, 4)$
e) No x-intercepts

f)

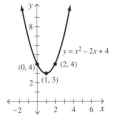

g) Domain: $\mathbb{R}$; range: $y \geq 3$

Chapter 7

Section 7.1, Page 388

1. Two or more linear equations form a system of linear equations.

3. A consistent system of equations is a system that has a solution.

5. An inconsistent system of equations is one that has no solution.

7. The graphs of the equations will be parallel.

9. The graphs of the equations will be the same line.

11. Yes: $(3, 0)$; no: $(2, -2)$, $(1, 2)$

13.

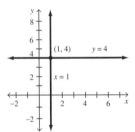

15.

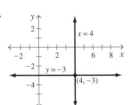

17.

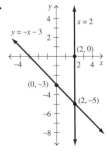

19.

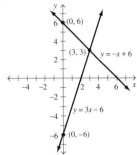

21.

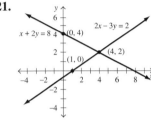

23.

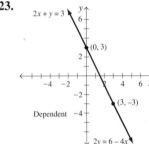

25.

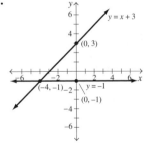

27.

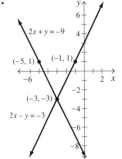

29.

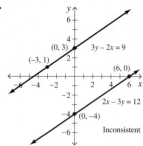

31.

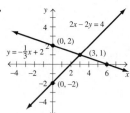

33. a) One unique solution; the lines intersect at one and only one point.
  b) No solution; the lines do not intersect.
  c) Infinitely many solutions; the lines coincide.

35. An infinite number of solutions   **37.** One solution

39. No solution   **41.** An infinite number of solutions

43. No solution   **45.** One solution

47. Not perpendicular   **49.** Perpendicular

51. a) Tom's Tree and Landscape: $C = 60h + 200$
  Lawn Perfect: $C = 25h + 305$

  b)

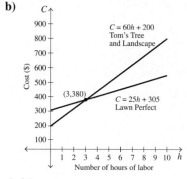

  c) 3 hours

53. a) $C = 15x + 400$
  $R = 25x$

  b)

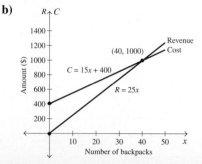

c) 40 backpacks   **d)** $P = 10x - 400$
e) Loss of $100   **f)** 140 backpacks

55. a) $C = 155x + 8400, R = 225x$

  b)

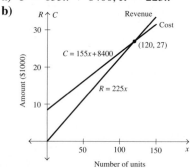

c) 120 units   **d)** $P = 70x - 8400$
e) Loss of $1400   **f)** 138 units

57. a) Job 1: $s = 0.15x + 300$
  Job 2: $s = 450$

  b)

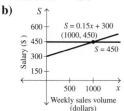

c) $1000 sales volume

59. a) One   **b)** Three   **c)** Six   **d)** Ten
  e) To find the number of points of intersection for n lines, add $n - 1$ to the number of points of intersection for $n - 1$ lines. For example, for 5 lines there were 10 points of intersection. Therefore, for 6 lines $(n = 6)$ there are $10 + (6 - 1) = 15$ points of intersection.

Section 7.2, Page 399

1. Answers will vary.

3. The system is dependent if the same value is obtained on both sides of the equal sign.

5. x, in the first equation   **7.** $(-1, 6)$ **9.** $(0, 2)$

11. No solution; inconsistent system   **13.** $\left(-2, \frac{8}{3}\right)$

15. An infinite number of solutions; dependent system

17. $(-3, -6)$ **19.** $\left(\frac{11}{5}, -\frac{13}{5}\right)$ **21.** $\left(-\frac{1}{5}, -\frac{8}{5}\right)$

23. No solution; inconsistent system

25. $(2, 4)$ **27.** $(6, 4)$ **29.** $(-2, 0)$ **31.** $(-4, 5)$

33. $(3, 5)$ **35.** $(1, -2)$

37. No solution; inconsistent system   **39.** $(2, -1)$

41. $s = 12,000 + 0.15p$
  $s = 27,000 + 0.05p$
  $150,000 annual profit

43. $m + l = 50$
$10.95m + 14.95l = 663.50$
21 medium, 29 large

45. $x + y = 10$
$0.25x + 0.50y = 0.40(10)$
4ℓ of 25%, 6ℓ of 50%

47. $y = 18 + 0.02x$
$y = 24 + 0.015x$
1200 copies

49. $x + y = 20$
$3x + y = 30$
Mix 5 lb of nuts with 15 lb of pretzels.

51. $x + y = 250$
$2x + 5y = 950$
100 student tickets and 150 nonstudent tickets

53. ≈ 26.7 years after 1981 or in 2007

55. $\left(\frac{1}{2}, \frac{1}{3}\right)$ **57.–59.** Answers will vary.

Section 7.3, page 408

1. A matrix is a rectangular array of elements.

3. A square matrix contains the same number of rows and columns.

5. 2   **7. a)** Answers will vary.   **b)** $\begin{bmatrix} 4 & 9 & -7 \\ 2 & 4 & 9 \end{bmatrix}$

9. a) The number of columns of the first matrix must be the same as the number of rows of the second matrix.
b) 2×3

11. a) $I = \begin{bmatrix} 1 & 0 \\ 0 & 1 \end{bmatrix}$ **b)** $I = \begin{bmatrix} 1 & 0 & 0 \\ 0 & 1 & 0 \\ 0 & 0 & 1 \end{bmatrix}$

13. $\begin{bmatrix} -4 & 2 \\ 12 & 9 \end{bmatrix}$ **15.** $\begin{bmatrix} 0 & 4 \\ 4 & 4 \\ 5 & -1 \end{bmatrix}$

17. $\begin{bmatrix} 6 & -7 \\ -12 & 4 \end{bmatrix}$ **19.** $\begin{bmatrix} 2 & 11 \\ 16 & 13 \\ -2 & 2 \end{bmatrix}$

21. $\begin{bmatrix} 6 & 4 \\ 10 & 0 \end{bmatrix}$ **23.** $\begin{bmatrix} 0 & 13 \\ 22 & 0 \end{bmatrix}$

25. $\begin{bmatrix} 13 & 0 \\ 7 & 0 \end{bmatrix}$ **27.** $\begin{bmatrix} 4 & 12 \\ 14 & 22 \end{bmatrix}$

29. $\begin{bmatrix} 15 \\ 22 \end{bmatrix}$ **31.** $\begin{bmatrix} 4 & 7 & 6 \\ -2 & 3 & 1 \\ 5 & 1 & 2 \end{bmatrix}$

33. $A + B = \begin{bmatrix} 6 & 2 & 1 \\ 6 & -2 & 4 \end{bmatrix}$; cannot be multiplied

35. Cannot be added; $A \times B = \begin{bmatrix} 26 & 38 \\ 24 & 24 \end{bmatrix}$

37. Cannot be added; $\begin{bmatrix} 1 \\ -1 \end{bmatrix}$

39. $A + B = B + A = \begin{bmatrix} 5 & 7 \\ 8 & 4 \end{bmatrix}$

41. $A + B = B + A = \begin{bmatrix} 8 & 0 \\ 6 & -8 \end{bmatrix}$

43. $(A + B) + C = A + (B + C) = \begin{bmatrix} 7 & 10 \\ 6 & 13 \end{bmatrix}$

45. $(A + B) + C = A + (B + C) = \begin{bmatrix} 5 & 5 \\ 7 & -37 \end{bmatrix}$

47. No   **49.** No   **51.** Yes

53. $(A \times B) \times C = A \times (B \times C) = \begin{bmatrix} 41 & 13 \\ 56 & 16 \end{bmatrix}$

55. $(A \times B) \times C = A \times (B \times C) = \begin{bmatrix} 16 & -10 \\ -24 & 2 \end{bmatrix}$

57. $(A \times B) \times C = A \times (B \times C) = \begin{bmatrix} 17 & 0 \\ -7 & 0 \end{bmatrix}$

59. Large Small   **61.** [$36.04 $47.52]
$\begin{bmatrix} 38 & 50 \\ 56 & 72 \\ 17 & 26 \\ 10 & 14 \end{bmatrix}$

63. Answers will vary.   **65.** Yes   **67.** False

69. a) $28.70   **b)** $60.10   **c)** $\begin{bmatrix} 28.7 & 24.6 \\ 41.3 & 35.7 \\ 69.3 & 60.1 \end{bmatrix}$

71. Yes. Answers will vary. One example is

$$A = \begin{bmatrix} 2 & 7 & 6 \\ -3 & 0 & 8 \end{bmatrix}, \quad B = \begin{bmatrix} 1 & 2 \\ 3 & 4 \\ 5 & 6 \end{bmatrix}.$$

Section 7.4, Page 417

1. a) An augmented matrix is a matrix formed with the coefficients of the variables and the constants. The coefficients of the variables are separated from the constants by a vertical bar.
b) $\left[\begin{array}{cc|c} 1 & 3 & 7 \\ 2 & -1 & 4 \end{array}\right]$

3. If you obtain an augmented matrix in which one row of numbers on the left side of the vertical line are all zeroes but a zero does not appear in the same row on the right side of the vertical line, the system is inconsistent.

5. Change the -2 to a 1 by multiplying the numbers in the second row by $-\frac{1}{2}$.

7. $(3, 0)$ **9.** $(3, 2)$

11. An infinite number of solutions; dependent system

13. $\left(\frac{7}{2}, -1\right)$ **15.** $\left(\frac{1}{2}, -6\right)$

17. No solution; inconsistent system   **19.** (3, 5)

21. 20 small flags and 35 large flags

23. Truck driver: $7\frac{1}{9}$ hours; laborer: $9\frac{1}{9}$ hours

25. Nonrefillable pencils: 125; refillable pencils: 75

Section 7.5, Page 420

1. The solution set of a system of linear inequalities is the set of points that satisfy all inequalities in the system.

3.

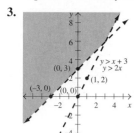

$y > x + 3$
$y > 2x$

5.

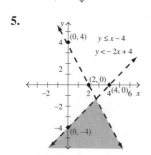

$y \leq x - 4$
$y < -2x + 4$

7.

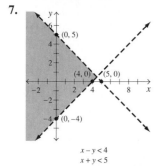

$x - y < 4$
$x + y < 5$

9.

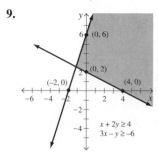

$x + 2y \geq 4$
$3x - y \geq -6$

11.

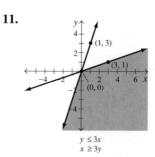

$y \leq 3x$
$x \geq 3y$

13.

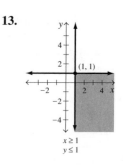

$x \geq 1$
$y \leq 1$

15.

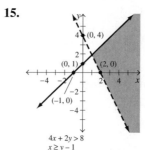

$4x + 2y > 8$
$x \geq y - 1$

17.

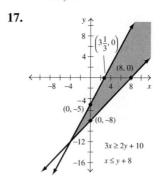

$3x \geq 2y + 10$
$x \leq y + 8$

19. a) $P \geq 2S$, $P \geq 10$, $S \geq 5$, $600P + 900S \leq 18,000$

b)

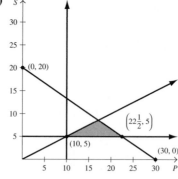

c) One example is (15, 6); $14,400 of inventory cost

21. a) No   **b)** One example: $x + y > 4$
$$x + y < 1$$

23. No, every line divides the plane into two half planes, only one of which can be part of the solution.

25. Answers will vary.

Section 7.6, Page 426

1. Constraints are restrictions that are represented as linear inequalities.

3. Vertices   **5.** Answers will vary.

7. Maximum is 30 at (5, 0), minimum is 0 at (0, 0).

9. a)

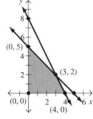

b) Maximum is 23 at (3, 2), minimum is 0 at (0, 0).

11. a)

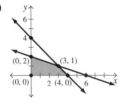

b) Maximum is 28 at (4, 0), minimum is 0 at (0, 0).

13. a)

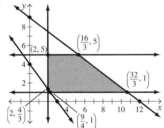

b) Maximum is ≈ 25.12 at $\left(\frac{32}{3}, 1\right)$, minimum is 6.6 at $\left(\frac{9}{4}, 1\right)$ or $\left(2, \frac{4}{3}\right)$.

15. a) $x + y \leq 24,\ x \geq 2y,\ y \geq 4,\ x \geq 0,\ y \geq 0$
b) $P = 0.35x + 0.50y$
c)

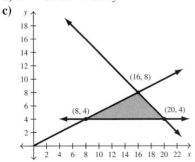

d) (8, 4), (16, 8), (20, 4)
e) 16 rolls of Kodak and 8 rolls of Fuji
f) \$9.60

17. a) $3x + 4y \geq 60,\ 10x + 5y \geq 100,\ x \geq 0,\ y \geq 0$
b) $C = 28x + 33y$
c)

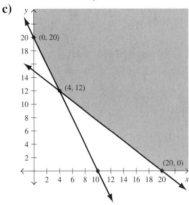

d) (0, 20), (4, 12), (20, 0)
e) 4 hours for Machine I and 12 hours for Machine II
f) \$508

19. Three car seats and seven strollers, \$320

Review Exercises, Page 428

1.

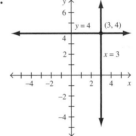

2.

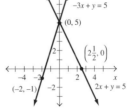

3.

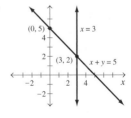

4.

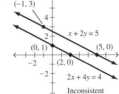

Inconsistent

5. An infinite number of solutions   **6.** No solution

7. One solution   **8.** One solution   **9.** $(-9, 3)$

10. $(-1, -5)$ **11.** $(-2, -8)$

12. No solution; inconsistent   **13.** $(3, 1)$ **14.** $(-7, 16)$

15. $(4, -2)$ **16.** An infinite number of solutions; dependent

17. $(30, -15)$ **18.** $(2, 0)$

19. $\begin{bmatrix} -1 & -8 \\ 8 & 7 \end{bmatrix}$ **20.** $\begin{bmatrix} 3 & 2 \\ -4 & 1 \end{bmatrix}$

21. $\begin{bmatrix} 2 & -6 \\ 4 & 8 \end{bmatrix}$ **22.** $\begin{bmatrix} 8 & 9 \\ -14 & -1 \end{bmatrix}$

23. $\begin{bmatrix} -20 & -14 \\ 20 & 2 \end{bmatrix}$ **24.** $\begin{bmatrix} -12 & -14 \\ 12 & -6 \end{bmatrix}$

25. $(2, 2)$ **26.** $(-2, 2)$ **27.** $(3, -3)$

28. $(1, 0)$ **29.** $\left(\frac{12}{11}, \frac{7}{11}\right)$ **30.** $(1, 2)$

31. $350,000 at 8%, $250,000 at 10%

32. Mix $83\frac{1}{3}\ell$ of 80% acid solution with $16\frac{2}{3}\ell$ of 50% acid solution.

33. $500 salary, 4% commission rate

34. a) 32.5 months   **b)** Model 6070B

35. a) 3 hr   **b)** All-Day parking lot

36.

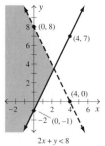

$y \le 3x - 1$
$y > -2x + 1$

37.

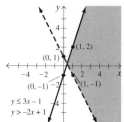

$2x + y < 8$
$y \ge 2x - 1$

38.

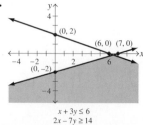

$x + 3y \le 6$
$2x - 7y \ge 14$

39.

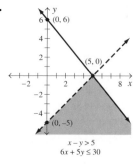

$x - y > 5$
$6x + 5y \le 30$

40. The maximum is 54 at $(9, 0)$.

Chapter Test, Page 429

1. If the lines do not intersect (are parallel) the system of equations is inconsistent. The system of equations is consistent if the lines intersect. If both equations represent the same line, then the system of equations is dependent.

2.

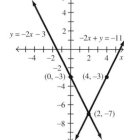

$y = -2x - 3$
$-2x + y = -11$

3. One solution   **4.** $(2, -3)$ **5.** $(-2, -3)$

6. $(3, -1)$ **7.** $(-1, 3)$ **8.** $(2, 0)$

9. $(-2, 2)$ **10.** $\begin{bmatrix} 1 & -8 \\ 6 & 5 \end{bmatrix}$

11. $\begin{bmatrix} 7 & -12 \\ -2 & 7 \end{bmatrix}$ **12.** $\begin{bmatrix} -27 & -16 \\ 14 & 3 \end{bmatrix}$

13.

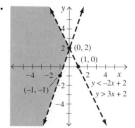

$y < -2x + 2$
$y > 3x + 2$

14. 20 lb at $7.50, 10 lb at $6.00

15. a) 40 checks   **b)** Citrus Bank

16. a)

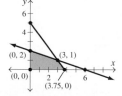

b) Maximum is 18.75 at $(3.75, 0)$, minimum is 0 at $(0, 0)$.

Chapter 8

Section 8.1, Page 437

1. The metric system

3. It is the standard of measurement accepted worldwide. There is only one basic unit of measurement for each quantity. It is based on the number 10, which makes many calculations easier than the U.S. customary system.

5. a) Answers will vary. b) 0.007 146 km
   c) 30 800 dm

7. Answers will vary.

9. a) 100 times greater b) 100 dm c) 0.01 dam

11. 2   13. 5   15. 22   17. (d)   19. (c)   21. (f)

23. a) 10 b) $\dfrac{1}{100}$ c) $\dfrac{1}{1000}$ d) $\dfrac{1}{10}$ e) 1000 f) 100

25. mg; $\dfrac{1}{1000}$ g   27. dg; $\dfrac{1}{10}$ g   29. hg; 100 g

31. 320 000 g   33. 200   35. 9.5   37. 0.024 26

39. 0.040 36   41. 13 400   43. 92 500 g

45. 895 000 mℓ 47. 0.024 hg   49. 4.0302 daℓ

51. 590 cm, 5.1 dam, 0.47 km

53. 2.2 kg, 2400 g, 24 300 dg

55. 203 000 mm, 2.6 km, 52.6 hm

57. Jim, 1 m > 1 yd

59. The pump that removes 1 daℓ per minute

61. a) 346 cm b) 3460 mm

63. a) 108 m b) 0.108 km c) 108 000 mm   65. 3.2 km

67. a) 2160 mℓ b) 2.16 ℓ c) $1.13 per liter

69. a) 6900 g b) 23 000 dg   71. 1000

73. 1×10^{24} = 1 000 000 000 000 000 000 000 000

75. $\approx$ 30 eggs   77. $\approx$ 4.1 cups   79. 5 dam   81. 6 mg

83. 2 daℓ 85. gram   86. decigram   87. liter

88. dekaliter   89. meter   90. milliliter   91. kilometer

92. centimeter   93. degrees celsius   94. hectogram

Section 8.2, Page 446

1. Volume   3. Area   5. Volume   7. Volume   9. Area

11. Length   13.–17. Answers will vary.

19. A cubic decimeter   21. A cubic centimeter   23. Area

25. Centimeters   27. Centimeters or millimeters

29. Centimeters   31. Millimeters

33. Centimeters or millimeters   35. Kilometers

37. (c)   39. (c)   41. (a)   43. (b)

45.–49. Answers will vary.   51. centimeter, kilometer

53. meter   55. a centimeter   57. Square centimeters

59. Square meters   61. Square meters or hectares

63. Square centimeters or square millimeters

65. Square kilometers or hectares

67. (b)   69. (a)   71. (c)   73. (c)

75.–79. Answers will vary.   81. Kiloliters

83. Milliliters   85. Liters   87. Cubic meters

89. Liters or milliliters   91. (c)   93. (c)   95. (a)

97. (a)   99. b) 152 561 cm^3 101. $\approx$ 0.20 m^3

103. Longer side = 4 cm, shorter side = 2.2 cm, area = 8.8 cm^2

105. 2984 cm^2 107. a) 5.25 km^2 b) 525 ha

109. a) 450 m^3 b) 450 kℓ

111. a) 56 000 cm^3 b) 56 000 mℓ c) 56 ℓ

113. 100 times larger   115. 1000 times larger

117. 1 000 000   119. 100   121. 0.001   123. 1 000 000

125. 435   127. 76   129. 600 000 dℓ

131. Answers will vary.   133. 6700

135. a) 4,014,489,600 sq in. b) Answers will vary.

137. Answers will vary.

138. a) 100 cm longer b) 3 times longer

139. a) Answers will vary. The average use is 5150.7 ℓ/day.
   b) Answers will vary. The average use is 493.2 ℓ/day.

Section 8.3, Page 455

1. Kilogram   3. 2   5.–7. Answers will vary.

9. Grams   11. Grams   13. Grams   15. Kilograms

17. Grams   19. (b)   21. (b)   23. (b)

25.–27. Answers will vary.   29. (c)   31. (b)   33. (b)

35. (c)   37. (b)   39. 86°F   41. $\approx$ 33.3°C   43. $\approx$ 82.2°C

45. 98.6°F   47. $\approx$ −10.6°C   49. 113°F   51. $\approx$ −28.9°C

53. 71.6°F   55. 95.18°F   57. 64.04°F–74.30°F

59. $4.34   61. 444 g

63. a) 2304 m^3 b) 2304 kℓ c) 2304 t

65. Yes: 78°F is about 25.6°C.   67. 0.0042

69. 17 400 000 g   71. a) 1200 g b) 1200 cm^3

73. a) 5.625 ft^3 b) $\approx$351.6 lb c) $\approx$ 42.4 gal   74. 1500 g

75. a) −79.8°F b) 36.5°F c) 510 000 000°C

Section 8.4, Page 465

1. Dimensional analysis is a procedure used to convert from one unit of measurement to a different unit of measurement.

3. $\dfrac{60 \text{ seconds}}{1 \text{ minute}}$ or $\dfrac{1 \text{ minute}}{60 \text{ seconds}}$ 5. $\dfrac{1 \text{ ft}}{30 \text{ cm}}$ 7. $\dfrac{3.8 \ell}{1 \text{ gal}}$

9. 132.08 cm   11. 1.26 m   13. 12 m^2 15. 62.4 km

17. 1687.5 acres   19. $\approx$ 33.19 pints   21. 1.52 fl oz

23. 54 kg   25. 28 grams   27. 0.45 kilogram

29. 2.54 centimeters, 1.6 kilometers   31. 9 meters

33. ≈ 561.11 yd   **35.** ≈ 1146.67 ft   **37.** ≈ 53.13 mph
39. 43.2 m²   **41.** ≈ 14.29 oz   **43.** 240 mℓ   **45.** 360 m³
47. $0.495 per pound   **49.** ≈ 9078.95 gal
51. a) ≈ 50.91 kg   **b)** ≈ 113.13 lb
53. a) −8460 cm   **b)** −84.6 m
55. a) 10.89 ft²   **b)** 35.937 ft³   **57.** 25.2 mg
59. 6840 mg, or 6.84 g   **61. a)** 25 mg   **b)** 900 mg
63. a) 289.2 m   **b)** 76 500 t   **c)** 44.8 kph
65. a) ≈ 41.1 yd   **b)** 231,337.5 mi
   c) 27.5 mi   **d)** 2300°F
   e) 209.375 mph   **f)** 65,520 lb
   g) 5 yd × 20 yd   **h)** ≈ 45,104.21 gal/min
   i) ≈ 16,733.68 gal/min   **j)** 52.1 yd
   k) ≈ 9.33 yd   **l)** 1,406,160 lb
   m) 235,871.11 lb   **n)** −419.8°F
67. 7.8 lb   **69.** A meter   **70.** A kilogram   **71.** A hectare
72. A liter   **73.** A tonne   **74.** A decimeter   **75.** wonton
76. 1 microscope   **77.** 1 kilohurtz   **78.** 1 pound cake
79. 1 megaphone   **80.** 2 megacycles   **81.** 2 kilomockingbird
82. 1 decacards   **83.** 1 decoration   **84.** 1 microfiche

Review Exercises, Page 469

1. $\frac{1}{100}$ of base unit   **2.** 1000 × base unit

3. $\frac{1}{1000}$ of base unit   **4.** 100 × base unit

5. 10 times base unit   **6.** $\frac{1}{10}$ of base unit   **7.** 0.20 g

8. 320 cℓ   **9.** 0.004 mm   **10.** 1 kg   **11.** 4620 ℓ
12. 19 260 dg   **13.** 3000 mℓ, 14 630 cℓ, 2.67 kℓ
14. 0.047 km, 47 000 cm, 4700 m   **15.** Centimeters
16. Grams   **17.** Degrees Celsius
18. Millimeters or centimeters   **19.** Square meters
20. Milliliters or cubic centimeters   **21.** Millimeters
22. Kilograms or tonnes   **23.** Kilometers
24. Meters or centimeters   **25. a) and b)** Answers will vary.
26. a) and b) Answers will vary.   **27.** (c)   **28.** (b)   **29.** (c)
30. (a)   **31.** (a)   **32.** (b)   **33.** 2.5 t   **34.** 6 300 000 g
35. 64.4°F   **36.** 20°C   **37.** ≈ −21.1°C   **38.** 102.2°F
39. $l = 4$ cm, $w = 1.6$ cm, $A = 6.4$ cm²
40. $r = 1.5$ cm, $A ≈ 7.07$ cm²
41. a) 80 m³   **b)** 80 000 kg
42. a) 660 m²   **b)** 0.000 66 km²
43. a) 96 000 cm³   **b)** 0.096 m³
   c) 96 000 mℓ   **d)** 0.096 kℓ
44. 10,000 times larger   **45.** ≈ 7.87 in.   **46.** ≈ 233.33 lb
47. 74.7 m   **48.** ≈ 111.11 yd   **49.** 72 kph   **50.** ≈ 42.11 qt

51. 57 ℓ   **52.** ≈ 52.63 yd³   **53.** ≈ 12.77 in.²   **54.** 3.8 ℓ
55. 11.4 m³   **56.** 99.2 km   **57.** 0.9 ft   **58.** 82.55 mm
59. a) 1050 kg   **b)** ≈ 2333.33 lb   **60.** 32.4 m²
61. a) 190 kℓ   **b)** 190 000 kg
62. a) 56 kph   **b)** 56 000 meters per hour
63. a) 252 ℓ   **b)** 252 kg
64. $1.58 per pound

Chapter Test, Page 471

1. 0.204 daℓ   **2.** 123 000 000 mm   **3.** 100 times greater
4. 2.4 km   **5.** (b)   **6.** (a)   **7.** (c)   **8.** (c)   **9.** (b)
10. 10,000 times greater   **11.** 1,000,000,000 times greater
12. 1148.08 cm   **13.** ≈ 166.67 yd   **14.** ≈ −23.33°C
15. 68°F
16. 360 cm or 365.76 cm, depending on which conversion factor you used
17. a) 3200 m³   **b)** 3 200 000 ℓ (or 3200 kℓ)
   c) 3 200 000 kg
18. $245

Chapter 9

Section 9.1, Page 482

1. a) Undefined terms, definitions, postulates (axioms), and theorems
   b) First, Euclid introduced undefined terms. Second, he introduced certain definitions. Third, he stated primitive propositions called postulates about the undefined terms and definitions. Fourth, he proved, using deductive reasoning, other propositions called theorems.
3. Two lines in the same plane that do not intersect are parallel lines.
5. Two angles in the same plane are adjacent angles when they have a common vertex and a common side but no common interior points.
7. Two angles the sum of whose measure is 90° are called complementary angles.
9. An angle whose measure is greater than 90° but less than 180° is an obtuse angle.
11. An angle whose measure is 90° is a right angle.
13. Half line, $\overrightarrow{AB}$ **15.** Line segment, $\overline{AB}$ **17.** Line, $\overleftrightarrow{AB}$
19. Open line segment, $\overset{\circ\circ}{AB}$ **21.** $\overline{BD}$ **23.** $\overrightarrow{BD}$
25. {B, F}   **27.** {C}   **29.** $\overline{BC}$ **31.** $\overrightarrow{BC}$ **33.** ∅
35. $\overline{BC}$ **37.** $\angle ABE$ **39.** $\angle EBC$ **41.** $\overleftrightarrow{AC}$ **43.** $\overrightarrow{BE}$
45. Obtuse   **47.** Straight   **49.** Right   **51.** None of these
53. 71°   **55.** $57\frac{1}{4}°$ **57.** 25.3°   **59.** 89°   **61.** 159.5°
63. $136\frac{2}{7}°$ **65.** (d)   **67.** (c)   **69.** (e)

71. $m\angle 1 = 47°$, $m\angle 2 = 43°$

73. 134° and 46°

75. Angles 3, 4, and 7 each measure 125°; angles 1, 2, 5, and 6 each measure 55°.

77. Angles 2, 5, and 6 each measure 25°; angles 1, 3, 4, and 7 each measure 155°.

79. $m\angle 1 = 70°$, $m\angle 2 = 20°$

81. $m\angle 1 = 33°$, $m\angle 2 = 57°$

83. $m\angle 1 = 115°$, $m\angle 2 = 65°$

85. $m\angle 1 = 29°$, $m\angle 2 = 151°$

87. a) An infinite number **b)** An infinite number

89. An infinite number

For Exercises 91–97, the answers given are one of many possible answers.

91. Plane ABG and plane JCD

93. $\overrightarrow{BG}$ and $\overrightarrow{DG}$

95. Plane AGB ∩ plane ABC ∩ plane $BCD = \{B\}$

97. $\overleftrightarrow{BC}$ ∩ plane $ABG = \{B\}$

99. Always true. If any two lines are parallel to a third line, then they must be parallel to each other.

101. Sometimes true. Vertical angles are only complementary when each is equal to 45°.

103. Sometimes true. Alternate interior angles are only complementary when each is equal to 45°.

105. No. Line m and line n may intersect.

107.

109. a)

Other answers are possible.

b) 30° **c)** 60° **d)** 90°

Section 9.2, Page 491

1. A polygon is a closed figure in a plane determined by three or more straight line segments.

3. The different types of triangles are acute, obtuse, right, isosceles, equilateral, and scalene. Descriptions will vary.

5. If the corresponding sides of two similar figures are the same length, the figures are congruent figures.

7. a) Rectangle **b)** Not regular

9. a) Hexagon **b)** Regular

11. a) Rhombus **b)** Not regular

13. a) Octagon **b)** Not regular

15. a) Scalene **b)** Right

17. a) Isosceles **b)** Obtuse

19. a) Equilateral **b)** Acute

21. a) Scalene **b)** Obtuse

23. Parallelogram **25.** Rhombus **27.** Trapezoid

29. 17° **31.** 150°

33. $m\angle 1 = 50°$, $m\angle 2 = 63°$, $m\angle 3 = 67°$, $m\angle 4 = 67°$, $m\angle 5 = 50°$, $m\angle 6 = 113°$, $m\angle 7 = 50°$, $m\angle 8 = 130°$, $m\angle 9 = 67°$, $m\angle 10 = 113°$, $m\angle 11 = 130°$, $m\angle 12 = 50°$

35. 540° **37.** 720° **39.** 3240° **41. a)** 60° **b)** 120°

43. a) 135° **b)** 45° **45. a)** 150° **b)** 30°

47. $x = 6$, $y = \frac{16}{5}$ **49.** $x = \frac{12}{5}$, $y = \frac{15}{2}$

51. $x = 1.2$, $y = 0.625$ **53.** 6 **55.** $\frac{20}{3}$ **57.** 14 **59.** 28

61. 28° **63.** 8 **65.** 16 **67.** 70° **69.** 55° **71.** 35°

73. 70 ft **75. a)** 246.25 mi **b)** 270.875 mi

77. $\overline{D'E'} = 4$, $\overline{E'F'} = 5$, $\overline{D'F'} = 3$

79. a) $m\angle HMF = m\angle TMB$, $m\angle HFM = m\angle TBM$, $m\angle MHF = m\angle MTB$

  b) 44 ft

Section 9.3, Page 503

Throughout this section, we used the π key on a scientific calculator to determine answers in calculations involving π. If you use 3.14 for π, your answers may vary slightly.

1. a) Answers will vary.

  b) Answers will vary.

  c)

The area of this rectangle is 12 square units. The perimeter of this rectangle is 16 units.

3. a) To determine the number of square inches, multiply the number of square feet by 144.

  b) To determine the number of square feet, divide the number of square inches by 144.

5. 35 in.² **7.** 17.5 cm²

9. Area = 105 ft²; perimeter = 44 ft

11. Area = 6000 cm²; perimeter = 654 cm

13. Area = 288 in.²; perimeter = 74 in.

15. ≈ 153.94 in.², 43.98 in.

17. ≈ 63.62 ft², 28.27 ft

19. a) 9 in.   **b)** 36 in.   **c)** 54 in.²

21. a) 26 cm   **b)** 60 cm   **c)** 120 cm²

23. ≈ 21.99 cm²   **25.** 8 in.²   **27.** ≈ 65.73 in.²

29. ≈ 114.90 ft²   **31.** ≈ 41.20 in.²   **33.** ≈ 11.89 yd²

35. 132.3 ft²   **37.** 234,000 cm²   **39.** 0.1075 m²

41. a) $3239.50   **b)** $4889.50   **43.** $1700   **45.** $2908.80

47. $38.93   **49. a)** 177.1 m²   **b)** 0.01771 hectare

51. ≈ 103.94 ft   **53.** 40 ft

55. a) $A = s^2$ **b)** $A = 4s^2$ **c)** Four times larger

57. 24 cm²   **59.** Answers will vary.

Section 9.4, Page 515

Throughout this section, we used the π key on a scientific calculator to determine answers in calculations involving π. If you use 3.14 for π, your answers may vary slightly.

1. Volume is a measure of the capacity of a figure.

3. A polyhedron is a closed surface formed by the union of polygonal regions. A regular polyhedron is one whose faces are all regular polygons of the same size and shape.

5. Answers will vary.   **7.** 27 ft³   **9.** 150.80 in.³

11. 131.95 cm³   **13.** 2400 in.³   **15.** 381.70 cm³

17. 524.33 cm³   **19.** 106.67 in.³   **21.** 59.43 m³

23. 30.49 ft³   **25.** 31.42 m³   **27.** 24 ft³   **29.** 189 ft³

31. ≈ 5.67 yd³   **33.** 5,900,000 cm³   **35.** 3 m³

37. a) 28,750 in.³   **b)** ≈ 16.64 ft³   **39.** ≈ 2.50 qt

41. a) The container with the larger diameter holds more.
   b) ≈ 188.50 in.³

43. 82,944,000 ft³   **45.** ≈ 283.04 in.³

47. a) ≈ 323.98 in.³   **b)** ≈ 0.19 ft³

49. a) Round pan base ≈ 63.62 in.²; rectangular pan base = 63 in.²
   b) Round pan volume ≈ 127.24 in.³; rectangular pan volume = 126 in.³
   c) Round pan

51. a) 4320 in.³   **b)** 2.5 ft³   **53.** Nine edges

55. Six vertices   **57.** Fourteen edges   **59.** ≈ 21.46%

61. a)–e) Answers will vary.
   f) If we double the radius of a sphere, the new volume will be eight times the original volume.

63. a) Answers will vary.
   b) $V_1 = a^3$; $V_2 = a^2b$; $V_3 = a^2b$; $V_4 = ab^2$; $V_5 = a^2b$; $V_6 = ab^2$; $V_7 = b^3$
   c) ab^2

64. a) 330 in.³   **b)** ≈ 300.84 in.³

Section 9.5, Page 532

1. The act of moving a geometric figure from some starting position to some ending position without altering its shape

or size is called rigid motion. The four main rigid motions studied in this section are reflections, translations, rotations, and glide reflections.

3. A reflection is a rigid motion that moves a figure to a new position that is a mirror image of the figure in the starting position.

5. A translation is a rigid motion that moves a figure by sliding it along a straight line segment in the plane.

7. A rotation is a rigid motion performed by rotating a figure in the plane about a specific point.

9. A glide reflection is a rigid motion formed by performing a translation (or glide) followed by a reflection.

11. A geometric figure is said to have reflective symmetry if the positions of a figure before and after a reflection are identical (except for vertex labels).

13. A tessellation is a pattern consisting of the repeated use of the same geometric figures to entirely cover a plane, leaving no gaps.

This figure contains the answers for Exercises 15 and 16.

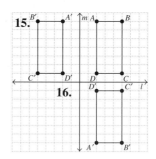

This figure contains the answers for Exercises 17 and 18.

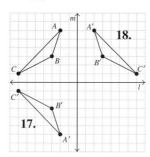

This figure contains the answers for Exercises 19 and 20.

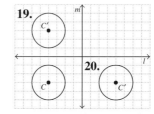

This figure contains the answers for Exercises 21 and 22.

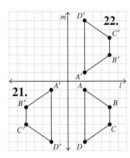

This figure contains the answers to Exercises 23 and 24.

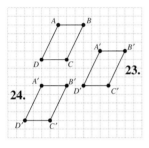

This figure contains the answers to Exercises 25 and 26.

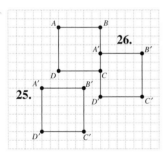

This figure contains the answers to Exercises 27 and 28.

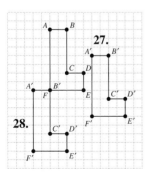

29.

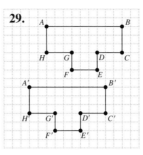

This figure contains the answers to Exercises 31 and 32.

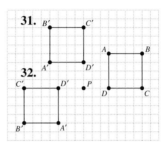

This figure contains the answers to Exercises 33 and 34.

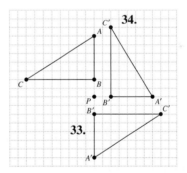

This figure contains the answers to Exercises 35 and 36.

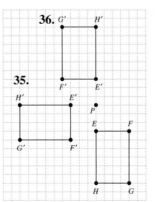

This figure contains the answers to Exercises 37 and 38.

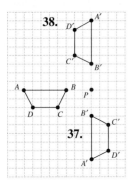

This figure contains the answers to Exercises 39 and 40.

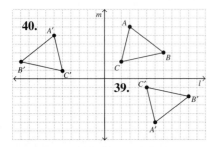

This figure contains the answers to Exercises 41 and 42.

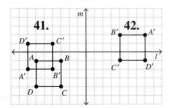

This figure contains the answers to Exercises 43 and 44.

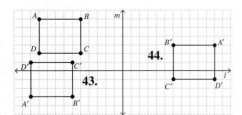

This figure contains the answers to Exercises 45 and 46.

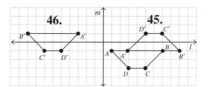

47. a)

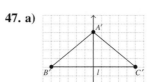

b) Yes
c) Yes

49. a)

b) No
c) No

51. a)

b) No
c) No
d)

e) Yes
f) Yes

53. a)–c)

d) No. Any 90° rotation will result in the figure being in a different position than the starting position.

55. a)–b)

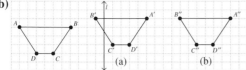

c) No.

d) The order in which the translation and the reflection are performed is important. The figure obtained in part (a) is the glide reflection.

57. Answers will vary.

59. a) Answers will vary.

b) A regular pentagon cannot be used as a tessellating shape.

60. Although answers will vary depending on the font, the following capital letters have reflective symmetry about a horizontal line drawn through the center of the letter: B, C, D, E, H, I, K, O, X.

61. Although answers will vary depending on the font, the following capital letters have reflective symmetry about a vertical line drawn through the center of the letter: A, H, I, M, O, T, U, V, W, X, Y.

62. Although answers will vary depending on the font, the following capital letters have 180° rotational symmetry about a point in the center of the letter: H, I, O, S, X, Z.

Section 9.6, Page 542

1. Topology is sometimes referred to as "rubber sheet geometry" because it deals with bending and stretching of geometric figures.

3. Take a strip of paper, give one end a half twist, and tape the ends together.

5. Four

7. A Jordan curve is a topological object that can be thought of as a circle twisted out of shape.

9. The number of holes in the object determines the genus of an object.

11.–19. Answers will vary.   **21.** Outside   **23.** Outside

25. Outside   **27.** Inside   **29.** 1   **31.** 1   **33.** Larger than 5

35. 5   **37.** 0   **39.** 5   **41. a)–d)** Answers will vary.

43. One   **45.** Two

47. The smaller one is a Möbius strip; the larger one is not.

49. Yes. "Both sides" of the belt experience wear.

51. Answers will vary.

53. a) 1   **b)** 1   **c)** Answers will vary.

Section 9.7, Page 552

1.–5. Answers will vary.

7. a) *Euclidean:* Given a line and a point not on the line, one and only one line can be drawn parallel to the given line through the given point.

b) *Elliptical:* Given a line and a point not on the line, no line can be drawn through the given point parallel to the given line.

c) *Hyperbolic:* Given a line and a point not on the line, two or more lines can be drawn through the given point parallel to the given line.

9. A plane   **11.** A pseudosphere

13. Spherical: elliptical geometry; flat: Euclidean geometry; saddle-shaped: hyperbolic geometry

15.

17.

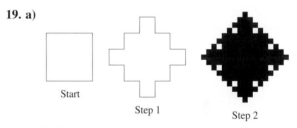

19. a)

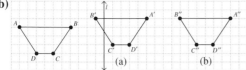

Start   Step 1   Step 2

b) Infinite

c) Finite

Review Exercises, Page 554

In the Review Exercises and Chapter Test questions, the π key on the calculator is used to determine answers in calculations involving π. If you use 3.14 for π, your answers may vary slightly.

1. $\{F\}$ **2.** $\triangle BFC$ **3.** $\overleftrightarrow{BC}$ **4.** $\overrightarrow{BH}$ **5.** $\{F\}$

6. $\{\ \}$ **7.** 38.8°   **8.** 55.3°   **9.** 10.2 in.   **10.** 2 in.

11. 58°   **12.** 92°

13. $m\angle 1 = 70°$, $m\angle 2 = 60°$, $m\angle 3 = 120°$, $m\angle 4 = 70°$, $m\angle 5 = 110°$, $m\angle 6 = 70°$

14. 720°   **15.** 63 cm^2 **16.** 35 in.^{2} **17.** 13 in.^{2}

18. 84 in.^{2} **19.** ≈ 530.93 cm^2 **20.** \$616

21. 1178.10 in.^{3} **22.** 120 cm^3 **23.** 28 ft^3 **24.** 432 m^3

25. 603.19 mm^3 **26.** 1436.76 ft^3

27. a) ≈ 67.88 ft^3 **b)** 4617.5 lb; yes   **c)** ≈ 511.14 gal

This figure contains the answers for Exercises 28 and 29.

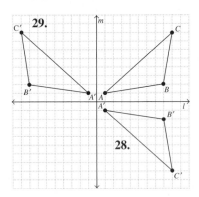

This figure contains the answers for Exercises 30 and 31.

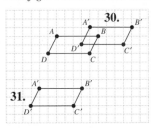

This figure contains the answers for Exercises 32–34.

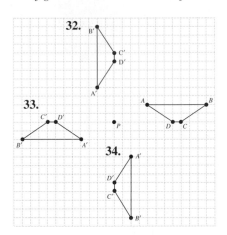

This figure contains the answers for Exercises 35 and 36.

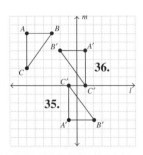

37. Yes

38. No

39. No

40. Yes

41. 1   **42.** Answers will vary.   **43.** Outside

44. Euclidean: Given a line and a point not on the line, one and only one line can be drawn parallel to the given line through the given point. Elliptical: Given a line and a point not on the line, no line can be drawn through the given point parallel to the given line. Hyperbolic: Given a line and a point not on the line, two or more lines can be drawn through the given point parallel to the given line.

45.

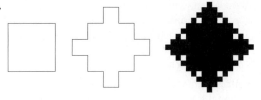

Chapter Test, Page 557

1. $\overleftrightarrow{EF}$ **2.** $\triangle BCD$ **3.** $\{D\}$ **4.** $\overleftrightarrow{AC}$ **5.** 53.1°

6. 78.5°   **7.** 64°   **8.** 1080°   **9.** $\approx$ 2.69 cm

10. a) 12 in.   **b)** 30 in.   **c)** 30 in.^{2}

11. $\approx$ 2144.66 cm^3 **12.** $\approx$ 42.14 yd^3 **13.** 112 ft^3

14.

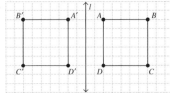

15.

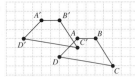

16.

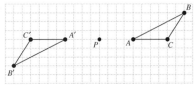

17.

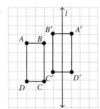

18. a) No **b)** Yes

19. A surface with one side and one edge

20. Answers will vary.

21. Euclidean: Given a line and a point not on the line, one and only one line can be drawn parallel to the given line through the given point. Elliptical: Given a line and a point not on the line, no line can be drawn through the given point parallel to the given line. Hyperbolic: Given a line and a point not on the line, two or more lines can be drawn through the given point parallel to the given line.

Chapter 10

Section 10.1, Page 566

1. A binary operation is an operation, or rule, that can be performed on two and only two elements of a set. The result is a single element.

3. a) When we add two numbers, the sum is one number: $4 + 5 = 9$.
  b) When we subtract two numbers, the difference is one number: $5 - 4 = 1$.
  c) When we multiply two numbers, the product is one number: $5 \times 4 = 20$.
  d) When we divide two numbers, the quotient is one number: $20 \div 5 = 4$.

5. A mathematical system is a commutative group if all five of the following conditions hold.
  1. The set of elements is closed under the given operation.
  2. An identity element exists for the set.
  3. Every element in the set has an inverse.
  4. The set of elements is associative under the given operation.
  5. The set of elements is commutative under the given operation.

7. If a binary operation is performed on any two elements of a set and the result is an element of the set, then that set is *closed* under the given binary operation. For all integers a and b, $a + b$ is an integer. Therefore, the set of integers is closed under the operation of addition.

9. When a binary operation is performed on two elements in a set and the result is the identity element for the binary operation, then each element is said to be the *inverse* of the other. For the set of rational numbers, the additive inverse of 2 is -2 since $2 + (-2) = 0$ and the multiplicative inverse of 2 is $\frac{1}{2}$ since $2 \times \frac{1}{2} = 1$.

11. No; every commutative group is also a group.

13. d); The commutative property need not apply.

15. $(a + b) + c = a + (b + c)$, for any elements a, b, and c; $(3 + 4) + 5 = 3 + (4 + 5)$

17. $a \cdot b = b \cdot a$ for any elements a and b; $2 \cdot 3 = 3 \cdot 2$

19. $4 \div 2 \neq 2 \div 4$

21. $(6 - 4) - 1 \neq 6 - (4 - 1)$
$$2 - 1 \neq 6 - 3$$
$$1 \neq 3$$

23. No; there is no identity element.

25. Yes; satisfies the five properties needed.

27. No; the system is not closed.

29. No; there is no identity element.

31. No; not all elements have inverses.

33. Yes; satisfies the four properties needed.

35. No; the system is not closed. For example, $\frac{1}{0}$ is undefined.

37. No; does not satisfy the associative property.

39. No; the system is not closed. For example, $\sqrt{2} + (-\sqrt{2}) = 0$, which is rational. There is also no identity element.

41. Yes **43.** Answers will vary. **44.** $(9^9)^9$ **45.** 20

Section 10.2, Page 574

1. Numbers are obtained by starting at the first addend (on a clock face), then moving clockwise the number of hours equal to the second addend.

3. a) Add $4 + 10$ to get 2, then add $2 + 3$.
  b) 5

5. a) Add 12 to 5 to get $17 - 9$.
  b) 8
  c) Since 12 is the identity element, you can add 12 to any number without changing the answer.

7. Yes, the sum of any two numbers in clock 12 arithmetic is a number in clock 12 arithmetic.

9. Yes; 1:11, 2:10, 3:9, 4:8, 5:7, 6:6, 7:5, 8:4, 9:3, 10:2, 11:1, and 12:12

11. Yes, $6 + 9 = 9 + 6$ since both equal 3

13. a) 5 **b)** 3. If you add 5 to any number, then you get the number you started with. Thus, in clock 5 arithmetic, 5 is the identity element. Three is the additive inverse of 2 since $2 + 3 = 5$.

15. Yes; the elements are symmetric about the main diagonal.

17. Yes; C is the identity element since the row next to C is identical to the top row and the column under C is identical to the left-hand column.

19. The inverse of A is B since $A \otimes B = C$ and $B \otimes A = C$.

21. 11 **23.** 5 **25.** 4 **27.** 8 **29.** 6 **31.** 6 **33.** 3 **35.** 4 **37.** 7 **39.** 1 **41.** 12 **43.** 12

45.

+	1	2	3	4	5	6
1	2	3	4	5	6	1
2	3	4	5	6	1	2
3	4	5	6	1	2	3
4	5	6	1	2	3	4
5	6	1	2	3	4	5
6	1	2	3	4	5	6

47. 1   **49.** 3   **51.** 2   **53.** 4

55.

+	1	2	3	4	5	6	7
1	2	3	4	5	6	7	1
2	3	4	5	6	7	1	2
3	4	5	6	7	1	2	3
4	5	6	7	1	2	3	4
5	6	7	1	2	3	4	5
6	7	1	2	3	4	5	6
7	1	2	3	4	5	6	7

57. 4   **59.** 6   **61.** 4   **63.** 7

65. Yes; it satisfies the five required properties.

67. a) $\{0, 1, 2, 3\}$

b) ✈

c) Yes

d) Yes; 0

e) Yes; 0–0, 1–3, 2–2, 3–1

f) $(2 \ ✈ \ 3) \ ✈ \ 1 = 2 \ ✈$
$(3 \ ✈ \ 1)$

g) Yes; $2 \ ✈ \ 3 = 3 \ ✈ \ 2$

h) Yes

69. a) $\{r, s, t, u\}$

b) 🛸

c) Yes

d) Yes; t

e) Yes; $r–r$, $s–u$, $t–t$, $u–s$

f) $(r \ 🛸 \ s) \ 🛸 \ u = r \ 🛸 \ (s \ 🛸 \ u)$

g) Yes; $s \ 🛸 \ r = r \ 🛸 \ s$

h) Yes

71. a) $\{f, r, o, m\}$ **b)** 🐦   **c)** Closed
d) m **e)** f **f)** f **g)** m **h)** r

73. Not associative:
$$\left(M \otimes 🔔\right) \otimes M \neq M \otimes \left(🔔 \otimes M\right);$$
not commutative: $🔔 \otimes M \neq M \otimes 🔔$

75. No inverse for $\odot$ or for $*$, not associative

77. No identity element, no inverses, not associative, not commutative

79. a)

+	E	O
E	E	O
O	O	E

b) Yes, it is a commutative group; it satisfies the five properties.

81. Answers will vary.

83. a) Is closed; identity element is 6; inverses: 1–5, 2–2, 3–3, 4–4, 5–1, 6–6; is associative—for example,
$(2 \infty 5) \infty 3 = 2 \infty (5 \infty 3)$
$3 \infty 3 = 2 \infty 2$
$6 = 6$

b) $3 \infty 1 \neq 1 \infty 3$
$2 \neq 4$

85. a)

*	R	S	T	U	V	I
R	V	T	U	S	I	R
S	U	I	V	R	T	S
T	S	R	I	V	U	T
U	T	V	R	I	S	U
V	I	U	S	T	R	V
I	R	S	T	U	V	I

b) Yes, the associative property will hold.

c) No, it is not commutative. For example,
$R * S \neq S * R$

87.

+	0	1	2	3	4
0	0	1	2	3	4
1	1	2	3	4	0
2	2	3	4	0	1
3	3	4	0	1	2
4	4	0	1	2	3

89. Add the number in the top row and the number in the left-hand column and divide the sum by 4. The remainder is placed in the table.

Section 10.3, Page 585

1. A modulo m system consists of m elements, 0 through $m - 1$, and a binary operation.

3. 5;

0	1	2	3	4
0	1	2	3	4
5	6	7	8	9
10	11	12	13	14
.	.	.	.	.
.	.	.	.	.

5. 12 classes   **7.** (b), (c) or (d)   **9.** Saturday   **11.** Friday
13. Saturday   **15.** Thursday   **17.** July   **19.** March
21. September
23. July   **25.** 4   **27.** 2   **29.** 3   **31.** 2   **33.** 1   **35.** 2
37. 0   **39.** 0   **41.** 6   **43.** 2   **45.** 2   **47.** 9   **49.** 5
51. 1   **53.** 2   **55.** 5   **57.** 5   **59.** { }
61. 1 and 6   **63.** 4   **65.** 0
67. a) 2016, 2020, 2024, 2028, 2032   **b)** 3004
c) 2552, 2556, 2560, 2564, 2568, 2572

69. a) Resting (for the second of two days)
  b) Resting (for the second of two days)
  c) Morning and afternoon practice
  d) No

71. a) 5   **b)** No   **c)** 54 weeks from this week

73. a) Evening   **b)** Day   **c)** Day

75. a)

+	0	1	2	3
0	0	1	2	3
1	1	2	3	0
2	2	3	0	1
3	3	0	1	2

  b) Yes   **c)** Yes, 0   **d)** Yes; 0–0, 1–3, 2–2, 3–1
  e) $(1 + 2) + 3 = 1 + (2 + 3)$
  f) Yes; $2 + 3 = 3 + 2$ **g)** Yes   **h)** Yes

77. a)

×	0	1	2	3
0	0	0	0	0
1	0	1	2	3
2	0	2	0	2
3	0	3	2	1

  b) Yes   **c)** Yes, 1
  d) No; no inverse for 0 or for 2, inverse of 1 is 1, inverse of 3 is 3
  e) $(1 \times 2) \times 3 = 1 \times (2 \times 3)$
  f) Yes, $2 \times 3 = 3 \times 2$ **g)** No

79. 2   **81.** 1, 2, 3   **83.** 0   **85.** 2   **87.** 0

88. Halfway up the mountain   **89.** Math is fun.

Review Exercises, Page 589

1. A mathematical system consists of a set of elements and at least one binary operation.

2. A binary operation is an operation that can be performed on two and only two elements of a set. The result is a single element.

3. Yes; the sum of any two integers is an integer.

4. No; for example $2 - 3 = -1$ and -1 is not a natural number.

5. 7   **6.** 5   **7.** 10   **8.** 8   **9.** 9   **10.** 11

11. Closure, identity element, inverses, and associative property

12. A commutative group   **13.** No; no identity element

14. No; no inverse for any integer except 1 and -1 **15.** Yes

16. No; no inverse for 0   **17.** No identity element

18. Not associative. For example, $(!\,\square\,p)\,\square\,? \neq !\,\square\,(p\,\square\,?)$

19. Not every element has an inverse; not associative. For example, $(P\,?\,P)\,?\,4 \neq P\,?\,(P\,?\,4)$.

20. a) $\{\vdash, \odot, ?, \triangle\}$ **b)** $\jmath$ **c)** Yes   **d)** Yes; $\vdash$
  e) Yes; $\vdash - \vdash$, $\odot - \triangle$, $? - ?$, $\triangle - \odot$

  f) $(\odot \,\jmath\, ?) \,\jmath\, \triangle = \odot \,\jmath\, (? \,\jmath\, \triangle)$
  g) Yes; $\odot \,\jmath\, ? = ? \,\jmath\, \odot$ **h)** Yes

21. 0   **22.** 7   **23.** 1   **24.** 3   **25.** 4   **26.** 2   **27.** 4

28. 12   **29.** 9   **30.** 9   **31.** 4   **32.** 3   **33.** { }   **34.** 1

35. 0, 2, 4, 6   **36.** 10   **37.** 5   **38.** 9   **39.** 7   **40.** 8

41.

+	0	1	2	3	4	5
0	0	1	2	3	4	5
1	1	2	3	4	5	0
2	2	3	4	5	0	1
3	3	4	5	0	1	2
4	4	5	0	1	2	3
5	5	0	1	2	3	4

Yes, it is a commutative group.

42.

×	0	1	2	3
0	0	0	0	0
1	0	1	2	3
2	0	2	0	2
3	0	3	2	1

No; no inverse for 0 or 2

43. a) No, she will be off.
  b) Yes, she will have the evening off.

Chapter Test, Page 590

1. A set of elements and a binary operation

2. Closure, identity element, inverses, associative property, commutative property

3. No, not all elements have inverses.

4.

+	1	2	3	4	5
1	2	3	4	5	1
2	3	4	5	1	2
3	4	5	1	2	3
4	5	1	2	3	4
5	1	2	3	4	5

5. Yes, it is a commutative group.   **6.** 4   **7.** 2

8. a) $\square$ **b)** Yes   **c)** Yes, T **d)** S **e)** S

9. No, not closed.   **10.** Yes, it is a commutative group.

11. Yes, it is a commutative group.   **12.** 1   **13.** 3

14. 6   **15.** 2   **16.** 5   **17.** 2   **18.** { }   **19.** 5

20. a)

×	0	1	2	3	4
0	0	0	0	0	0
1	0	1	2	3	4
2	0	2	4	1	3
3	0	3	1	4	2
4	0	4	3	2	1

  b) No; no inverse for 0

Chapter 11

Section 11.1, Page 599

1. A percent is a ratio of some number to 100.

3. Divide the numerator by the denominator, multiply the quotient by 100, and add a percent sign.

5. Percent change $= \dfrac{\left(\begin{array}{c}\text{amount in}\\\text{latest period}\end{array}\right) - \left(\begin{array}{c}\text{amount in}\\\text{previous period}\end{array}\right)}{\text{amount in the previous period}} \times 100$

7. 50.0%   **9.** 40.0%   **11.** 0.8%   **13.** 378%   **15.** 0.04

17. 0.0134   **19.** 0.0025   **21.** 0.002   **23.** 0.01   **25.** ≈ 2.7%

27. 4.7 grams   **29.** $47.28 million   **31.** $159.57 million

33. $5.6848 billion   **35.** $9.8838 billion   **37.** 19.2%

39. 19.6%   **41.** ≈ 5.8%

43. a) 17.3%   **b)** 43.6%   **c)** 54.3%   **d)** 53.9%

45. a) 4.9%   **b)** 27.0%   **c)** 23.5%   **d)** 10.6%

47. $6.75   **49.** 25%   **51.** 300

53. a) $2.61   **b)** $46.11   **c)** $6.92   **d)** $53.03

55. 12 students   **57.** $39,055   **59.** ≈ 5.3% decrease

61. ≈ 20.9%   **63.** ≈ 18.6% decrease   **65.** $3750

67. He will have a loss of $10.   **69.** $21.95

Section 11.2, Page 610

1. Interest is the money the borrower pays for the use of the lender's money.

3. Security or collateral is anything of value pledged by the borrower that the lender may sell or keep if the borrower does not repay the loan.

5. i is the *interest*, p is the *principal*, r is the interest *rate* expressed as a percent, and t is the *time*.

7. The United States rule states that if a partial payment is made on a loan, interest is computed on the principal from the first day of the loan until the date of the partial payment.

9. $60.00   **11.** $2.81   **13.** $15.85   **15.** $80.06

17. $113.20   **19.** 10%   **21.** $600   **23.** 2 years   **25.** $1015

27. a) $131.25   **b)** $3631.25

29. a) $182.50   **b)** $3467.50   **c)** ≈ 7.9%

31. $23,793.75   **33.** 168 days   **35.** 266 days   **37.** 264 days

39. June 14   **41.** March 24   **43.** $1615.31   **45.** $3635.85

47. $5278.99   **49.** $850.64   **51.** $6086.82   **53.** $2646.24

55. a) November 3, 2004   **b)** $978.06   **c)** $21.94
   d) ≈ 4.44%

57. a) ≈ 409.0%   **b)** ≈ 204.5%   **c)** ≈ 102.3%

59. a) 6.663%   **b)** ≈ 7.139%   **c)** $6663   **d)** $6996.15

60. a) $6.42   **b)** $14.20   **c)** $22.47   **d)** Answers will vary.

Section 11.3, page 618

1. An investment is the use of money or capital for income or profit.

3. A variable investment is one in which neither the principal nor the interest is guaranteed.

5. a) The effective annual yield is the simple interest rate that gives the same amount of interest as a compound rate over the same period of time.
   b) Another name for effective annual yield is annual percentage yield.

7. a) $2122.42   **b)** $122.42

9. a) $3942.72   **b)** $442.72

11. a) $1728.28   **b)** $228.28

13. a) $2831.95   **b)** $331.95

15. a) $4806.08   **b)** $806.08

17. $8336.15   **19.** $1653.36   **21.** $2341.82

23. a) $4195.14   **b)** $4214.36

25. $3106.62   **27.** $7609.45

29. a) $1040.60, $40.60   **b)** $1082.43, $82.43
   c) $1169.86, $169.86   **d)** No

31. a) $1125.51, $125.51   **b)** $1266.77, $266.77
   c) $1604.71, $604.71

   d) Yes; new amount $= \dfrac{(\text{old amount})^2}{1000}$

33. ≈ 3.53%   **35.** Yes, the APY should be 2.43%.

37. He will earn more interest in the account that pays the 5% simple interest

39. a) $129,210.47   **b)** $134.88

41. $23,202.23   **43.** $12,015.94   **45.** $1.53

47. a) 24 years   **b)** 12 years   **c)** 9 years   **d)** 6 years
   e) 3.27%

49. $27,550.11   **51. a)** $55,726.01   **b)** $55,821.15

Section 11.4, page 631

1. An open-end installment loan is one with which you can make different payments each month. A fixed installment loan is one in which you pay a fixed amount each month for a set number of months.

3. The APR is the true rate of interest charged on a loan.

5. The total installment price is the sum of all the monthly payments and the down payment, if any.

7. The unpaid balance method and the average daily balance method

9. a) $5339.96   **b)** $698.17

11. a) $809.20   **b)** $80.15

13. a) $628.40   **b)** 9.0%

15. a) $1752 **b)** 9%

17. a) 6% **b)** $726.00 **c)** $7858.00

19. a) $2818.20 **b)** $689.39 **c)** $347.90 **d)** $8614.17

21. a) $1344.87 **b)** $181.04 **c)** $761.64 **d)** $5936.84

23. a) $27.63 **b)** $1032.10

25. a) $18 **b)** $630.86

27. a) $31 **b)** $553.02

29. a) $19.76 **b)** $743.41

31. a) $1.56 **b)** $133.11

33. a) $512.00 **b)** $6.66 **c)** $638.43

35. a) $121.78 **b)** $1.52 **c)** $133.07
   d) The interest charged using the average daily balance method is $0.04 less than the interest charged using the unpaid balance method.

37. a) $8.87 **b)** $608.87

39. a) $25 **b)** $35.60 **c)** 8.5% **d)** 6.5%

41. a) 6 months **b)** $83.95
   c) The installment loan saves them $49.45.

43. a) $6872.25 **b)** $610.37 **c)** $2637.42 **d)** $2501.05

45. Since Martina's billing date is June 25th, she can buy the camera from June 26th through June 29th and the purchase will appear on her July 25th bill. Since she has a 20-day grace period, she can pay for the camera on August 5th without paying interest.

Section 11.5, Page 644

1. A mortgage is a long-term loan in which the property is pledged as security for payment of the difference between the down payment and the sale price.

3. The major difference is that the interest rate for a conventional loan is fixed for the duration of the loan, whereas the interest rate for a variable-rate loan may change every period, as specified in the loan agreement.

5. A buyer's adjusted monthly income is found by subtracting any fixed monthly payments with more than 10 months remaining from the gross monthly income.

7. An amortization schedule lists payment dates and payment numbers. For each payment it lists the amount that goes to pay the interest and the principal. It also gives the balance remaining on the loan after each payment.

9. Equity is the difference between the appraised value of your home and the loan balance.

11. a) $37,500 **b)** $1625.63

13. a) $21,000 **b)** $1247.40

15. a) $39,000 **b)** $156,000 **c)** $3120

17. a) $2865 **b)** $802.20 **c)** $1411.50 **d)** No

19. a) $187,736.40 **b)** $112,736.40 **c)** $38.68

21. a) $31,780 **b)** $2451.60 **c)** $4330 **d)** $1212.40
   e) $789.42 **f)** $916.09 **g)** Yes. **h)** $108.42

23. Bank B

25. a) 805
   b)

Payment Number	Interest	Principal	Balance of Loan
1	$750.00	$55.00	$99,945.00
2	$749.59	$55.41	$99,889.59
3	$749.17	$55.83	$99,833.76

   c) 9.38%
   d)

Payment Number	Interest	Principal	Balance of Loan
4	$780.37	$24.63	$99,809.13
5	$780.17	$24.83	$99,784.30
6	$779.98	$25.02	$99,759.28

   e) 9.46%

27. a) $113,095.24 **b)** $150,793.65

Review Exercises, page 647

1. 60.0% **2.** 66.7% **3.** 62.5% **4.** 4.1%

5. 0.98% ≈ 1.0% **6.** 314.1% **7.** 0.03 **8.** 0.121

9. 1.23 **10.** 0.0025 **11.** $0.008\overline{3}$ **12.** 0.0000045

13. ≈17.6% **14.** ≈11.0% **15.** 31.25% **16.** 275

17. 91.8 **18.** $6.42 **19.** 40 people **20.** 26.7%

21. $16.67 **22.** 9.5% **23.** $450 **24.** 0.5 year

25. $6214.25 **26. a)** $162 **b)** $3162

27. a) $1380 **b)** $4620 **c)** ≈14.9%

28. a) $7\frac{1}{2}$% **b)** $830 **c)** $941.18

29. a) $1610.51, $610.51 **b)** $1628.89, $628.89
   c) $1638.62, $638.62 **d)** $1645.31, $645.31
   e) $1648.61, $648.61

30. $5076.35 **31.** 5.76% **32.** $13,415.00

33. a) 6.0% **b)** 253.16 **c)** $4150.34

34. a) $109.18 **b)** $2014.11

35. a) 4.5% **b)** $32.06 **c)** $1420.43

36. a) $6.31 **b)** $847.61 **c)** $508.99 **d)** $6.62
   e) $847.92

37. a) $2.60 **b)** $546.92 **c)** $382.68 **d)** $5.36
   e) $549.68

38. a) $10,400 **b)** $41,600 **c)** $3040.96 **d)** 3.5%

39. a) $10.44 **b)** 8.5%

40. a) $33,925 **b)** $4805.33 **c)** $1345.49
   d) $855.93 **e)** $1172.60 **f)** Yes

41. a) $13,485 **b)** $756.51 **c)** $24.20 **d)** $285,828.60
   e) $195,928.60

42. a) $550.46 **b)** 8% **c)** 7.75%

Chapter Test, page 650

1. $40   **2.** 3 years   **3.** $637.50   **4.** $5637.50
5. $2523.20   **6.** $123.20   **7.** $7961.99, $461.99
8. $3036.68, $536.68   **9.** $1997.50   **10.** $181.46
11. 8.5%   **12. a)** $105.05   **b)** $3155.90
13. a) 4.5%   **b)** $64.02   **c)** $2836.28
14. a) $12.30   **b)** $1146.57   **c)** $765.67   **d)** $10.72
   e) $1144.99
15. $21,675   **16.** $6603.33   **17.** $1848.93   **18.** $1123.85
19. $1428.02   **20.** Yes   **21. a)** $426,261   **b)** $281,761

Chapter 12

Section 12.1, Page 659

1. An experiment is a controlled operation that yields a set of results.

3. Empirical probability is the relative frequency of occurrence of an event. It is determined by actual observation of an experiment.

$$P(E) = \frac{\text{number of times event has occurred}}{\text{number of times experiment was performed}}$$

5. Answers will vary.

7. No, it means that if a coin was flipped many times, about $\frac{1}{2}$ of the tosses would land heads up.

9. No, it means that the average person with traits similar to Mr. Duncan's will live another 43.21 years.

11.–13. Answers will vary.

15. a) $\frac{7}{15}$ **b)** $\frac{1}{3}$ **c)** $\frac{1}{5}$ **17. a)** $\frac{8}{19}$ **b)** $\frac{7}{19}$ **c)** $\frac{1}{19}$

19. a) The percents are relative frequencies of the events occurring.
   b) 0.32   **c)** 0.22   **d)** 0.19

21. a) 1   **b)** Yes

23. a) $\frac{11}{40}$ **b)** $\frac{9}{40}$ **c)** $\frac{1}{4}$ **d)** $\frac{7}{40}$ **e)** $\frac{3}{40}$

25. a) $\frac{6}{20} = \frac{3}{10}$ **b)** $\frac{14}{20} = \frac{7}{10}$ **c)** $\frac{14}{20} = \frac{7}{10}$
   d) $\frac{2}{20} = \frac{1}{10}$

27. a) 0   **b)** $\frac{50}{250} = 0.2$ **c)** 1

29. a) $\frac{224}{929} \approx 0.24$ **b)** $\frac{705}{929} \approx 0.76$

31. Answers will vary.

Section 12.2, Page 667

1. If each outcome of an experiment has the same chance of occurring as any other outcome, they are said to be equally likely outcomes.

3. $P(A) + P(\text{not } A) = 1$ **5.** 0.7   **7.** $\frac{7}{12}$

9. Answers will vary.   **11.** 0 and 1   **13. a)** $\frac{1}{5}$ **b)** $\frac{1}{4}$

15. $\frac{1}{50}$ **17.** $\frac{1}{13}$ **19.** $\frac{12}{13}$ **21.** $\frac{1}{2}$ **23.** 1   **25.** $\frac{4}{13}$

27. a) $\frac{1}{2}$ **b)** $\frac{1}{4}$ **c)** $\frac{1}{4}$ **d)** 0

29. a) $\frac{1}{2}$ **b)** 0   **c)** $\frac{1}{3}$ **d)** $\frac{1}{6}$

31. $\frac{2}{5}$ **33.** $\frac{9}{10}$ **35.** $\frac{1}{12}$ **37.** $\frac{1}{6}$ **39.** $\frac{23}{50}$ **41.** $\frac{33}{50}$

43. $\frac{11}{17}$ **45.** $\frac{12}{17}$ **47.** $\frac{4}{11}$ **49.** $\frac{4}{11}$ **51.** 1   **53.** $\frac{1}{11}$

55. $\frac{4}{11}$ **57.** $\frac{1}{26}$ **59.** $\frac{5}{26}$ **61.** $\frac{345}{715} = \frac{69}{143}$ **63.** $\frac{533}{715} = \frac{41}{55}$

65. $\frac{97}{715}$ **67.** $\frac{50}{159}$ **69.** $\frac{66}{159} = \frac{22}{53}$ **71.** $\frac{23}{159}$ **73.** $\frac{13}{36}$

75. $\frac{1}{3}$ **77.** $\frac{23}{36}$ **79. a)** 0   **b)** 1   **81. a)** $\frac{1}{4}$ **b)** $\frac{1}{4}$ **c)** $\frac{1}{4}$

83. 29 dots

Section 12.3, Page 674

1. Answers will vary.   **3.** Odds against

5. 9 to 5   **7. a)** $\frac{1}{2}$ **b)** $\frac{1}{2}$

9. a) $\frac{8}{27}$ **b)** $\frac{19}{27}$ **c)** 19 : 8   **d)** 8 : 19

11. 5 : 1   **13.** 4 : 2 or 2 : 1   **15.** 12 : 1, 1 : 12
17. 10 : 3, 3 : 10   **19.** 1 : 1   **21.** 5 : 3
23. a) 8 : 7   **b)** 7 : 8   **25.** 8 : 7   **27.** 14 : 1   **29.** 8 : 7

31. a) $\frac{5}{9}$ **b)** 4 : 5   **33.** 1 : 18   **35. a)** $\frac{8}{13}$ **b)** $\frac{5}{13}$

37. $\frac{11}{15}$ **39.** $\frac{1}{5}$ **41.** 1 : 4   **43.** 74 : 1   **45.** 0.34   **47.** 33 : 17

49. 43 : 57   **51.** 1 : 9   **53.** 7 : 1   **55. a)** $\frac{20}{21}$ **b)** 20 : 1

57. Horse 1, $\frac{2}{9}$; Horse 2, $\frac{1}{3}$; Horse 3, $\frac{1}{16}$; Horse 4, $\frac{5}{12}$;
   Horse 5, $\frac{1}{2}$

59. $\approx 97 : 3$

Section 12.4, Page 683

1. The expected value is the expected gain or loss of an experiment over the long run.

3. The fair price is the amount that should be charged for the game to be fair and result in an expectation of 0.

5. To obtain the fair price, add the cost to the expected value.

7. $0.50. Since you would lose $1.00 on average for each game you played, the price of the game should be $1.00 less than the actual cost. Then the expectation would be $0, and the game would be fair. The results could also be obtained from the fair price formula, fair price = expectation + cost to play.

9. $-$1.20   **11.** 176 people   **13.** 70 points

15. 1.44 million viewers   **17.** $3840   **19.** $1.60 off

21. a) $\approx -$0.67   **b)** $\approx $0.67

23. a) Yes, because you have a positive expectation of $\frac{1}{5}$

   b) Yes, because you have a positive expectation of $\frac{1}{2}$

25. a) $-1.20   **b)** $0.80   **27. a)** $-2.00   **b)** $1.00

29. $5.50   **31.** $-1.25   **33. a)** $1   **b)** $3

35. a) $2.25   **b)** $4.25   **37.** 0.75 base   **39.** 2.9 points

41. 381.4 employees   **43.** $\approx$ 15.65 min   **45.** 3.5

47. $\approx$141.51 service calls

49. a) $\frac{9}{16}, \frac{1}{4}, \frac{1}{8}, \frac{1}{16}$ **b)** $11.81   **c)** $11.81

51. An amount greater than $1200

53. $-$0.053 or $-5.3¢   **55. a)** $458.33   **b)** $308.33

Section 12.5, Page 692

1. If a first experiment can be performed in M distinct ways and a second experiment can be performed in N distinct ways, then the two experiments in that specific order can be performed in $M \cdot N$ distinct ways.

3. 14

5. The first selection is made. Then the second selection is made without the first selection being returned to the group of items being selected.

7. a) 2500   **b)** 2450   **9. a)** 216   **b)** 120

11. a) 4

   b)

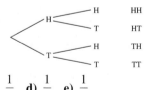

   c) $\frac{1}{4}$ **d)** $\frac{1}{2}$ **e)** $\frac{1}{4}$

13. a) 9

   b)

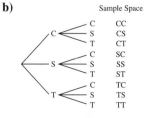

c) $\frac{1}{9}$ **d)** $\frac{1}{9}$ **e)** $\frac{5}{9}$

15. a) 12

   b)

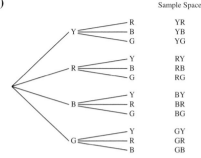

   c) $\frac{1}{2}$ **d)** 1   **e)** $\frac{1}{2}$

17. a) 8

   b)

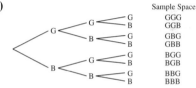

   c) $\frac{1}{8}$ **d)** $\frac{7}{8}$ **e)** $\frac{3}{4}$ **f)** $\frac{1}{8}$

19. a) 36

   b)

Sample Space

1	1, 1
2	1, 2
3	1, 3
4	1, 4
5	1, 5
6	1, 6
1	2, 1
2	2, 2
3	2, 3
4	2, 4
5	2, 5
6	2, 6
1	3, 1
2	3, 2
3	3, 3
4	3, 4
5	3, 5
6	3, 6
1	4, 1
2	4, 2
3	4, 3
4	4, 4
5	4, 5
6	4, 6
1	5, 1
2	5, 2
3	5, 3
4	5, 4
5	5, 5
6	5, 6
1	6, 1
2	6, 2
3	6, 3
4	6, 4
5	6, 5
6	6, 6

c) $\frac{1}{6}$ **d)** $\frac{1}{6}$ **e)** $\frac{1}{36}$ **f)** No

21. a) 6

b)

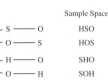

Sample Space

H	S — O	HSO
	O — S	HOS
S	H — O	SHO
	O — H	SOH
O	H — S	OHS
	S — H	OSH

c) $\dfrac{1}{3}$ **d)** $\dfrac{1}{6}$ **e)** $\dfrac{1}{6}$

23. a) 16

b) In the tree diagram, K represents the Magic Kingdom and M represents MGM Studios.

Sample Space

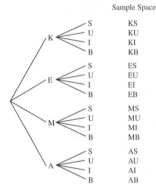

K	S	KS
	U	KU
	I	KI
	B	KB
E	S	ES
	U	EU
	I	EI
	B	EB
M	S	MS
	U	MU
	I	MI
	B	MB
A	S	AS
	U	AU
	I	AI
	B	AB

c) $\dfrac{1}{2}$ **d)** $\dfrac{7}{16}$ **e)** $\dfrac{1}{8}$

25. a) 27

b)

Sample Space

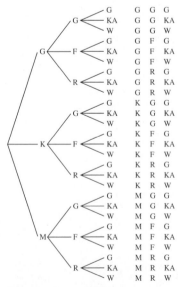

c) $\dfrac{1}{27}$ **d)** $\dfrac{8}{27}$ **e)** $\dfrac{19}{27}$

27. a) 24

b)

Sample Space

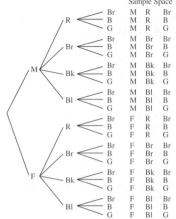

c) $\dfrac{1}{24}$ **d)** $\dfrac{1}{8}$

29. a) $\dfrac{1}{3}$ **b)** $\dfrac{2}{3}$ **c)** No, the probability of selecting a red chip is not the same as the probability of selecting a white chip. **d)** Answers will vary.

31. 3; 1 red, 1 blue, and 1 brown **32.** 5 faces

Section 12.6, Page 703

1. a) At least one event, A *or* B, must occur.
  b) Both events, A *and* B, must occur.

3. a) Events that cannot happen simultaneously are mutually exclusive events.
  b) $P(A \text{ or } B) = P(A) + P(B)$

5. We assume that event *A* has already occurred.

7. Two events are dependent when the probability of one item being selected has an effect on the probability of a second item being selected.

9. a) No, both events can occur at the same time.
  b) Yes, the outcome of one event has no affect on the outcome of the other event.

11. Events *A* and *B* cannot occur at the same time. Therefore, $P(A \text{ and } B) = 0$.

13. 0.7 **15.** 0.5 **17.** $\dfrac{1}{3}$ **19.** $\dfrac{1}{2}$ **21.** $\dfrac{2}{13}$ **23.** $\dfrac{8}{13}$

25. $\dfrac{31}{52}$ **27. a)** $\dfrac{1}{16}$ **b)** $\dfrac{1}{19}$

29. a) $\dfrac{1}{16}$ **b)** $\dfrac{5}{76}$ **31. a)** $\dfrac{3}{80}$ **b)** $\dfrac{3}{76}$

33. a) $\dfrac{9}{25}$ **b)** $\dfrac{33}{95}$ **35.** $\dfrac{11}{20}$ **37.** $\dfrac{2}{5}$ **39.** $\dfrac{1}{4}$

41. $\dfrac{1}{8}$ **43.** $\dfrac{9}{64}$ **45.** $\dfrac{1}{8}$ **47.** $\dfrac{3}{8}$ **49.** $\dfrac{1}{8}$ **51.** $\dfrac{1}{8}$

53. a) $\dfrac{1}{16}$ **b)** $\dfrac{1}{2}$ **55. a)** $\dfrac{4}{49}$ **b)** $\dfrac{2}{21}$

57. a) $\dfrac{24}{49}$ **b)** $\dfrac{11}{21}$ **59.** $\dfrac{5}{12}$ **61.** $\dfrac{7}{12}$ **63.** $\dfrac{969}{4060}$

65. $\dfrac{5}{812}$ **67.** 0.7 **69.** 0.343 **71.** $\dfrac{1}{4}$ **73.** $\dfrac{27}{1024}$

75. $\dfrac{243}{1024}$ **77.** $\dfrac{3}{22}$ **79.** $\dfrac{1050}{1331}$ **81.** $\dfrac{1}{48}$ **83.** $\dfrac{5}{12}$

85. 0.36 **87.** 0.36

89. a) No **b)** 0.001 **c)** 0.00004 **d)** 0.00096
e) 0.000999 **f)** 0.998001

91. $\dfrac{32}{1000}$, or 0.032 **93.** $\dfrac{484}{15,625}$, or 0.030976 **95.** $\dfrac{14}{45}$

97. Favors dealer, the probability of at least one diamond is ≈ 0.44, which is less than 0.5

99. $\dfrac{1}{9}$ **100.** $\dfrac{1}{4}$ **101.** $\dfrac{1}{2}$ **102.** 1 **103.** Answers will vary.

Section 12.7, Page 710

1. The probability of E_2 given that E_1 has occurred

3. $\dfrac{1}{3}$ **5.** $\dfrac{1}{3}$ **7.** $\dfrac{2}{3}$ **9.** $\dfrac{2}{3}$ **11.** $\dfrac{3}{4}$ **13.** $\dfrac{2}{3}$ **15.** $\dfrac{2}{3}$ **17.** $\dfrac{1}{3}$

19. $\dfrac{1}{3}$ **21.** $\dfrac{3}{5}$ **23.** $\dfrac{1}{7}$ **25.** $\dfrac{1}{16}$ **27.** $\dfrac{1}{7}$ **29.** $\dfrac{5}{36}$

31. $\dfrac{1}{6}$ **33.** $\dfrac{2}{3}$ **35.** $\dfrac{107}{217}$ **37.** $\dfrac{25}{56}$ **39.** $\dfrac{6}{11}$ **41.** $\dfrac{4}{9}$

43. $\dfrac{11}{20}$ **45.** $\dfrac{22}{39}$ **47.** $\dfrac{133}{300}$ **49.** $\dfrac{1}{2}$ **51.** $\dfrac{21}{43}$

53. ≈ 0.3197 **55.** ≈ 0.0795 **57.** ≈ 0.1928 **59.** $\dfrac{10}{11}$

61. $\dfrac{3}{19}$ **63.** $\dfrac{44}{47}$ **65.** $\dfrac{11}{27}$ **67.** $\dfrac{10}{29}$ **69.** $\dfrac{11}{29}$ **71.** $\dfrac{93}{200}$

73. $\dfrac{15}{52}$ **75. a)** 140 **b)** 120 **c)** $\dfrac{7}{10}$ **d)** $\dfrac{3}{5}$
e) $\dfrac{2}{3}$ **f)** $\dfrac{4}{7}$
g) Because A and B are not independent events

77. a) 0.3 **b)** 0.4 **c)** Yes; $P(A\,|\,B) = P(A) \cdot P(B)$

78. $\dfrac{1}{3}$ **79.** $\dfrac{2}{3}$ **80.** $\dfrac{1}{3}$ **81.** $\dfrac{1}{3}$ **82.** 100 **83.** $\dfrac{1}{3}$

Section 12.8, Page 721

1. Answers will vary.
3. $n! = n(n - 1)(n - 2) \cdots (3)(2)(1)$
5. The number of permutations of n items taken r at a time.
7. $_nP_r = \dfrac{n!}{(n - r)!}$ **9.** 720 **11.** 30 **13.** 1 **15.** 1
17. 3024 **19.** 6720 **21.** 10,000
23. a) 11,232,000 **b)** 17,576,000

25. a) $5^5 = 3125$ **b)** $\dfrac{1}{3125} = 0.00032$
27. 57,106,944 **29.** 720 systems
31. a) 720 **b)** 120 **c)** 24 **d)** 600 **33.** 720
35. a) 479,001,600 **b)** 3,628,800 **c)** 14,400
37. 3,276,000 **39.** 131,040 **41.** 676,000 **43.** 104,000
45. a) 8,000,000 **b)** 6,400,000,000
c) 64,000,000,000,000
47. 3,603,600 **49.** 5040 **51.** 280 **53.** 362,880
55. 1,663,200 **57.** 630 **59.** 6720
61. a) 40,320 **b)** 362,880
63. a) 3125 **b)** ≈ 128 **c)** 0.00032
65. 12,600 sec, or 3.5 hr **67.** No **68.** 56 **69.** 600

Section 12.9, Page 727

1. Answers will vary.
3. $_nC_r = \dfrac{n!}{(n - r)!\,r!}$ **5.** Answers will vary.
7. 10 **9. a)** 15 **b)** 360 **11. a)** 1 **b)** 1
13. a) 120 **b)** 720 **15.** $\dfrac{1}{6}$ **17.** 2 **19.** 72
21. 84 **23.** 5 **25.** 210 **27.** 126 **29.** 495
31. 45 **33.** 28 **35.** 6160 **37.** 560 **39.** 294,000
41. 560 **43.** 1200 **45. a)** 45 **b)** 56
47. a) and b)

```
                1
            1       1
          1   2   1
        1   3   3   1
      1   4   6   4   1
    1   5   10   10   5   1
```

49. a) 24 **b)** 24
51. a) The order is important. Since the numbers may be repeated, it is not a true permutation lock.
b) 64,000 **c)** 59,280

Section 12.10, Page 733

1. $\dfrac{_6C_4}{_{10}C_4}$ **3.** $\dfrac{_5C_3}{_{26}C_3}$ **5.** $\dfrac{_{10}C_5}{_{18}C_5}$ **7.** $\dfrac{_{14}C_9}{_{30}C_9}$ **9.** $\dfrac{5}{42}$ **11.** $\dfrac{4}{143}$

13. $\dfrac{1}{12}$ **15.** $\dfrac{4}{33}$ **17.** $\dfrac{1}{9,366,819}$ **19.** $\dfrac{3}{10}$ **21.** $\dfrac{7}{10}$

23. $\dfrac{1}{115}$ **25.** $\dfrac{27}{230}$ **27.** $\dfrac{646,646}{3,910,797,436} \approx 0.0001653$

29. $\dfrac{923,410,488}{3,910,797,436} \approx 0.236$ **31.** $\dfrac{20}{1001}$ **33.** $\dfrac{200}{1001}$

35. $\dfrac{1}{77}$ **37.** $\dfrac{5}{77}$ **39.** $\dfrac{5}{506} \approx 0.010$

41. a) $\dfrac{1}{123,760}$ **b)** $\dfrac{1}{30,940}$

43. a) $\dfrac{33}{54,145}$ **b)** $\dfrac{1}{2,598,960}$

45. a) $\dfrac{1}{2,162,160}$ **b)** $\dfrac{1}{6435}$

47. 1; Since there are more hairs than people, two or more people must have the same number of hairs on their head.

Section 12.11, Page 742

1. A probability distribution shows the probability associated with each specific outcome of an experiment. In a probability distribution every possible outcome must be listed and the sum of all the probabilities must be 1.

3. $P(x) = (_nC_x)p^x q^{n-x}$

5. 0.2646 **7.** 0.3456 **9.** 0.015625

11. a) $P(x) = (_nC_x)(0.14)^x (0.86)^{n-x}$
   b) $P(2) = (_{12}C_2)(0.14)^2 (0.86)^{10}$

13. 0.05954 **15.** 0.11059 **17.** 0.06877 **19.** 0.4096

21. a) 0.01024 **b)** 0.98976

23. a) ≈ 0.1119 **b)** ≈ 0.2966

25. 0; it will be midnight.

Review Exercises, Page 745

1. Answers will vary. **2.** Answers will vary.

3. $\dfrac{1}{5}$ **4.** Answers will vary. **5.** $\dfrac{2}{5}$ **6.** $\dfrac{1}{2}$ **7.** $\dfrac{7}{10}$

8. 1 **9.** $\dfrac{1}{5}$ **10.** $\dfrac{5}{24}$ **11.** $\dfrac{1}{6}$ **12.** $\dfrac{1}{3}$ **13.** $\dfrac{19}{24}$

14. a) 9 : 1 **b)** 1 : 9 **15.** 5 : 3 **16.** $\dfrac{3}{85}$ **17.** 7 : 3

18. a) $-\$1.20$ **b)** $-\$3.60$ **c)** \$0.80

19. a) $-\$0.23$ **b)** \$0.23 **c)** Lose \$23.08

20. 660 people

21. a) 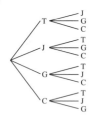   **b)** Sample Space   **c)** $\dfrac{1}{12}$

TJ
TG
TC
JT
JG
JC
GT
GJ
GC
CT
CJ
CG

22. a) 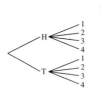 **b)** Sample Space **c)** $\dfrac{1}{4}$ **d)** $\dfrac{3}{4}$

H1
H2
H3
H4
T1
T2
T3
T4

23. $\dfrac{1}{4}$ **24.** $\dfrac{9}{64}$ **25.** $\dfrac{5}{16}$ **26.** $\dfrac{7}{8}$ **27.** 1 **28.** $\dfrac{3}{16}$

29. $\dfrac{1}{22}$ **30.** $\dfrac{14}{55}$ **31.** $\dfrac{41}{55}$ **32.** $\dfrac{1}{22}$ **33.** $\dfrac{1}{4}$

34. Against, 3 : 1; in favor, 1 : 3 **35.** \$13.75

36. $\dfrac{1}{8}$ **37.** $\dfrac{5}{8}$ **38.** In favor, 3 : 5; against, 5 : 3 **39.** \$3.75

40. $\dfrac{7}{8}$ **41.** $\dfrac{89}{106}$ **42.** $\dfrac{55}{74}$ **43.** $\dfrac{19}{74}$ **44.** $\dfrac{17}{106}$

45. $\dfrac{23}{40}$ **46.** $\dfrac{3}{17}$ **47.** $\dfrac{3}{4}$ **48.** $\dfrac{12}{17}$

49. a) 24 **b)** \$4500 **50.** 30 **51.** 720 **52.** 504

53. 20 **54. a)** 3003 **b)** 3,628,800

55. a) $\dfrac{1}{2,598,960}$ **b)** $\dfrac{1}{135,145,920}$ **56.** 5880 **57.** 560

58. $\dfrac{1}{221}$ **59.** $\dfrac{1}{12}$ **60.** $\dfrac{1}{18}$ **61.** $\dfrac{1}{24}$ **62.** $\dfrac{11}{12}$ **63.** $\dfrac{5}{182}$

64. $\dfrac{45}{364}$ **65.** $\dfrac{2}{13}$ **66.** $\dfrac{11}{13}$

67. a) $P(x) = (_nC_x)(0.6)^x (0.4)^{n-x}$
   b) $P(75) = (_{100}C_{75})(0.6)^{75}(0.4)^{25}$

68. 0.0512 **69. a)** 0.0256 **b)** 0.9744

Chapter Test, Page 748

1. $\dfrac{11}{15}$ **2.** $\dfrac{2}{9}$ **3.** $\dfrac{5}{9}$ **4.** $\dfrac{7}{9}$ **5.** $\dfrac{1}{3}$ **6.** $\dfrac{1}{6}$ **7.** $\dfrac{1}{6}$

8. $\dfrac{5}{18}$ **9.** $\dfrac{5}{12}$ **10.** $\dfrac{8}{13}$ **11.** 18

12.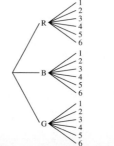

Sample Space

R1
R2
R3
R4
R5
R6
B1
B2
B3
B4
B5
B6
G1
G2
G3
G4
G5
G6

13. $\dfrac{1}{18}$ **14.** $\dfrac{4}{9}$ **15.** $\dfrac{5}{6}$ **16.** 608,400

17. a) $5 : 4$ **b)** $5 : 4$ **18.** $\dfrac{2}{7}$ **19.** \$0

20. a) $\dfrac{107}{228}$ **b)** $\dfrac{115}{228}$ **c)** $\dfrac{68}{115}$ **d)** $\dfrac{60}{107}$

21. 120   **22.** $\dfrac{14}{95}$ **23.** $\dfrac{81}{95}$ **24.** $\dfrac{175}{396}$ **25.** 0.0081

Chapter 13

Section 13.1, Page 756

1. Answers will vary.

3.–5. Answers will vary.

7. a) A population is all items or people of interest.
b) A sample is a subset of the population.

9. a) A random sample is a sample drawn in such a way that each item in the population has an equal chance of being selected.
b) Number each item in the population. Write each number on a piece of paper and put each numbered piece of paper in a hat. Select pieces of paper from the hat and use the numbered items selected as your sample.

11. a) A stratified sample is one that includes items from each part (or strata) of the population.
b) First identify the strata in which you are interested. Then select a random sample from each strata.

13. An unbiased sample is one that is a small replica of the entire population with regard to income, education, gender, race, religion, political affiliation, age, and so forth.

15. Stratified sample   **17.** Cluster sample

19. Systematic sample   **21.** Convenience sample

23. Random sample   **25. a)–c)** Answers will vary.

27. President; four out of 42 U.S. presidents have been assassinated (Lincoln, Garfield, McKinley, Kennedy).

Section 13.2, Page 759

1. Answers will vary.

3. There may have been more car thefts in Baltimore, Maryland than Reno, Nevada because many more people live in Baltimore than in Reno. But, Reno may have more car thefts per capita than Baltimore.

5. Although the cookies are fat free, they still contain calories. Eating many of them may still cause you to gain weight.

7. More people drive on Saturday evening. Thus, one might expect more accidents.

9. People with asthma may move to Arizona because of its climate. Therefore, more people with asthma may live in Arizona.

11. Although milk is less expensive at Star Food Markets than at Price Chopper Food Markets, other items may be more expensive at Star Food Markets.

13. There may be deep sections in the pond, so it may not be safe to go wading.

15. Half the students in a population are expected to be below average.

17. a)

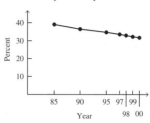

Percent of National Expenditures Spent on Hospital Care

b)

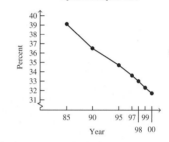

Percent of National Expenditures Spent on Hospital Care

19. a)

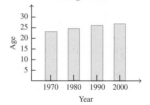

Median Age at First Marriage for Males

b)

Median Age at First Marriage for Males

21. a)

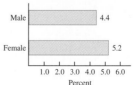

Percent of Survey Respondents That Purchased Clothing Accessories Online, Nov. 2000–Jan. 2001

b) Yes. Answers will vary.

23. A decimal point

Section 13.3, Page 765

1. A frequency distribution is a listing of observed values and the corresponding frequency of occurrence of each value.

3. a) 7 **b)** 16–22 **c)** 16 **d)** 22

5. The modal class is the class with the greatest frequency.

7. a) 18 **b)** 7 **c)** 19 **d)** 16–22 **e)** 51–57

9.

Number Sold	Number of Days
0	3
1	8
2	3
3	5
4	2
5	7
6	2
7	3
8	4
9	1
10	2

11.

IQ	Number of Students
78–86	2
87–95	15
96–104	18
105–113	7
114–122	6
123–131	1
132–140	1

13.

IQ	Number of Students
80–90	8
91–101	22
102–112	11
113–123	7
124–134	1
135–145	1

15.

Placement Test Scores	Number of Students
472–492	9
493–513	9
514–534	5
535–555	2
556–576	3
577–597	2

17.

Placement Test Scores	Number of Students
472–487	4
488–503	9
504–519	7
520–535	3
536–551	2
552–567	2
568–583	2
584–599	1

19.

Circulation (thousands)	Number of Newspapers
209–458	36
459–708	8
709–958	3
959–1208	1
1209–1458	0
1459–1708	0
1709–1958	1
1959–2208	1

21.

Circulation (thousands)	Number of Newspapers
209–408	34
409–608	9
609–808	3
809–1008	1
1009–1208	1
1209–1408	0
1409–1608	0
1609–1808	1
1809–2008	0
2009–2208	1

23.

Population (millions)	Number of Counties
1.4–2.1	15
2.2–2.9	6
3.0–3.7	2
3.8–4.5	0
4.6–5.3	0
5.4–6.1	1
6.2–6.9	0
7.0–7.7	0
7.8–8.5	0
8.6–9.3	0
9.4–10.1	1

25.

Population (millions)	Number of Counties
1.0–2.5	19
2.6–4.1	4
4.2–5.7	1
5.8–7.3	0
7.4–8.9	0
9.0–10.5	1

27.

Price ($)	Number of States
0.35–0.44	6
0.45–0.54	10
0.55–0.64	11
0.65–0.74	3
0.75–0.84	2
0.85–0.94	4
0.95–1.04	1
1.05–1.14	2
1.15–1.24	2
1.25–1.34	1
1.35–1.44	0
1.45–1.54	1

29.

Price ($)	Number of States
0.35–0.54	16
0.55–0.74	14
0.75–0.94	6
0.95–1.14	3
1.15–1.34	3
1.35–1.54	1

31. February, since it has the fewest numbers of days

32. a) Did You Know?, page 762: There are 6 F's.
  b) Answers will vary.

Section 13.4, page 774

1. Answers will vary.   **3.** Answers will vary.

5. a) Answers will vary.
  b)

Children in Selected Families

7. a) Answers will vary.
  b)

Observed values	Frequency
45	3
46	0
47	1
48	0
49	1
50	1
51	2

9. Occasionally: 295; most times: 125; every time: 35; never: 45

11.

Using Online Travel Websites

13. a) and **b**)

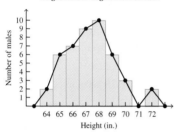

15. a) and **b**)

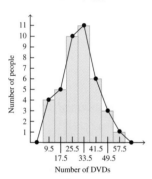

17. a) 30   **b**) 4   **c**) 2   **d**) 75

e)

Number of Soft Drinks Purchased	Number of People
0	2
1	7
2	8
3	5
4	4
5	3
6	1

19. a) 7   **b**) 16   **c**) 36

d)

Response Time (min)	Number of Calls	Response Time (min)	Number of Calls
3	2	7	3
4	3	8	8
5	7	9	6
6	4	10	3

e)

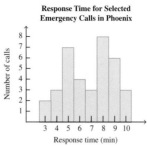

Response Time for Selected Emergency Calls in Phoenix

21.

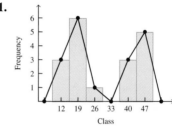

23. 1 | 5 represents 15

```
1 | 0  5  7
2 | 4  4
3 | 6  0  3
4 | 8  5  2  5  8
5 | 3  4
6 | 0  2  0
```

25. a)

Salaries (1000s of dollars)	Number of Companies
27	1
28	7
29	4
30	3
31	2
32	3
33	3
34	2

b) and **c**)

Starting Salaries for 25 Different Social Workers

d) 2 | 3 represents 23

```
2|7  8  8  8  8  8  8  8  9  9  9  9
3|0  0  0  1  1  2  2  2  3  3  3  4  4
```

27. a)

Advertising Spending (millions of dollars)	Number of Companies
597–905	19
906–1214	14
1215–1523	7
1524–1832	3
1833–2141	2
2142–2450	3
2451–2759	1
2760–3068	0
3069–3377	1

b) and c)

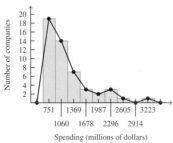

29. a)–e) Answers will vary.

Section 13.5, Page 784

1. Ranked data are data listed from the lowest value to the highest value or from the highest value to the lowest value.

3. The median is the value in the middle of a set of ranked data. To find the median rank the data and select the value in the middle.

5. The mode is the most common piece of data. The piece of data that occurs most frequently is the mode.

7. The median should be used when there are some values that differ greatly from the rest of the values in the set, for example, salaries.

9. The mean is used when each piece of data is to be considered and "weighed" equally, for example, weights of adult males.

11. 11, 10, 10, 14   **13.** 69.3, 72, none, 66

15. 8, 8, none, 8   **17.** 13.1, 11, 1, 18.5

19. 11.9, 12.5, 13, 11.5   **21.** 6.5, 5, 3 and 5, 10.5

23. a) 4.9, 5, 5, 6   **b)** 5.3, 5, 5, 6
   c) Only the mean   **d)** The mean and the midrange

25. A 79 mean average on 10 quizzes gives a total of 790 points. An 80 mean average on 10 quizzes requires a total of 800 points. Thus, Jim missed a B by 10 points, not 1 point.

27. a) 8.8 million   **b)** 8.0 million   **c)** None
   d) 12.2 million

29. a) $5.1 billion   **b)** $2.3 billion
   c) $2.3 billion and $1.5 billion   **d)** $14 billion
   e) Answers will vary.

31. 510   **33.** One example is 72, 73, 74, 76, 77, 78.

35. a) Yes   **b)** No   **c)** No   **d)** Yes
   e) Mean = 200; midrange = 275

37. a) 33 or greater
   b) It is not possible if 100 is the maximum possible grade.
   c) 22 or greater   **d)** 82 or greater

39. One example: 1, 2, 3, 3, 4, 5, changed to 1, 2, 3, 4, 4, 5.

41. No, by changing only one piece of the 6 pieces of data you cannot alter both the median and the midrange.

43. The data must be ranked.

45. He is taller than approximately 35 percent of all kindergarten children.

47. a) $430   **b)** $350   **c)** $650

49. Second quartile, median

51. a) $490   **b)** $500   **c)** 25%
   d) 25%   **e)** 17%   **f)** $51,000

53. a)

Ruth	Mantle
0.290	0.300
0.359	0.365
0.301	0.304
0.272	0.275
0.315	0.321

b) Mantle's is greater in every case.
c) Ruth: 0.316; Mantle: 0.311; Ruth's is greater.
d) Answers will vary.
e) Ruth: 0.307; Mantle: 0.313; Mantle's is greater.
f) Answers will vary.   **g)** Answers will vary.

55. 90   **57. a)–c)** Answers will vary.

Section 13.6, Page 793

1. Range = highest value − lowest value

3. Answers will vary.   **5.** Answers will vary.   **7.** σ

9. Answers will vary.

11. They would be the same since the spread of data about each mean is the same.

13. a) The grades will be centered about the same number since the mean, 75.2, is the same for both classes.
   b) The spread of the data about the mean is greater for the evening class since the standard deviation is greater for the evening class.

15. 11, $\sqrt{16.5} \approx 4.06$ **17.** 6, $\sqrt{4.67} \approx 2.16$

19. 11, $\sqrt{15.2} \approx 3.90$ **21.** 5, $\sqrt{3} \approx 1.73$

23. $32, $\sqrt{137.78} \approx \$11.74$ **25.** $150, $\sqrt{2600} \approx \$50.99$

27. a) $63, $\sqrt{631.6} \approx \$25.13$ **b)** Answers will vary.

c) Answers remain the same, range: $63, standard deviation ≈ $25.13.

29. a)–c) Answers will vary.

d) If each number in a distribution is multiplied by n, the mean and standard deviation of the new distribution will be n times that of the original distribution.

e) The mean of the second set is $4 \times 5 = 20$, and the standard deviation of the second set is $2 \times 5 = 10$.

31. a) The standard deviation increases. There is a greater spread from the mean as they get older.

b) ≈ 133 lb   **c)** ≈ 21 lb

d) Mean: ≈ 100 lb; normal range: ≈ 60 to 140 lb

e) Mean: ≈ 62 in.; normal range: ≈ 53 to 68 in.   **f)** 5%

33. a)

East		West	
Number of Oil Changes Made	Number of Days	Number of Oil Changes Made	Number of Days
15–20	2	15–20	0
21–26	2	21–26	0
27–32	5	27–32	6
33–38	4	33–38	9
39–44	7	39–44	4
45–50	1	45–50	6
51–56	1	51–56	0
57–62	2	57–62	0
63–68	1	63–68	0

b)

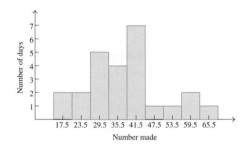

Number of Oil Changes Made Daily

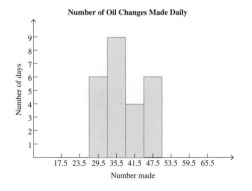

Number of Oil Changes Made Daily

c) They appear to have about the same mean since they are both centered around 38.

d) The distribution for East is more spread out. Therefore, East has a greater standard deviation.

e) East: 38, West: 38   **f)** East: ≈ 12.64, West: ≈ 5.98

35. 6, 6, 6, 6, 6

Section 13.7, Page 804

1. A rectangular distribution is one in which all the values have the same frequency.

3. A bimodal distribution is one in which two nonadjacent values occur more frequently than any other values in a set of data.

5. A distribution skewed to the left is one that has "a tail" on its left.

7. a) B **b)** C **c)** A **9.–11.** Answers will vary.

13. Normal   **15.** Skewed right

17. The mean is the greatest value. The median is lower than the mean. The mode is the lowest value.

19. Answers will vary.   **21.** They all have the same value.

23. A z-score will be negative when the piece of data is less than the mean.

25. 0   **27.** 0.500   **29.** 0.818   **31.** 0.034   **33.** 0.037

35. 0.019   **37.** 0.053   **39.** 26.1%   **41.** 89.8%

43. 97.1%   **45.** 97.5%   **47.** 2.9%

49. a) Jake, Sarah, Carol   **b)** Marie, Kevin   **c)** Omar, Justin, Kim

51. 50%   **53.** 10.6%   **55.** 69.2%   **57.** 24.1%   **59.** 44.0%

61. 29.1%   **63.** 59.9%   **65.** 50.0%   **67.** 10.6%

69. ≈ 21 women   **71.** 86.2%   **73.** 4.5%   **75.** 69.2%

77. 0.6%   **79.** ≈ 83 children   **81.** 1.8%

83. The standard deviation is too large.

85. a) Katie: $z = 2.4$; Stella: $z = 1.7$

b) Katie. Her z-score is higher than Stella's z-score, which means her sales are further above the mean than Stella's sales.

87. Answers will vary.   **89.** −1.18   **91.** 2

Section 13.8, Page 816

1. The correlation coefficient measures the strength of the relationship between the quantities.

3. 1   **5.** 0

7. A positive correlation indicates that as one quantity increases, the other increases.

9. The level of significance is used to identify the cutoff between results attributed to chance and results attributed to an actual relationship between the two variables.

11. –13. Answers will vary.

15. Yes   **17.** Yes   **19.** No   **21.** No

The answers in the remainder of this section may differ slightly from your answers, depending on how your answers are rounded and which calculator you used. The answers given here were obtained from a Texas Instruments TI-36x solar calculator.

23. a)

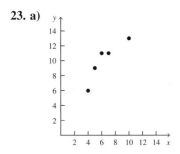

b) 0.903 **c)** Yes **d)** No

25. a)

b) 0.228 **c)** No **d)** No

27. a)

b) 0.999 **c)** Yes **d)** Yes

29. a)

b) −0.968 **c)** Yes **d)** Yes

31. $y = 1.0x + 3.4$ **33.** $y = 0.2x + 23.8$

35. $y = 0.8x + 5.8$ **37.** $y = -0.1x + 9.5$

39. a) 0.960 **b)** Yes **c)** $y = 1.3x + 4.8$

41. a) 0.950 **b)** Yes **c)** $y = 0.8x + 24.9$

43. a) −0.782 **b)** Yes **c)** $y = -0.7x + 22.3$
  d) 12.5 muggings

45. a) 0.800 **b)** Yes **c)** $y = 0.2x + 2.3$ **d)** ≈ 25 units

47. a) −0.977 **b)** Yes **c)** $y = -12.9x + 99.6$
  d) 41.6%

49. a) and b) Answers will vary.
  c)

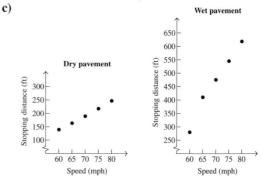

  d) 0.999 **e)** 0.990 **f)** Answers will vary.
  g) $y = 5.4x - 183.4$ **h)** $y = 16.2x - 669.8$
  i) Dry, 232.4 ft; wet, 577.6 ft

51. Answers will vary.

53. a) 0.991 **b)** Should be the same.
  c) 0.991, the values are the same.

Review Exercises, Page 821

1. a) A population consists of all items or people of interest.
  b) A sample is a subset of the population.

2. A random sample is one where every item in the population has the same chance of being selected.

3. The candy bars may have lots of calories, or fat, or sodium. Therefore, it may not be healthy to eat them.

4. Sales may not necessarily be a good indicator of profit. Expenses must also be considered.

5. a)

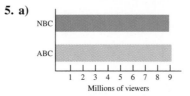

  b)

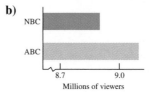

6. a)

Class	Frequency
35	1
36	3
37	6
38	2
39	3
40	0
41	4
42	1
43	3
44	1
45	1

b) and c)

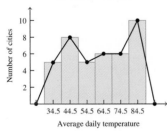

7. a)

High temperature	Number of Cities
30–39	5
40–49	8
50–59	5
60–69	6
70–79	6
80–89	10

b) and c)

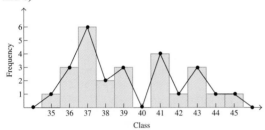

Average Daily High Temperature in January for Selected Cities

d) 3 | 6 represents 36

```
3 | 0  3  4  5  6
4 | 1  2  2  3  4  7  8  8
5 | 0  4  4  5  6
6 | 5  6  6  7  8  9
7 | 3  5  5  7  7  9
8 | 0  1  3  3  4  6  6  7  8  9
```

8. 80   **9.** 81   **10.** None   **11.** 78   **12.** 30

13. $\sqrt{104} \approx 10.20$ **14.** 13   **15.** 13   **16.** 7 and 12

17. 13.5   **18.** 19   **19.** $\sqrt{40} \approx 6.32$ **20.** 68.2%

21. 95.4%   **22.** 94.5%   **23.** 5.5%   **24.** 72.6%

25. 34.1%   **26.** 34.5%   **27.** 29.0%   **28.** 2.3%

29. a)

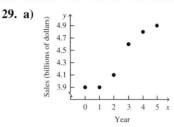

b) Yes; positive   **c)** 0.964   **d)** Yes   **e)** $y = 0.2x + 3.8$

30. a)

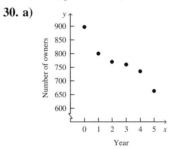

b) Yes; negative   **c)** −0.952   **d)** Yes
e) $y = -39.3x + 869.0$

31. a)

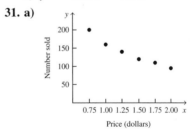

b) Yes; negative   **c)** −0.973   **d)** Yes
e) $y = -79.4x + 246.7$ **f)** ≈ 120 sold

32. 175 lb   **33.** 180 lb   **34.** 25%   **35.** 25%   **36.** 14%

37. 18,700 lb   **38.** 233 lb   **39.** 145.6 lb   **40.** ≈ 3.57

41. 2   **42.** 3   **43.** 7   **44.** 14   **45.** $\sqrt{8.105} \approx 2.85$

46.

Number of Children	Number of Presidents
0–1	8
2–3	15
4–5	10
6–7	6
8–9	1
10–11	1
12–13	0
14–15	1

47. and 48.

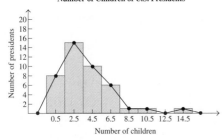

Number of Children of U.S. Presidents

49. No, it is skewed to the right.   **50.** Answers will vary.

51. Answers will vary.

Chapter Test, Page 824

1. 36   **2.** 37   **3.** 37   **4.** 33.5   **5.** 25   **6.** $\sqrt{84} \approx 9.17$

7.

Class	Frequency
25–30	7
31–36	5
37–42	1
43–48	7
49–54	5
55–60	3
61–66	2

8.

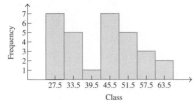

9.

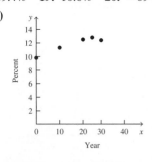

10. $695   **11.** $670   **12.** 75%   **13.** 79%

14. $70,000   **15.** $740   **16.** $640   **17.** 31.8%

18. 89.4%   **19.** 10.6%   **20.** ≈69 cars

21. a)

b) Yes   **c)** 0.932   **d)** Yes   **e)** $y = 0.1x + 10.1$
f) 14.1%

Chapter 14

Section 14.1, Page 833

1. A graph is a finite set of points, called vertices, that are connected with line segments, called edges.

3. One example: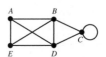

5. If the number of edges connected to the vertex is even, the vertex is even. If the number of edges connected to the vertex is odd, the vertex is odd.

7. a) A path is a sequence of adjacent vertices and the edges connecting them.
b) A circuit is a path that begins and ends at the same vertex.
c) In the following graph:

The path A, B, D, C is a path that is not a circuit. The path A, B, D, C, A is a path that is also a circuit.

9.

11.

13.

15. No. There is no edge connecting vertices B and C. Therefore, A, B, C, D, E is not a path.

17. Yes. One example is A, C, E, D, B.

19. Yes. One example is C, A, B, D, E, C, D.

In Exercises 21–31, one graph is shown. Other graphs are possible.

21.

23.

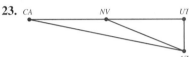

25.

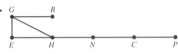

27.

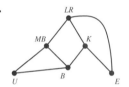

29.

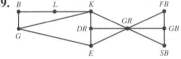

31.

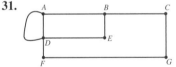

33. Disconnected   **35.** Connected   **37.** Edge *AB*

39. Edge *EF*

41.

Other answers are possible.

43. It is impossible to have a graph with an odd number of odd vertices.

45. a) and b) Answers will vary.

Section 14.2, Page 845

1. a) An Euler path is a path that must include each edge of a graph exactly one time.
   b) The path *A, B, E, D, C, A, D, B* is an Euler path.

c) In the graph above, path *A, B, E, D, C* is a path that is not an Euler path.

3. a) Yes   **b)** Yes   **c)** No

5. If all the vertices are even, the graph has an Euler circuit.

7. *A, B, C, D, E, B, E, D, A, C*; other answers are possible.

9. No. This graph has exactly two odd vertices. Each Euler path must begin with an odd vertex. *B* is an even vertex.

11. *A, B, A, C, B, E, C, D, A, D, E*; other answers are possible.

13. No. A graph with exactly two odd vertices has no Euler circuits.

15. *A, B, C, E, F, D, E, B, D, A*; other answers are possible.

17. *C, B, A, D, F, E, D, B, E, C*; other answers are possible.

19. *E, F, D, E, B, D, A, B, C, E*; other answers are possible.

21. a) Yes. There are zero odd vertices.
   b) Yes. There are zero odd vertices.

23. a) No. There are more than two odd vertices.
   b) No. There are more than zero odd vertices.

25. a) Yes
   b) They could start on either island and finish at the other.

In Exercises 27–31, one graph is shown. Other graphs are possible.

27. a)

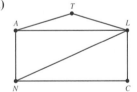

b) Yes; *A, T, L, C, N, L, A, N*
c) No

29. a)

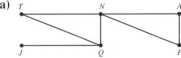

b) Yes; *J, Q, T, N, A, P, N, Q*
c) No

31. a)

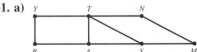

b) Yes; *A, S, M, N, T, Y, B, A, T, S*
c) No

33. a) No
   b) No such path exists.

35. a) Yes **b)** One path is A, D, B, E, C, B, A, C.

37. a) Yes
  b) The residents would need to start at the intersection of Maple Cir., Walnut St., and Willow St. or at the intersection of Walnut St. and Oak St.

39. $F, G, E, F, D, E, B, D, A, B, C, E$; other answers are possible.

41. $H, I, F, C, B, D, G, H, E, D, A, B, E, F$; other answers are possible.

43. $A, B, E, F, J, I, E, D, H, G, C, D, A$; other answers are possible.

45. $A, E, B, F, C, G, D, K, G, J, F, I, E, H, A$; other answers are possible.

47. $A, B, C, E, B, D, E, F, I, E, H, D, G, H, I, J, F, C, A$; other answers are possible.

49. $F, C, J, M, P, H, F, M, P$; other answers are possible.

51. $B, E, I, F, B, C, F, J, G, G, C, D, K, J, I, H, E, A, B$; other answers are possible.

53. $J, F, C, B, F, I, E, B, A, E, H, I, J, G, G, C, D, K, J$; other answers are possible.

55. It is not possible to draw a graph with an Euler circuit that has a bridge. Therefore, a graph with an Euler circuit has no bridge.

56. a)

  b)

  c)

  Other answers are possible.

Section 14.3, Page 857

1. a) A Hamilton circuit is a path that begins and ends at the same vertex and passes through all other vertices exactly one time.
  b) Both Hamilton and Euler circuits begin and end at the same vertex. A Hamilton circuit passes through all other *vertices* exactly once, whereas an Euler circuit passes through each *edge* exactly once.

3. a) A weighted graph is a graph with a number, or weight, assigned to each edge.
  b) A complete graph is a graph in which there is an edge between each pair of vertices.
  c) A complete, weighted graph is a graph in which there is an edge between each pair of vertices and each edge has a number, or weight, assigned to it.

5. a) The number of unique Hamilton circuits in a complete graph with n vertices is found by computing $(n-1)!$
  b) $3! = 6$ **c)** $8! = 40,320$

7. Answers will vary.

9. A, B, C, G, F, E, D and E, D, A, B, F, G, C; other answers are possible.

11. A, B, C, D, G, F, E, H and E, H, F, G, D, C, A, B; other answers are possible.

13. A, B, C, E, D, F, G, H and F, G, H, E, D, A, B, C; other answers are possible.

15. A, B, D, E, G, F, C, A and A, C, F, G, E, D, B, A; other answers are possible.

17. $A, B, C, F, I, E, H, G, D, A$ and $A, E, B, C, F, I, H, G, D, A$; other answers are possible.

19.

21. $7! = 5040$ ways   **23.** $10! = 3,628,800$ ways

In Exercises 25–31, other graphs are possible.

25. a)
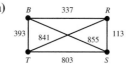

  b) S, T, B, R, S or S, R, B, T, S
  c) \$1646

27. a)
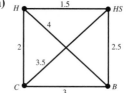

  b) H, HS, B, C, H or H, C, B, HS, H
  c) 9 miles

29. a)
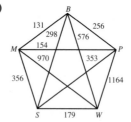

  b) B, M, P, S, W, B for \$1393
  c) Answers will vary.

31. a)
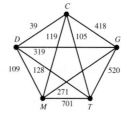

b) *C, D, M, G, T, C* for $1044

c) Answers will vary.

33. a–d) Answers will vary.

35. *A, E, D, N, O, F, G, Q, P, T, M, L, C, B, J, K, S, R, I, H, A*; other answers are possible.

Section 14.4, Page 868

1. A tree is a connected graph in which each edge is a bridge.

3. Yes, because removing the edge would create a disconnected graph.

5. A minimum-cost spanning tree is a spanning tree that has the lowest cost or shortest distance of all spanning trees for a given graph.

7.

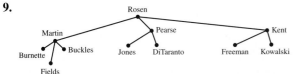

9.

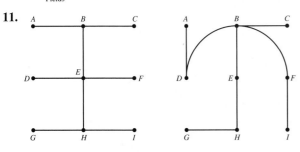

11.

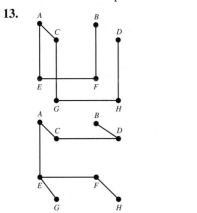

Other answers are possible.

13.

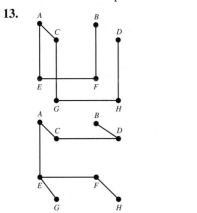

Other answers are possible.

15.

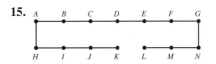

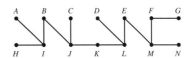

Other answers are possible.

17.

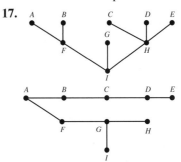

Other answers are possible.

19.

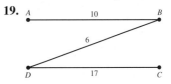

21.

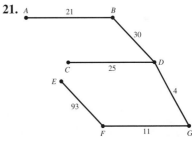

23.

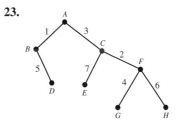

25.

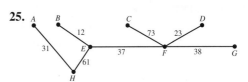

27. a)

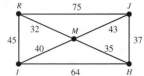

Other answers are possible.

b)

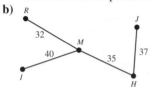

c) $2160

29. a)

b) $189,919

31. a)

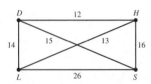

Other answers are possible.

b)

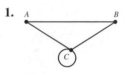

c) $140,000

33. a)

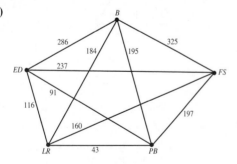

Other answers are possible.

b)

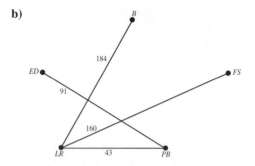

c) $1,195,000

35.–37. Answers will vary.

38. a) EULER
   b) FLEURY
   c) HAMILTON
   d) KRUSKAL

Review Exercises, Page 873

1.

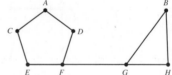

Other answers are possible.

2.

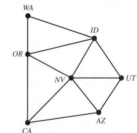

Other answers are possible.

3. *A, B, C, A, D, C, E, D*; other answers are possible.

4. No. To trace each edge in the graph with a path would require you to trace at least one edge twice (the graph has more than two odd vertices).

5.

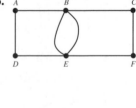

6.

7. Connected   **8.** Disconnected   **9.** Edge *CD*

10. *C, B, A, F, E, D, C, G, B, A, G, E, D, G, F*; other answers are possible.

11. *F, E, G, F, A, G, D, E, D, C, B, A, B, G, C*; other answers are possible.

12. *B, C, A, D, F, E, C, D, E, B*; other answers are possible.

13. E, F, D, E, C, D, A, C, B, E; other answers are possible.

14. a)

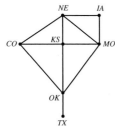

b) Yes. CO, NE, IA, MO, NE, KS, MO, OK, CO, KS, OK, TX; other answers are possible.

c) No.

15. a) Yes
   b) The person may start in any room and will finish in the room where he or she started.

16. a) Yes
   b) The officer would have to start at either the intersection of Dayne St., Gibson Pl., and Alvarez Ave. or at the intersection of Chambers St., Fletcher Ct., and Alvarez Ave.

17. A, B, F, A, E, F, G, C, D, G, H, D; other answers are possible.

18. A, B, C, D, H, G, C, F, G, B, F, E, A; other answers are possible.

19. A, C, B, F, E, D, G and A, C, D, G, F, B, E; other answers are possible.

20. A, B, C, D, F, E, A and A, E, F, B, C, D, A; other answers are possible.

21.

22. 4! = 24 ways

23. a)

b) P, D, M, C, P or P, C, M, D, P
c) $2088

24. a)

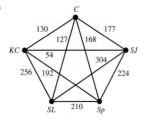

b) SJ, KC, C, SL, Sp, SJ traveling a total of 745 miles

c) Sp, C, SL, KC, SJ, Sp traveling a total of 829 miles

25.

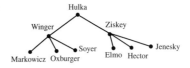

26.

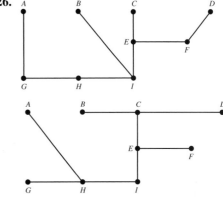

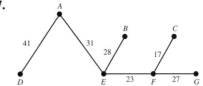

Other answers are possible.

27.

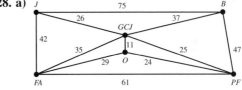

28. a)

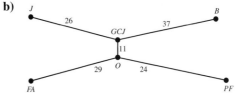

b)

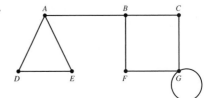

c) $317.50

Chapter Test, Page 876

1.

Other answers are possible.

2.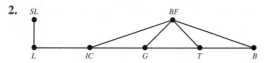

3. One example: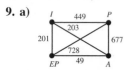

4. *D, A, B, C, E, B, D, E*; other answers are possible.

5. Yes. The person may start in any room and the person will end in the room where he or she started.

6. *A, D, E, A, F, E, H, F, I, G, F, B, G, C, B, A*; other answers are possible.

7. *A, B, C, D, H, I, L, K, J, G, F, E, A*; other answers are possible.

8. 7! = 5040 ways

9. a)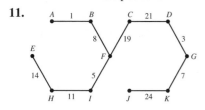

b) *I, P, A, EP, I* or *I, EP, A, P, I* for $1376
c) *I, EP, A, P, I* for $1376

10.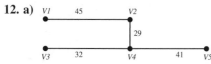

Other answers are possible.

11.

12. a)

b) $183.75

Chapter 15

Section 15.1, Page 892

1. When a candidate receives more than 50% of the votes, he or she receives a majority.

3. Voters rank candidates from most favorable to least favorable. Each last-place vote is awarded 1 point, each

next-to-last-place vote is awarded 2 points, each third-from-last-place vote is awarded 3 points, and so forth. The candidate receiving the most points is the winner.

5. Voters rank the candidates. A series of comparisons is conducted in which each candidate is compared with each of the other candidates. If candidate A is preferred to candidate B, A receives 1 point. If candidate B is preferred to candidate A, B receives 1 point. If the candidates tie, each receives $\frac{1}{2}$ point. The candidate receiving the most points is declared the winner.

7. A preference table summarizes the results of an election.

9. a) Jeter   **b)** No

11.

Number of Votes	3	1	2	2	1
First	B	A	C	C	A
Second	A	B	B	A	C
Third	C	C	A	B	B

13. 19   **15.** Mop   **17.** Vacuum   **19.** Beach   **21.** No winner

23. San Antonio

25. No winner, a tie between Honolulu and San Antonio

27. Williams   **29.** Johnson   **31.** Williams   **33.** Erie

35. Erie   **37. a)** TI   **b)** TI   **c)** TI   **d)** TI

39. a) C   **b)** A   **c)** A   **d)** Tie between B and C

41. a) If there were only two columns, only two of the candidates were the first choice of the voters. If each of the 15 voters cast a ballot, one of the voters must have received a majority of votes because 15 cannot be split evenly.

b) An odd number cannot be divided evenly so one of the two first-choice candidates must receive more than half of the votes.

43. a) Warriors, Rams and Tigers tied, Comets
b) Rams, Tigers, Warriors, Comets

45. a) 150   **b)** 50   **c)** Yes

47. One possible answer is:

Number of Votes	5	5	2
First	A	B	C
Second	B	A	B
Third	C	C	A

Section 15.2, Page 906

1. If a candidate receives a majority of first-place votes, then that candidate should be declared the winner.

3. If a candidate is favored when compared individually with every other candidate, that candidate should be declared the winner.

5. A candidate that is preferred to all others will win each head-to-head comparison and is selected with the pairwise comparison method.

7. If a candidate receives a majority of votes, that candidate also has the most votes and wins by the plurality method.

9. Pizza wins with the Borda count method but tacos has a majority of first-place votes.

11. No. B is the Borda count winner, but A has a majority of first-place votes.

13. No. Lounge areas wins by the Borda count method, but Parking is preferred to Security and to Lounge areas.

15. Yes. B wins by plurality with elimination and is preferred over each of the other candidates using head-to-head comparisons.

17. No. A wins the first election by plurality. If B drops out, C wins by plurality.

19. No. B wins by the Borda count method. If A drops out, C wins.

21. No. C wins by plurality with elimination. If the voters change their preference, B wins by plurality with elimination.

23. No. B wins by plurality with elimination. If A drops out, C wins by plurality with elimination.

25. No. B wins by pairwise comparison. If A, C, and E drop out, D wins by pairwise comparison.

27. No. B wins by the Borda count method, but A has a majority of first-place votes.

29. a) Museum of Natural History
   b) Museum of Natural History
   c) Museum of Natural History
   d) Museum of Natural History
   e) Museum of Natural History
   f) None of them

31. a) Jennifer Aniston   **b)** Denzel Washington   **c)** Yes

33. A candidate who holds a plurality only gains strength and holds an even larger lead if more favorable votes are added.

35.–37. Answers will vary.

Section 15.3, Page 924

1. If we divide the total population by the number of items to be apportioned, we obtain a number called the standard divisor.

3. The upper quota is the standard quota rounded up to the nearest whole number.

5. An apportionment should always be either the upper quota or the lower quota.

7. Jefferson's method, Webster's method, and Adams's method

9. a) Webster's method   **b)** Adams's method
   c) Jefferson's method

11. a) 50,000   **b)** 24.4, 54.6, 17.14, 53.86
   c) 24, 55, 17, 54

13. a) 24.70, 55.26, 17.35, 54.51   **b)** 24, 55, 17, 54

15. a) 24.06, 53.85, 16.90, 53.12   **b)** 25, 54, 17, 54

17. a) 24.38, 54.55, 17.12, 53.81   **b)** 24, 55, 17, 54

19. a) 11.86, 8.29, 6.01   **b)** 11, 8, 6

21. a) 10.55, 7.38, 5.34   **b)** 11, 8, 6   **23.** 11, 8, 6

25. a) 18   **b)** 4.17, 5.39, 7.78, 12.67

27. 4, 5, 8, 13   **29.** 4, 5, 8, 13

31. 34, 136, 41, 18, 21   **33.** 34, 136, 41, 18, 21

35. a) 90   **b)** 53.33, 40.09, 33.22, 23.36

37. 54, 40, 33, 23   **39.** 54, 40, 33, 23

41. 53, 26, 31, 35, 37, 28   **43.** 53, 26, 31, 35, 37, 28

45. a) 12   **b)** 62.58, 81.67, 41.92, 13.83

47. 63, 82, 42, 13   **49.** 62, 82, 42, 14

51. a) Divisor   **b)** Adams   **c)** Webster
   d) Modified   **e)** Hamilton

Section 15.4, Page 932

1. The Alabama paradox occurs when an increase in the total number of items to be apportioned results in a loss of items for a group.

3. The population paradox occurs when group A loses items to group B, although group A's population grew at a higher rate than group B's.

5. Hamilton's method, Jefferson's method

7. No. The new apportionment is still 12, 9, 9, 10, 11. No school suffers a loss so the Alabama paradox doesn't occur.

9. a) 6, 8, 16
   b) Yes. When the number of seats increases, states B and C gain a seat and state A loses a seat.

11. a) 65, 32, 103   **b)** No

13. a) 7, 16, 9, 11, 11
   b) Yes. Division B loses an internship to division A even though the population of division B grew faster than the population of division A.

15. a) 8, 40
   b) Yes, the apportionment is now 9, 39, 7 and group B loses a manager.

17. a) 5, 17, 44
   b) Yes, the apportionment is now 4, 17, 44, 6 and state A loses a seat.

Review Exercises, Page 935

1. a) Robert Rivera   **b)** No

2. a) Michelle MacDougal   **b)** Yes

3.

Number of Votes	3	2	1	1	3
First	B	A	D	D	C
Second	A	C	C	A	B
Third	C	D	A	B	A
Fourth	D	B	B	C	D

4.

Number of Votes	2	2	2	1
First	C	A	B	C
Second	A	B	C	B
Third	B	C	A	A

5. 17 **6.** Park City **7.** Park City **8.** Park City

9. Park City **10.** Park City **11.** 110

12. Volleyball **13.** Soccer **14.** Volleyball

15. None **16.** Soccer

17. a) Yes, American Association of Retired Persons
  b) American Association of Retired Persons
  c) American Association of Retired Persons
  d) American Association of Retired Persons
  e) American Association of Retired Persons

18. a) No **b)** New Orleans **c)** Las Vegas
  d) Las Vegas **e)** Las Vegas

19. a) A tie between *Encyclopedia Britannica* and *World Book*
  b) *World Book*
  c) A tie between *Encyclopedia Britannica* and *World Book*

20. No. A has a majority, but B wins by the Borda count method.

21. No. B wins by the Borda count method, but A is preferred over each of the other candidates using head-to-head comparisons.

22. a) C wins the election by plurality with elimination.
  b) When the order is changed A wins. Therefore, the monotonicity criterion is not satisfied.
  c) No. If B drops out, A is the winner by plurality with elimination. Therefore, the irrelevant alternatives criterion is not satisfied.

23. a) Starbucks **b)** Maxwell House **c)** Folger's
  d) Eight O'Clock **e)** Starbucks
  f) Plurality method, Borda count method, and plurality with elimination method all violate the head-to-head criterion.

24. a) Fleetwood Mac **b)** Boston **c)** Fleetwood Mac
  d) ABBA **e)** Fleetwood Mac
  f) The plurality method and the plurality with elimination method

25. The Borda count method

26. The plurality method and the plurality with elimination method

27. The pairwise comparison method and the Borda count method

28. 4, 3, 3 **29.** 5, 2, 3 **30.** 4, 3, 3 **31.** 5, 2, 3

32. Yes. The apportionment is 5, 2, 4. Region B loses one truck.

33. 11, 7, 5 **34.** 11, 7, 5 **35.** 10, 7, 6 **36.** 11, 7, 5

37. No. The apportionment with the additional population is still 11, 7, 5.

38. 5, 50 **39.** 4, 51 **40.** 5, 50 **41.** 5, 50

42. Yes. The new apportionment is 5, 49, 6. State B loses a seat.

Chapter Test, page 938

1. 12 **2.** No **3.** Chris **4.** Chris **5.** Donyall

6. Donyall

7. a) Snail **b)** Iguana **c)** Hamster **d)** Ladybug

8. Plurality method, Borda count method, and plurality with elimination method

9. Yes

10. a) 6, 9, 15 **b)** 6, 9, 15
  c) No. The apportionment is 6, 9, 16.
  d) No. The apportionment is 6, 9, 15.
  e) No. The apportionment is 6, 9, 15, 5.

shopping at busy mall © Corbis; Page 630, photo of ATM machine © PhotoDisc Blue; Page 631, photo of a woman looking at appliances © PhotoDisc; Page 632, photo of a furniture store © PhotoDisc; Page 632, photo of Portland, Oregon © PhotoDisc; Page 634, photo of a family watching television © Digital Vision; Page 636, photo of a small house © PhotoDisc Blue; Page 637, photo of a large house © PhotoDisc; Page 641, photo of a Real Estate sign © PhotoDisc; Page 644, photo of a house with Sold sign © PhotoDisc; Page 645, photo of couple applying for mortgage © PhotoDisc Page 646, photo of a house on waterfront © Digital Vision; Page 648, photo of a skateboarder © Duomo/Corbis; Page 649, photo of skiing © PhotoDisc; Page 650, photo of a house for sale with sign © PhotoDisc; Page 651, photo of someone in a fishing boat © PhotoDisc; Page 653, photo of Cheetahs © PhotoDisc Blue; Page 654, photo of Jacob Bernouilli © Corbis/Bettman; Page 656, photo of a dog © Allen R. Angel; Page 658, photo of Queen Victoria and family © Corbis/Bettman; Page 659, photo of Barry Bonds © Duomo/Corbis; Page 660, photo of birds at birdfeeder © PhotoDisc; Page 664, photo of a bird © Corbis; Page 668, photo of tennis courts © Allen R. Angel; Page 669, photo of manatees © Allen R. Angel; Page 676, photo of a bingo board © Allen R. Angel; Page 677, photo of horse race © Kevin R. Morris/Corbis; Page 677, graph Multiple Births in the United States in 2000 © *USA Today*, 1/2/03 "Stork Strain." Reprinted with permission. Page 678, photo of a man receiving a parking ticket © PhotoDisc; Page 684, photo of Diana Taurasi of the UCONN Huskies © AP Wide World Photos/Jeffrey Phelps; Page 694, photo of Epcot Center © Allen R. Angel; Page 695, photo of a flowering pea plant © PhotoDisc; Page 699, photo of family with eight girls © Corbis/Bettman; Page 700, photo of large group of people © PhotoDisc; Page 702, photo of a slot machine © Allen R. Angel; Page 704, photo of people playing golf © Allen R. Angel; Page 705, photo of a slot machine © Allen R. Angel; Page 711, photo of assortment of paper money © Beth Anderson; Page 714, illustration of Slot Machine as found in *Scientific American* 1996 © Tomo Narashima. Reprinted with permission. Page 716, photo of The Three Stooges © Bettmann/Corbis; Page 717, photo of seven children in a line © Corbis Royalty-Free; Page 719, photo of people in a hiking club © Corbis Royalty-Free; Page 720, photo of bicycle club © Corbis Royalty-Free; Page 724, Monet's *The Water Lily Pond, Pink Harmony* © Musée d'Orsay Paris/Lauros-Giraudon, Paris/SuperStock;Page 726, photo of 13-card bridge hand © Beth Anderson; Page 728, photo of theater district in NYC © Allen R. Angel; Page 728, photo of a jai alai game © Tom McCarthy/Photo Edit; Page 731, photo of Wild Bill Hickock's poker hand © Allen R. Angel; Page 731, photo of men moving furniture © Digital Vision; Page 733, photo of Mickey Mantle rookie baseball card © Allen R. Angel; Page 734, photo of a horse farm © Corbis Royalty-Free; Page 735, photo of a baseball game © Allen R. Angel; Page 743, photo of dolphins © Allen R. Angel; Page 745, photo of a national park © Allen R. Angel; Page 746, photo of a baseball field © Allen R. Angel; Page 747, photo of family riding on a dogsled © Corbis Royalty-Free; Page 748, photo of people fishing in a lake © Digital Vision; Page 749, photo of Golden Gate bridge © Allen R. Angel; Page 751, photo of a Woman with cat and dog © PhotoDisc; Page 752, photo of family watching TV © Neilsen Media Research; Page 756, photo of a bingo board © Corbis; Page 765, photo of Portland, Oregon most wired city © PhotoDisc; Page 766, photo of a car dealership © Beth Anderson; Page 767, photo of a chicken farm © PhotoDisc; Page 769, graph "Poll of Polls" © 10/23/03 *U.S. News and World Report, L.P.* Reprinted with permission. Page 772, photo of Captain Fairfield Inn Bed and Breakfast © courtesy Janet and Rick Wolf; Page 774, graph "Where Teens Work" © Rochester Democrat & Chronicle 5/8/01. Reprinted with permission. Page 775, photo of a saxophone player © BrandX Pictures; Page 777, photo of a Broadway show © Allen R. Angel; Page 779, photo of San Francisco © Allen R. Angel; Page 779, photo of Beaumont/Port Arthur, Texas © Cody Sewell; Page 781, photo of a smiling baby © Bruce Anderson; Page 784, photo of books on display at bookstore © Corbis Royalty-Free; Page 785, photo of a national park © Allen R. Angel; Page 786, photo of Blue Lagoon Water Park © Allen R. Angel; Page 787, photo of Babe Ruth © Bettmann/Corbis; Page 787, photo of Mickey Mantle © Bettmann/Corbis; Page 791, photo of Sydney opera house © Corbis Royalty-Free; Page 793, photo of someone fishing © Allen R. Angel; Page 799, photo of Blackwell; courtesy of David Blackwell, University of California at Berkeley; Page 806, photo of coffee in vending machine © Allen R. Angel; Page 806, photo of students studying © PhotoDisc Red; Page 818, photo of people eating pizza © PhotoDisc; Page 819, Photo of a movie theater © PhotoDisc; Page 819, Photo of a pool © Allen R. Angel; Page 832, map of MBTA Subway system © 2002 Massachusetts Bay Transportation Authority. Reprinted with permission. Page 844, photo of Pac-Man screen © Roger Ressmeyer/Corbis; Page 852, photo of Kevin Bacon © Reuters NewMedia Inc./Corbis; Page 853, photo of WNBA © Duomo/Corbis; Page 858, photo of big trucks at a weigh station © PhotoDisc Blue; Page 858, photo of Alan Greenspan © AFP/Corbis; Page 859, photo of St. Louis gateway Arch © PhotoDisc; Page 859, photo of Eliza Kelly Hall © courtesy of Clarke College; Page 861, photo of Icosian game © Royal Irish Academy ; Page 866, photo of Solomon Lefschetz © Archive Photos; Page 870, photo of a hibiscus © Beth Anderson; Page 878, photo of a ballot box © David Butow/Corbis SABA; Page 879, photo of a garden with flowers © PhotoDisc; Page 880, photo of a husky © PhotoDisc; Page 880, photo of students at computers © PhotoDisc; Page 881, photo of Arnold Schwarzenegger © Reuters NewMedia Inc./Corbis; Page 881, photo of Gray Davis © Reuters NewMedia Inc./Corbis; Page 882, photo of Harry Truman © Bettmann/Corbis; Page 883, photo of statue of Jean-Charles de Borda courtesy Musée de Borda; Page 885, photo of an ice sculpture © Beth Anderson; Page 888, photo of building a snowman © PhotoDisc Blue; Page 891, photo of University of Wisconsin-Platteville courtesy University of Wisconsin-Platteville; Page 892, photo of Rutherford Hayes © Library of Congress; Page 893, photo of The Grand Canyon © Corbis Royalty-Free; Page 894, photo of Honolulu © PhotoDisc Blue; Page 894, photo of scene from M*A*S*H © The Kobal Collection; Page 895, photo of bank carpeting © PhotoDisc; Page 895, photo of kittens © PhotoDisc; Page 896, photo of Tony Bennett at 45th annual Grammy Awards © Reuters NewMedia Inc./Corbis; Page 898, photo of voting booths © Mark Richards; Page 899, photo of Marquis de Cordorcet © The Granger Collection; Page 901, photo of people in voting booths © David Butow/Corbis SABA; Page 903, photo of East Lake High School © Allen R. Angel; Page 905, photo of Kenneth Arrow © AP/Wide World Photos; Page 906, photo of 5th grade class having a party © Digital Vision; Page 907, photo of Mall of America Underwater Adventure © Owen Franken/Corbis; Page 908, photo of National Air and Space Museum © Corbis Royalty-Free; Page 909, photo of Campbell's Soup can © Beth Anderson; Page 915, photo of Congress © Corbis;Page 925, photo of hotel staff © PhotoDisc; Page 925, photo of Princeton University © Princeton University; Page 926, photo of Chicago © Allen R. Angel; Page 930, photo of Texas Instruments calculator © Texas Instruments;Page 933, photo of film on shelves © Allen R. Angel; Page 935, photo of a skier © Allen R. Angel; Page 936, photo of Las Vegas © Allen R. Angel; Page 937, photo of ABBA © Archive Photos; Page 937, photo of a postal worker delivering mail © Mary Kate Denny/PhotoEdit; Page 939, photo of New Orleans © Allen R. Angel.